D1258192

Architectural Drafting

George K. Stegman

Harry J. Stegman

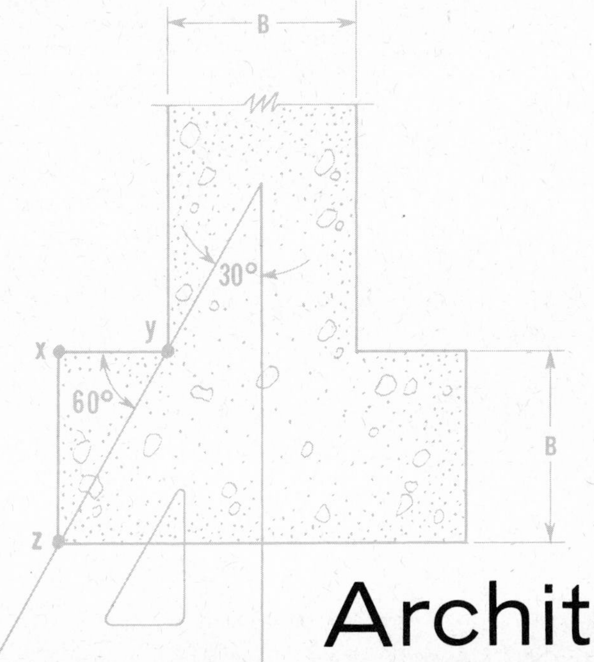

Architectural Drafting

Functional Planning and Creative Design

American Technical Society, Chicago

Library of Congress Card Catalog No.: 65-24313

Printed in the United States of America

preface

Each year, throughout the world, millions of new homes are constructed. In the United States alone in the past five years over 6,000,000 homes were built. *Each new home requires architectural planning and drafting.* The demand for professionally trained architects and architectural draftsmen has greatly expanded.

As the need for the trained professional increases, educators more-and-more require professionally oriented textbooks. *Architectural Drafting: Functional Planning and Creative Design* is designed to meet this need. The organization of this text is based on the professional operations of the practicing architect and architectural draftsman.

A student learns when he has a strong purpose or desire to learn. Motivation will be provided when the environment of the classroom, the problem, and the work on the drafting board is similar to that of the practicing architect. With this as a primary objective, this text has been professionally organized in both content and direction. The content has been determined by observing the needs of a large number of students in various sections of the country. The direction is determined by the duties and responsibilities of the professional architect. The successful architect has found by observation and experience that a basic series of steps are common to all residential construction. For example, once the client has selected a site, the architect analyzes the client's needs and requirements, examines the site layout, and then suggests solutions in the form of sketches, cost estimates, etc. By following the actual working conditions, the student will gain a professional feel for the job. With this approach, stimulus is given toward creative thinking and problem solving.

Each unit begins with basic principles and progresses forward from that point. All illustrative material, both written and graphical, is given in clear-cut form, with numerous step-by-step illustrations and explanations. All problems have been selected to give a maximum amount of experience in different graphical methods. A check list with a set of working drawings is included to aid the student with his drafting problems. The more difficult or unfamiliar architectural terms are explained in a glossary located, for easy reference, in the index.

So that this text may be used by students with little or no drafting experience, a discussion of basic drawing instruments and techniques is given in Appendix A. To interest students in continuing in the architectural field, guidance information is given in Appendix B. Other allied professions and the construction trades are also covered by the guidance information.

The drawings used in the text have been tested on thousands of students in the authors' classes. Many of these students have won top honors in state and national competition.

Both of the authors have experience in construction work. Both have on the board experience in residential and commercial design and drafting. We believe that the *Professional Plan* of this text will be a definite asset to those who are interested in the graphical aspects of architecture, as well as those who are novice home planners.

The authors wish to thank the many students, teachers, businessmen, and craftsmen who contributed their time to read the manuscript, give counsel, and prepare some of the illustrations. Among those to whom the authors are indebted are: Phillip Barber, Norman Bennett, Carl Betke, John Bosenetto, Donald Brown, Conrad Chojnacki, Allen den Bleyker, Phillip Hatfield, Gerry Lind, Garret Moerdyk, Richard Monroe, Howard Olson, William Palm, Jr., Tiit Telmet, Richard Tetzlaf, and James M. Thorne. The authors also wish to express their appreciation to the many industries and associations that have contributed illustrations. The authors wish to thank Mrs. Lois Stegman for the countless hours spent in typing.

THE PUBLISHERS

Books are the best of things, well used; abused, among the worst. What is the right use? What is the one end which all means go to effect? They are for nothing but to inspire.

Ralph Waldo Emerson

contents

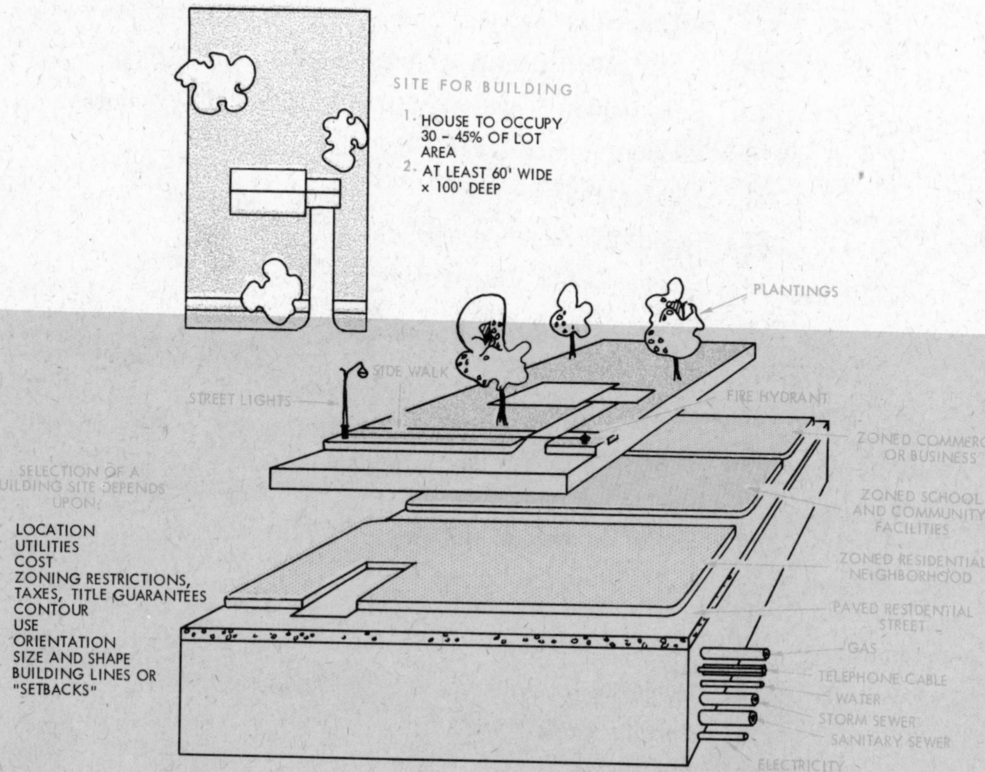

These are some of the important features to consider when selecting a building site.

Home Site Considerations 1

Next to the house itself, there is no greater investment than the home site. The site should not be viewed merely as an isolated plot of land, it must also be seen as part of the total community situation. A home site is more than a place upon which to build a house. It is a permanent location for the family residence. Great care, therefore, must be exercised to insure a site and neighborhood suited to the present and future needs of the family.

Neighborhood

Often, prospective site owners visit with the neighbors to gain a first-hand impression prior to purchasing. A tour of the surrounding neighborhood may reveal many features not discussed with the realtor. Look for factors which may detract from the neighborhood: below average housing, housing not in the same general price range, busy or noisy through streets, dumping areas, swamps, railroads, airports, factories, etc. Each of these undesirable features reduces the value of the site. The happiness of the new owner depends not only upon those who live nearby, but also upon the available facilities, the surrounding physical features of the neighborhood, and local ordinances.

Available Facilities

Schools. Closeness and quality of schools are particularly important to families with children. When choosing the site, investigate the location of all the nearest schools. Transportation to and from the schools may be a problem if they are not within walking distance. Information concerning nearby schools, such as enrollment, class size, school boundary lines, and school bus facilities or pick-up routes should be obtained from the local board of education.

Transportation facilities. The present trend in the design of residential areas is such that community facilities (schools, churches, theaters, etc.) and commercial areas are not located within walking distance. Distance is measured in terms of the time required for traveling, rather than in terms of mileage. *Time is the essential factor.* When selecting a site, investigate the public transportation facilities and major traffic arteries which go to commercial and community facility areas. Fig. 1-1 illustrates the recommended maximum distances between the home site to be chosen and the different community facilities. The distance between the home and the place of employ-

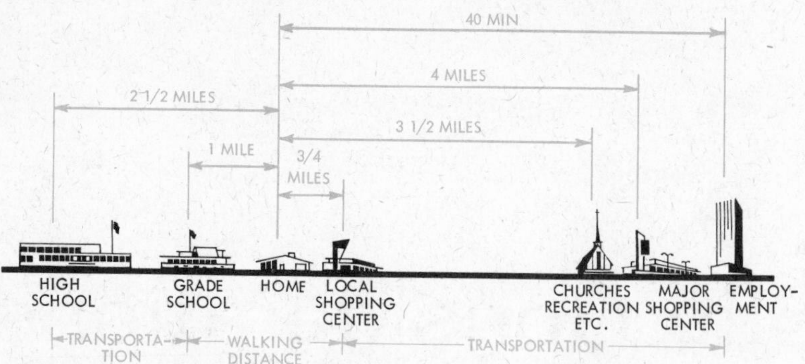

Fig. 1-1. Maximum distances from home to employment and other facilities are measured not only in miles, but also in time.

ment is shown in time measure rather than in terms of miles.

Utilities. It is considered essential today to have available such utilities as water, electricity, gas, municipal sewage disposal, storm sewer system, and telephone. In some fringe or suburban areas all such facilities are not available. A nominal fee may be charged for the extension of some or all of these utilities to the prospective site. It is sound business to investigate all these matters to determine who assumes the financial responsibility.

Physical Features

Topography is an important factor to consider when choosing a lot. Note the physical features of the site such as rocks, land slope, and soil condition. Excavations for the footings in rocky or steep sites may prove costly and exceedingly difficult. Lots which are too rocky eliminate the possibility of having a basement. Sloping land offers advantages as well as disadvantages. A slope is an aid to drainage, and a sloping lot lends itself to a partially or fully exposed walk-out basement. However, lots having steep slopes generally require retaining walls and earth fill. *Be especially wary of lots which have been filled.* If a portion or all of the lot has been recently filled, or will require filling prior to the construction of the building, it is possible that the building will settle and crack the foundation. Such damage may occur either during the building construction or at a later date depending upon how fast the fill below the structure settles. If the conditions of the earth are doubtful, it is always wise to have a soil engineer check the site before buying or starting building construction. If the site appears to be questionable, obtain all the necessary information, including excavation cost estimates, prior to any decision to purchase or to build.

Lot size. Some families enjoy spacious lawns, while others are interested in a minimal amount of yard work. Most experts recommend 50′ wide by 100′ deep as the minimum lot size unless neighborhood conditions, local customs, or land values dictate otherwise. Narrow lots may present difficulties in orientation of the major living areas and/or the placement of the building. Where building restrictions are such that an odd placement of the house is not permitted, a lot frontage of 60′ is almost mandatory for sufficient light and ventilation. In many developments, lots vary from 80′ to 130′ in width and by 100′ to 150′ in depth.

Local Ordinances

Zoning is an important matter for the prospective site purchaser to investigate. Some zones permit only the erection of apartments and business structures. Other areas are solely residential. It is wise to investigate the zoning restrictions in the immediate and adjoining neighborhoods. A multiple family dwelling or a business establishment may cause an appreciable loss in property values. Zoning restrictions, in part, determine the future of the neighboring area. A city concerned with its municipal pride permits very few amendments for *spot zoning* in single family residential areas.

Building codes vary from area to area. It is wise to investigate the building restrictions in the area prior to any lot commitment. Some restrictions are for the benefit of home builders; others outlaw many newly developed building materials and construction methods because they do not conform to extremely antiquated rules. Be very skeptical of areas which do not conform to contemporary practices as well as those which have no building codes.

Assessments and tax rates should be investigated before choosing a site. A quick check at the local, municipal, or county offices will reveal the amount of taxes and assessments (or impending assessments) which may be due on the lot in question. Prospective buyers frequently have the opinion that taxes are lower in the suburban areas. This is often not actually true. Large cities and some large communities may have higher taxes because they offer as many as 300 services, while suburbs or fringe areas may offer as few as 20. Extra charges for water, refuse collection, or sewage disposal have considerable effect on the actual total costs of suburban living. Low taxes do not always indicate a desirable area in which to locate.

Title Search and Deed

Prior to purchase of the site, a *title search* should be instituted to determine if there are any claims (legal or monetary) against the property. This service is usually performed by an agency specializing in title searches. Reputable loan institutions will not lend money on a house or property unless the title has been searched and found to be satisfactory (no legal claims against the property). The deed to the site should be inspected for any restrictions and *easements*. Easements are rights given by the owner to the utility companies to cross the lot with gas, water, and power lines. This also includes a right for entry on the land for service and repair. Some easements may cause inconvenience or possible hazard after the building is constructed. The buyer should accept only a *warranted deed*. This is a guarantee, given by the seller, stating that there are no liens, encumbrances, easements, or claims against the property. With a warranted deed the seller will defend the title against all legal claims by other persons. The deed is valid when it has been (1) prepared in writing describing the property fully, (2) agreed upon by both the buyer and the seller, and (3) witnessed by a notary public.

Site Cost

It is impossible to project an average site cost because of the varying conditions in the different localities. A rule of the thumb states that approximately 12 to 20 per cent of the total cost of the house (materials and construction) should be expended for a lot. This percentage is not a hard-and-fast rule and will vary according to local land, material, and construction costs.

The site may require additional improvements and maintenance such as grading, additional top soil, or provisions for drainage. These expenses must also be considered in the total cost of the lot. Frequently, these are completely forgotten and come as an economic shock to the budget.

The initial cost of the lot is also dependent upon its location within a normal city block. A lot in the middle of a block is less expensive than one at a corner. Proportionally higher tax assessments are usually levied on a corner lot for streets, sewers, and other improvements.

Community Considerations

Some communities or neighborhoods are so poorly planned that neighborhood stability is almost non-existant. Those communities, having grown without a plan, eventually become transitional (i.e., deteriorate both economically and socially). Antiquated or inadequate zoning laws hinder the land developer in completing well planned community subdivisions. A properly planned community depends to a large degree on zoning. Zoning provides separation of land masses for basic use and restricts the size of lots and buildings.

Restrictions may be carried further by means of *protective covenants*. These are legal devices which allow a developer or a group of citizens within an area to establish and maintain minimum standards of quality. Covenants protect the home owner against impairment of home values by the addition of sub-standard buildings. Covenants also detail the standards of housing and provide for legal means of enforcement.

Much of today's building is in suburban or outlying areas, encompassing whole tracts of land which are subdivided by professional land developers. Many of these tracts are planned as virtually separate communities. These areas may include shopping centers, social centers, parks, recreational

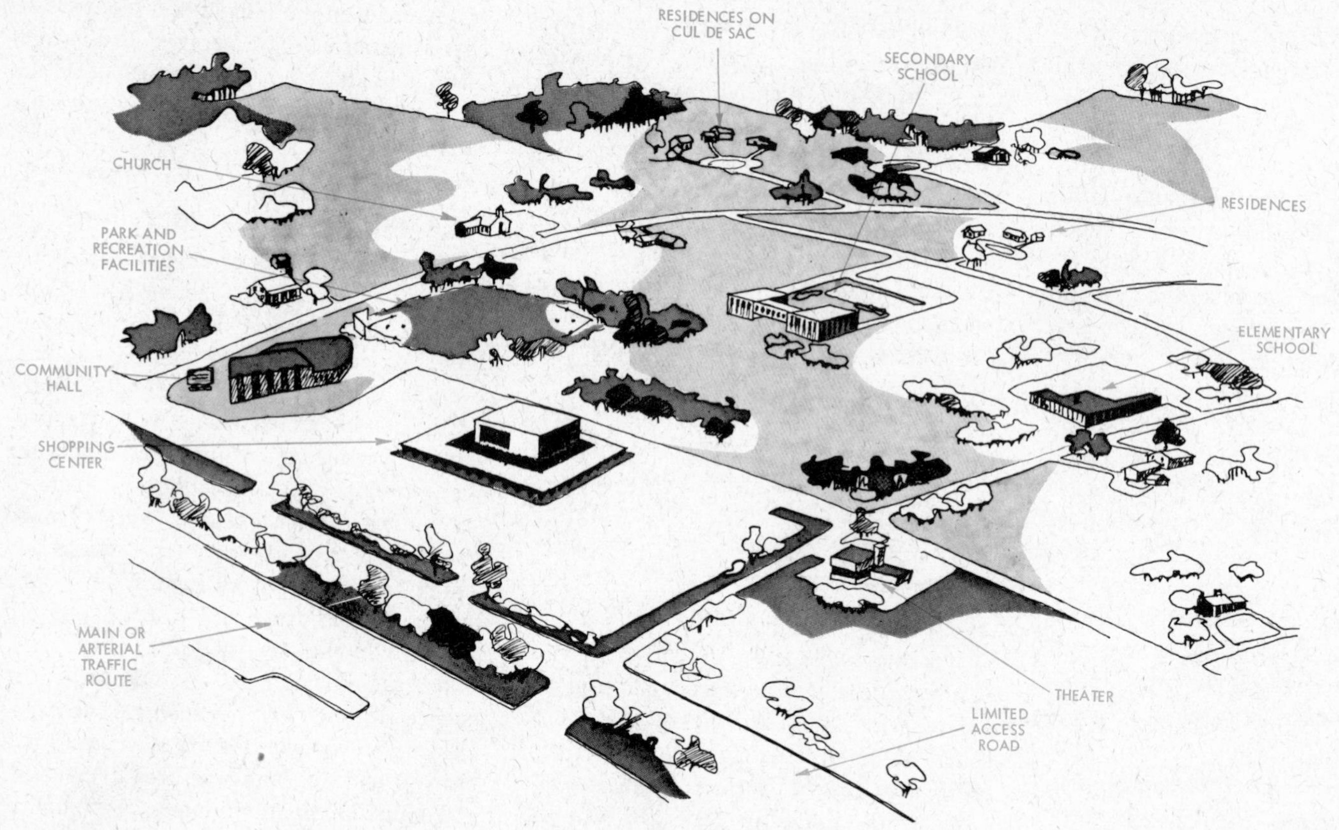

Fig. 1-2. Modern housing developments may be planned as virtually separate communities.

facilities, athletic fields, and churches. Fig. 1-2 illustrates such an area.

A recent trend in community planning, known as *clustering,* places houses closer together. Lot sizes are slightly reduced and houses are grouped around a *cul-de-sac* (a dead end street which terminates in a circle) or *access court* (a cluster of houses without street access). The excess area, available from the reduced lot sizes, may then be made available as a common park area for all residents in the subdivision.

Street paving, sidewalks, and streetlights are assets to any well-planned community. This is true not only in terms of practicality and beautification, but also in terms of safety. Residential streets should be planned to eliminate through traffic. Small cul-de-sacs, courts, and minor residential streets discourage heavy traffic. Some communities use limited access roads which branch off into less direct, curved streets.

Site and House Relationship

Lot Shape and Topography

The shape and topographic features of the

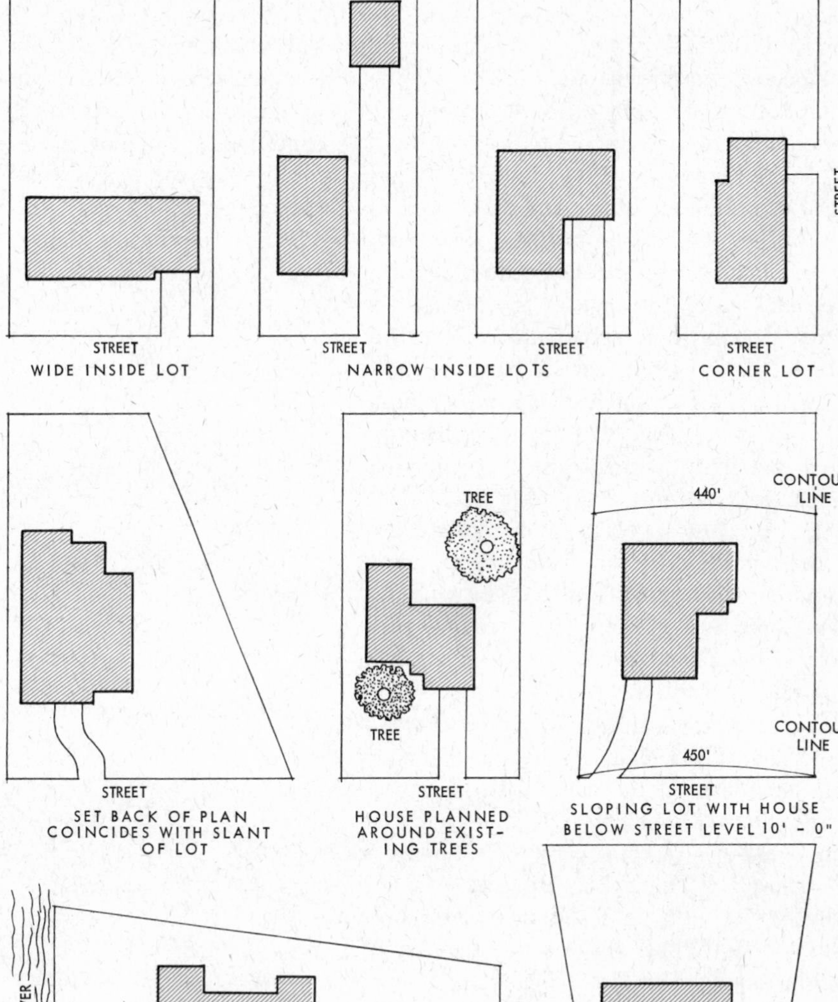

Fig. 1-3. The shape of the lot affects the plan and the placement of the house.

lot have an important influence on house planning. As suburban living becomes more popular, areas which offer a variety of lot shapes are being opened for development. The plan of many American communities is based on a rectangular grid system. This usually leads to a monotonous division of small land plots. In cities the lots are long and narrow so that a maximum number of sites per city block can be obtained. In the suburbs, however, the lots are often wide and deep and have irregular shapes (trapezoidal, triangular, etc.) which deviate from the basic rectangular grid. Fig. 1-3 graphically illustrates how the shape and topographic features of the lot affect the planning and the orientation of a house.

There are several factors to consider when planning a house which conforms to the physical features of the lot. The following statements indicate the manner in which the shape and topography of the site affects the orientation plan of a house to be erected.

Shape. Frequently, the outline of a lot may determine the shape and orientation of the house. A triangular lot shape, for example, will probably have a house built with *set backs* (i.e., the face of the building is moved back) to coincide with the sides of the lot. See Fig. 1-3 (center left).

Size. A house which is excessively large for the lot is out of place. It is particularly so if the lots are small and the adjoining houses are well proportioned in size.

Topography. Irregular and sloping land, together with ledge rock, may offer an ideal situation for a multi-level type of a house. These physical features often produce very interesting plans provided excessive costs are not incurred.

Trees. The position and number of trees may control placement and room planning of the house on the site. Well developed trees may add as much as $1,000 or more to the value of a building site.

View. The length of lot frontage, or a desirable view in front of the house, may suggest a controlling position for the family room, dining room, or living room.

House Placement

Placement of the house on a site deserves much thoughtful consideration. The best approach is to study the particular conditions of the lot. Each building site, whether suburban or city, has individual characteristics such as size, location, topography, trees, bushes, direction of view, and number of improvements. Architects utilize these conditions in planning and designing, so that the site and the structure may complement each other.

When determining the proper placement of the house on a site, the lot may be divided into three functional areas. These areas are (1) *public,* that portion of the lot which is exposed to the public view, usually the front area; (2) *service,* that portion used for the kitchen entry, garage, laundry, delivery, and possibly the children's play area, the front, rear, or side; and (3) *private,* that area allotted for recreation, gardening, and outdoor living, usually at the rear or side. Location of the house relative to these three functional areas is also dependent upon the sun and the prevailing winds.

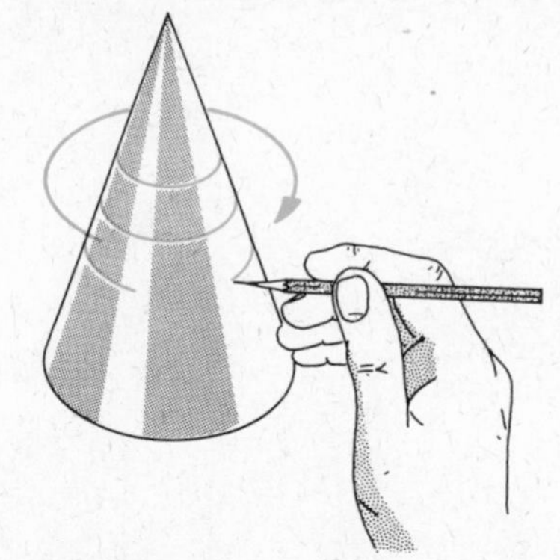

Fig. 1-4A. A contour is an imaginary line that connects points of the same elevation.

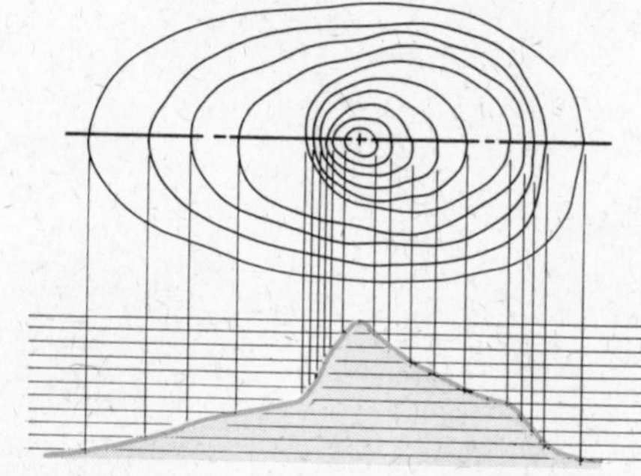

Fig. 1-4B. A profile gives an understandable expression of a slope along a certain line.

The house is best located forward on the lot unless prohibited by zoning restrictions. This permits the private area in the rear to be maximum in size. Houses placed in this manner eliminate long driveways and sidewalks which are expensive to construct. Privacy screens or plantings in the private area offer a further retreat from neighbors, provide shade, and serve as wind breakers. An attached garage may also provide privacy and act as a screen for the service area. Complete privacy in the living area may be obtained by making use of plantings and screenings, garage position, and the house placement.

Plot Plan

The first step after purchasing a home site and before constructing a house is drafting the plot plan. This presents a graphic picture of existing conditions and reveals possible problems which may arise. Plot planning is not necessarily detailed or involved, but it does require attention to a few basic facts.

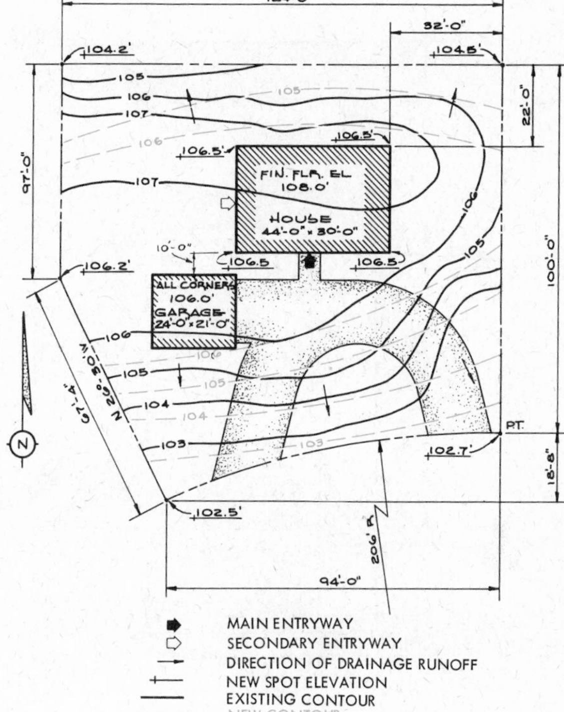

Fig. 1-5. This portion of a plot plan shows the original contour lines and the new contour lines (in color) after grading.

The plot plan is based upon a survey made of the site. The survey shows existing features (such as trees) and the grade of the lot. The grade is shown by means of contour lines. Fig. 1-4 illustrates how contour lines represent the land slope. The site usually must be graded to level the lot for construction. Fig. 1-5 graphically illustrates a plot plan with the existing contours (heavy lines) over-laid with the projected house location (with garage and driveway) and the new contours (colored broken lines) after grading. Higher ground is graded down and may be used as fill for the low ground, thus making a more uniform site for the house. Fig. 1-6 shows the necessary information and dimensioning required for the plot plan.

The following procedure lists some of the essential steps necessary for adequate planning.

Step 1. Make an outline sketch of the area surrounding the site, and indicate the following:

a. Compass direction
b. Direction of prevailing summer and winter winds
c. Location of neighbor's houses and garages
d. Zoning and building restrictions which may affect the site
e. Location of pleasant views with respect to the site

Step 2. On the outline sketch, indicate the proposed areas for the following:

a. Play area for children
b. Garage and driveway area
c. Refuse storage area
d. Outdoor living area
e. Flower garden area

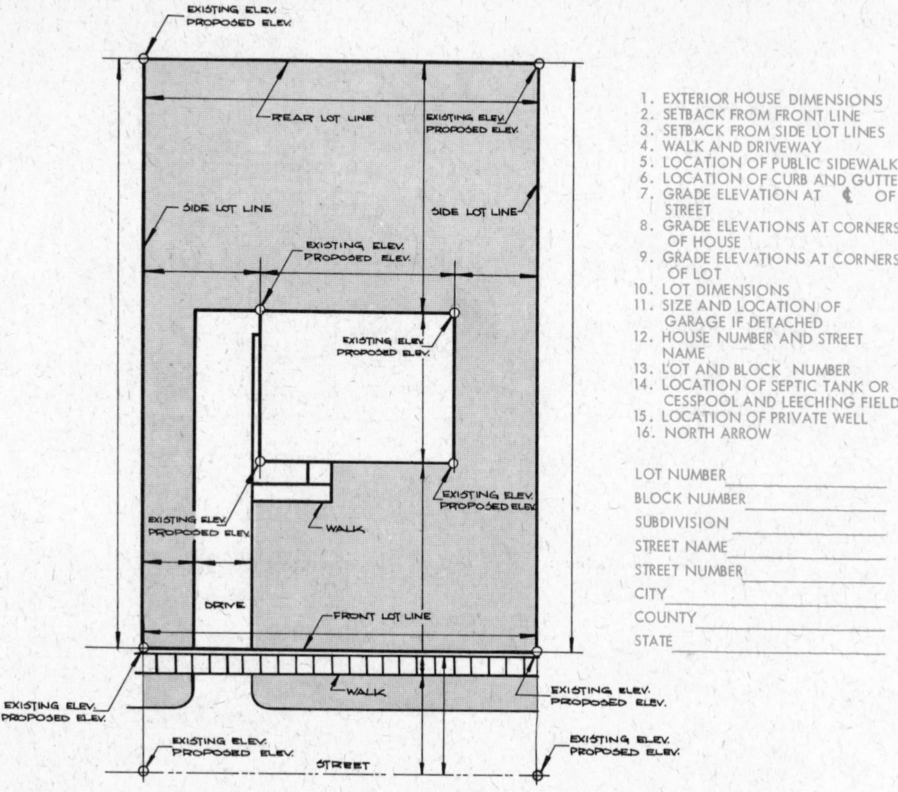

Fig. 1-6. The plot plan must include the dimensions listed here.

f. Laundry drying area (if necessary)

Step 3. Next, arrange the house in relation to public, service, and private areas. The shape of the house should be approximately rectangular. No detailed shape is necessary at this point. When planning the arrangement of the house, make the most advantageous use of the site conditions.

a. Observe the physical features of the site. House placement on the higher area of a sloping lot is most desirable. (The site should be graded so there is a slight drop away from the house for ground water run-off.)

b. Observe the tentative location of the house with respect to the neighbor's view. The house should be located for privacy.

c. Attractive views may determine the location of outdoor living areas.

d. Private areas should be properly screened from public and service areas.

Landscaping

The final consideration is the landscaping. Landscaping lends a finished appearance to the home—it should not be omitted. A landscape plan is a long term investment in the property, not a luxury. Consideration given to grading, planting, and screening determine the success of landscaping.

Most local nurserymen or landscapers willingly supply a planning service for the home owner. Frequently, the planting plan will extend over a period of several years. The plan consists of initially planting the necessary trees and shrubs and then adding more plantings each successive year. This method allows the home owner to budget the cost of landscaping and to have a definite system for planting.

Top Soil

Fertile top soil is essential to the growth of any plant life. A valuable supply is available from areas where grading or excavating is required, such as the driveway, sidewalks, patio, and the house site. The top soil from these areas should be skinned or stripped (removed) from the surface and then piled separately prior to any construction. After the building is completed and the excavation is *backfilled,* a 4″ layer of top soil is usually spread over the site.

Japanese Spreading Yew

Hatfield Yew

Japanese Upright Yew

Douglas Fir

Cannaerti Juniper

Andorra Juniper

Juniper Pfitzer

Fig. 1-7. Plantings have an almost infinite variety of shapes and sizes.

ILLUSTRATIONS: SWEENEY, KRIST & DIMM, HORTICULTURAL PRINTERS; PORTLAND, OREGON.

Caution must be exercised in checking for discarded scrap materials in the excavated area adjacent to the foundation. All scrap materials should be burned or hauled away and not disposed of in the excavated areas. Large voids and depressions will develop as the fill and top soil settles around these pieces of discarded materials. More dirt will be required as the fill continues to settle. These areas adjacent to the footing and foundation that are scrap filled may lead to water problems at a later date.

Trees, Shrubs, and Evergreens

Nature has provided an abundance of plant sizes, shapes, and colors. Therefore, utmost consideration should be given to their efficient placement and combination. Fig. 1-7 illustrates, as an example, various plant shapes that may be employed. Individual creative ingenuity here may be allowed a wide range. It must be remembered, however, that adequate space must be left for growth. Home owners who have neglected this find that after several years their plantings have grown too close together and too near the house. Properly placed plantings, with allowance for spreading and growth, should result in a well planned landscaping. It is necessary, of course, to choose native plants, or plants that have demonstrated their growth ability under local soil and climatic conditions.

Trees are usually placed so they provide a maximum amount of shade from the afternoon sun, as shown in Fig. 1-8. Selection of trees should be based on their maximum mature height and spread, rapidity of growth, and color. For example, an American Elm will reach an adult height of 75′, develops a spread of about 50′, and grow at a medium rate. The Chinese Elm, on the other hand, reaches a height of about 50′, has a maximum spread of about 40′, and grows at a faster rate.

Fig. 1-8. Proper placement of trees is necessary to provide afternoon shade.

Small flowering trees may be used for accent; they usually provide a contrast to shrub plantings. The Redbud, for example, has a spread of approximately 18′, grows to a height of 25′, and has pink flowers early in the spring prior to its leafing. A Purple Leaf Plum provides colorful foliage through the season and attains a height of 25′ with a spread of about 15′.

Evergreens, shrubs and hedges are used to separate the plot from streets and neighbors, as well as to divide the driveway, garage, and rear entrance from other parts of the lot.

Plantings around the house, especially the front and sides, add beauty to the house and serve to conceal the concrete foundation. Slow-growing compact varieties of plantings should be chosen for this purpose. Higher growing specimens, such as Pfitzer Juniper which reaches a height between 6′ and 8′ or Cannarti Juniper which grows up to 15′, may be placed around corners or along large bare walls where there are no windows.

Low growing evergreens together with annually flowering shrubs are ideal for plantings near the house foundation, for boundary plantings, and for providing color to the landscape. Low evergreens (4′ or less), such as Andora Juniper, Dwarf Japanese Quince, Spirea Frobelli, and Mugho Pine are ideal when mixed with low-growing shrubs and annual flowers (e.g., the Flowering Almond, Flowering Quince, and Virginal Mock Orange). Taller shrubs (8′ to 12′), such as the French Lilac, Nanking Cherry, and Viburnum, are generally used to bound the site, to screen the private and service areas, and to soften the lines of the house.

Fig. 1-9. Examples of Improper and Proper Landscaping. Improper (Top): Tall trees centrally located. High shrubs and evergreens obstruct view from windows. House is dwarfed by tall planting. **Proper (Bottom):** Small trees for low house. Low shrubs and evergreens do not obstruct view. Proper planting accents entryway.

Plantings and House Relationship

A good relationship between the plantings and the house is generally the product of a well planned landscaping. Fig. 1-9 demonstrates the difference between a poorly planned landscape and one that is ideally planned. For example, Fig. 1-9 (top) shows a tree planted in front of and towering over the house. Tall evergreens and shrubs surround the house in such a manner as to block the view from the windows. The house appears dwarfed by these plantings, so that the relationship between it and the surrounding landscape cannot be defined.

In Fig. 1-9 bottom, however, this is not the case. Here a few small shrubs at the house corner are sufficient. Low shrubs and evergreens are located below the windows so as not to cover the view. Smaller trees, located off center and away from the picture window, give contrast between the landscape and the house. Small trees or shrubs at the sides of doorways or garage doors lend beauty to the general appearance of the house, especially at the main entryway.

Houses which are long and low, such as those shown in Figs. 1-8 and 1-9, look well with plantings at each end. This gives the appearance that the house is tied to the ground. Houses built on a slab generally need very little shrubbery or evergreens because they are built closer to the ground than those houses with a basement or crawl space.

Check List

When considering or investigating a site, it is always good practice to make a check list. The check list should call attention to important facts relating to the site and its surrounding areas, to the availability of public facilities, and to the home builder's needs and desires.

The following is a suggested check list based on the points covered in the preceding sections of this chapter.

Neighborhood or Community Characteristics:

	Yes	*No*
Residential	—	—
Below average housing	—	—
Developed areas	—	—

	Yes	No
Far away from industrial or commercial areas	—	—
Far away from dumping areas, railroads, airports, factories, etc.	—	—
Excessive traffic and noises	—	—
Air pollution—unpleasant odors	—	—
Pleasant surrounding views	—	—
Good prevailing winds	—	—
Properly zoned areas	—	—
Well planned street layout	—	—

Community Facilities:

	Yes	No
Quality schools nearby	—	—
School and public transportation facilities	—	—
Shopping centers nearby	—	—
Churches	—	—
Theaters	—	—
Playgrounds and athletic fields	—	—
Well paved streets with sidewalks	—	—
Good street drainage system	—	—

Availability of Public Utilities and Services:

	Yes	No
Water, electricity, and gas	—	—
Sewerage: storm and sanitary	—	—
Telephone	—	—
Fire and police protection	—	—
Garbage and trash removal	—	—
Street lights	—	—

Building Protection and Limitations:

	Yes	No
Good zoning laws	—	—
Proper restrictions on use of lot area	—	—
Proper type and use of structure indicated	—	—
Long duration of protection	—	—
Adequate building codes	—	—

Site and House Relationship:

	Yes	No
House plan fits into site	—	—
House plan adequate for site conditions	—	—
Site and house conforms with general neighborhood character	—	—

Site and Landscaping Considerations:

	Yes	No
Adequate size and shape	—	—
Good topographic features	—	—
Trees, shrubs, and evergreens	—	—
Firm soil	—	—
Little fill and grading required	—	—
Sufficient drainage	—	—

Purchasing Transaction:

	Yes	No
Satisfactory appraisal	—	—
Satisfactory tax status	—	—
Adequate land contract terms	—	—
Satisfactory title search	—	—

The following is a list of items to consider and calculate when purchasing a lot for a building site.

Total price	$________
Down payment	$________
Balance of purchase price, plus interest	$________
Possible special assessments (street, curb, sewer, etc.)	$________
Assessed value	$________
Tax rate per year	$________

FROM: PRACTICAL BUILDER, CHICAGO, ILLINOIS

Fig. 1-10. Housing Development.

Questions and Problems

Each of the following questions is concerned with the important points in this chapter. Answer each question carefully.

1. Various factors have been explained as a basis for site selection. List six which may be considered as the most important.
2. List the requisites of a good building site.
3. What are the advantages and disadvantages of the placement of your present home? If you live in an apartment, imagine that its floor plan were moved to ground level. What are the advantages and disadvantages of its placement?
4. Select a lot near your home; sketch the lot and give the approximate size and compass direction. Evaluate the lot in terms of (a) size; (b) orientation; (c) wind and sun; (d) shape of plan best suited to the shape of the lot; (e) availability of transportation; and (f) general neighborhood.
5. What are some of the factors which may be used when evaluating a neighborhood?
6. Using your own observations, what items would you consider as essential in landscaping a new home?
7. Study the waterside housing development shown in Fig. 1-10. In what ways has the site determined the house placement? Under these conditions what landscaping improvements could you suggest?
8. What are the advantages in selecting a home in an area zoned for single family as opposed to multi-family dwellings?

LOUVRE MUSEUM, PARIS, FRANCE.

The Chaldean statue of Gudea (found at Tello, Mesopotamia) is the oldest known technical drawing.

LOUVRE MUSEUM, PARIS, FRANCE.

Close up of the temple or fortress being planned by Gudea. Note the scale at the bottom edge and the stylus along the left of the tablet.

Floor Plan Characteristics 2

Floor plans are two-dimensional (length and width) drawings which show the location and relationship of the rooms on a particular level of a building. The design characteristics of a floor plan should ideally demonstrate the **functional,** the **comfortable,** and the **livable** conditions of rooms in their basic relationships. When making floor plans, it is always good practice to come as close as possible to the ideal design.

The following characteristics of **good** floor plans should be studied in detail:

1. Adequate traffic circulation
2. Proper house and room orientation as well as good sun control
3. Adaptability to indoor-outdoor living
4. Open planning concept
5. Proper window location
6. Privacy in living areas
7. Adequate storage space
8. Well planned furniture arrangement
9. Flexibility for expansion

An understanding of these inter-related design qualities, which are studied in this chapter, will enable the student to evaluate and design good floor plans.

Adequate Traffic Circulation

The term *circulation,* when applied to floor planning, refers to the movement of traffic from room to room, floor to floor, or to the outside of the house. Hallways, stairways, and rooms, as well as interior and exterior doorways, are passageways for the circulation of traffic.

Good circulation, or ease of movement in and about the house, is one of the most desirable features of a good floor plan. This, however, is not always possible—particularly in the floor design of small houses. In any case, every route or path of circulation should be direct, well lighted, and have ample room for movement. Figs. 2-1 and 2-2 show paths of good traffic circulation in single and double level homes.

Privacy is an important factor in design-

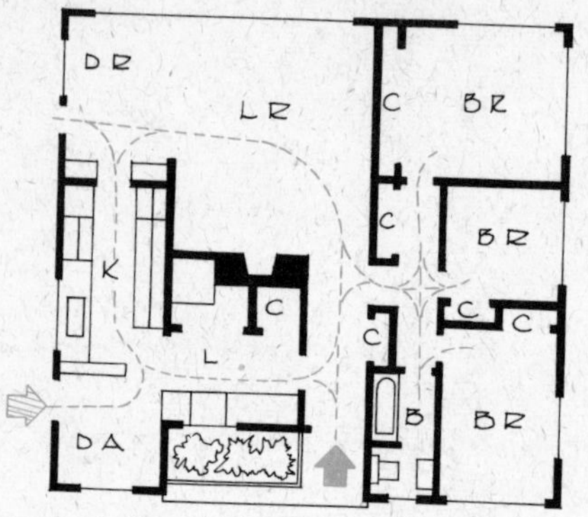

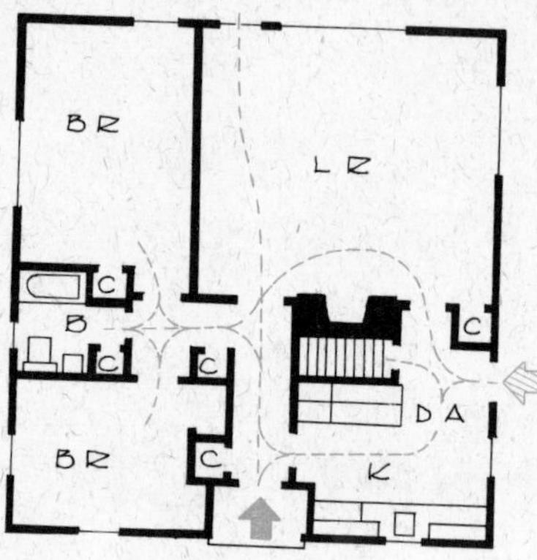

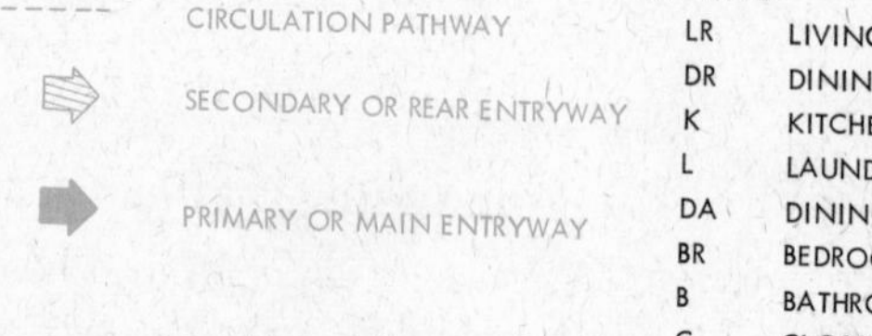

Fig. 2-1. Two examples of single-level homes showing well planned paths of traffic circulation.

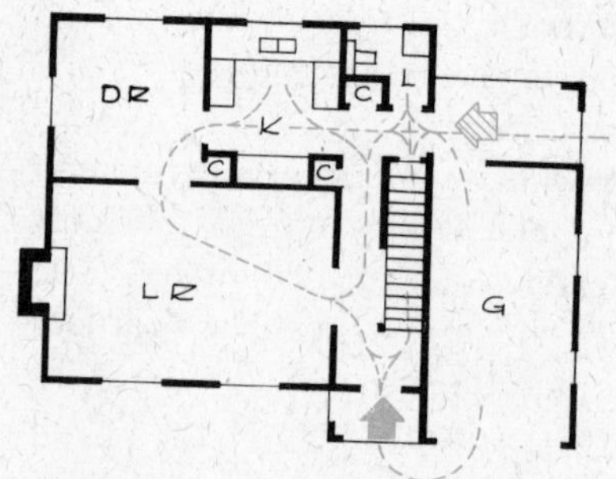

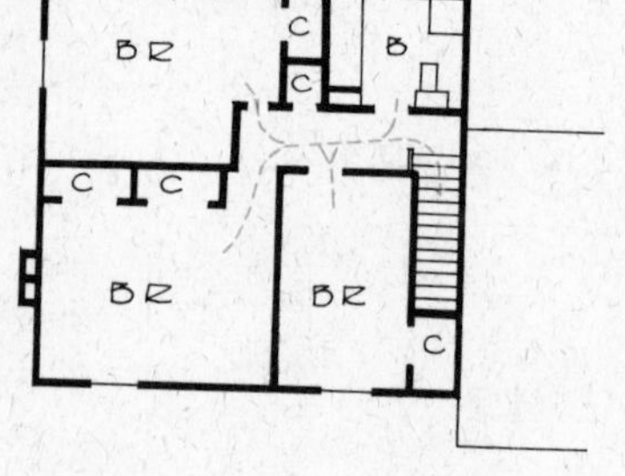

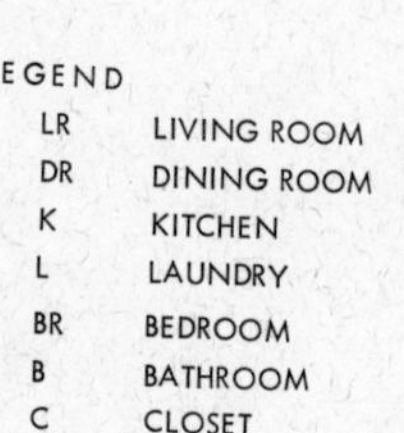

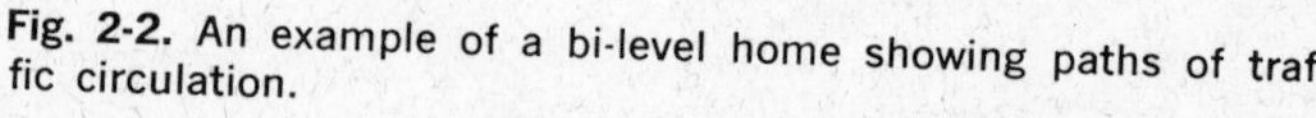
Fig. 2-2. An example of a bi-level home showing paths of traffic circulation.

ing good circulation paths in floor plans. Notice in Figs. 2-1 and 2-2 that paths of circulation are designed to end where particular privacy is desired, such as in bedrooms or bathrooms. If possible, these rooms should not be used as circulation pathways or traffic lanes.

Passageways

Hallways, particularly in small houses where there may be only one, serve mainly to provide better circulation. A small family of two or three people requires very little space for traffic circulation. However, a large family in a large house has a greater

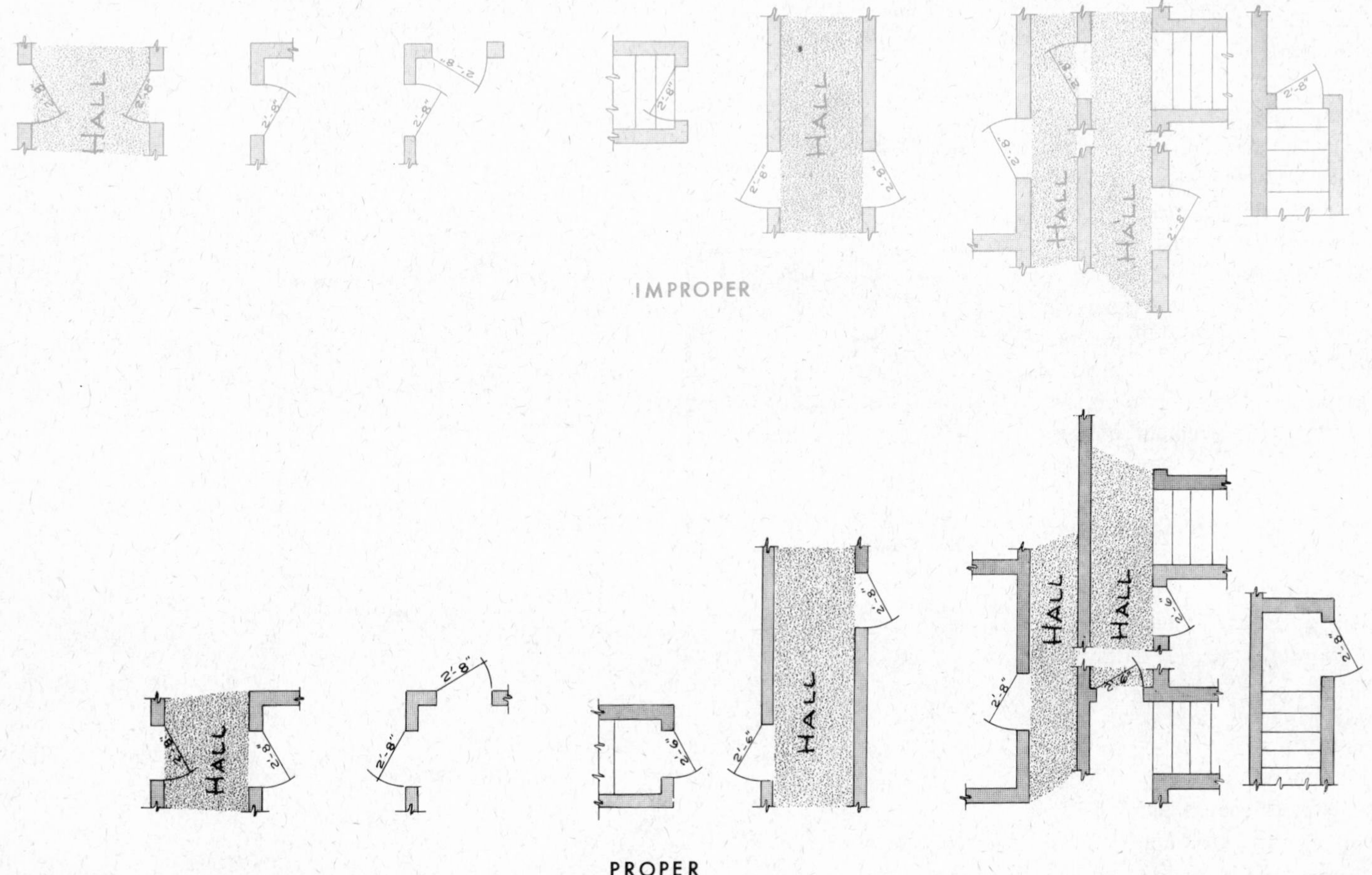

Fig. 2-3. Proper and Improper Placement of Doors: Improper method is shown in color at top; proper method is shown in black at bottom. Doors must be placed so that safety is the first consideration. They should not collide with other doors; as much floor space as possible should be saved.

need for space. In this case, more hallways are sometimes necessary.

The ease with which traffic can move through hallways is controlled by the width. In order to be practical, the hall should have a width ranging between 3′-0″ and 3′-4″, and should, ideally, be confined to within 10 per cent of the total floor area. Every effort should be made to keep hallways as short as possible.

When hallways are entirely eliminated from a floor plan, the circulation path must, of necessity, be through rooms having at least two doorways. Sometimes, for convenience, bedrooms, bathrooms, and other rooms designed for privacy have two doors. However, these rooms should never be considered as pathways for traffic. The rooms commonly used for circulation pathways are the living room, the dining room, and the kitchen. Furniture placement in these rooms should be such that they will not obstruct the traffic lanes.

In many cases, traffic circulation is not confined to one house level alone. Houses with more than one level, require stairways for traffic movement. The characteristics of good stairways are: (1) safety, (2) economy of space, (3) handrails, (4) landings (5) adequate lighting, and (6) a minimum width of 3′-0″.

The size, placement, and swing of doors are of utmost importance in planning the home. To facilitate the movement of furniture, doors should be at least 2′-6″ to 3′-0″ wide. Depending upon the size and the extent of door swing (90° to 180°), between six and seven square feet of floor space may be eliminated from the room. Great care, therefore, should be taken to place doorways so they cause minimum interference with the living area. Doors located at the ends (or along the sides) of small hallways or stairwells should be placed so there is no conflicting swing. Fig. 2-3 shows the proper and improper placement of doorways, and also the proper and improper direction of door swing.

Doorways for entrance to and exit from

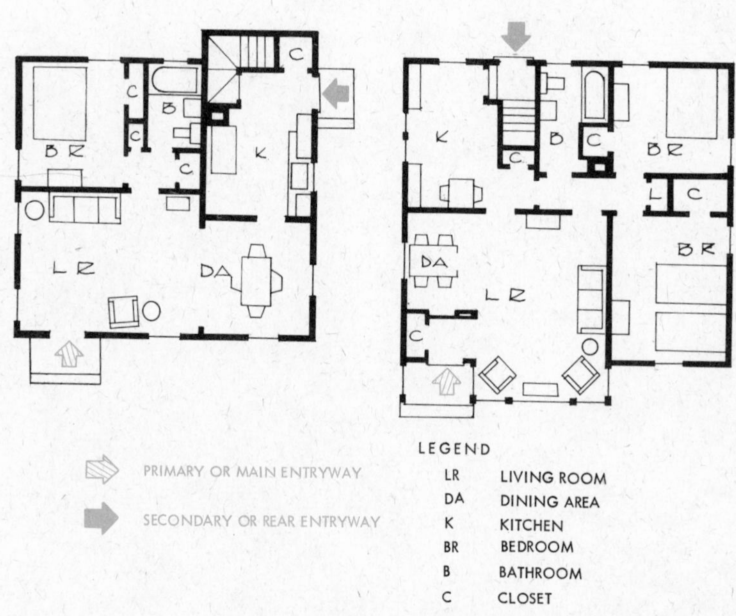

Fig. 2-4. Check the paths of circulation on these two plans.

the house should be located for ease of movement. Activities such as carrying groceries into the house, disposing of refuse, or carrying wet laundry from the kitchen or basement to the rear yard or service area must be considered in planning doorway locations. Circulation paths between the house and the outside facility areas (such as garage, driveway, patio, rear yard, etc.) should be designed for maximum convenience.

Good Circulation Factors

The most important factors influencing good circulation are:

1. Direct routes between rooms
2. Each room as independent from another as possible
3. Rooms free from traffic lanes
4. Rooms designed for minimum interruption of social groups
5. No space wasted by unnecessary hallways
6. Traffic routed through "not too busy" areas to avoid unnecessary floor wear and extra cleaning

Check Points

To check any floor plan for adequate circulation, move from one area or zone within the floor plan. Each route should be as short and direct as possible. Where applicable, use the following check points in the two floor plans shown in Fig. 2-4.

Check the circulation path from:

1. Kitchen to front entrance
2. Kitchen to dining room
3. Kitchen to porch
4. Living room to kitchen
5. Living room to dining room
6. Front entrance to living room
7. Rear entrance to basement
8. Rear entrance to second floor rooms
9. Bedrooms to bathroom
10. Front or rear entrance to coat closets
11. Various areas of the first floor to any room on the upper level
12. Outside or basement to lavatories or bathrooms

Proper Orientation

In floor planning, *orientation* refers to the house and room arrangement which takes into consideration the sun's rays, prevailing breezes, and scenic views.

Solar Orientation

Solar orientation, or house arrangement which obtains benefits from the sun, is an ancient concept. Even the earliest cave dwellers preferred a southern exposure. To efficiently apply solar orientation in floor planning, the position of the sun and the approximate latitude of the building site must be known.

Solar orientation of the home can best be achieved on a wide lot (between 75 and 100 feet), because the extra space allows more design freedom in floor planning. For example, a one-story house is feasible within a wide area. On a narrow lot, however, liberty in designing the single-level house is very limited because complete privacy from the public or neighbor's view may not be obtainable. This is generally true in areas where adjacent buildings are too close to the home site. In such areas, a two-story house design is more suitable.

Planning the house to take advantage of the benefits from the sun (in the northern hemisphere) almost always makes it necessary to place the most lived-in areas (living room, dining room, family room, or kitchen) on the southern part of the site. Placement and type of windows in these rooms usually depend upon (1) the activities for which the room will be used; (2) the surrounding views; and (3) the interior and exterior aesthetic effects. However, in cases where solar orientation is of prime importance, some of these factors may be neglected. The areas of the house in which sunlighting is not of primary importance (garage, hallways, stairways, bathrooms, etc.) are usually located on the northern part of the site. (In the southern hemisphere or in warm or desert areas, the orientation of the house normally would be reversed.)

Orientation towards the sun may be applied to any house design. Generally, the *non-traditional* type of architectural design offers more liberty in planning and results in the best use of sunlight and solar heat. Non-traditional architecture includes styles such as the ranch type and contemporary, as opposed to the pure or true Cape Cod, Southern Colonial, New England Colonial,

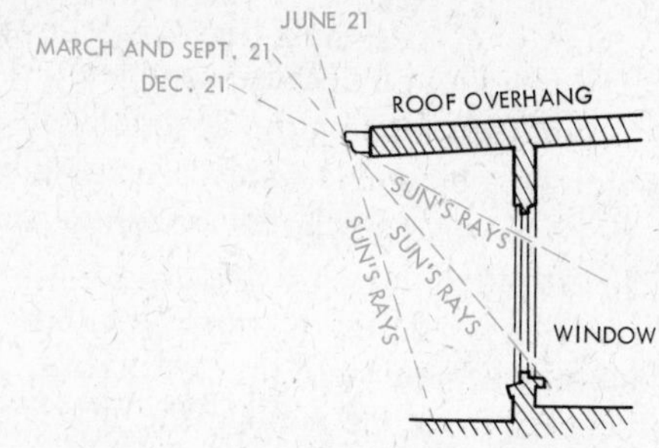

Fig. 2-5. The elevation angle of the sun with respect to a building changes during the four seasons of a year. The roof overhang is designed accordingly. (This building is set at 42° North latitude.)

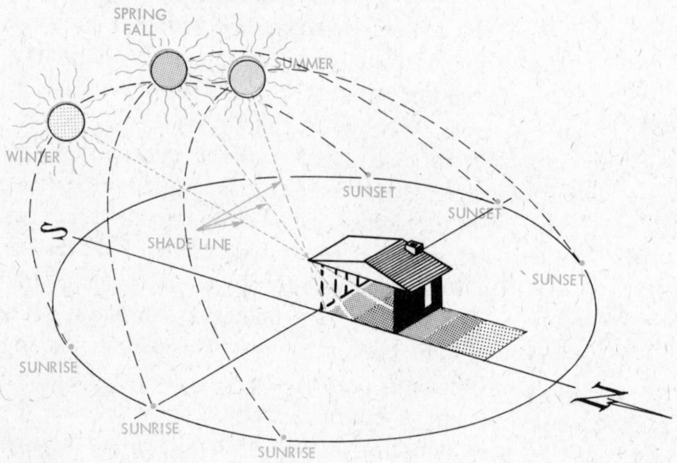

Dutch Colonial, etc. The rancher and contemporary do not have any fixed or set locations for living areas, or any fixed size or style for the windows. Non-traditional designs, therefore, permit the use of large glass areas, such as picture windows, sliding glass doors, or window walls. This type of window allows more sunlight and radiant heat to come into the house during the winter months. To obtain utmost heat benefit from the sun without losing the interior heat of the house, window panes are double in thickness. Sealed dead air spaces between the panes allow radiant heat to enter and prevent the loss of internal heat. The size and angle of roof overhang on each window controls the amount of sunlight that enters the house (see Fig. 2-5, top).

Best sun advantage (in the northern hemisphere) is obtained when window walls face toward the south. During the winter months, maximum heat may be received from a southern exposure. During the summer, however, windows with southern exposure receive less heat than those oriented towards the east or west. This effect is due mainly to the elevated angle of the sun with respect to the house. During the summer months, the sun's angle of elevation is much higher than at any other time of the year. Fig. 2-5 (bottom) shows how the elevation angle of the sun changes during the four seasons of the year. The height of the sun at any particular time of day is dependent upon the time of year and the latitude of the site. The greatest change in the sun's angle occurs in the areas where the latitude of the building site is furthest from the equator. The illustrations in Figs. 2-6 and 2-7 have been set at 40° North latitude to show the effects of the sun's high arc in summer and low arc in winter. In Fig. 2-6 the patio side faces west; in Fig. 2-7 the patio side faces south. The shadow on the east and north side is evident.

Wind and View Orientation

Orientation of large windows should not only be toward the sun, but also, if possible, toward the direction of prevailing breezes and scenic views. In areas where the winter season is very cold, however, large glass areas should not face towards the prevailing winter winds.

Orientation toward prevailing winds is important only if the breezes are able to aid in cooling the house during the summer

Fig. 2-6A. Patio faces west. December 21, 11 A.M. A patio placed on the west side will provide shade when it is neither needed or wanted. To benefit from the winter sun extend the patio around the south side.

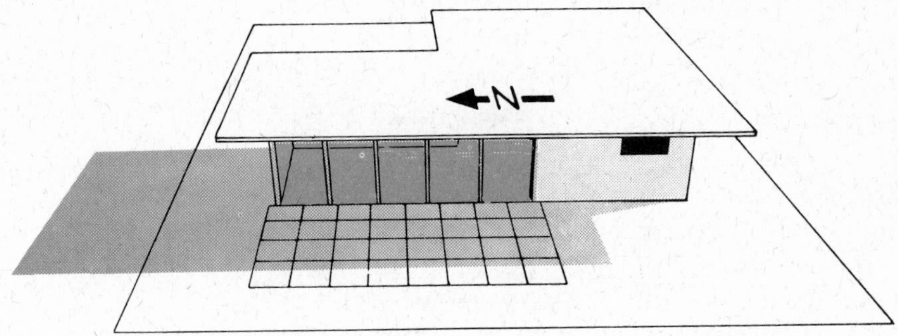

FROM: LANE PUBLICATIONS, MENLO PARK, CALIFORNIA.

Fig. 2-6B. West. December 21, 4 P.M. The late, low afternoon sun can sweep across the patio and into the living room. The angle of the sun may be discomforting to some occupants; a screen or plantings can block some of the low angle sun.

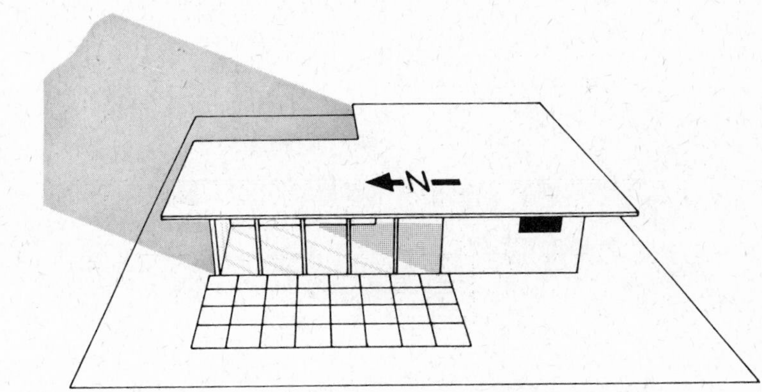

FROM: LANE PUBLICATIONS, MENLO PARK, CALIFORNIA.

Fig. 2-6C. West. March 21-September 21, 11 A.M. A patio and living room oriented to the west offers no sun problem in the morning hours; however, no warmth can be derived from the sun on cool March mornings.

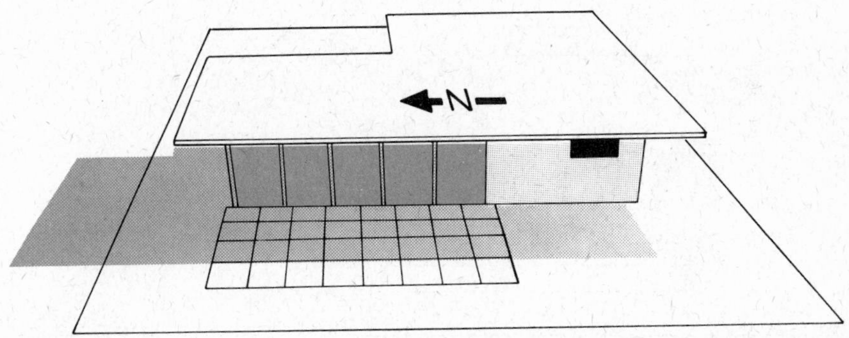

FROM: LANE PUBLICATIONS, MENLO PARK, CALIFORNIA.

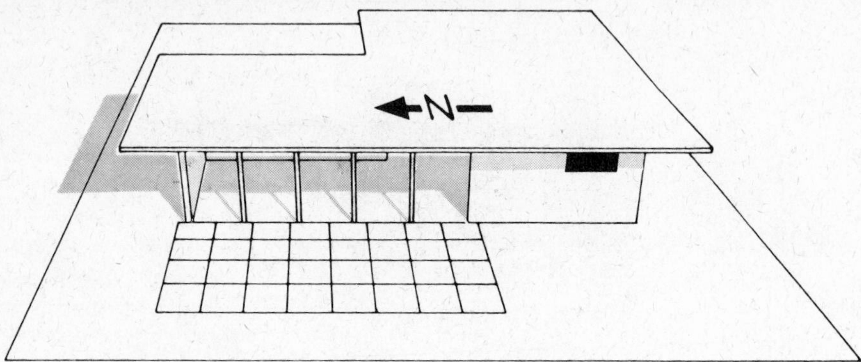

FROM: LANE PUBLICATIONS, MENLO PARK, CALIFORNIA.

Fig. 2-6D. West. March 21-September 21, 4 P.M. During the warm season, the western sun is at its most punishing angle. Vertical baffles and an extended overhang will help. A line of trees, tall shrubs, vertical screens, or louvers may provide the best solution.

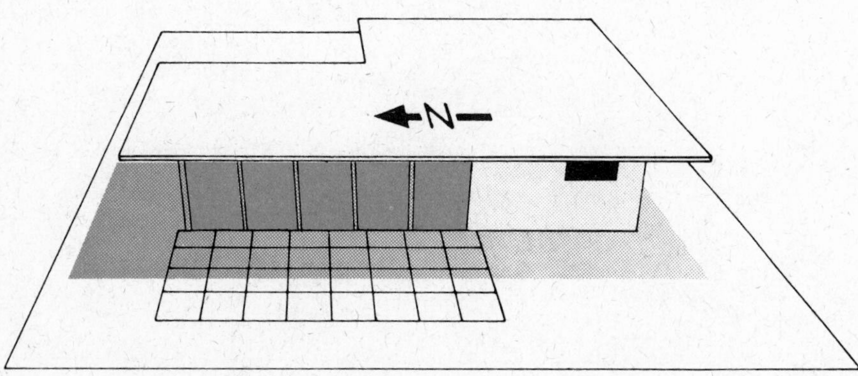

FROM: LANE PUBLICATIONS, MENLO PARK, CALIFORNIA.

Fig. 2-6E. West. June 21, 11 A.M. All during the year the west side of the house is in the morning shade. On the west side during the summer months temperatures vary more than in any other location.

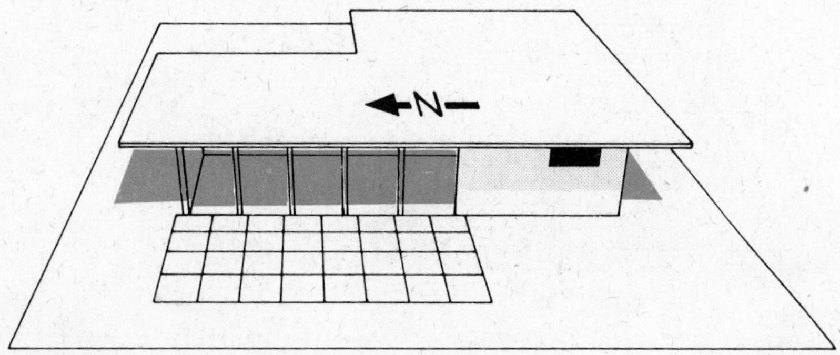

FROM: LANE PUBLICATIONS, MENLO PARK, CALIFORNIA.

Fig. 2-6F. West. June 21, 4 P.M. The sun's rays may be intercepted on the west side by vines, trees, or screens. This avoids the west wall's input of radiated heat long after sundown.

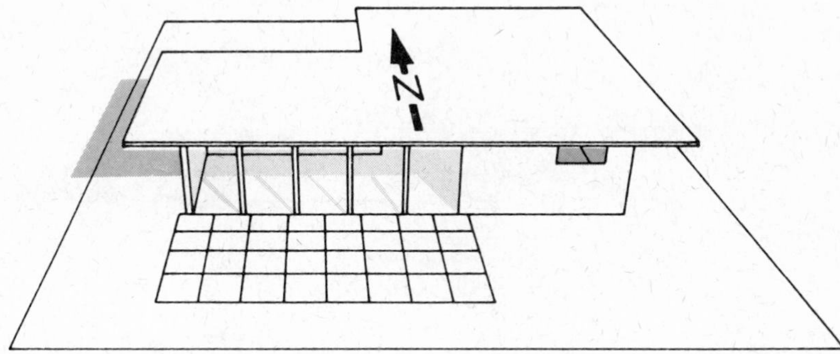

FROM: LANE PUBLICATIONS, MENLO PARK, CALIFORNIA.

Fig. 2-7A. Patio faces south. December 21, 11 A.M. The sun's arc is at its lowest point on December 21 when the sun's rays stream across the patio and into the living area.

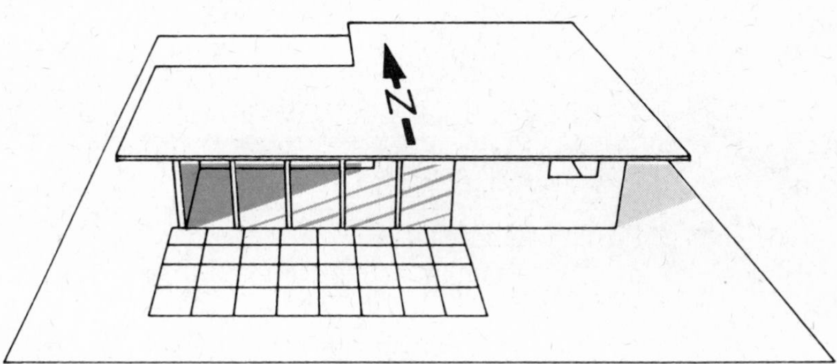

FROM: LANE PUBLICATIONS, MENLO PARK, CALIFORNIA.

Fig. 2-7B. South. December 21, 4 P.M. In cold winter areas the sun should be allowed to enter unimpeded into the living areas. In milder winter areas this pattern can't be used without causing too much heat in October and November. A screening of trees will overcome this problem.

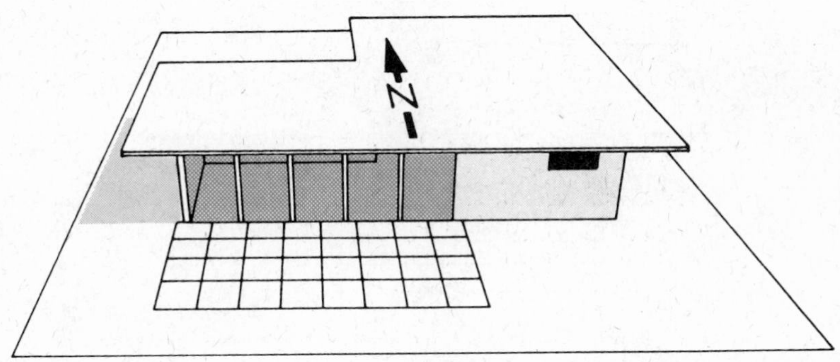

FROM: LANE PUBLICATIONS, MENLO PARK, CALIFORNIA.

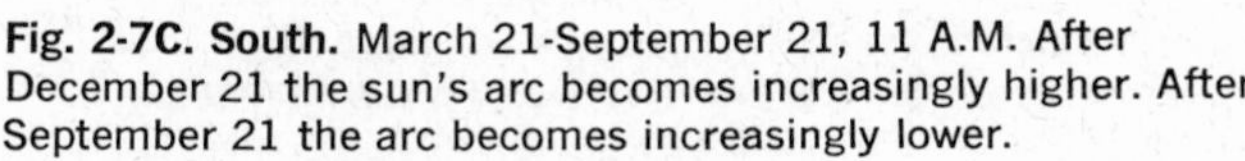
Fig. 2-7C. South. March 21-September 21, 11 A.M. After December 21 the sun's arc becomes increasingly higher. After September 21 the arc becomes increasingly lower.

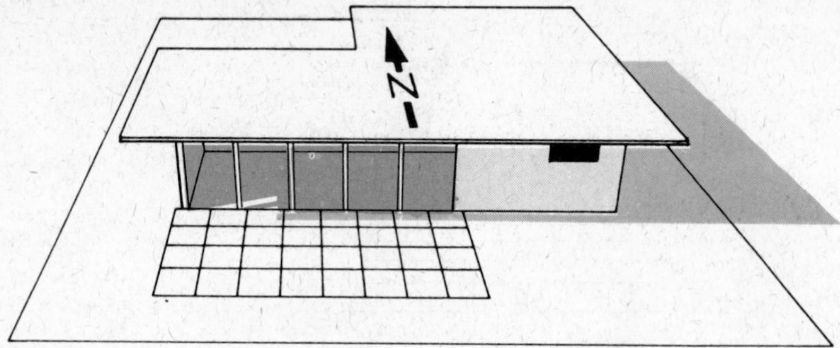

FROM: LANE PUBLICATIONS, MENLO PARK, CALIFORNIA.

Fig. 2-7D. South. March 21-September 21, 4 P.M. Living areas oriented in this direction will obtain adequate protection during the late afternoon. To shade the patio in mild areas, a vertical screening must be built or grown on the west side of the patio.

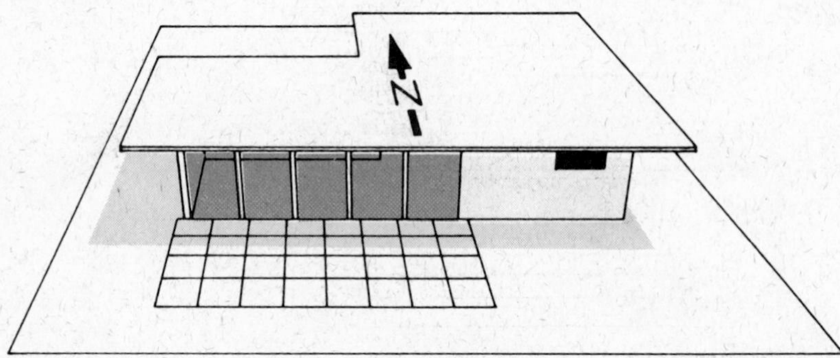

FROM. LANE PUBLICATIONS, MENLO PARK, CALIFORNIA.

Fig. 2-7E. South. June 21, 11 A.M. An adequate roof overhang will provide some protection for the patio at this time.

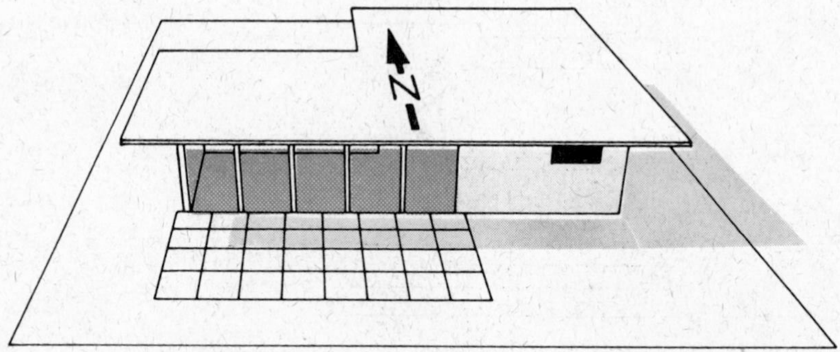

FROM: LANE PUBLICATIONS, MENLO PARK, CALIFORNIA.

Fig. 2-7F. South. June 21, 4 P.M. The late afternoon shade pattern leaves much of the patio in the sun while the living area is shaded. There will be less shade from this day on. Plantings can be utilized to add shade to the patio.

season. Cooling or ventilating the house can be achieved by placing *louvered openings* (slatted openings) above and below the large glass walls or windows.

Prior to planning the orientation of major rooms, it is advisable to contact the nearest weather bureau office or local airport for information regarding the direction of the prevailing breezes in the area. Breezes in Illinois, for example, are out of the southwesterly direction during the summer, and out of the northwesterly during the winter.

Existing trees and landscaping, as well as planned future landscaping, must be taken into account to ensure the most pleasing scenic view.

Room Orientation

Not all the rooms can be oriented toward the most desirable location. Some rooms may have to be placed in locations where their orientation with respect to sunlight, prevailing breezes, or scenic views is undesirable. When making the preliminary floor plan sketches of the house, major consideration should be given to its room orientation. The following paragraphs list the suggested orientation of major rooms.

The Living Room should face south and west (corner location is preferable) so it may receive an ample amount of sunshine at all times during the year. This room may view the garden or the patio.

Dining Room. It is generally agreed that the dining room should have an easterly exposure in order to receive the morning sunlight. Also, the dining room may be located in the southern part of the house.

Kitchen. Most architects suggest that the kitchen face north and/or east. Since most housewives do a considerable part of their work in the morning, sunlight is desirable. A kitchen with a northern exposure remains cool during hot summer afternoons. The kitchen, for convenience, should be located as near as possible to the driveway.

Bedrooms. Usually, bedrooms are oriented according to personal preferences. If possible, however, it is better to have the master bedroom oriented towards the south, and the child's bedroom oriented towards the south or southwest.

Studios and Work Rooms. These rooms should be oriented towards the north because natural light is desirable for close work.

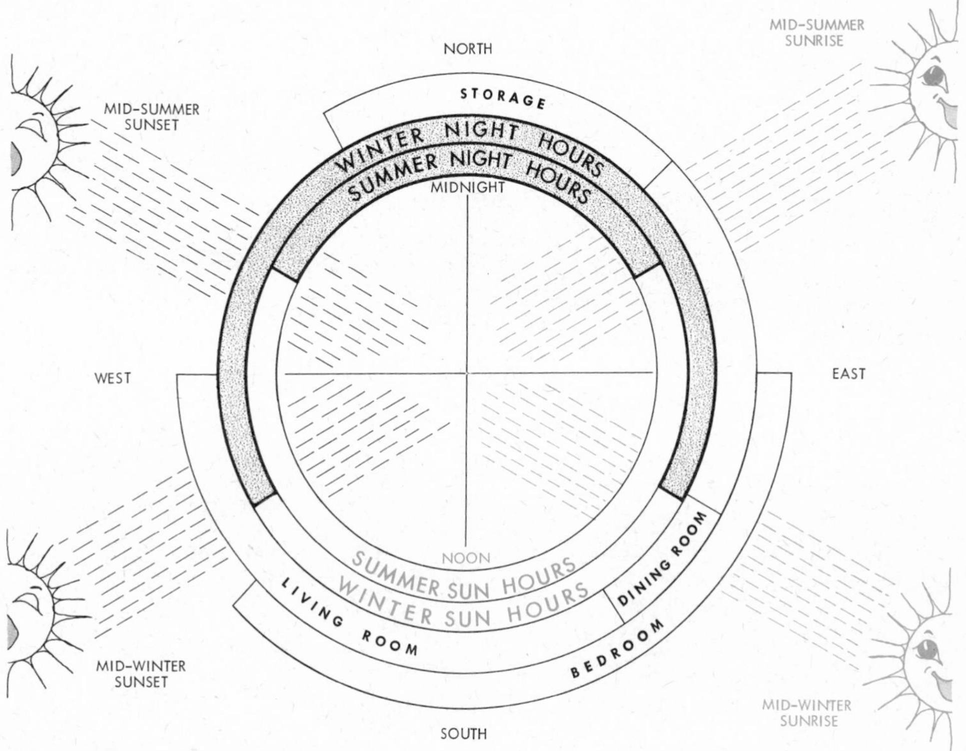

Fig. 2-8. Orientation Chart: Sketch a small scale plan, place it on the center of the chart, then revolve the plan to get the best position for maximum sunlight in the rooms.

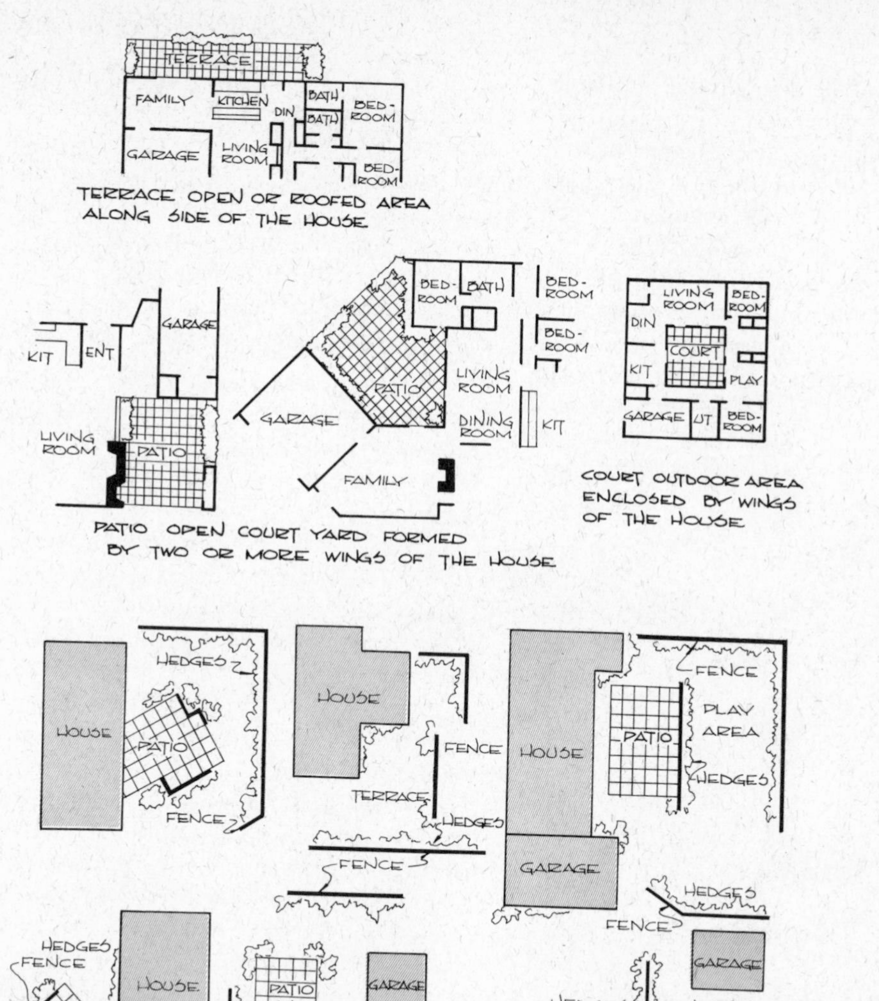

Fig. 2-9. The outdoor living area may be extended by using screenings associated with patios, terraces, and courts.

Porches and Terraces are generally used for relaxation in late afternoons. It is important, therefore, that these areas either face away from the late afternoon sun, or be protected with plantings, privacy screens, or awnings.

The Laundry and Utility Rooms should have direct access to the driveway. These rooms may be placed in the least desirable location on the site.

Orientation Check List

Make a small sketch of a one story dwelling showing the basic living areas, and place it at the center of the orientation chart on Fig. 2-8. Revolve the sketch on the chart to get the best position for maximum sunlight in the rooms. Use the following check list for the ideal orientation of the rooms.

1. Principal living areas should face towards the south.
2. Living room should face south and/or west, and toward the prevailing breezes, if possible.
3. Kitchen should face either towards the north, the east, or the northeast.
4. Dining room should have either an eastern or southern exposure.

Adaptability to Indoor-Outdoor Living

The present trend in home building is toward back-yard outdoor living. Floor plans reflect this change by orienting the major living area to the rear, as shown in Fig. 2-9.

Many new homes have the major rooms (living room, dining room, and/or family room) oriented away from the street. Living rooms (with large window areas) commonly face the rear of the lot. Orientation of the living areas in this manner allows a large amount of sunlight to enter the interior living area, and permits the possibility of future expansion of this area to the open space of the garden, the patio, or the terrace. Doors opening to the patio or terrace make the outdoor living area easily accessible from the living room, the dining room, and the other major rooms.

The house with a separate or an attached garage is usually placed well towards the front of the lot to provide the rear area with larger space for outdoor living. The proper orientation and placement of the house is always important in the consideration of an area for indoor-outdoor living activities. However, a house should not be arbitrarily placed merely to facilitate back yard living.

Lots which are small and extremely close to adjoining lots may have their outdoor-living area enclosed with either wall panels or fences as shown in Fig. 2-9. This form of enclosure is often considered temporary. In that event, shrubs, evergreens, or hedges may be planted close to the wall panels or fences. When the plantings reach their mature height, they may replace the temporary enclosure.

Figs. 2-10 and 2-11 show two types of privacy screens used for enclosure. Placement of such screens around the outdoor living area provides a location blocked off from the neighbor's view. A barbeque fireplace, a good flooring, a ceiling made of open trellis work or corrugated plastic, or some built-in furniture may be included in the design of this area. Often, the outdoor living area is one of the most pleasant in the home.

The location of the patio has a direct bearing on the adaptability of an area to indoor-outdoor living. Fig. 2-12 shows the proper placement of patios at different lo-

MASONITE CORP., CHICAGO, ILLINOIS

Fig. 2-10. A privacy screen adds a decorative touch. Hardboard panels and clay tile fill the openings.

MASONITE CORP., CHICAGO, ILLINOIS

Fig. 2-11. Complete privacy is assured by using this type of screen made of plastic sheets.

cations on the lot. A patio located at the side of the house, for example, is ideally suited to lots which are wide and shallow. A patio located at the rear of the house is generally best suited for narrow and deep lots, as the view from the street may be blocked or screened by the house itself. However, a patio located on the street side of the lot usually poses a design problem. This may be overcome by using aesthetically designed screening which complements the landscape as well as the home. Most patios are oriented toward the eastern or southern side of the house for the best protection from the warm rays of the afternoon summer sun.

An outdoor living area which may be enclosed on all sides by the house (Fig. 2-12, bottom right) is ideal for a small lot. This type of house design permits every room to have a pleasant view of the patio or courtyard, while having maximum privacy from the neighbor's view. House designs of this form are best suited for areas where heating is not a problem and mild seasonal weather is predominant.

To determine the adaptability of floor plans to the indoor-outdoor living conditions, note the following questions.

1. Does the living area face the best outdoor area?
2. Is area oriented for best sunlight?
3. Are the indoor areas accessible from the outside by convenient openings (i.e., sliding or hinged doors)?
4. Does the indoor-outdoor area have privacy and is it shielded by house wings, fences, or plantings?

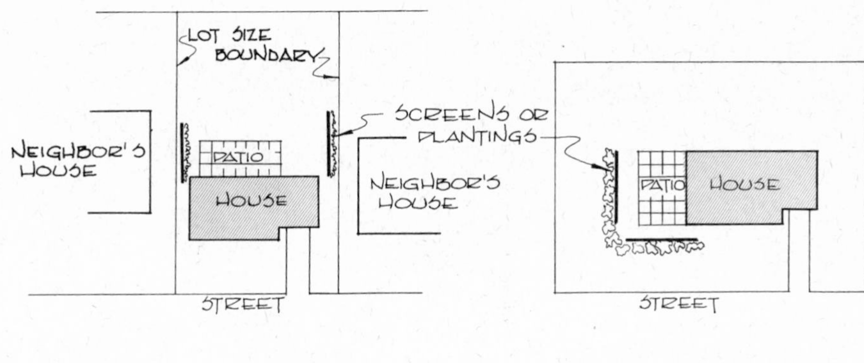

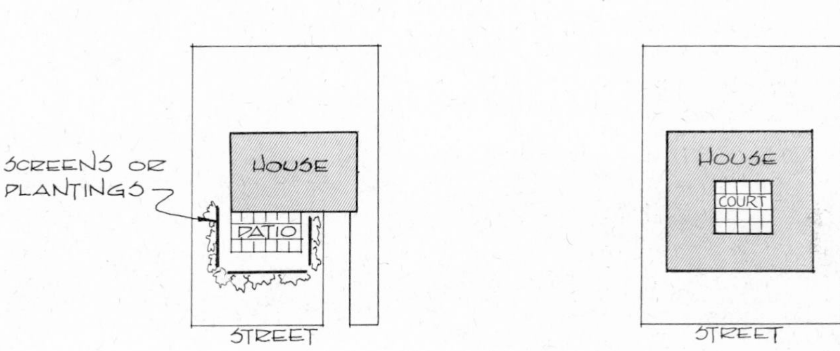

Fig. 2-12. The shape and size of the lot has a major influence on the design of the patio.

Open Planning Concept

To increase the livability of a small house, various design features may be employed to make some rooms appear larger. Open planning is one means by which this may be accomplished. When open planning is applied to a floor plan, the wall, which generally separates two adjoining rooms, is eliminated. Some examples of adjoining room combinations in which open planning may be applied are (1) kitchen and family room; (2) dining ell and living room; (3) dining room and kitchen; (4) kitchen and laundry areas; (5) dining room and living room; and (6) kitchen, dining area, and living room.

In essence, open planning does not limit the view to the four walls of the room. The illusion of spaciousness is created by eliminating the partition wall between adjoining rooms and adding a large glass window which faces the back yard or a scenic view. Fig. 2-13 demonstrates the effect of spaciousness when special interior designing is incorporated in the plan of a room. The interior design of the living room area may create a spacious effect when the ceiling is of the *cathedral* type (ceiling which parallels the roof), and the partial partition between this room and the next does not extend all the way to the ceiling.

Room partitions or dividers separate one area from another and are usually not permanently placed within the room. Generally, dividers make area boundaries for activities less definite, thus allowing a more versatile use of the room. Examples of room partitions or dividers are: partial walls, draw drapes, screens, accordion-pleated or folding doors, pocket doors (doors sliding out of sight when not in use), dividers of translucent material, and furniture groups. An example of a room divider is shown in Fig. 2-14.

Fig. 2-13. A cathedral ceiling, wide expanse of glass, and low partitions create a feeling of spaciousness.

KHOURY BROS., INC.; CHICAGO, ILLINOIS.

Fig. 2-14. A movable room divider may add to the general decor as well as serve a functional purpose.

In open planning, walls often become functional because furniture or appliances are built into them. Generally, walls with built-in units (such as a bookcase, storage unit, desk, high fidelity-stereo system, television set, beverage cooler, washer, dryer, water heater, dishwasher, etc.) give more floor space to the room and add beauty to the interior design.

Open planning, because of the large open space involved, requires some form of sound control. Examples of materials which aid in reducing sound within a room are: acoustical tile (generally for the ceiling), wood (for wall panelling), and rubber or asphalt tile (usually for the floors).

Floor plans with open planning deviate from the traditional concept of living areas as places for specific activities. Today's floor plan design permits flexible use of areas for different purposes. Fig. 2-15 shows examples of open planning as it is applied to floor plans. Note how different methods create the illusion of spaciousness and partial separation of activities.

Proper Window Location

In residential or commercial architecture, windows have long been the dominant element in the design of building exteriors and interiors. When windows are properly selected and located, they become functional, aesthetic parts of the home plan design. Today's millworks and window manufacturers offer a wide variety of windows which accent the character, the comfort, and the convenience of the home.

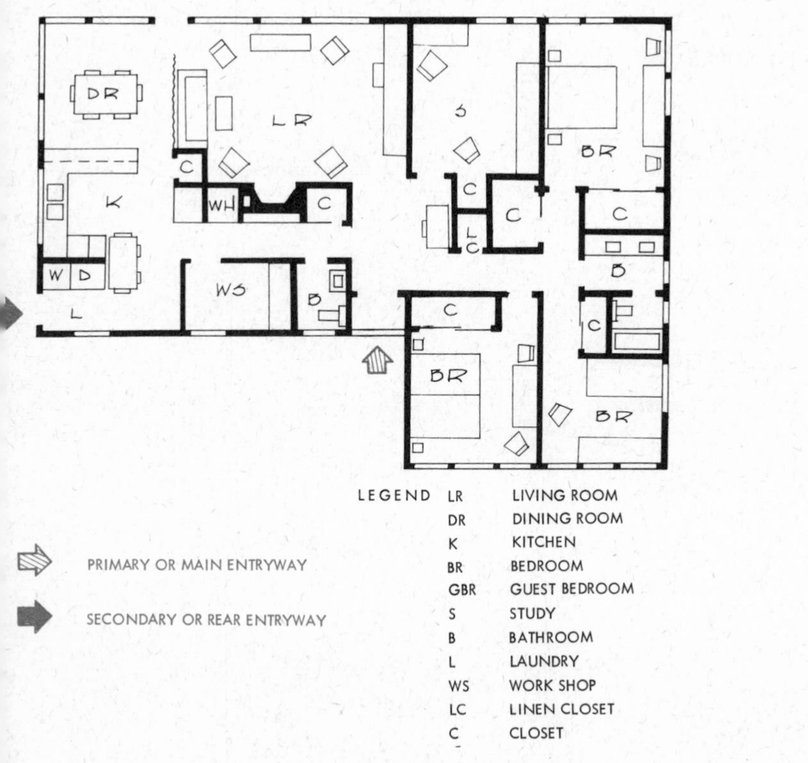

Fig. 2-15. Open planning creates the illusion of spaciousness and adds flexibility when folding or sliding doors are used to create privacy when desired.

LIVING ROOM

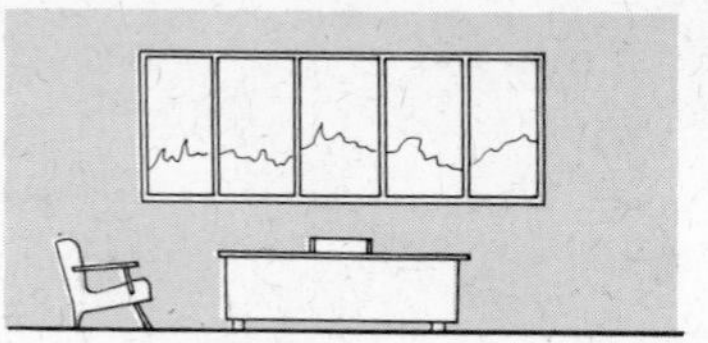

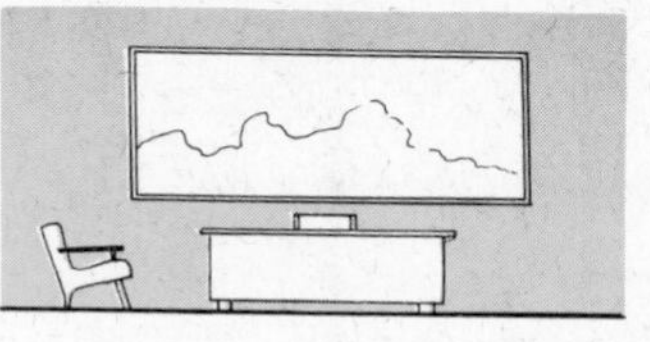

DON'T BREAK THE VIEW

Fig. 2-16. Windows should be planned with regard to view and privacy.

LIVING ROOM

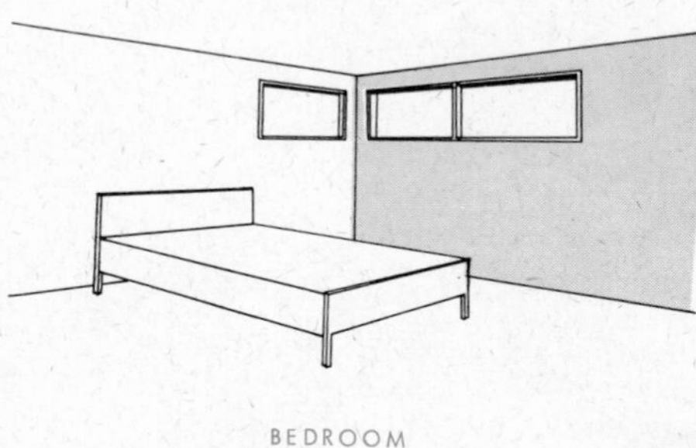

BEDROOM

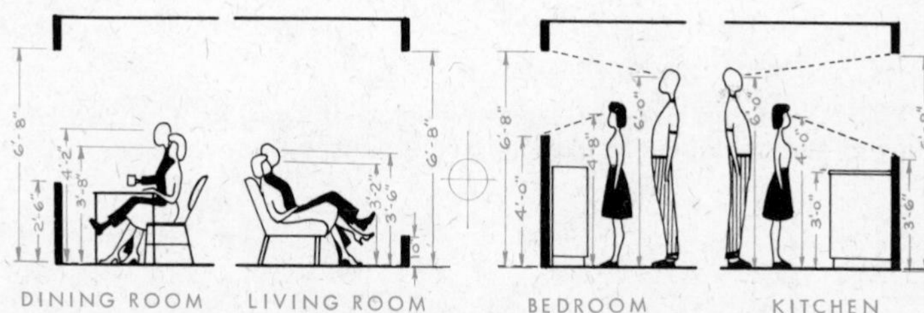

Fig. 2-17. Suggested Sill Heights: Sill heights should be in accordance with the use and purpose of the room.

Window location should be planned so as to face the most pleasing view, while producing some degree of privacy in the room (see Fig. 2-16). Large windows give rooms the effect of spaciousness by "borrowing" the outside light and view. Windows in all cases should be related to the exterior design. For example, a competent architect or designer would not consider specifying twelve pane *double-hung windows* for the living room of a home designed in the flat-roof *contemporary* style. A window of this type is better suited to the *Cape Cod* or the *colonial* style of home design.

A room becomes very pleasant if the window sills are located below the eye level of a seated person. However, placing certain windows above the eye level, as in bed rooms, is sometimes desirable. Fig. 2-17 gives suggestions on sill heights for various types of rooms.

Cross ventilation within an individual room is directly related to the arrangement and proportioning of windows. This is sometimes called *fenestration*. Window arrangement, in this context, refers not only to the location of windows in elevation and plan, but also to their type (i.e., double-hung, casement, sliding, hopper, etc.). Fig. 2-18 shows the flow of air through a room with different window openings and arrangement.

Bedrooms located in the front or the rear area of a house should have their windows located near the *interior wall-partitions* to allow as much ventilation as possible. Fig. 2-19 illustrates the flow of prevailing breezes through the house. Note that by placing the windows adjacent to the interior wall-partitions, the breezes will cross ventilate the room. Windows placed at a room corner would only ventilate that corner, with very little ventilating benefits for the rest of the room. Some windows cannot be placed directly adjacent to the interior wall partitions. Windows such as those in front of the house, for example, are often centered on the wall.

Fig. 2-18. The window opening determines the air flow through a room.

Fig. 2-19. The location of the windows also determines the air flow. Correct window placement allows cross ventilation.

The absolute minimum window glass area, according to the Federal Housing Administration (FHA) standards, is 10 per cent of the floor area. About 4 per cent of the floor area is an adequate proportion for natural (window opening) ventilation. For example, according to minimum standards, a 10′ x 13′ bedroom must have 13 sq. ft. for window area; of the 13 sq. ft. approximately 5¼ sq. ft. must be given to natural ventilation. Conditions allowing, about 25 per cent of the floor space would be a more satisfactory window glass area. Excessive glass area, however, often contributes to cold rooms. Good insulation to a certain extent will decrease the heat loss. For adequate daytime illumination in the house, the window area should be equal to 17 per cent of the floor area.

Privacy in Living Areas

Sociologists have indicated that with increasing population, privacy of the individual, the family, or the group is becoming increasingly important. Many of our daily activities require an area where there is privacy. It is often difficult, however, to incorporate provisions for maximum privacy, especially in the plan of a small house. Small houses have some design limitations on the living areas.

Privacy in living areas is the result of careful planning. Activities requiring an area for privacy are sleeping, bathing, dressing, studying, etc. Generally, the rooms where these activities take place can be grouped into three areas: (1) living area, (2) quiet or sleeping area, and (3) service or work area.

The door location and swing direction generally adds to the privacy of an area. The bedroom door, for example, should not show the bed and dressing areas in full view of the other rooms or the hallway. The dining room and kitchen doors should not expose the working part of the kitchen. Similarly, the main entryway door should not offer an immediate view of the living room.

Privacy is possible in the outdoor living area with proper screening. The shape of the house, its orientation on the lot, or the slope and elevation of the lot may offer good screening for the outdoor living area. Other forms of screening used are: the garage or service sheds, wood fences, low masonry walls, hedges, low-growing fruit or ornamental trees, shrubs, and fast-growing vines on trellises.

Privacy should be thought of not only in terms of sight, but also in terms of sound. Extraneous sounds can be reduced by using good quality, close-fitted doors between adjoining rooms, and by using acoustical materials (rugs, drapery, acoustical tile, insulation, etc.). Sounds or noises from the living room, for example, may be isolated from the bedroom area by designing the floor plan with sound baffles such as hallways, closets, bathrooms, and quality doors.

Adequate Storage Space

Adequate storage space is a primary household need. In floor planning, closets should be functionally designed to meet all the requirements for storing or accommodating the family's accumulated possessions.

Closet Space

The closet space costs the same as almost any other space in the house. Houses in the medium price category must have their

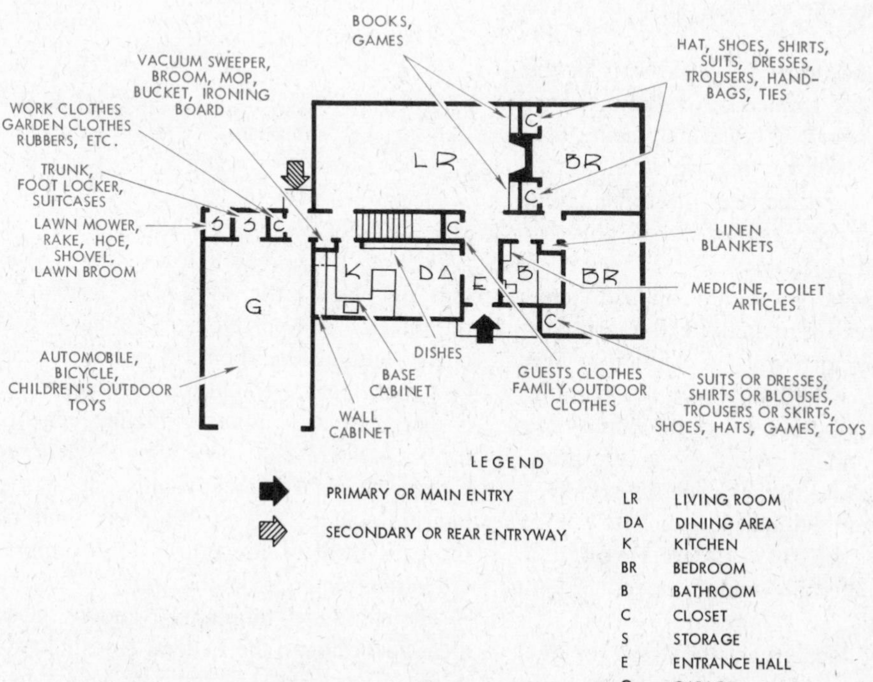

Fig. 2-20. Household articles are associated with particular storage areas. In planning, this should be taken into consideration.

TABLE 2-1

MINIMUM AND SUGGESTED SIZE OF CLOSETS IN A SIX-ROOM HOUSE

Closet Location	Minimum Size	Suggested Size
FIRST FLOOR:		
MAIN ENTRYWAY (Guest or Coat Closet)	2'-0" x 3'-0"	3'-6" x 3'-6"
HALLWAY OR KITCHEN (Cleaning or Broom Closet)	2'-0" x 1'-0"	2'-6" x 3'-6"
BACK ENTRYWAY (Utility or Sports Closet)		2'-6" x 3'-0"
LIVING ROOM (Living Room Closet)		2'-6" x 3'-0"
SECOND FLOOR:		
HALLWAY (Linen Closet)	2'-0" x 2'-0"	2'-0" x 4'-0"
MASTER BEDROOM (Bedroom Closets)	2'-0" x 3'-0"*	2'-6" x 4'-0"*
SINGLE BEDROOM (Bedroom Closet)	2'-0" x 3'-0"	2'-6" x 4'-0"
SINGLE BEDROOM (Bedroom Closet)	2'-0" x 2'-6"	2'-6" x 3'-0"

*Master bedroom generally requires two closet spaces.

closets well planned so as to keep the total costs within reason.

In order to obtain maximum benefit from storage areas, the space should be specifically designed for the items to be stored. In addition, these storage spaces should be located as near as possible to where the stored articles are to be used. Fig. 2-20 shows some of the more basic storage areas and associated articles. Unless closet spaces are planned carefully, considerable floor space will be wastefully consumed.

Although closet planning is often thought of as just making use of excess spaces in floor planning, the size of these spaces are important in order to functionally utilize them for storage purposes. Table 2-1 gives

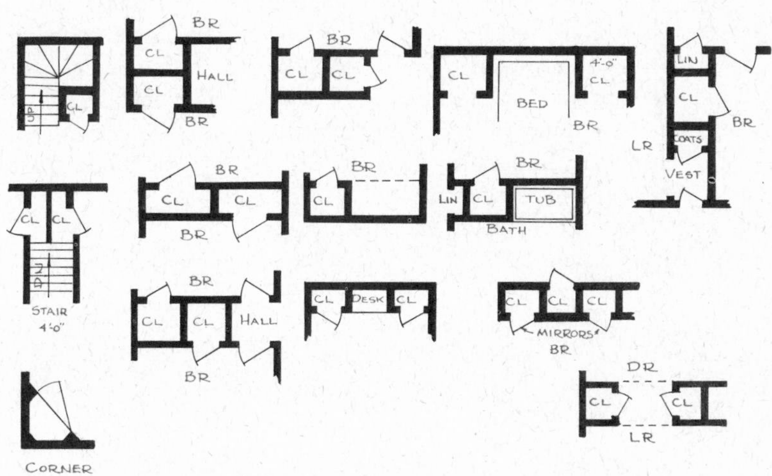

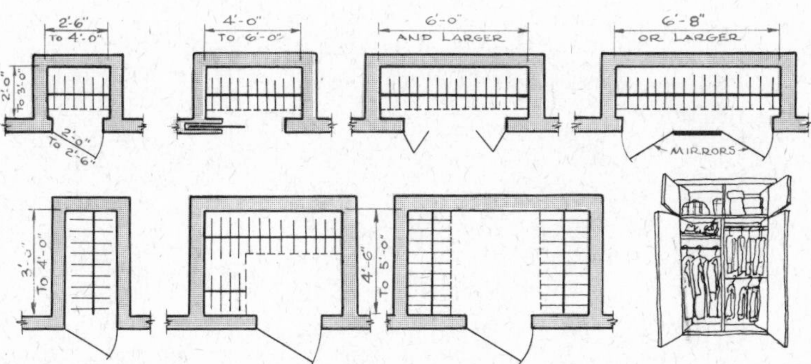

Fig. 2-21. Closets should be planned in relation to the available space.

the *minimum* and the *suggested* closet space for a typical six-room, one story or multi-level home.

The place where closets are to be located, and the type of items to be stored, are the controlling factors in good closet designs. Bedroom closets, for example, should be conveniently located and designed for accessibility of stored items such as clothes, shoes, and other personal articles. The guest closet, located near the main entrance, should be used for storing such articles as coats, rubbers, etc. The broom or cleaning closet, located near to or in the kitchen, should be used for storing such items as brooms, the vacuum cleaner, wet mops, dust mops, and other things generally used for cleaning. Fig. 2-21 shows various types of closet designs and arrangements for bed rooms and other areas.

Storage Space Check List

In the following list storage space is associated with the items common to each type.

1. Master bedroom closets: suits, shirts, blouses, dresses, shoes, hats, neckties, etc.
2. Children's bedroom closet: clothes, shoes, toys, etc.
3. Guest bedroom closet: clothes, storage space, luggage, etc.
4. Guest closet: summer or winter outer garments, rain apparel, umbrellas, hats, rubbers, etc.
5. Linen closet: sheets, blankets, pillowcases, towels, bathroom supplies, table cloths, napkins, etc.
6. Cleaning closet: brooms, dust mops, cleaning supplies, vacuum cleaner, brushes, etc.
7. Game room or utility closets: sport equipment and games, tools, hobby supplies, etc.
8. Kitchen cabinets: food, staples, cooking utensils, kitchen utensils, etc.
9. Bathroom cabinet: medicines, etc.
10. Garage closet: lawn and garden equipment, garden clothes, car cleaning equipment, charcoal grill, etc.

Arrangement of Room Furnishings

Room size depends not only upon purpose, but also upon the number of pieces and the types of furniture the room must contain. Since most room furnishings are

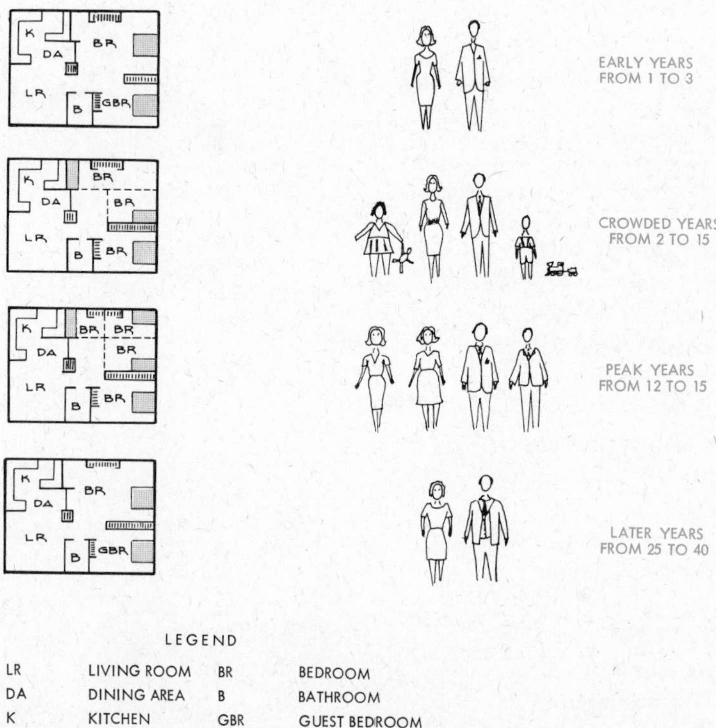

Fig. 2-22. Family changes directly affect the floor plan of the home. With a **flexible plan** these changes may be made without great difficulty.

standardized, odd sized or odd shaped rooms are normally avoided. A 9′ by 12′ rug, for example, is the most common size. An odd sized room therefore may necessitate the purchase of non-standard and expensive rugs or carpeting.

Room furnishings should be arranged in accordance with traffic circulation. The fireplace and the furniture adjacent to it, for example, should always be out of the traffic path. When the height of the furniture is above the waist, single passage width between 2′-0″ and 2′-6″ is desirable. Space between low furniture, such as the coffee table and the sofa, should never be less than 12″.

Rooms should be planned so that more than one furniture arrangement is possible. The size and location of windows and their sill height — and consequently the amount of sunlight and the view—plays a major role in the possible furniture combinations. Furniture should not, for example, obstruct the view.

In all cases, simplicity in furniture arrangement is better than complexity, which may result in overcrowding.

Flexibility of Expansion

In home planning, adequacy of space includes both the present and the future family needs. Provisions for later home expansion is always desirable, since most families normally change their manner of living and their activities. Possible family additions should also be taken into consideration. Future needs should not, however, dominate the main plan or the overall appearance of the floor plan. Fig. 2-22 shows how family changes affect the floor plan of a home.

One of the most effortless and economical methods of expansion is *conversion.* Conversion entails changing the purpose of a room or area to suit the changing family pattern. This may be accomplished by simply changing the nature of the furniture or

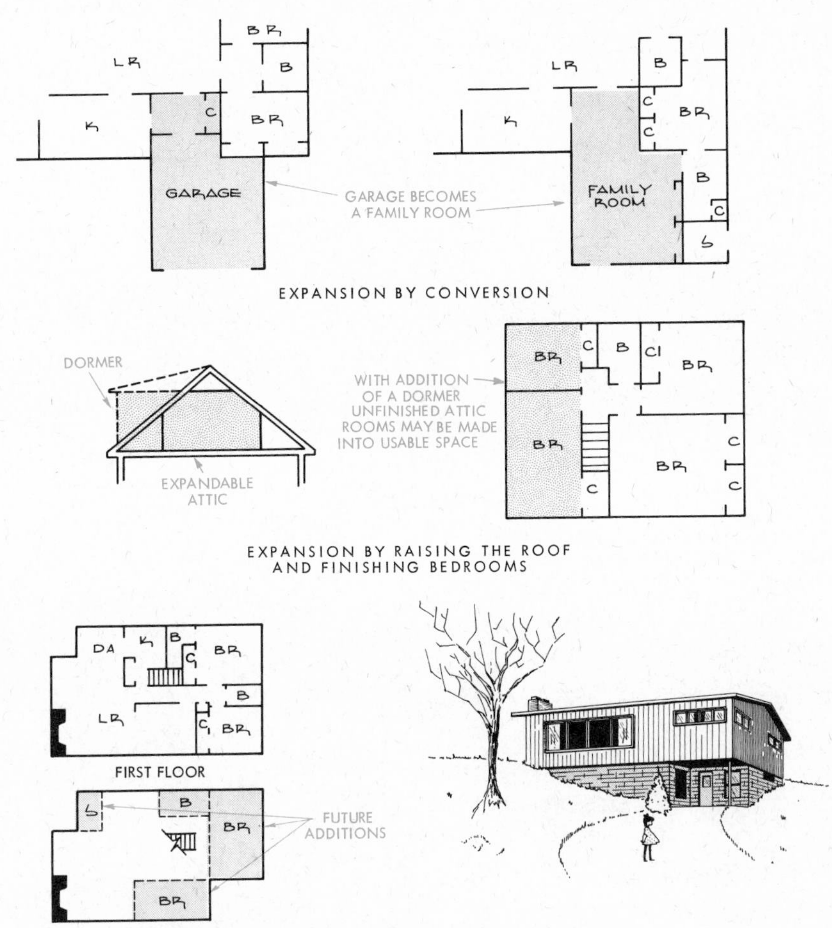

Fig. 2-23. Additional space may be gained by conversion, finishing, or expansion.

by adding storage space and removing or adding a partition wall. Fig. 2-23 shows some methods of conversion.

Another method is expansion by *addition*. This is illustrated in Figs. 2-24 and 2-25. Expansion by addition is dependent upon time, family requirements, and economic factors. Under this method, the complete house is built, then, as needed, extensions are added to the basic living areas. The sequence of additions to the basic unit should be determined and planned with minimum waste of space and maximum convenience of traffic circulation.

The house should be complete at each stage of expansion both in appearance and in function. The basic rooms must provide all the necessary facilities for the normal life of a family. In some cases, where the house is small, the utilization of all available floor space for family living is very important. When the available floor space is such that it becomes impossible to accommodate rooms having different functions, a room designed to serve a dual purpose is often incorporated into a small house plan. The following are examples of those rooms which serve dual or multipurposes.

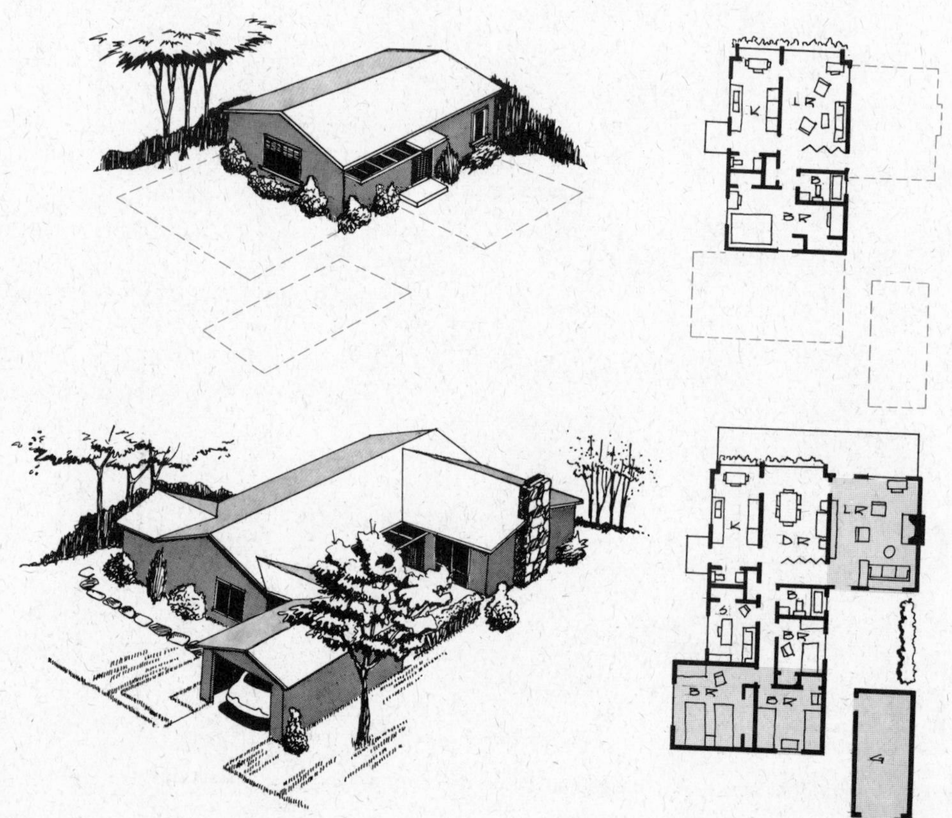

Fig. 2-24. A house may also be expanded by addition.

Fig. 2-25. Wings may be added to the basic structure.

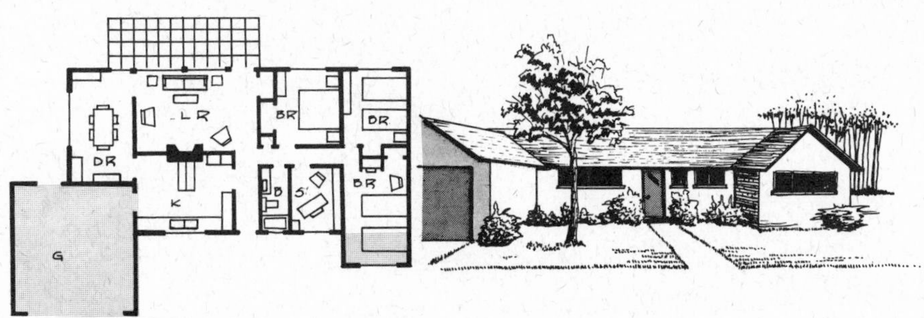

1. Living room
   Used for a variety of family purposes and for entertaining guests or social groups.
2. Dining room
   Used for dining as well as for children's playing or studying.
3. Kitchen
   Used for cooking, dining, and/or laundering.
4. Bedroom
   Used for sleeping, studying, and radio or record listening.
5. Recreation room and den(s)
   Used for playing, sewing, or other recreational activities — may be used as guest bedroom.
6. Garage extension
   Used for garage, hobby work, summer family room, photo darkroom, laundry facilities, laundry drying, and storage.

Questions and Problems

The following questions are based on essential factors related to the characteristics of a good floor plan.

1. Sketch a floor plan or copy one from some floor plan source. Check this plan for indoor and outdoor privacy. What can be modified on this plan to increase the privacy factor?
2. What approximate percentage of floor area should be adequate for natural lighting and ventilation?
3. State the advantages and disadvantages of placing a garage near the front of a lot. Would the lot shape, either long and shallow, or narrow and deep, have an effect on your analysis?
4. Open planning is used in varying degrees in many plans. What are some factors which might influence a decision to use open planning?
5. What are the possible methods by which a house could be expanded?
6. Which are considered to be the essential rooms in a house?
7. A house is to be built on a lot near

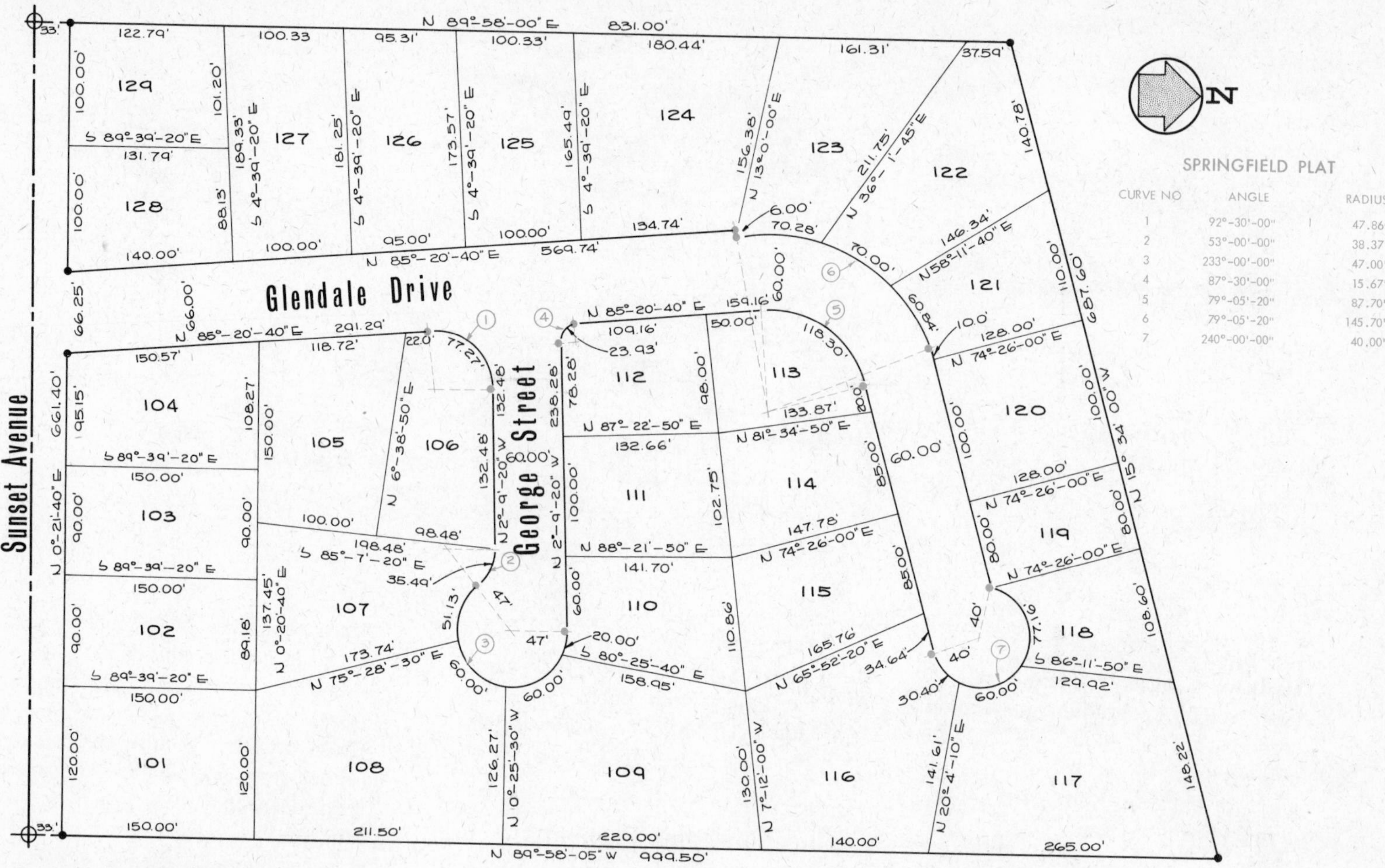

CURVE NO	ANGLE	RADIUS
1	92°-30'-00"	47.86'
2	53°-00'-00"	38.37'
3	233°-00'-00"	47.00'
4	87°-30'-00"	15.67'
5	79°-05'-20"	87.70'
6	79°-05'-20"	145.70'
7	240°-00'-00"	40.00'

Fig. 2-26. Springfield Plat.

the street. How would this influence the room arrangement?

8. List the necessary storage facilities required by a family of four planning to build a three-bedroom home.
9. Quickly sketch a plan of your home, including the street, compass direction, adjacent topographic features, and neighboring houses. Check this sketch for all plan characteristics. How could this plan be improved?
10. Assume a proposed house plan has been developed with all the features presented in this chapter. However, the kitchen window faces west. What remedy can you suggest without changing the kitchen plan?
11. In the past, rooms were designed for

a specific use. Today, rooms are designed for a number of uses. List the other uses for the following main rooms: living room, dining room, kitchen, bedroom, and garage.

12. What are the agencies of circulation in a house?
13. What criteria are used to check a plan for adequate circulation and orientation?
14. Select a lot from the plat shown in Fig. 2-26 and lay out a house that will illustrate the correct orientation for the following rooms:
    a. Living Room
    b. Dining Room
    c. Kitchen
    d. Family Room
    e. Three Bedrooms
    f. Attached Garage

THE ARCHITECT'S COLLABORATIVE.
PHOTO BY PICTOR.

Contemporary living areas and rooms are designed for comfort and beauty.

Individual Room Plans 3

Planning the component areas of a home requires a knowledge of the family's social and recreational activities and the number and ages of the family members. In general, each room or area should be planned with regard to (1) the different activities that may take place; (2) the frequency and degree of use; (3) the age, sex, and number of occupants; and (4) the furniture requirements. Ideally, a good house design would satisfy the prospective owner's needs and desires.

Regardless of the criteria used, the possibility of resale must be seriously considered. The mobility of our population has increased greatly over the past twenty-five years. It is wise, therefore, to plan a home that will be not only pleasing to the owner, but also to a future purchaser. The attractiveness which the potential home may have for others is an important economic factor in present planning.

This chapter is devoted to a study of component areas of the home. Room requirements, sizes, and shapes are shown in detail. By combining the material presented here with the information in the preceding chapter, the student should be ready to design the individual rooms of a home.

One-Quarter Inch Furniture Cutouts

In planning the individual rooms, the student may find it difficult to visualize furniture dimensions, and clearances. Cutouts will aid in determining adequate room size. Individual pieces of furniture are shown in Fig. 3-1. These may be drawn to scale on *detail paper,* cut out, and placed on ⅛″ or ¼″ co-ordinate paper. The scale of the furniture cutouts depends on the grid size of the co-ordinate paper. By arranging the cutouts on the co-ordinate paper, various possibilities of furniture arrangement may be suggested. As these cutouts are being ar-

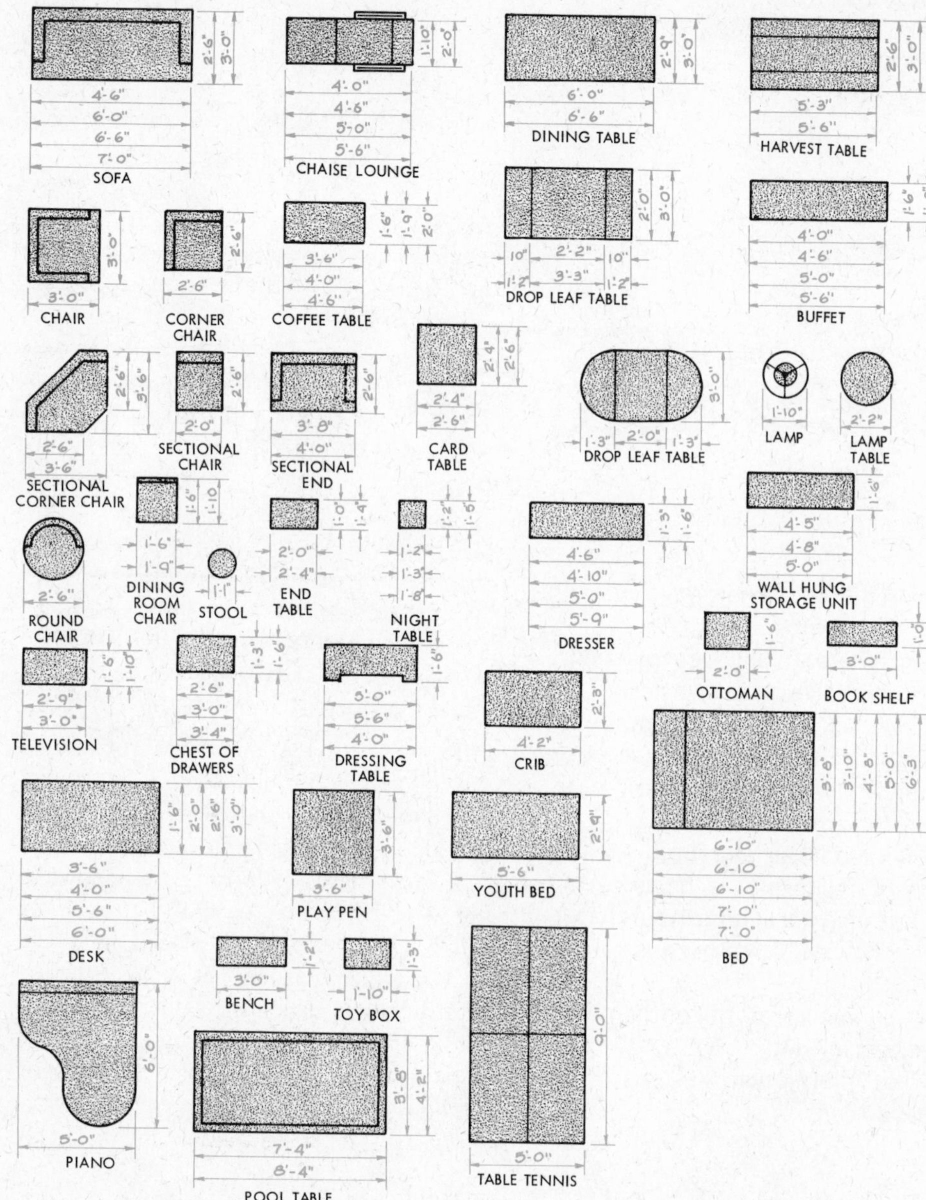

Fig. 3-1. Furniture Outlines: Furniture pieces may be copied to scale on co-ordinate paper. Additional furniture sizes may be found in **Architectural Graphics Standards** or by writing for descriptive brochures from furniture manufacturers.

ranged, consideration must also be given to the possible window, door, and closet locations. These will invariably influence the furniture placement, and possibly the room size. Each component area or room in the house must be studied to determine the proper clearances between the pieces of furniture.

Living Room

The living room, with its large floor area, is the most versatile room in the house. It may, for example, provide a place for receiving guests during the evening or afternoon hours. It may also be used as a place for listening to music, viewing television, or as a quiet place for reading a book or magazine. Sometimes, the living room is used as a rumpus room or as a supervised play area for the pre-school children in the home. Its interior design or plan is determined by the daily living requirements of the owner or family.

Size and Design Factors

The size and design of the living room will depend on several factors. The most important factors (exclusive of finance) are: (1) the frequency with which the owner or the family expects to entertain guests, (2) the number of people the room is expected to accommodate, (3) the expected requirement for furniture essential to comfort and relaxation, and (4) the possibility of using the design concept of open planning. For aid in designing the living room, minimum furniture clearances are given in Fig. 3-2.

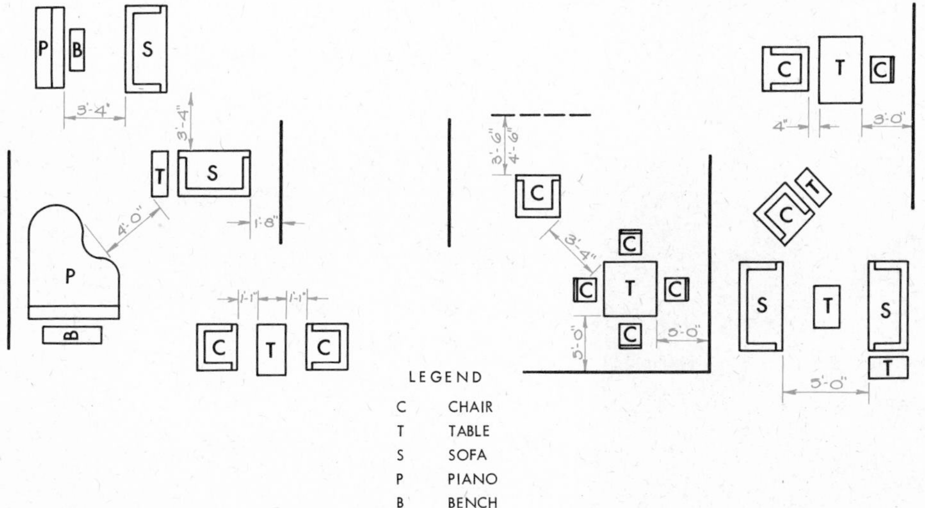

Fig. 3-2. Minimum Furniture Clearances: These may be used in designing the living room.

Open Planning

The living room need not be limited by the enclosing walls—it may be extended in several ways. One way to create the illusion of spaciousness within the room is to use open planning. For instance, large windows and a sliding door oriented towards the patio or porch may extend the living room to the outside, as shown in Fig. 3-3. However, a living room that is extended to the outside in this manner may require exterior screening provisions for privacy. Orientation toward a pleasant view is also desirable. This adds to the charm and the beautiful appearance of the living room.

As explained in Chapter 2, open planning will extend the living room to the dining room, thus creating the effect of more space. The living room-dining room combination not only allows free and easy movement of traffic within the area, but also allows greater freedom for arranging the furniture. This combination is also very convenient for circulation from the kitchen for entertaining guests.

Window Type and Placement

The type and proper placement of windows in the living room are important factors to consider. Windows not only control the natural lighting of the room, but also the arrangement of furniture within the room. In general practice, for adequate natural lighting, the window area should be equal to about one-fourth the total floor space of the room. The windows should be selected so that a person who is either seated or standing

Fig. 3-3. The appearance of spaciousness in a room may be increased by using sliding glass doors.

in the living room has a view to the outside unobstructed by the window sills. Some window types, such as windows which extend from the floor to the ceiling, greatly limit the amount of free wall space for arranging furniture. Generally, living rooms with large glass areas have the furniture arranged away from the windows so as not to obstruct the view. Large windows should face toward the south or southwest (corner location) to receive as much natural light as possible.

Traffic Circulation

As mentioned in the previous chapter, traffic paths in and through a room (1) should be direct and short, (2) should have ample space for freedom of movement, and (3) should not disturb those areas requiring privacy. In some plans the living room is regarded as a type of hall carrying traffic from one part of the house to the other. This can be minimized by changing the door placement. Doors should be placed close together so one may pass through the living room without traveling the full length of the room. An ideal location for entrance and exit doorways is in the corner of the room. Doors and windows should be located so as to leave large unbroken spaces for location of major furniture pieces. When a fireplace is to be included in the design, its location should be either at the center of a living room wall or at a corner. Unless the room is wide, a fireplace located on the side will tend to make the room look narrow. On the other hand, if placed at the end of a room, seating space may be limited. In every case, the fireplace should be away from doors and windows.

Dining Room or Dining Area

Until the early 1940's the dining room was considered an essential part of most home plans. However, during the years which followed, surveys of prospective home owners indicated that a separate dining room was considered costly and unnecessary since it was not used more than three hours a day. In the 1960's, this trend reversed again. The dining room and dining ell have begun to appear with greater frequency in moderately priced homes.

The size of the dining area, whether separate or part of the living room, is partially determined by the dimensions of the table and the number of persons to be seated around it. For families who entertain informally, the dining area may be included as part of the living room, or as an extension of the kitchen. An effective dining-living room arrangement may be achieved by planning an "L" shaped room, the short leg of which may be the dining area. A room that is planned to have this shape will appear to be more spacious. Less floor area is required in an arrangement of this type than for a dining room which is separate from the living room. Generally, a minimum of 9′-6″ and a maximum 12′-0″ for the width of this area is ample. A smaller space may be used by placing the table in a corner with built-in benches on two or three sides. If space is limited, the dining room may be converted to accommodate other activities or uses, such as children's study, after school gatherings, family room, supervised play area, etc.

Screens, draperies, or movable partitions, and sometimes furniture arrangements, may be used to separate the dining area from the

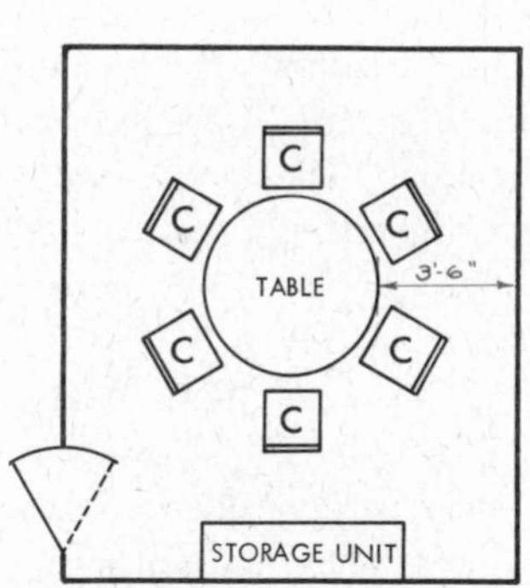

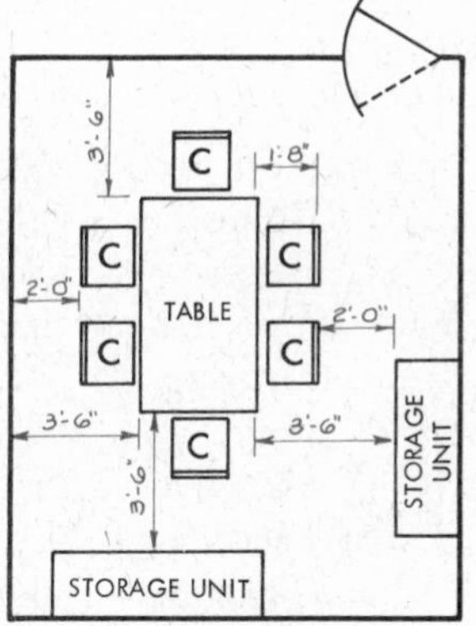

Fig. 3-4. Dining Room Furniture Clearances: When designing this room leave ample space for seating and serving.

living quarters. If the dining area is part of the kitchen, it is frequently separated by a partial partition or breakfast bar.

Dining rooms require a considerable amount of free wall space because the wall often accommodates a china closet, a hutch, a serving table, or a buffet. Ample clearance should be allowed around the dining room table for seating space and serving. Minimum clearances for dining room furniture are shown in Fig. 3-4.

Multi-purpose Rooms

Family Room

The family room is the first new room to be added to the home since the advent of the bathroom. During the early 1800's, most families ate, socialized, and relaxed in the kitchen. Later the parlor, now generally called the living room, was added for these activities and a separate dining room assumed some of these functions. Over the past years, factors such as increased building costs, scarcity of household help, smaller families, and entertainment away from the home have influenced the living pattern of the family group. If a comparison of residential building plans were made between the 1900's and the present, it would be evident that the size of the living room has decreased. The changing structure of society and the demands made by various sociological and economic factors have created a number of new family needs. These demands influence the design of the family room.

Family life has been changed by the many technological developments in our time. Television, for example, has had a great influence on family living. Prior to its advent, spectator sports, movies, concerts, etc., attracted the family away from the home. Because these attractions are now being televised, this trend has been reversed. Today, many families are staying home.

According to U.S. Census reports, families are now becoming larger. Increased salaries and higher hourly wages have created a greater demand for conveniences. The work week of many blue and white collar workers is being shortened. This allows more time for hobbies, television viewing, and leisure activities with the family. Greater demands are being made upon the home to accommodate more possessions. Also, more people with a broader scope of activities stay at home for a longer period of time. A pattern of greater social-group informality in home living is being formed.

The family room, as the name implies, is the center of family activity. This major room may contain, or be adjacent to, cooking and dining facilities. The family room may contain such furnishings as lounge chairs, game or utility tables, hi-fi, stereo, and TV. Space should also be provided for hobbies and children's recreation. Many units (sewing machines, hi-fi, TV, washer, dryer, desk, etc.) may be concealed behind sliding or bi-fold doors. These units are usually placed along an inside wall. If a cooking area in the family room is to be included, it is often separated by a divider, base cabinets, or a fireplace. Sometimes the cooking area is planned as a cooking island.

The family room is often designed to open onto a terrace or patio through sliding doors. During mild weather, this arrangement greatly expands the group activities of the family.

Because a major portion of the family's time is spent in the family room, the tendency in planning has been to reduce the size of the living room. The living room in this case becomes a facility for formal entertainment.

Den, Study, or Guest Room

The extra room (called a den, study, or guest room) offers privacy for reading, studying, conversing, and working. It may also serve as sleeping quarters for guests.

Space should be provided for a hide-a-bed, lounge-type chair, desk, bookcase, closet, and possibly a lavatory. The minimum room area recommended is $9' \times 12'$. Its location should be near the living area. The closets should be designed to act as a baffle to reduce the noise which enters this room.

Bedrooms

In floor plans, the number of bedrooms is determined by the number of individuals in the family and the expected number of guests to be accommodated. The arrangement of bedrooms in a multi-level house is governed, to a great extent, by the first floor plan and the stair and window locations.

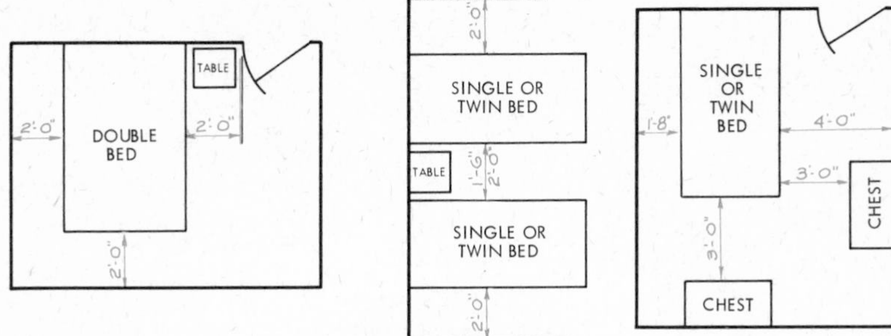

Fig. 3-5. Bedroom Furniture Clearances: Leave at least a 20″ clearance on both sides and at the foot of the bed.

To permit the greatest freedom for furniture arrangement, consideration must be given to free wall space and window location. Regardless of the size or shape of the bedroom, the glass area of the wall should be equal to no less than 15 per cent of the floor area. In recent years, the trend has been to design windows which are wider and shorter, with sills located approximately 4′-6″ to 5′-0″ above the floor. Careful selection and placement of windows give a maximum range of free wall space, thus permitting various furniture arrangements.

Bedroom windows should be located where maximum cross ventilation may be achieved. A well planned bedroom has windows placed in such a manner as to allow fresh air to enter one window and stale air to escape through the others. Air movement should not, however, be directly across the bed.

A further consideration in planning the bedroom is the number and size of the furniture pieces to be included. For example, the usual furnishings in a master bedroom include: one double bed, or a pair of twin beds; one dresser (single, double, or triple); one chest of drawers; one or two bedside tables; and one or two chairs. Children's or guest's bedrooms usually contain the same furniture with the exception of a dresser.

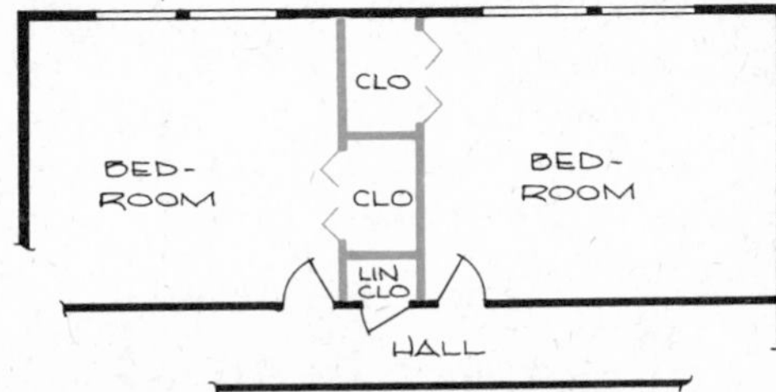

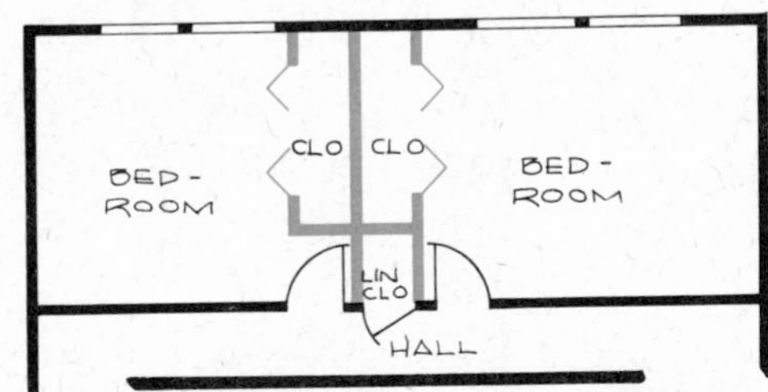

Fig. 3-6. The common wall between two bedrooms may be used for closet space.

Passage space at both sides of the bed and at the foot should be at least 20″ wide. Adequate clearance between beds, beds and walls, and beds and other furnishings are shown in Fig. 3-5. The bathroom, closets, and the hall should be easily accessible without walking around the bed.

If two bedrooms are planned side by side, as in Fig. 3-6, the common wall should be utilized for closet space. The closet walls shown in these figures compactly house a closet for each bedroom and a linen closet for the hall.

To provide maximum comfort, the following check points should be considered in the plan.

1. The bedrooms should be located as far away from the living area as possible.
2. The bedrooms should be located on the quiet side of the lot away from the street.
3. If the bedroom is expected to be used as a living area, it should have a southern or a south-eastern exposure.
4. Bedrooms should have direct access to the hall without passing through any other room.
5. The children's bedroom should be adjacent to or near the master bedroom.
6. Bedrooms should be provided with cross ventilation by planning the windows on two outside walls near the interior partitions. Avoid a room layout where the wind blows directly over the bed.

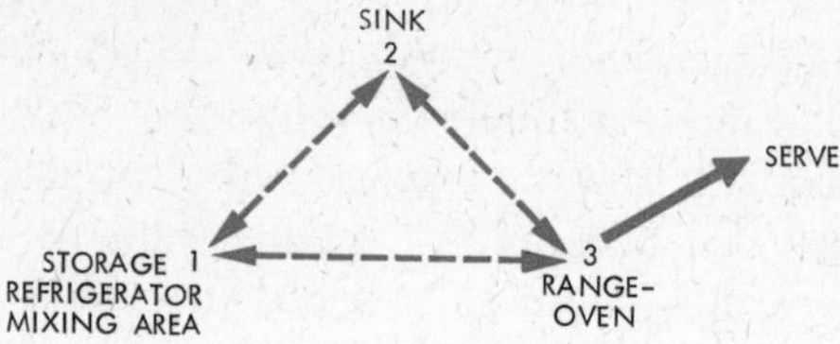

Fig. 3-7. The work triangle should have a perimeter of 12′ to 22′.

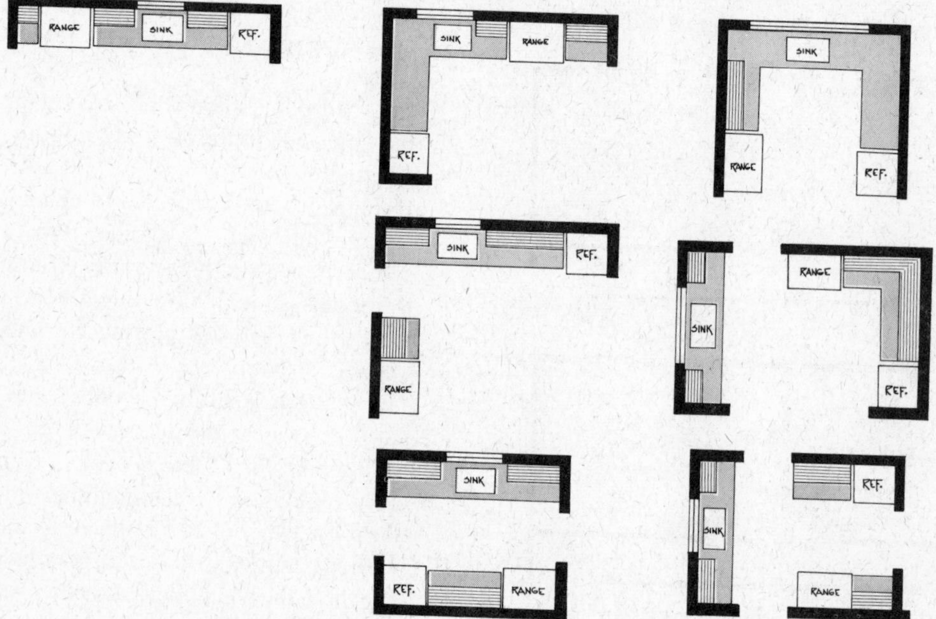

Fig. 3-8. Various kitchen arrangements are possible within the work triangle.

7. The plan should include one closet for each bedroom and two for the master bedroom.

Kitchen

Work Triangle

Kitchens planned for efficient operation depend upon the convenient location of cabinets, appliances, and work centers. The relationship of the three basic work centers, containing the refrigerator, the sink, and the kitchen range, is called the *work triangle*. Fig. 3-7 illustrates this concept. For maximum efficiency, the perimeter or the total distance around the work triangle (refrigerator-sink-kitchen range) should be between 12′ and 22′. The preparation of food should move through the pattern of the work triangle directly to the dining area or living room where it is finally served. The kitchen should be near to and connected with the dining area.

The kitchen sink is the main corner of the work triangle. The sink area serves as a preparation and clean-up center. Counter space should be planned on both sides of the sink for food cleaning, draining, and for an auxiliary mixing area.

The kitchen range should be accommodated with a counter space on either side, and a cabinet above if possible. The oven, if separate from the stove, may be located in a less important area. As a fire precaution, the kitchen range should never be placed below a window. For convenience, a range hood with an exhaust fan may be installed over the range.

Various kitchen arrangements are shown in Fig. 3-8. As with other areas of the house, the kitchen requires minimum clearances between cabinets, walls, doors, etc. Minimal clearances are shown in Fig. 3-9. Aver-

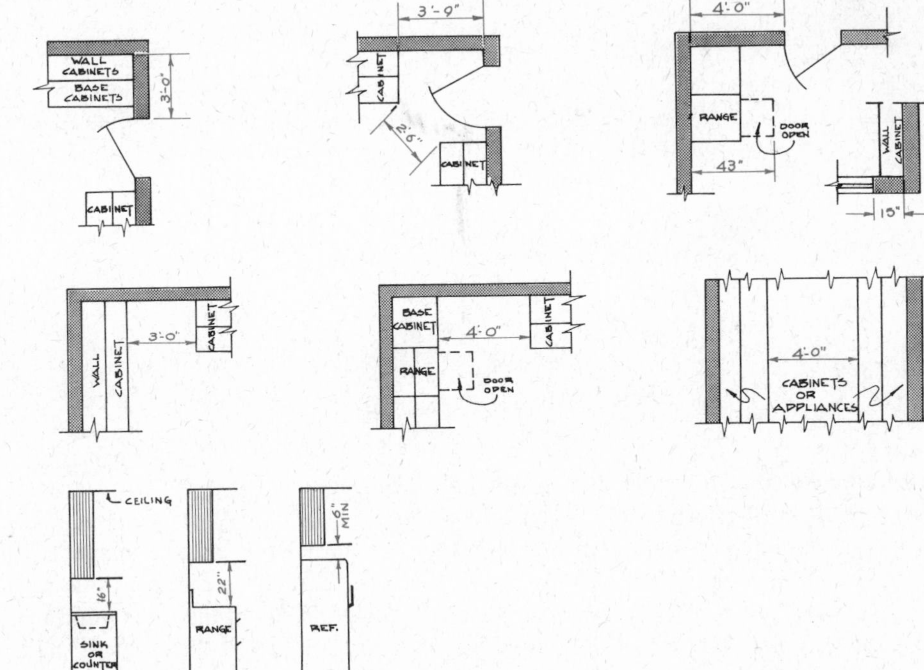

Fig. 3-9. Minimum Clearances for Kitchen Units.

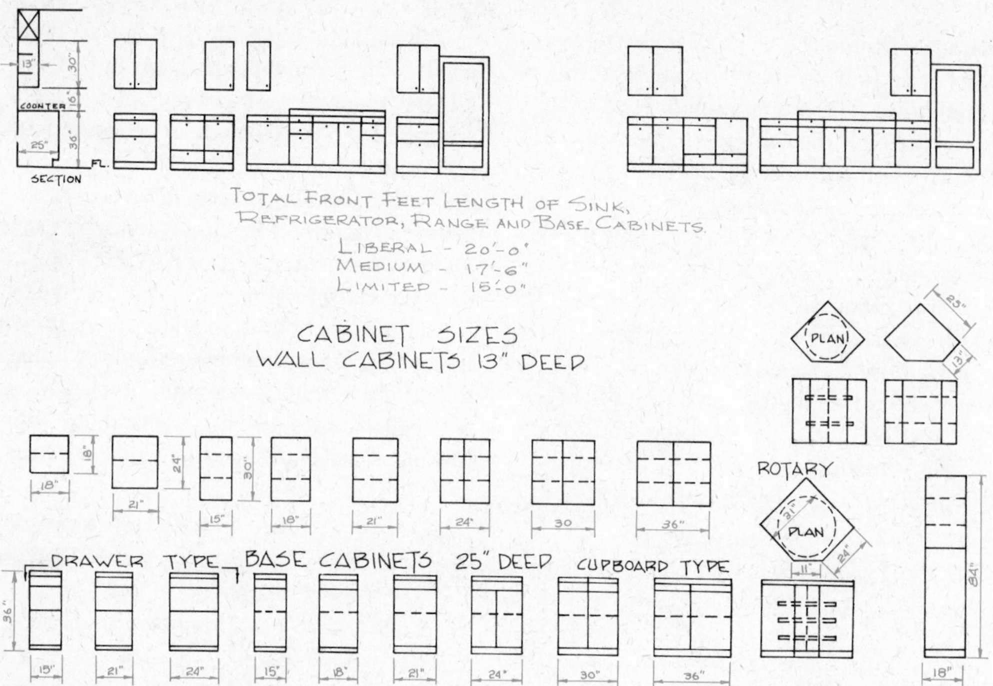

Fig. 3-10. Standardized Cabinet Sizes: Various combinations and arrangements may be used.

age cabinet sizes for both combined and individual work centers are illustrated in Fig. 3-10. (Views in Fig. 3-10 are shown from the front. The corner units are shown in both front and top, or plan, view.) Table 3-1 gives typical sizes of ranges, refrigerators, and sink bowls.

Storage

The amount of storage space is a prime consideration in kitchen planning. Food buying habits of the family and the amount of space required for dishes and utensils must be studied.

Supplies are usually stored where they are first used. For convenience, staple items should be stored adjacent to the mixing area. It is also convenient to store dormant vegetables (potatoes, onions, etc.) under or next to the sink where they are easily accessible for washing and peeling. Dishes should

TABLE 3-1

TYPICAL DIMENSIONS OF RANGES, REFRIGERATORS AND SINK BOWLS

RANGES								
BUILT IN OVEN			BUILT IN RANGE TOP			CONVENTIONAL UNIT		
WIDTH	HEIGHT	DEPTH	WIDTH	HEIGHT	DEPTH	WIDTH	HEIGHT	DEPTH
20"-24"	26"-39"	21"-24"	20"-40"	6"-11"	17"-20"	30"-43"	36"	23"-31"
						36"-48"	36"	30"

REFRIGERATORS			
CU FT	WIDTH	HEIGHT	DEPTH
3-4½	23½"-24½"	44"-54"	25½-29"
5-6¾	25½"-29"	50½"-60"	25"-29"
7-8¾	26"-31"	59"-65"	27"-31"
9-12	28"-33"	62'-70"	27"-31"

SINK BOWLS		
Single Compartment		
24"x 21"		30" x 20"
Double Compartment		
32"x 20"	42"x 20"	36" x 21"

be placed near the serving area where they are easily accessible.

Windows, Ventilation, and Lighting

Adequate window area is usually considered to be about 15 to 20 per cent of the total floor area. However, cabinet space on a kitchen wall must not be sacrificed for excessive window space.

In addition to window ventilation, provision is usually made for an exhaust fan, or more preferably a range hood. For maximum efficiency, the exhaust fan must be located directly over the range center. A fan mounted on the wall behind the range is not as effective as a fan mounted on the ceiling.

Adequate lighting is a must in the kitchen since the homemaker spends a large portion of her day in this area. In addition to a central ceiling fixture, other lighting may be placed over each of the main work centers to assure sufficient illumination. For convenience, electrical outlets should also be placed near each work area.

Traffic Circulation

Ideally, the kitchen should have easy access to both the front entryway and the rear service entrance. However, the kitchen normally should not have more than two doors and should not be used as a traffic lane. Door swings should not interfere with the arrangement of equipment, appliances, or other doors. Many kitchen designs make use of sliding doors in lieu of conventional hinged doors.

Bathroom and Lavatory

The bathroom in today's home is viewed from a different standpoint than it was in the 1930's and 1940's. During and preceding this era, most moderately priced homes were planned with only one bathroom. Contrasting this with current planning practice, today's home buyer anticipates one and a half or two bathrooms for an average six room house. If conditions allow, the *ideal* plan would provide a bathroom for each bedroom. However, one bathroom will be sufficient for three people in a small home. In large homes a bathroom for every two additional bedrooms (after the first two) will insure adequate facilities.

The number and arrangement of fixtures, the number of persons these fixtures will serve, and the character of the dwelling will influence the bathroom size. Bathrooms are not difficult to plan. Fixtures are standardized and do not vary greatly in size. Fig. 3-11 shows some basic fixture sizes. If the budget permits, the bathroom should be planned to be larger than the minimum sizes of 5′ × 7′ or 6′ × 8′.

There are several methods of grouping bathroom fixtures around the walls. Plumbing fixtures may be arranged along one wall, on opposite walls, scattered along the walls, or divided by means of partitions. Many arrangement variations are possible by merely including extra fixtures, such as another water closet (with a partition) and another lavatory in the room. With the addition of extra fixtures, the design of two-bathroom efficiency is possible. The construction cost of this design is considerably less than that of the two separate bathrooms. Minimum clearances between fixtures and between adjacent or opposite walls are illustrated in Fig. 3-12.

If the home is to have only one bathroom, it should be accessible from the rear entryway as well as from the bedrooms. Traffic lanes must be well planned. Two doors entering into the bathroom may solve this problem. Another solution is to design an

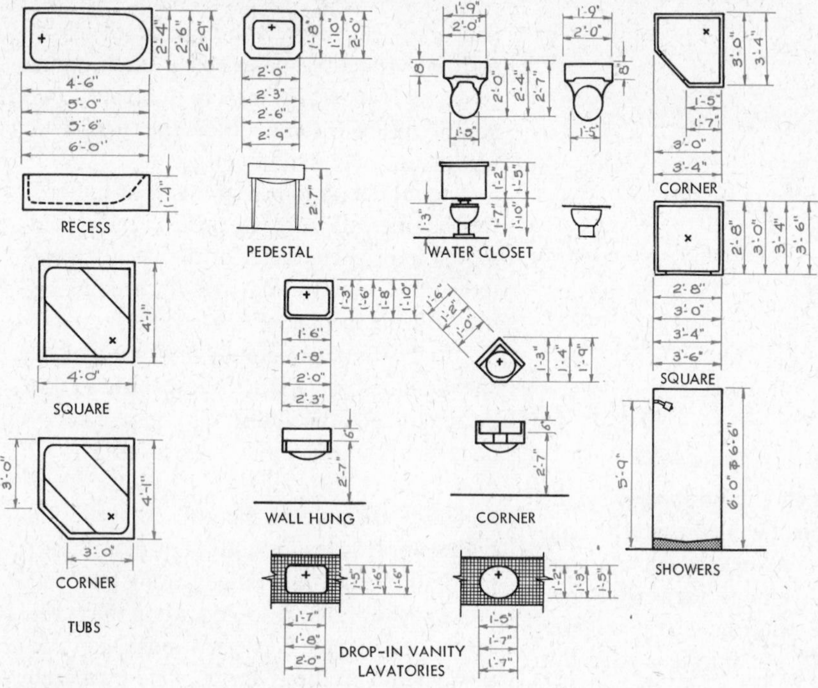

Fig. 3-11. Basic Bathroom Fixture Sizes.

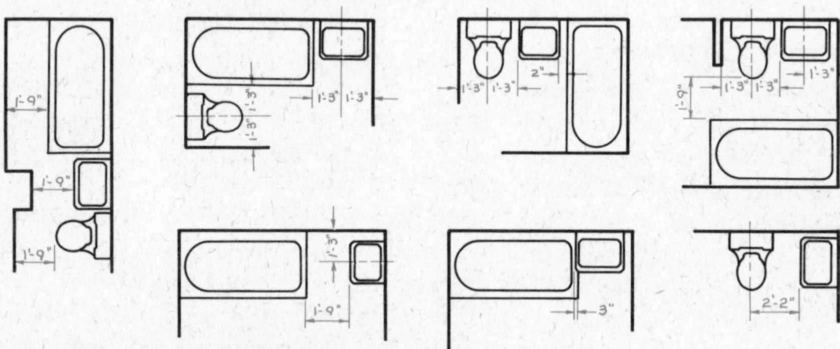

Fig. 3-12. Minimum Bathroom Clearances.

additional room, with a lavatory and water closet, near the rear of the house by the service entry or kitchen. This solution is advantageous when there are guests for it eliminates excessive traffic.

The greatest saving is gained in one-story or multi-level dwellings if the bathrooms are located over each other, adjacent to each other (especially if fixtures are backed up to each other in a common wall), or over the kitchen and laundry plumbing. It is false economy, however, to sacrifice convenience and utility for a savings in piping. Usually, good planning and piping economy are natural complements.

In order to plan the bathroom for economy, efficiency, and convenience, the following points should be considered.

1. The bathroom should be located near the bedrooms.
2. It should be located near the head of the stairs or where it is accessible from the hall.
3. The entrance to the bathroom should be from the hall, near the head of the stairs in a two-story or split-level house.
4. When bedrooms are located on different floors additional bathrooms should be considered.
5. As a minimum, one additional bathroom should be planned for every two *additional* bedrooms after the first two.
6. Bathroom windows should be located where they may be easily approached for opening and closing. Window sills should be four feet above the floor.

7. Bathroom fixtures should be planned so they do not interfere with each other. (Place the lavatory between water closet and tub in a small bathroom).
8. The water closet should be located as near to the vertical *soil stack* (waste pipe) as possible.

Laundry Area

In recent years the trend has been away from placing the laundry room area in the basement. Laundering is now generally done in a room specifically designed for this purpose. This room may be on the first floor in an area off the kitchen, recreation room, storage room, sewing room, or utility room. In areas where the climate is warm throughout the year, the laundry area may be located in the garage. In any case, it should be convenient to the service entry if the home maker desires to hang the wash outdoors.

In planning the laundry area, consideration must be given to pleasant lighting and step-saving. The laundry area should have space for work, storage, and equipment. Fig. 3-13 shows the general dimensions of laundry equipment and the necessary clearances.

The laundry-area plan is determined by the sequence of laundry operations. Equipment which is grouped according to the following work cycle should result in an efficient plan.

1. Receiving and Preparation Center
   a. Sorting table or counter

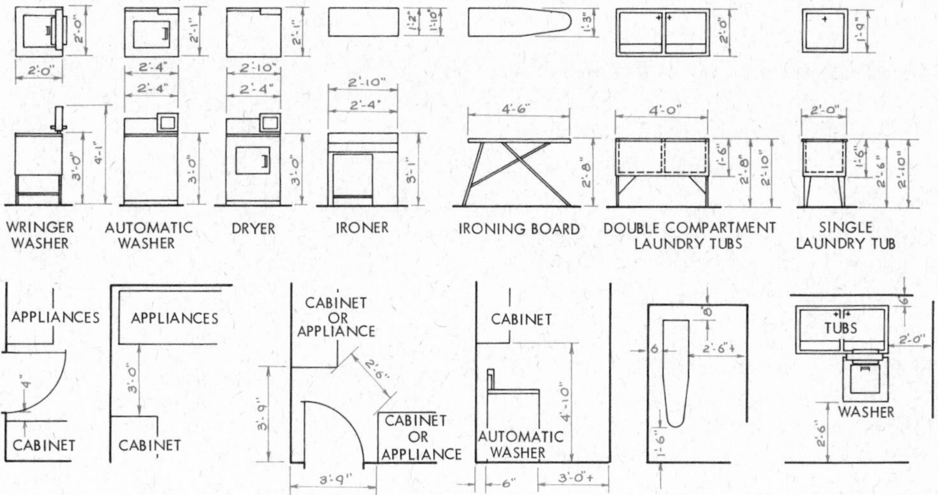

Fig. 3-13. Laundry Equipment and Clearances.

   b. Supply cabinet or shelves
2. Washing Center
   a. Automatic washer or washing machine
   b. Stationary tub(s)
3. Drying Center
   a. Electric or gas dryer (should be adjacent to outside wall for venting)
   b. Drying lines
4. Ironing and Storage Center
   a. Counter for sprinkling and folding
   b. Ironer or mangle
   c. Ironing board
   d. Rack or counter (may be the same as the one above) for finished laundry
   e. Storage cabinet

Basement

Whether a basement will be built depends on the following factors: (1) slope of the lot, (2) climatic conditions, (3) desire or need for recreational facilities, and (4) available money.

Building a basement may double the home size. The cost for this addition is only about one-tenth of the total cost of the home. This may be the most inexpensive way to get additional space for living, recreation, and storage. Plumbing and drainage problems are easier to solve when a basement is included in the plan. Studies have shown that the basement is the most economical and efficient location for the furnace and water heater. In colder, northern climates where the foundation walls must be supported below the *frost line,* an additional few feet (usually two feet) below this line would be sufficient for placing a footing for the basement.

The following points should be considered in efficient basement planning: (1) Plan as much natural light in the basement as possible—use ribbonlike *hopper windows* for this purpose and for ventilation. (Hopper windows are long, narrow windows that open inward with hinges along the lower edge.) (2) Make sure the basement construction is waterproof and that provisions are made for adequate exterior drainage. (3) The heating equipment and stairway should be located along one wall to make more space available in the basement. (4) If the house is built on a sloping lot, the basement may be planned with a large glass window located on the sloping side of the lot. If properly waterproofed, heated, and lighted, this type of basement may become the most used area in the home. (5) Whether the lot is sloping or level, it is desirable to have a basement with direct access to the outside.

To some home owners, the basement is not only an unnecessary space which must be cleaned and heated, but it is also an area where water problems may be encountered during rainy weather. When this situation exists, the basement may be regarded as unnecessary and costly. The money allotted for the basement could be utilized more efficiently for increasing the ground-level living area. In warm climates, the basement is usually omitted and a utility room is planned.

Fig. 3-14. Various layouts may be used to separate the entryway from the rest of living area.

Utility Room

If the area for the basement is wet and water seepage would be an evident problem, a basement is not feasible. A substitute plan is to build a utility room above the grade level.

If the basement is dispensed with, such

items as the furnace, hot water heater, automatic washer, and dryer should be located in the utility room. The utility room should be near the kitchen and the service entry. It is also possible to eliminate the utility room by placing these items along one wall of the kitchen behind louvered, sliding doors.

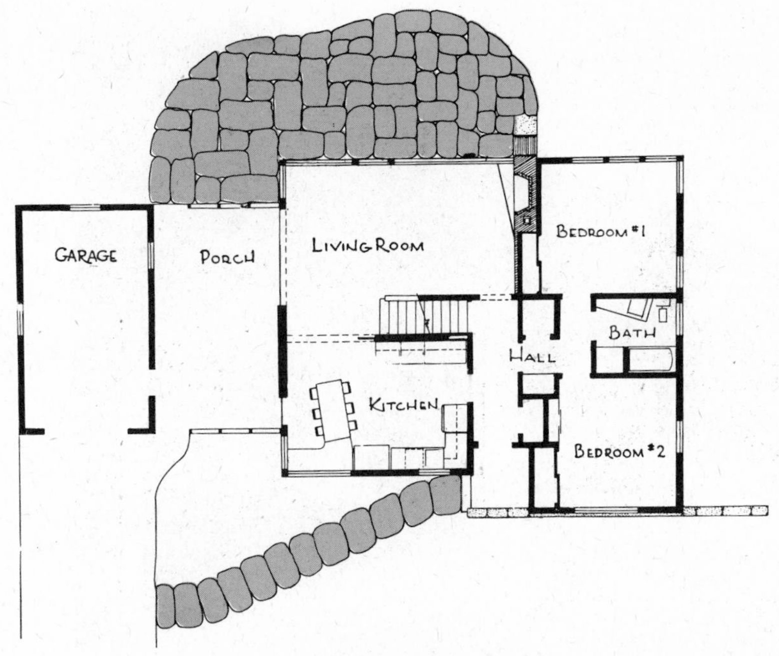

Fig. 3-15. Flagstones may be used to form an attractive terrace or walkway.

Entrances and Hallways

The front entrance or main entryway should be located so that it leads to the central area of the house. In planning the entryway, the relationship of the entrance to the driveway and the street is a prime consideration. If possible, the front entrance should open into a hall rather than directly into the living room. If the area is limited, a small portion of the living room may be used as a hall or vestibule. This can be accomplished by designing a vertical louvered divider, a closet divider that is elevated from the floor, or a storage unit which will separate the entrance area from the living room. Fig. 3-14 illustrates several entrance areas.

In areas where severe weather prevails part of the year, an entrance hall in a home is almost a necessity. An entry hall serves as a barrier or shield against cold drafts and damp air which may enter the living areas. This hall may also serve as an ideal location for a guest closet.

When planning the hallways of a house, the design should provide the most *direct routes* to the bathrooms, bedrooms, and other living areas. Also, hallways should be sufficiently wide to allow free flow of traffic circulation. Hallways must also be wide enough to permit passage of furniture. In general, the width of a hallway should be no less than 3′-0″. Hallways wider than 4′-0″ are wasted space, unless designed for a specific purpose, such as a passageway for handicapped persons or invalids. The total floor area of a hallway should be kept to a minimum so as not to reduce the area alloted for family living.

Porches and Outdoor Living Areas

The porch may take many shapes and may serve many purposes. Common types of porches are: living porches, entrance stoops, sleeping porches, outdoor covered porches, and garden rooms. A porch often complements the indoor areas of the house and may be used for dining, playing, sleeping, or sitting. For greatest versatility and privacy, the porch is usually located at the rear or side of the house. If it is to accommodate table and chairs, etc., it should be at least 8′ wide.

Outdoor living may also be facilitated by building a patio, terrace, or deck. (Decks are made of wood planks laid down as a floor.) The total area of the house may be

Fig. 3-16. A roof overhang is often used to shade the terrace area.

as much as doubled in this manner. Various paving materials may be used. The easiest and most economical are loose stone, asphalt, or concrete. Bricks, blocks, wood (planks, sawn tree trunks, etc.), stone, tile, adobe, etc., may also be used. One of the most popular materials, illustrated in Fig. 3-15, is flagstone. However, this is one of the most expensive paving materials. It is also one of the most permanent. Regardless of the material used, it should not be laid down haphazardly. Careful planning is necessary to create a pleasing, aesthetic effect. Both the shape and color must be considered. Existing features, such as trees and shrubs, must also be taken into account. A patio or deck may, for example, be built around trees.

Patios and decks may be joined to the house or they may be located away from the house in a garden area. They may, if desired, be wholly or partially covered. The house roof, for example, may be extended to provide a partial cover. Fig. 3-16 illustrates this possibility. If the surface does not drain easily, a slight grade should be provided. Locate south for the best sunlight, north for shade.

Lighting for night use should also be considered. Spot or flood lights may be used. Reflected light is the most comfortable and is recommended. In any case, light sources should not be located where they could shine in anyone's eyes.

Most patios and decks pose no serious construction problems. However, support is required for decks. Piers and footings will be required for a deck of any height. (Railings, depending on the height, may also be necessary.) With a simple low-level deck, however, little difficulty should be encountered. A simple footing may be used. In any event, local building codes should be consulted for requirements and restrictions. Fig. 3-17 illustrated a low-level deck. Here piers

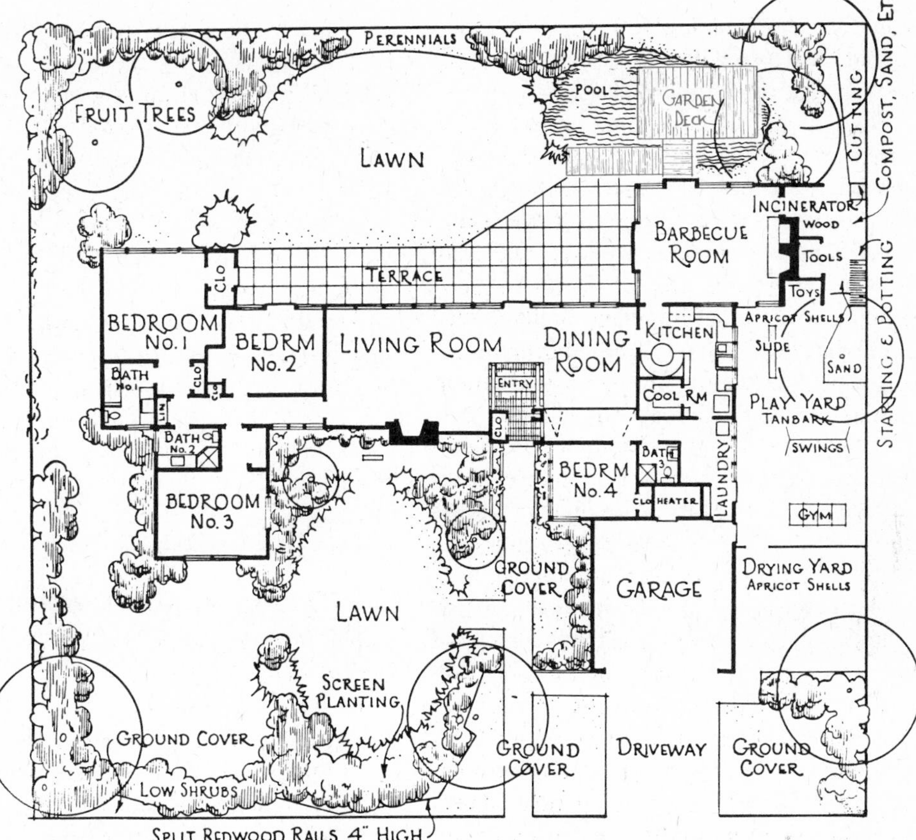

Fig. 3-17. A terrace may be combined with a deck to form an attractive outdoor area.

would be used. Note how the decking leads away from the terrace into the privacy of the pool area.

Garage or Carport

The garage today has developed from a simple shed-like structure to an all-purpose room or building. In some areas, however, a shed-like structure, known as a carport, has become very popular.

When the size of the lot permits, the garage is often designed as a separate building and combined with a porch, barbecue area, green house, or work shop. However, today's garages or carports are usually attached to the house. This has the economy of using a common wall and the convenience of direct and semi-sheltered access to the house. A garage that opens directly into the kitchen is especially desirable since carrying groceries long distances is eliminated. Also, an attached garage with an open or closed breezeway (covered passage) gives the illusion that the building is long, and widespread. A house with this design, however, is somewhat more expensive.

Since 1940, there has been an increasing tendency to locate the garage on the front portion of the lot near the street. In general, this not only locates the auto in the most convenient and practical place, but also frees the entire rear area of the lot for gardening and other development. In the northern areas where snow prevails during much of the winter season, this garage location eliminates excessive snow shoveling.

If a house is built without a basement, there may be a need for a garage with storage and work space. Although an allowance of 12′ × 22′ is sufficient for any car, space for car door clearances, storage, and work areas should also be included in the total garage area. The garage may also provide space for storing such items as bicycles, wagons, baby carriages, screens, storm windows, fireplace wood, garden tools, hose, lawn mower, ladders, etc. In some cases the garage is designed to house laundry equipment and a clothes drying area. It may also be a convenient location for a porch-type play room where the children may play without disturbing the rest of the household.

In warm areas, where the winter season is not very severe, the need to house the auto in a completely enclosed building is not very important. Recently, the use of carports has come into vogue, particularly in the southern and southwestern seaboard areas. Because of their simplicity, carports are very inexpensive. In design, carports are very much like a lean-to. One side of the roof is supported by the house, while the other is supported by columns. Carports may be open on two or three sides. In either case, the function is merely to provide a roofed shelter for the auto. The carport may be planned in such a manner as to allow conversion to a garage with a minimal amount of work.

The driveway should be designed simultaneously with the garage or carport. It should slope to the street and, if possible, conform to the level of the lawn. For safety, the view along the driveway should be unobstructed.

Questions and Problems

The following questions are designed as a self-checking device.

1. What are the most important factors to consider in making a plan for the living room? Assume the size has already been decided.
2. What are some other uses for main rooms such as the living room, dining room, kitchen, bedroom, and garage?
3. By what means can one be assured that certain pieces of furniture will fit into a specific room?
4. How much space is considered adequate between a wall and bed to allow sufficient clearance to make the bed?
5. What determines the size of a room?
6. What are the three activity centers or work areas in the kitchen?
7. What are some pros and cons for construction of a basement?
8. Make three thumbnail sketches of a kitchen and bathroom, using a common wall for plumbing and venting. Show the various items of equipment that would be necessary along each wall.
9. Draw or sketch the following rooms to scale (½″ = 1′-0″). Arrange all furniture with proper clearances; include doors, windows and closets.
   a. Living Room—Dining Room Combination—Size 16′ × 22′. A 2′ × 8′ divider serves as a screen between the living and dining room. The divider contains a desk, bookcase, radio, stereo, TV, and games on living room side and shelves for linen and china on the dining room side. Other furniture to be included: 4 chairs, 2 arm chairs, dining room table, sectional sofa, end table, piano and bench, cocktail table, and an upholstered chair.
   b. Study or Den—Size 9′ × 12′. Furniture to be included: a studio couch, low chest, table, 2 chairs, bookcase, desk, and storage closet.
   c. Master Bedroom — Size 12′ × 16′. Furniture to be included: a double bed, bedside table, chest, double dresser, lounge chair, and closet(s).
   d. Girl's Bedroom—Size 10′ × 12′. Furniture to be included: a single bed, night or bedside table, dress-

ing table or bench, desk chair, boudoir chair, bookcase, and closet.

e. Boy's Bedroom—Size 10′ × 12′. Furniture to be included: a single bed; upholstered chair; cabinets (12″ deep attached to wall) for games, athletic equipment, and books; an 18″ deep workbench placed below cabinets; desk and chair; chest; and closet.

f. Dining Room — Size 10′ × 12′. Furniture to be included: a dining room table, 6 chairs, a hutch or china cabinet, and a buffet.

g. Living Room—Size 18′ × 21′. Furniture to be included: a 4 piece sectional sofa (including a corner section); 2 occasional chairs; 2 large lounge chairs; coffee table; piano and bench; fireplace; radio; stereo; TV; and storage facilities for records, music, games, card table, and guests' coats.

h. Combination Kitchen and Laundry. Sketch a possible combination of these two areas, utilizing the following equipment and appliances: refrigerator, sink, separate range top and oven, washer dryer, furnace, and water heater.

10. Design a bedroom for two brothers age 8 and 12 years. Indicate on your sketch all the necessary furniture, and the appropriate dimensions.

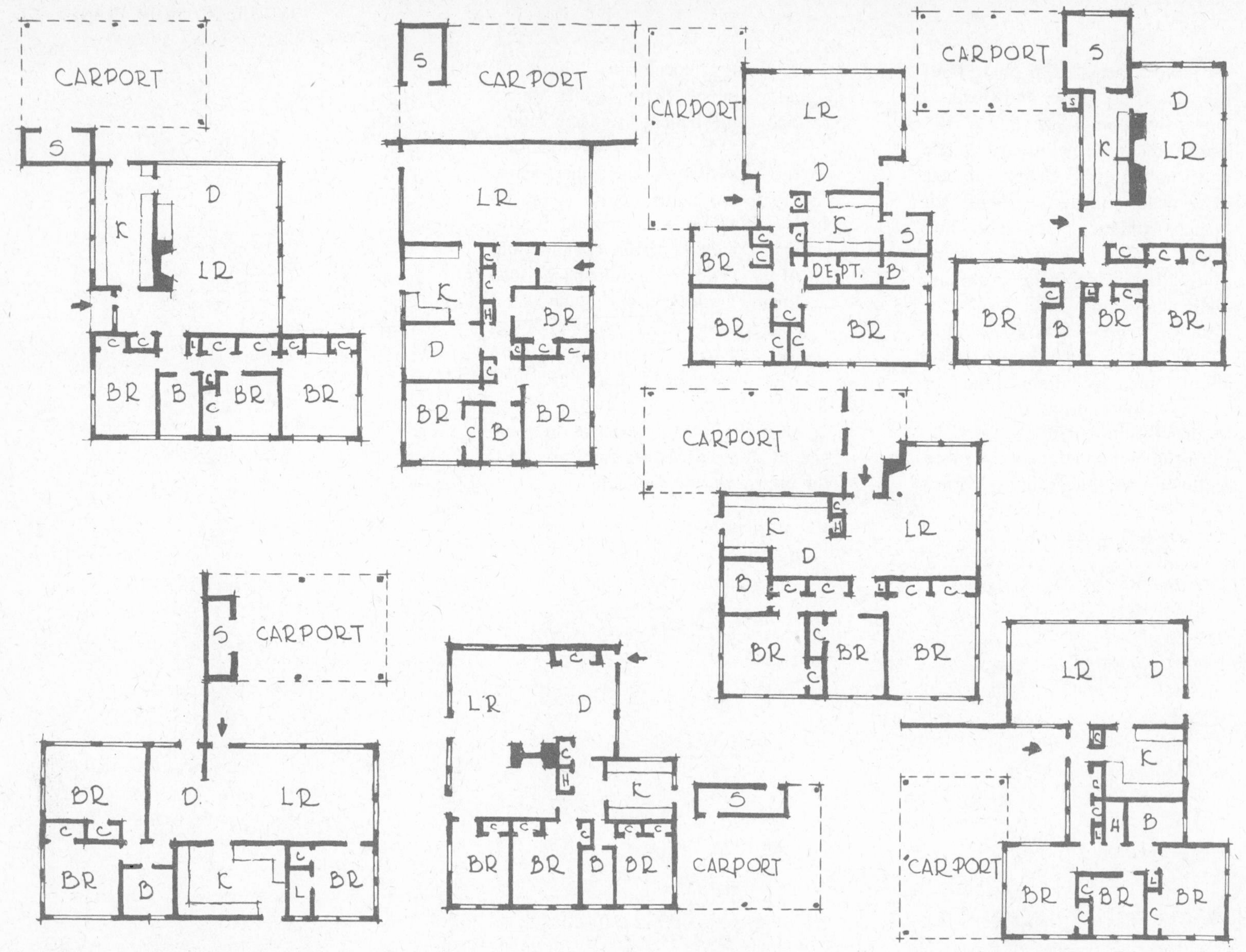

House plans take many different forms, depending upon the conditions of the site and the needs and desires of the prospective owner.

House Plans 4

Today's home is designed primarily for comfort and convenience. The livability of a house, regardless of size, depends upon good, sound planning. This involves **designing and placing rooms** in relation to family activities. Remember: Designing and planning should never be approached as separate entities.

Building materials, construction techniques, and methods of fabrication are changing constantly in the home construction field. In spite of research and development in housing, there is one problem which perpetually plagues the designer. This problem is determining the needs of the family. Because each family group has its own specific needs, pattern of living, and activities, it remains impossible for an outsider to generalize about the requirements of most families. It is evident that the requirements of an individual family should control the house plan. In order to find something that will suit the family needs, persons who seek to design a home usually search through numerous books and magazines on home planning, obtain ideas from existing floor plans, or visit homes which are for sale.

Searching For Ideas

All of us have considered how we might change our present living quarters. Most planning ideas generally originate from such contemplation. In addition to this, ideas on house planning may be found in publications and in existing homes. By finding planning ideas suited to the client's taste and combining them with your own ideas, a satisfactory house plan may be created.

The following procedure is useful in planning a house.

1. *Be a "Window Shopper."* Review houses on display at home shows, open houses, etc. Pick up brochures, plan sheets, and other home planning information which may be available. These are good sources for obtaining home planning ideas. It is advisable to look at all styles and types of homes. Usually, every house style and floor plan provides many different home planning principles. By shopping for ideas in this manner, the home designer is better able to devise a house which will meet the family requirements.

2. *Read Magazines.* Some of the better designed houses are no farther away than the public library or the corner news stand. Get in the habit of browsing through architectural and building magazines. Read books intended for the architect and builder. Check

home magazines for new ideas and for house plans which may be featured periodically. Some publishers put out an annual or semi-annual home planning magazine which compiles all of the best plans of the preceding six months or year. Many local newspapers carry a weekly home planning section describing plans or aspects of planning which are valuable. When selecting publications, be sure to choose the best home planning sources available. The following is a list of some of the most reliable sources for good planning ideas: *American Builder, Architectural Forum, Architectural Record, Arts and Architecture, House and Home, Interiors, House Beautiful,* and *Practical Builder.*

3. *Hold on to Your Ideas.* The purpose of "window shopping" and reading magazines is to obtain usable ideas. For easy reference, the collected information may be kept in a scrap book or "idea file." The clippings and sketches should be classified according to rooms or areas in the house (i.e., family room, dining room, bedroom, floor plans, fireplaces, etc.). Save only those ideas which seem useful or interesting.

Planning Considerations

When planning a house, each room must be considered as a *vital part of the total plan.* Each room should be thoroughly examined for its use, location within the plan, and possible furniture arrangements. The formative planning stage should give primary consideration to (1) the family's space requirements, (2) the routing and implementation of household tasks, (3) the normal traffic circulation through the house, and (4) the proper room orientation. Remember, it is much easier to make changes in the formative planning stage than later, when building commitments have been made with the contractor.

To devise an intelligent plan, it is essential that the various rooms be studied individually to ascertain their *sizes, location, requirements,* and *uses.* Each room must be related to the whole plan.

Family Activities

A well-planned house should provide enough space for all living activities. Every room or area in the house should be designed for a limited number of activities. Rooms or areas which are designed to accommodate a large variety of activities should always be avoided. Such a design can never fully satisfy any of the planned activities. "Seldom used" rooms may be adapted to accommodate additional living activities. Multi-purpose rooms or areas are desirable only if their design provides maximum functional conveniences with a minimum of wasted space.

The well-designed house plan must have: (1) all of the living space that the buyer can afford; (2) pleasing simplicity in its architectural treatment; and (3) utmost privacy from the neighbors. In home planning, the incorporation of these three home considerations may seem an impossible task with a limited budget, but clear thinking and a good evaluation of the family needs can produce excellent planning results.

Prior to designing the house, the requirements of the family must be analyzed and considered carefully. By gathering data about the family, it is possible to design the house plan according to their needs and desires. This gathered data, or inventory of the family, should provide: (1) the number, sex, and ages of the family members; (2) the number and type of family possessions, including those they expect to have in the future; (3) the family's design preferences in the home; and (4) the types of activities the family would ordinarily perform in certain areas of the home.

The test of the house plan is its ability to meet the requirements and needs of the family. Listed below are various family activities, both individual and group, and the rooms or areas involved.

Family Activities

Activities	*Areas or Rooms Involved*
Housework	
Food Preparing	Kitchen
Housekeeping	Cleaning storage cabinet
Laundering	Utility room, kitchen, basement, garage
Serving	Dining room, family room, kitchen
Sewing	Utility, kitchen, laundry, dining room, den, bedroom
Gardening	Basement, utility, garage

Activity	Room
House Upkeep	Basement, utility, garage
Family (Group)	
Conversing	Dining room, kitchen, living room, family room, patio, outdoors
Dining	Dining room, family room, kitchen, living room, patio, outdoors
Relaxing	Living room, den, family room, bedroom, basement, patio, outdoors
Entertaining	Living room, recreation room, family room, dining room, patio, outdoors
Playing (Recreation)	Recreation room, living room, family room, basement, patio
Partying	Recreation room, living room, dining room, patio, outdoors
Storing	Closets, storage cabinet, storage room, utility room
Working	Den, study, bedroom, workshop, garage
Family (Individual)	
Dressing	Bedroom, bath
Bathing	Bath, laundry
Studying, writing, reading	Living room, family room, dining room, dining areas, bedroom, patio, den, study
Storing clothes	Clothes closets, chests, storage cabinets, storage room
Hobbying	Utility room, workshop, basement, garage, den, storage room, kitchen, living room, studio, workshop
Accommodating Guests	Extra bedroom, living room, den, recreation room, or other room

TABLE 4-1

ROOM SIZE ACCORDING TO SPACE AND SIZE ALLOCATION

Room	Minimum	Small	Medium	Large
KITCHEN	51 Sq Ft 6'-0" x 8'-6"	92 Sq Ft 8'-0" x 11'-6"	108 Sq Ft 9'-0" x 12"	168 Sq Ft 12'-0" x 14'- 0"
DINING ROOM	100 Sq Ft 10'-0" x 10'-0"	117 Sq Ft 9'-0" x 13'-0"	140 Sq Ft 10'-0" x 14'-0"	160 Sq Ft 10'-0" x 16'-0"
DINING ALCOVE (Dinette)	25 Sq Ft 5'-0" x 5'-0"	49 Sq Ft 7'-0" x 7'-0"	566 Sq Ft 7'-6" x 7'-6"	76 Sq Ft 8'-9" x 8'-9"
LIVING ROOM	150 Sq Ft 10'-0" x 15'-0"	219 Sq Ft 12'-6"x 17'-6"	259 Sq Ft 14'-0"x 18'-6"	300 Sq Ft 15'-0"x 20'-0"
FAMILY ROOM	154 Sq Ft 11'-0"x14'-0"	192 Sq Ft 12'-0"x16'-0"	216 Sq Ft 12'-0"x18'-0"	273 Sq Ft 13'-0"x21'-0"
BEDROOM	90 Sq Ft 9'-0"x10'-0" (1 Bed)	120 Sq Ft 10'-0"x12'-0" (Twin Beds)	172 Sq Ft 12'-0"x14'-4" (Twin Beds)	219 Sq Ft 12'-0"x18'-4" (Twin Beds)
BATHROOM	35 Sq Ft 5'-0" 7'-0"	35 Sq Ft 5'-0" 7'-0"	40 Sq Ft 5'-0" 8'-0"	48 Sq Ft 6'-0" 8'-0"
GARAGE 1-Car*		193 Sq Ft 11'-0"x17'-6"	218 Sq Ft 11'-6"x19'-0"	258 Sq Ft 12'-0"x21'-6"
2-Car		288 Sq Ft 16'-6"x17'-6"	333 Sq Ft 17'-6"x19'-0"	410 Sq Ft 19'-0"x21'-6"

*Sizes shown indicate minimum width clearances.
Small, medium, and large refer to car sizes.
One-car garage for any car size is 11'-6" x 21'-6".
Two-car garage for any car size is 19'-0" x 21'-6".

Room Sizes

In discussing room sizes, it is fallacious to arbitrarily specify the *best size* of a room. Before a room size can be considered, the planner should answer at least three main questions. (1) Has the inventory of the famiy shown the room size to be adequate for their activities? (2) Has consideration been given to existing and future furniture or equipment to be placed in the room? (3) Has the location of windows and doors been considered in relation to furniture and equipment?

Ideal room sizes are helpful as a starting point in planning, but strict adherance to the ideal sizes is not necessary. Table 4-1 lists the basic rooms and indicates the suggested area and dimensions for each room.

Room Combinations

An examination of plans for small homes

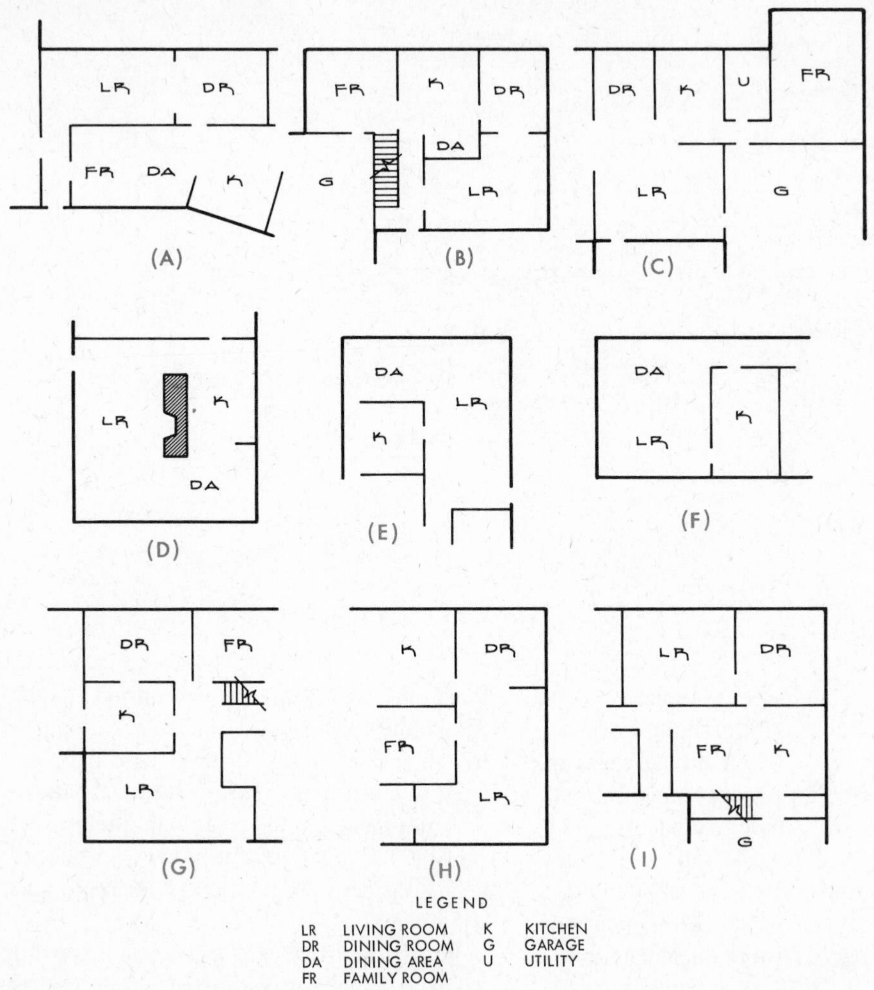

Fig. 4-1. Living, dining, and family room combinations go together for convenience and function.

will reveal that fundamental relationships exist between rooms. This is a crucial factor in home planning. Various areas belong together for convenience and function. For example, the dining room is usually placed next to the kitchen. In some cases, the dining area is incorporated as part of the kitchen. The family room sometimes serves as the dining area, so this room also is commonly placed adjacent to the kitchen (see Fig. 4-1).

Many home plans frequently have the living room placed near the dining room or dining area. Often, the dining room is combined with the living room to form a dining area or a dining ell at one end of the room. The front entrance is located in or adjacent to the living room. The basement stairway is often near the kitchen, the rear of the house, or occasionally the front entryway.

On most plans, bedroom and bathroom arrangements can be broken into specific combinations. Fig. 4-2 shows a few of the standard combinations. These room combinations may be used in most plans regardless of the number of bedrooms and bathrooms.

Any of the standard arrangements may be doubled by reversing the plan. To reverse a plan, one merely turns the paper over and views the image through the opposite side.

Closets play an important role in bedroom and bathroom combinations. By careful planning, space left between the end of the tub and a wall may be used as a closet for the adjoining bedroom. This and other suggestions are shown in Fig. 4-2. Closets also help to lessen noise travel from the bathroom to the bedroom.

A lavatory (that is, a room which contains a water closet and a sink only) may be placed adjacent to one of the bedrooms

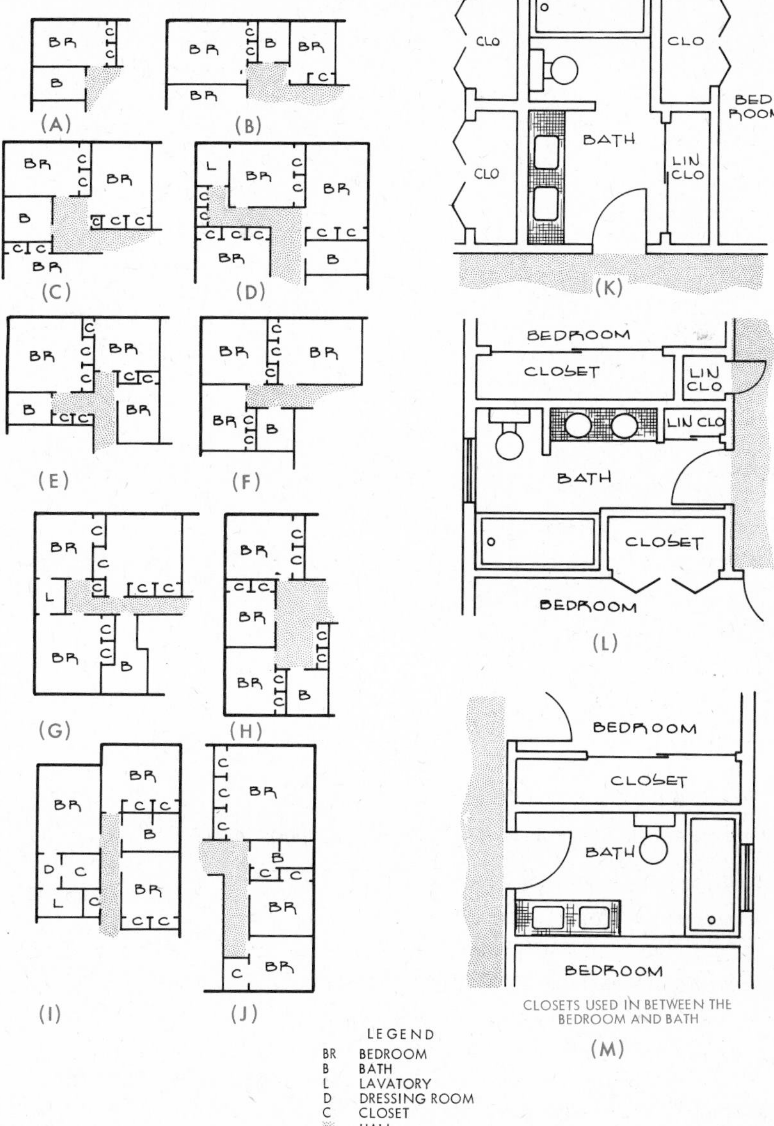

Fig. 4-2. Bedroom-bathroom combinations should be arranged for convenience.

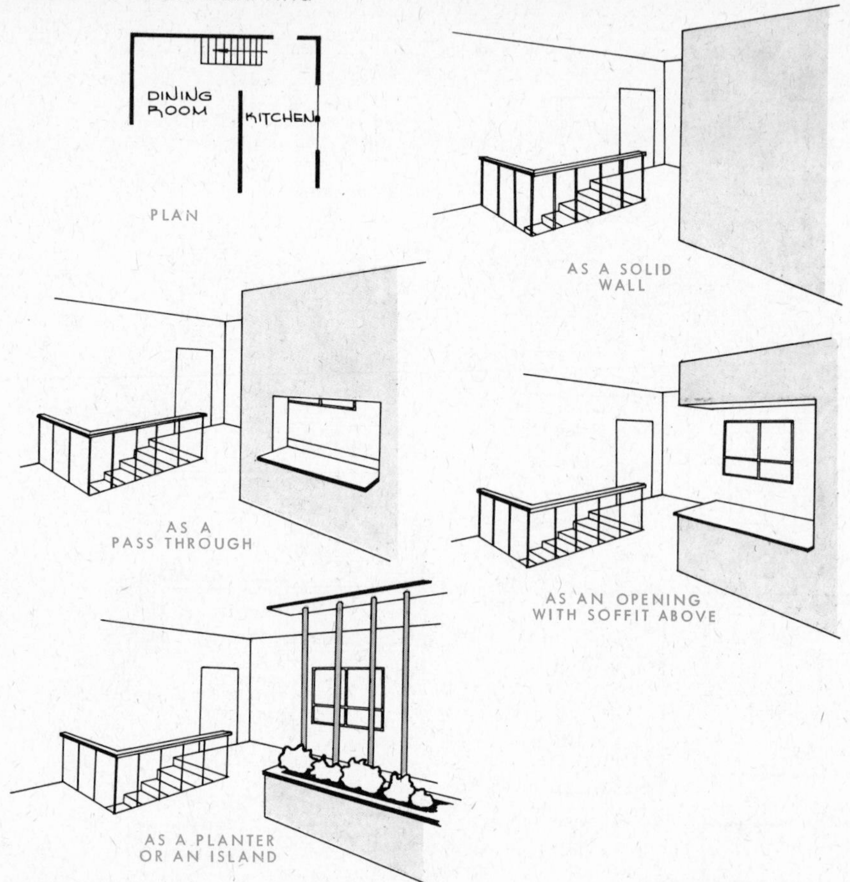

Fig. 4-3. A line on a rough preliminary sketch may have many interpretations.

or located in close proximity to an entryway. Prior to World War II, the lavatory was located near the front entryway. Since that time, the trend has been to place the lavatory near the rear door or service entryway for greater convenience. In some instances the lavatory adjoins a bedroom (or bedrooms) thereby freeing the main bath for others during conjested times.

Room Layout

The rooms included in the plan should be arranged for maximum efficiency with a minimum of wasted space. A great amount of wasted space influences not only the cost of the house, but also its livability. Livability is the key to the layout of a house plan.

Often, the novice designer begins the house plan by designing the outside before the inside. In other words, the treatment of the exterior appearance is paramount. It is good practice to design the house interior first and let the exterior design be considered when the plan has been roughed in.

All plans have many possible variations. The planner should not crystallize his thinking with only one arrangement. Devise several alternate plans based on the same number of rooms, requirements, livability, etc.

A factor often overlooked on the preliminary house plan sketch is that a line drawn on the paper really has three dimensions. The hastily sketched line on the plan represents not only length and width, but also height which cannot be shown. The planner must visualize in three dimensions whenever he draws. A line on a rough layout of the plan may have many meanings as shown in Fig. 4-3.

Layout is a problem that is never simple; it always requires careful thought and imagination. Here the scrapbook or file of newspaper and magazine photos, sketches, brochures, etc., may be very helpful. The main purpose of the file is to help stimulate thinking—not to copy.

On the plan, each room should be designed to function basically as a room, and not as a passageway. If every room, with the exception of the living room and kitchen, can be designed as a *dead-end room,* traffic lanes which make furniture arrangements nearly impossible will be

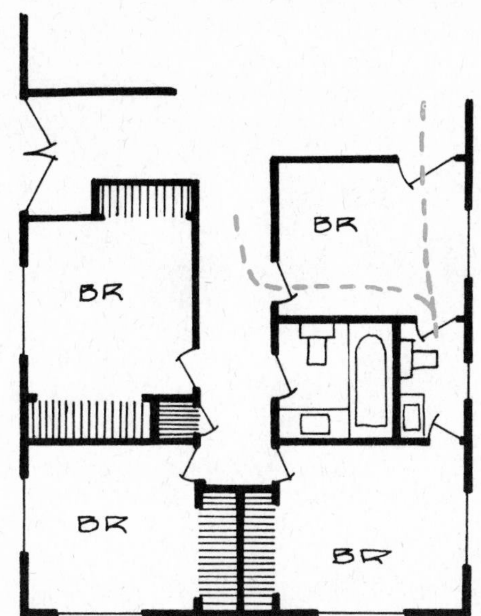

Fig. 4-4. A poorly placed traffic lane may make furniture placement impossible.

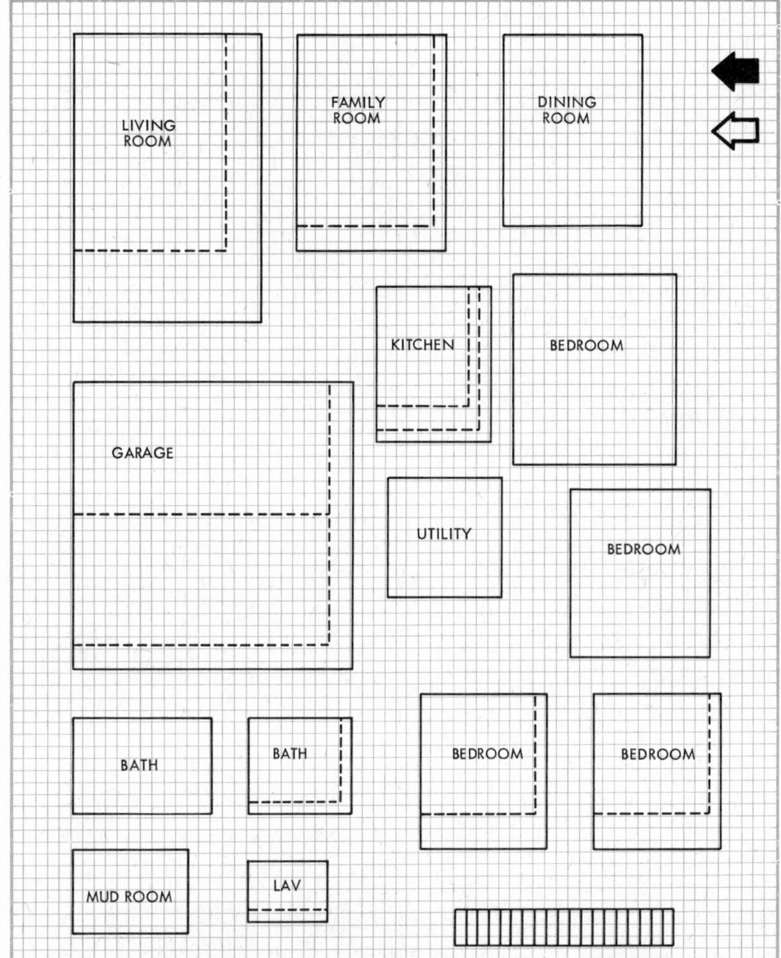

Fig. 4-5. Room templates may be drawn on co-ordinate paper and cut out.

avoided. Fig. 4-4 is an example of traffic lanes which have cut a room to pieces and made furniture arrangement highly difficult. An ideal plan layout should first be developed, disregarding functionality. The plan layout should then be made functional and workable by eliminating or making compromises on problems such as multiple traffic lanes. Another helpful suggestion is to develop several different layouts based on the number of rooms, the sizes, and the groupings desired. In this manner various sections of one layout may be combined with another.

Planning by Templates or Room Cutouts

As mentioned in Chapter 3, the use of room cutouts or templates is perhaps the most flexible method of home planning. Each cutout is made from ⅛″ or ¼″ co-ordinate paper so the planner may quickly identify the size required and the area of the room that is used. For ease of size identification and arrangement, the cutouts may be placed on another co-ordinate paper that is of the same co-ordinate size. By trial and error, various area or room combinations may be tried and evaluated. The following steps illustrate the template or cutout method that is used in planning.

Step 1. Sketch rooms on ⅛″ or ¼″ co-ordinate paper, and cut each sketch out. See Figs. 4-5 and 4-6, Step 1.

Step 2. Sketch boundaries of lot on another ⅛″ or ¼″ co-ordinate paper. (Draw lot plan on the same scale paper as used for cutouts.) On this sketch, indicate the topographical features such as existing trees, shrubs, nearby street (s), etc.; and also indicate north. See Fig. 4-7, Step 2.

Step 3. Arrange room templates on sketch of Step 2 by placing related rooms together to insure:

a. *Ease of service and control.* Related household activities are usually located in related rooms (i.e., kitchen and dining room, bedrooms and bath, living room and dining room, and laundry and utility room).

b. *Diversity of interests and activities.* Unrelated activities should be located at separate areas so activities in one area cannot disturb those in the others.

c. *Economy.* Greater economy may be afforded if plumbing fixtures in adjacent rooms are placed in proximity to each other. Hall space should also be reduced to a minimum.

d. *Full potential from each area.* The space allotted to each area must be justified in

Fig. 4-6. Step 1. Sketch rooms on co-ordinate paper and cut out.

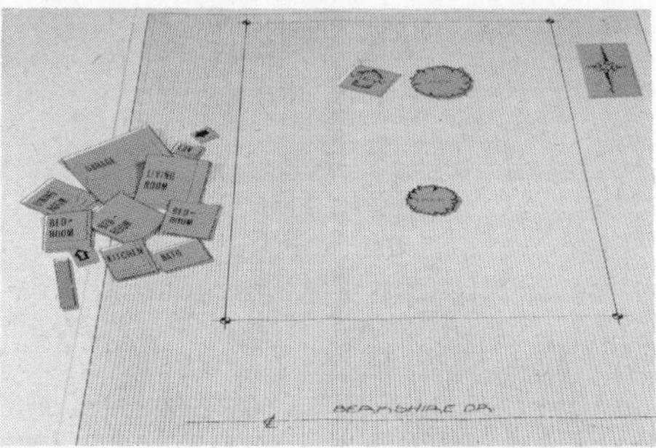

Fig. 4-7. Step 2. Sketch outline and indicate view, compass direction, streets, and existing trees.

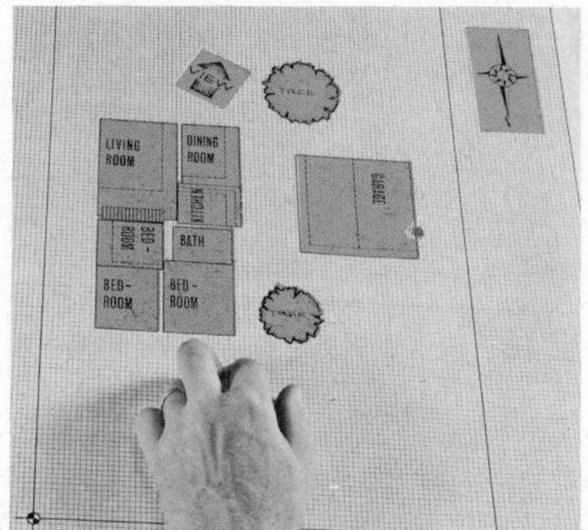

Fig. 4-8. Step 3A. Arrange templates on sketch.

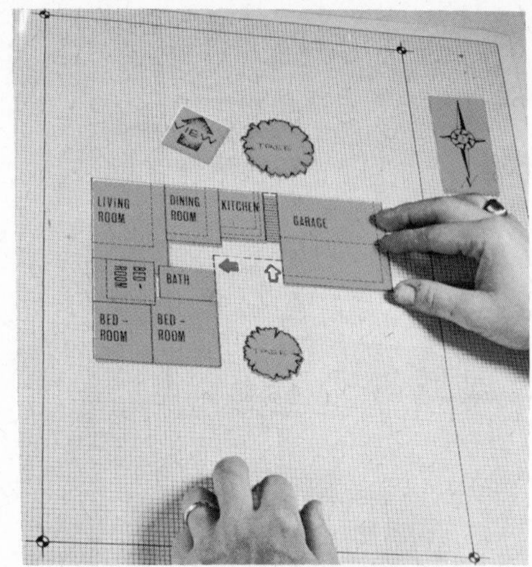

Fig. 4-9. Step 3B. Try for a better plan arrangement.

terms of need. Some activities, because of their nature, require more space.

See Figs. 4-8 and 4-9, Step 3.

Step 4. Compare the characteristics of the floor plan in Figs. 4-8 and 4-9 with a model plan in Fig. 4-10.

Step 5. Separate the rooms by allowing roughly 6″ (in scale) for interior walls, 6″ for frame exterior walls, and 10″ for brick veneer exterior walls. Also allow spaces for closets, halls, stairs, storage, etc. Straighten the outside walls and check room sizes. Lightly pencil in the outline of the rooms.

Step 6. Create and study a tentative plan for window and door locations. See Fig. 4-11, Steps 5 and 6.

Step 7. Consider possible furniture locations and arrangements relative to window and door locations.

Step 8. Inspect the tentative plan as it is oriented on the lot and check to see that it answers the following questions:

a. Can the room positions be improved?
b. Is the house too compact?
c. Will the house be economical to build, heat, and maintain?
d. Is the front door accessible

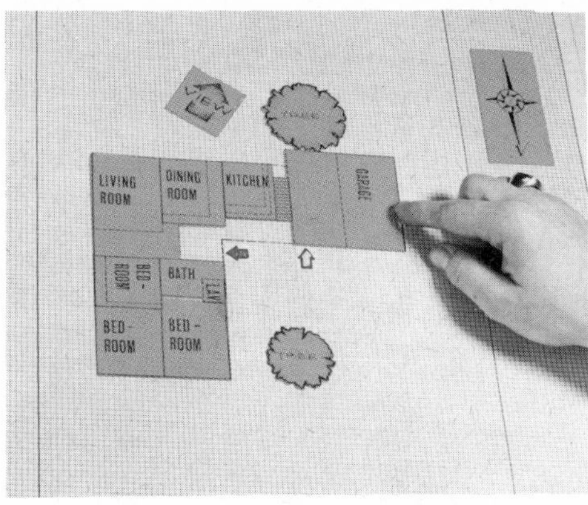

Fig. 4-10. Step 4. Adopt best plan.

from the other rooms?

e. Are the "quiet" areas away from the "noisy" areas?
f. Are the rooms located where they can best be utilized?
g. Can better room and **furni-**

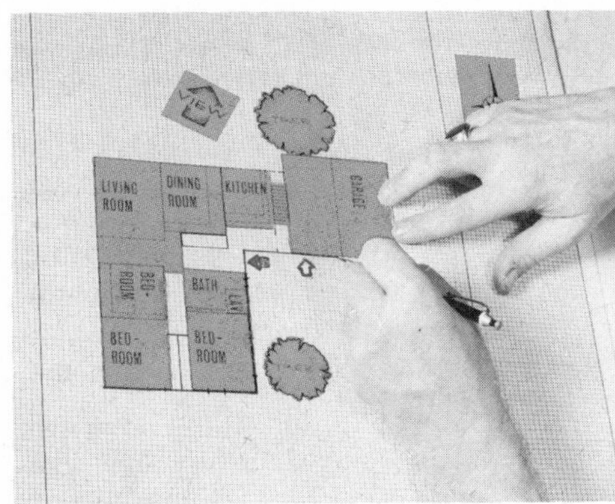

Fig. 4-11. Step 5. Allow room for closets, stairs, etc.; trace rooms. **Step 6.** Plan window and door locations.

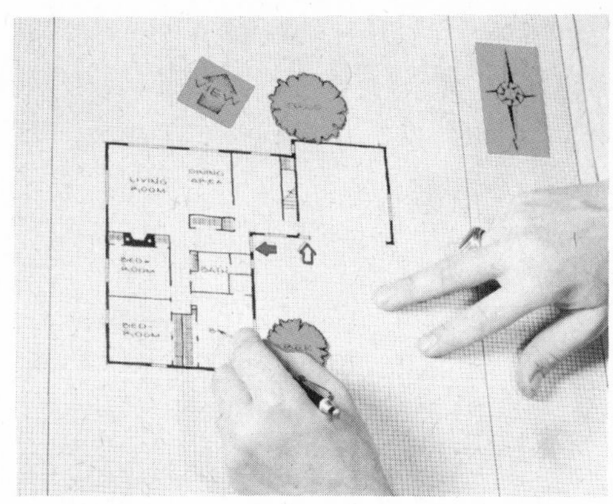

Fig. 4-12. Step 7. Consider furniture locations relative to windows and doors. **Step 8.** Inspect the plan. **Step 9.** Darken lines around rooms, halls, stairs, etc.

ture arrangements be made if shape of the rooms are altered?

h. Will "open planning" suit the layout better?
i. Does the room layout facilitate indoor-outdoor living?
j. Does the plan show adequate traffic circulation?

Step 9. Design the best plan, and darken the lines around rooms, halls. stairs, etc. Indicate room sizes, and entrance and window locations. See Fig. 4-12, Steps 7 to 9.

Planning by the Circle Method

Perhaps the simplest method of planning is called the *circle method.* This tentative

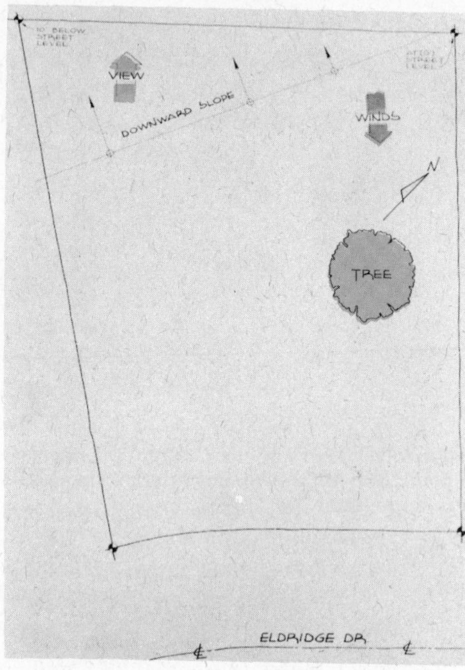

Fig. 4-13. Step 1. Sketch the lot outline and indicate view, compass direction, existing trees and bushes, prevailing winds, and any changes in elevation. Note: The changes in elevation need not be precisely indicated.

planning develops strictly from the most desirable placement of rooms according to the physical features of the lot and the climatic conditions of the area. Once the "room-locating" circles have been suitably arranged, the room sizes and closets are roughly determined. The circle method may also be used as a preliminary step to using cutouts or templates.

The following is the procedure for the circle method.

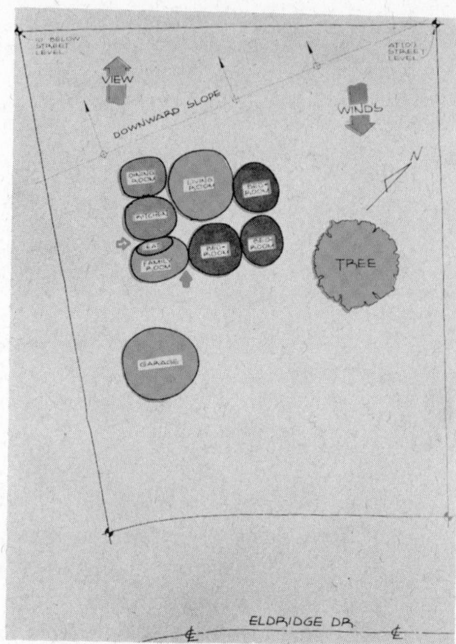

Fig. 4-14. Step 2. Draw circles or ellipses for the living room and family room. **Step 3.** Locate and draw a circle for the kitchen. **Step 4.** Locate and draw sleeping areas and bath rooms. **Step 5.** Locate and draw garage; locate entrances.

Step 1. Roughly sketch the lot, using any type of paper, and indicate the outstanding topographic features, views, streets, afternoon sun, prevailing seasonal winds, and direction. See Fig. 4-13, Step 1.

Step 2. Taking all lot conditions into consideration, draw a circle or ellipse to represent the approximate size and shape of living room and family room.

Step 3. Locate kitchen and dining areas in relation to living room and other living areas. The kitchen should be located where it can receive benefit from the morning sun, and should face the patio. It should also be near the living room, dining area, and family room.

Step 4. Locate sleeping rooms in relation to the orientation of the lot.

a. Locate bedrooms facing away from direct sunlight and away from the living areas where noise may prevail. If possible, also locate all the bedrooms away from the street.

b. Locate bathroom adjacent to the bedrooms and near the living areas of the house. Locate lavatory near family room, rear entryway, or master bedroom.

Step 5. Locate garage, utility room (if needed), entrances, and halls.

a. Locate garage near kitchen and utility room.

b. Locate the entrances, drawing a filled-in arrow for the main entryway and open arrows for secondary entryways. See Fig. 4-14, Steps 2 to 5.

Step 6. Locate halls, and darken these

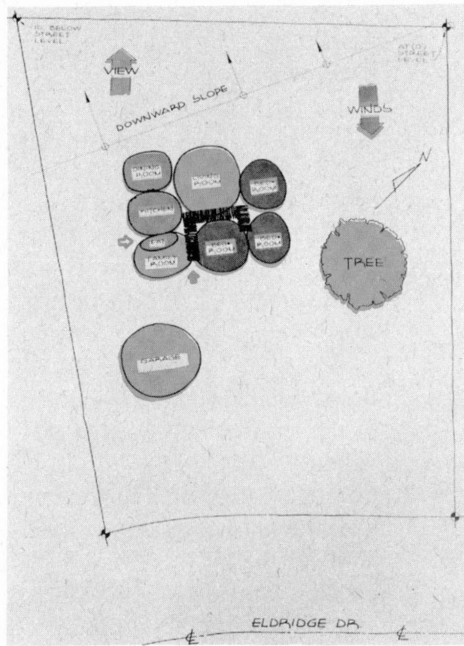

Fig. 4-15. Step 6. Locate and darken hall areas.

areas on the sketch. See Fig. 4-15, Step 6.

Step 7. Redraw the plan sketched in Steps 1 through 6 on ⅛″ or ¼″ co-ordinate paper by sketching the actual outline of the over-all plan. See Fig. 4-16, Step 7.

Sketch Planning

Room arrangements can be studied most effectively by making a series of sketch plans. The ideas and plans that were developed from the arrangements of *room cutouts* or *templates* and from the *circle*

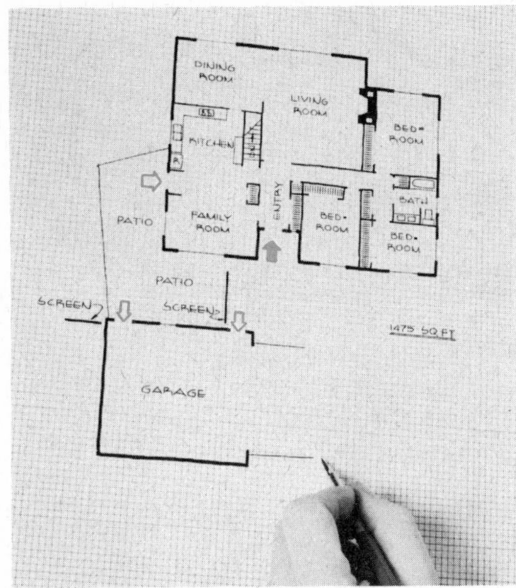

Fig. 4-16. Step 7. Redraw actual outline of overall plan.

method are best used in the beginning *sketch plan*. The component areas and rooms of the house *must* be in proportion to each other, otherwise little is gained in sketching. Hence, it is suggested that all plans be sketched freehand on co-ordinate paper. *Do not* use a straight edge or ruler to draw the lines. One is more reluctant to change a mechanically drawn line. A freehand sketched line is flexible, free, and psychologically easier to erase and change.

The following steps outline the approach to be used in planning.

Step 1. Draw the general outline of the house on co-ordinate paper. Use a single line to represent the exterior walls.

Step 2. Locate the partitions of the main rooms or areas. Check the room sizes to be sure they are sufficiently large to accommodate furniture, closets, etc. (Use the eraser freely; if the rooms or areas are too small, move out the walls.)

Step 3. Locate chimney and/or fireplace.

Step 4. Locate stairs.

Step 5. Locate secondary partitions such as closets, storage, etc.

Step 6. Locate opening.

a. Indicate windows by erasing a portion of the wall line and drawing a single light line across the opening.

b. Indicate doors by erasing a portion of the wall line.

Step 7. Locate any other desired features.

If a basement or second floor of a multilevel house plan is to be drawn, simply place a sheet of tracing paper over the first floor plan. Trace the outside wall lines, stairs, fireplaces, and chimneys; then proceed in general with the above procedure.

Elevation Planning

As the sketch floor plan develops, one must look to his "mind's eye" to determine what changes in the exterior are taking place as the room sizes and placement are altered. The planner should, after some experience, be able to perceive the roof line, exterior coverings, and the window style which will enhance the outside appearance.

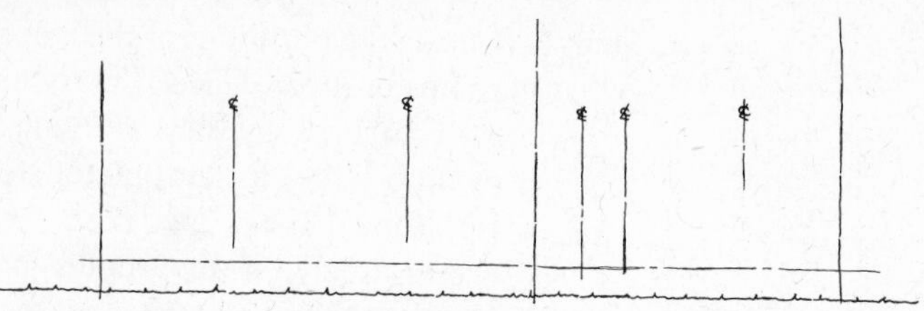

Fig. 4-17. Step 1. Place tracing paper over the floor plan. **Step 2.** Trace off center lines of opening and extremities of outside walls. **Step 3.** Draw in finished grade line. **Step 4.** Lightly draw in finished floor line (center line convention).

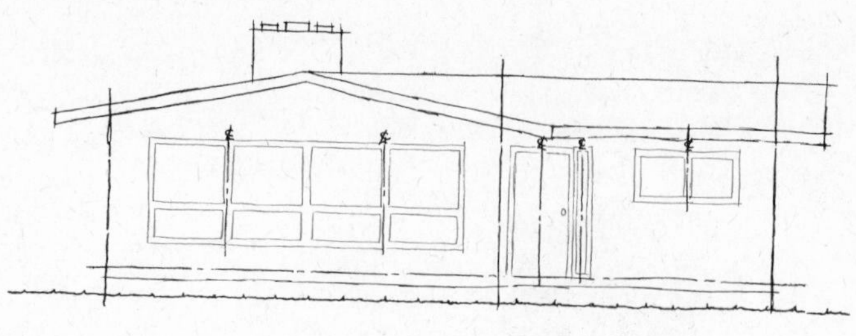

Fig. 4-19. Step 7. Sketch in the proper openings.

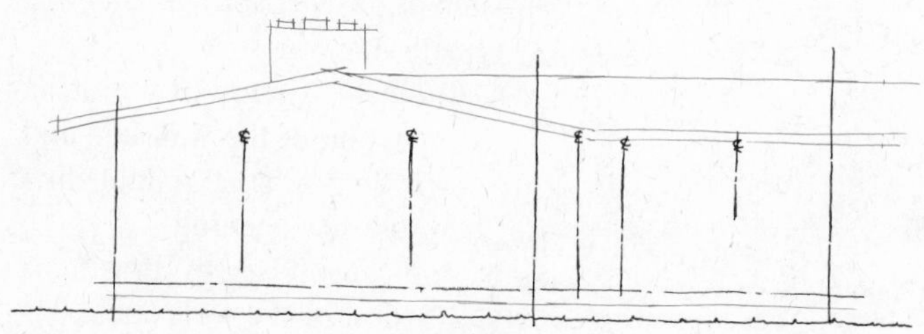

Fig. 4-18. Step 5. Block in elevation using sketchy, straight lines. **Step 6.** Sketch in roof type desired and chimney.

After several floor plans have been sketched, select the best one and draw it to scale (¼″ = 1′-0″ or ⅛″ = 1′-0″). Draw only the outside walls, and include the primary and secondary interior partitions. Do not draw in the doors, windows, fireplaces, or other details at this stage of the sketch design.

When the house is in the preliminary stages of design, it is helpful to sketch the house elevations along with the floor sketch plans. As the floor and elevation sketch plans are being drawn at the same time, greater co-ordination is achieved between the interior and exterior designs. By *sketching* the elevations, changes may easily be made in the appearance of the structure, thereby offering more freedom in producing a pleasing design.

For the development of the elevations, the following procedure is suggested.

Step 1. Place the sketch plan selected beneath a sheet of tracing paper.

Step 2. Draw vertical lines on the tracing paper locating the ℄ of windows, doors, and the extremities of the outside walls for that elevation.

Step 3. Locate, by drawing a horizontal line, the finished grade (ground level) of the lot.

Step 4. Locate, with a light horizontal line, the finished floor approximately 1′-6″ above the finished grade. This distance may be approximated or scaled using a corresponding piece of co-ordinate paper. See Fig. 4-17, Steps 1 to 4.

Step 5. "Block in" the elevation, using freehand straight lines. Draw the wall height as far as the *eave* or roof border, which is approximately 8′ above the floor.

Step 6. Draw the roof type desired and also the chimney. See Fig. 4-18, Steps 5 and 6.

Step 7. Sketch the window and door openings; approximate the sizes, or scale them with a co-ordinate paper. See Fig. 4-19, Step 7.

Step 8. Complete the finished sketch, suggesting most of the details by light or dark markings. Do not erase the preliminary lines unless an actual mistake has occurred. The preliminary lines serve as background to soften and add coherence to the sketch. Study and compare the opening sizes, proportion of masses, and balance of areas. Any feature which seems awry may be adjusted easily with an eraser. See Fig. 4-20, Step 8.

Fig. 4-20A. Step 8. Proceed to bring out the finished sketch. Study and compare openings, proportion, and balance of areas. Change any features which do not enhance design.

Fig. 4-20B. Finished Elevation Sketch.

Planning Points

Regardless of the methods used in home planning, the various aspects of the plan must be given careful consideration. Planning errors made by inexperienced planners are infinite and impossible to list. The following points, however, are those most frequently neglected or overlooked by students as they plan a house.

1. If the house has more than one floor, plan the chimney location first, because this may affect the upper levels or the basement arrangement.
2. Avoid using rooms as passageways, (i.e., going through a bedroom to get to another bed- or bathroom).
3. Plan halls within a minimum space and with some natural light. Hall space costs as much per square foot as sleeping, living, and eating areas.
4. Design the house to fit the lot. Do not neglect to consider the existing trees on the lot, as well as the shape, slope, and orientation.
5. Decide the location and the style of windows to be used and relate them to the street, adjoining lot, and the natural beauty.
6. Avoid an excessive number of windows and doors in the average size house design. Failure to consider this may cause problems in arranging furniture and will add to the cost of heating the house.
7. Avoid placing a bath room or lavatory over the living room.
8. If cost is a major factor, try to cover the tentative plan with a roof having as few breaks or *offsets* as possible. Every break in the roof line will increase the cost.
9. Allow roughly six inches for all interior partitions.
10. Plan all storage space so they are readily accessible and near to the area of their greatest use. The space must be large enough to contain items intended for storage.
11. Plan all bedrooms with windows which allow adequate ventilation.
12. Allow adequate space for a *stair run*. Do not end stairs against a blank wall.

Plan Types

In all aspects of life, advantages and

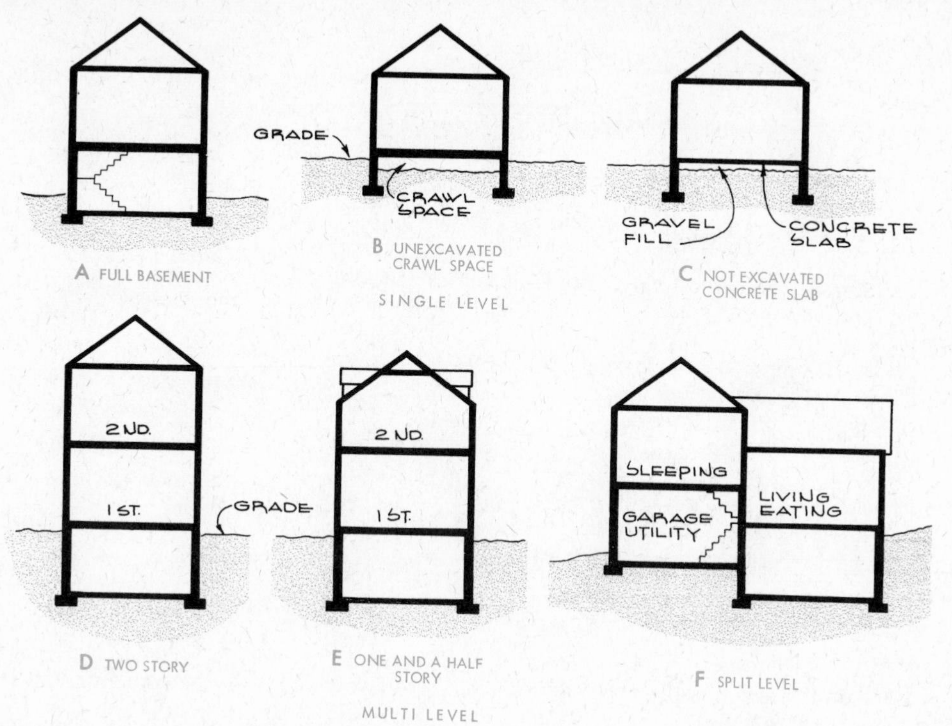

Fig. 4-21. These single- and multi-level designs represent the six basic elevations.

disadvantages must be weighed prior to making a decision. The same is true in deciding whether to build a one-story, two-story, one-and-a-half story, or split-level dwelling. In many instances the choice of the number of levels is a matter of personal preference. However, building factors should be taken into consideration before any final choice is made. Each family, depending on their circumstances, should base their decision on such factors as cost, comfort, climate, convenience, beauty, upkeep, and lot size.

Single-Story Dwellings

Single-story houses have proven to be very popular. Quite possibly this may be due to the family experiences as apartment dwellers since many apartment dwellers desire the open spaciousness of a ranch-type house. The single-story dwelling saves the house wife and older persons many trips up and down the stairs. Cost analysis of single-level versus multi-level dwellings show little difference in small homes of 1000 to 1500 sq. ft.

The single-story house, as shown in Fig. 4-21 (top) may be built with a full basement, a crawl space, or on a slab. The basement is not classified as an additional house level. Without a stairway to an upper level, a more open floor plan may be designed giving the interior a larger appearance. Larger basements with more usable areas are possible in the single-level dwelling.

Families that plan a home for future expansion will encounter little or no difficulty expanding the single-level home, as compared to a two-level dwelling. Also, a greater variation of exterior design is possible with the single-level house.

The maintenance cost is often greater with a one-story house because the exterior walls and roof have larger areas. More heat loss occurs with the larger roof areas. Depending upon the interior plan, the one-story house may require more hall space than a multi-level house. In addition, the one-story house may require a larger lot area than a multi-level dwelling.

Two-Story Dwelling

The two-story house (for the same volume) offers more living space and is more economical to heat because it has less roof and foundation area. The hall space in a two-story house can be greatly reduced. The two-story house does not usually lend itself to open planning because the rooms are enclosed and are not open to view from the outside. This type of home is commonly found in urban areas where the privacy of the family or individuals is important.

Often, the outside design appearance of a two-story dwelling is narrow and tall, giving a "box-like" appearance. This illusion is caused not only by the design, but also by the type of exterior covering materials which are used. Frequently, a garage may be planned at one end and a porch on the other to lower the height illusion.

It is unwise to plan a two-story house in an area populated with low, single-story dwellings. If the lots are extremely wide and the terrain is "rolling", however, a two-story house may be suitable. See Fig. 4-21 (lower left).

One-and-a-Half Story Dwellings

The one-and-a-half story house shown in Fig. 4-21 (lower middle) is essentially a single-story dwelling with a sufficiently high pitched roof to permit later expansion in the attic area. As indicated in the figure, a *dormer* (a raised roof and wall area to provide window space) may be added to increase the natural light and ventilation. Although the floor area of a one-and-a-half story house may be equivalent to the two-story house, it usually has the illusion of being lower. It has most of the advantages of the two-story with one possible exception. The upper floor areas of a one-and-a-half story house may be smaller, and a portion of its ceiling may slope. Because the upper rooms are immediately below the roof, these rooms are difficult to cool in the summer.

Split-Level Dwellings

The split-level house shown in Fig. 4-21 (lower right) is also referred to as a tri-level or bi-level. This type of plan has become very popular and has been widely adapted not only to sloping land terrain, but also to those areas where the terrain is level. The split-level house was originally intended for sloping or hilly land.

Split-level houses often present problems in design and construction. However, the construction cost per square foot, in relation to comparable materials and floor area, is often less than that of a single-level type.

The general arrangement of a split-level offers the basic functions, such as sleeping eating, and living, on separate levels of the house. The eating and living areas are usually located on the ground level, so that they are easily integrated to the out-of-doors. The sleeping area is separated from the living area by a half or partial flight of stairs. The utility room, recreation or family room, and sometimes the garage may be located in a semi-basement. This is one of the economical attributes of the split-level because the foundation depth is a little more than that required for basementless construction. As with the two-story dwelling, split-level homes have more living space with less roof and foundation area, thus they are more economical to heat. Hall space may also be completely or greatly reduced. In addition to being economical, the split-level has other advantages. The raised sleeping area with a short flight of stairs gives a greater feeling of privacy, quietness, and security than does the conventional, single-level type of house plan.

Because of the frequent use of open planning, the heating system must be carefully planned to insure even heat in all the rooms. Frequently, *zoned heating* (a thermostat in every room or a group of rooms) is incorporated in the split-level home. Though the initial cost of heating equipment may be greater, savings introduced through heating economy, and the additional comfort, may repay the investment in the long run.

Exposed Basement

Depending on the topographic features

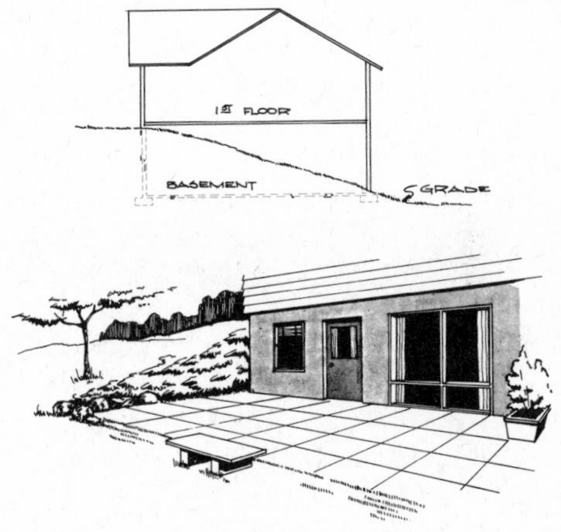

Fig. 4-22. An exposed basement adds living area to the home.

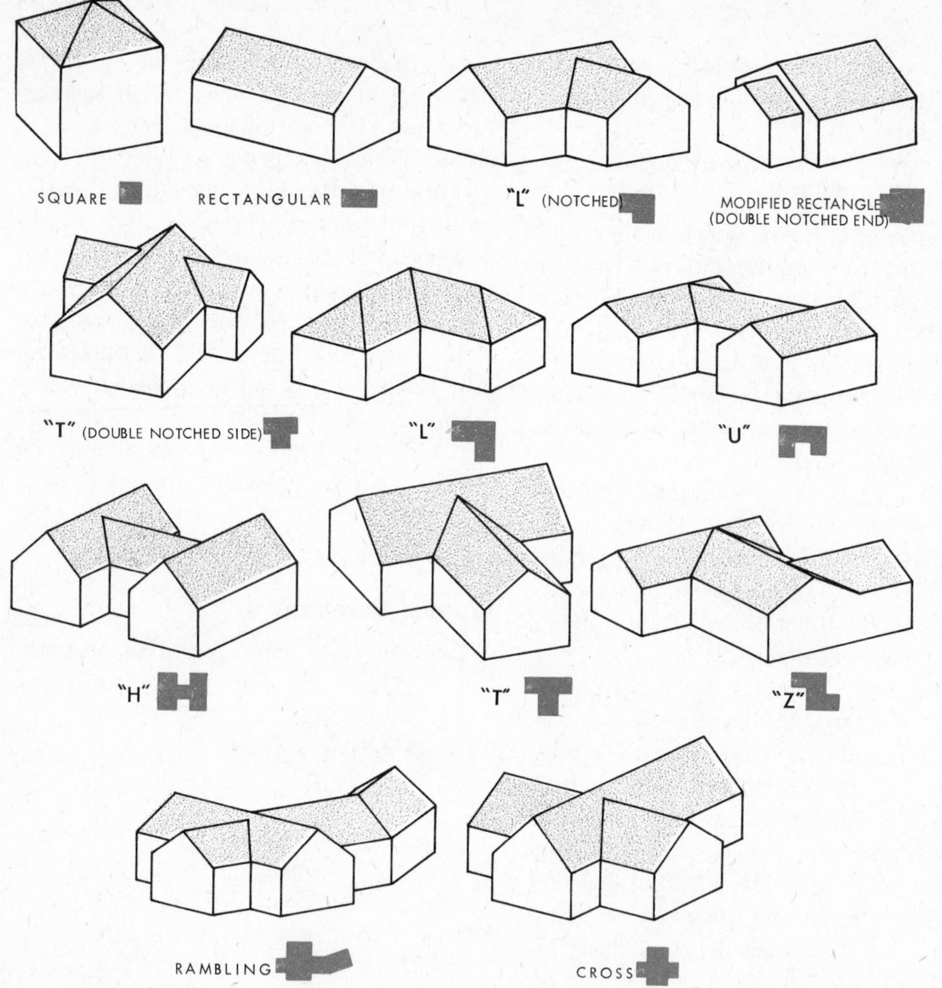

Fig. 4-23. Most house plans are derivations of these basic types.

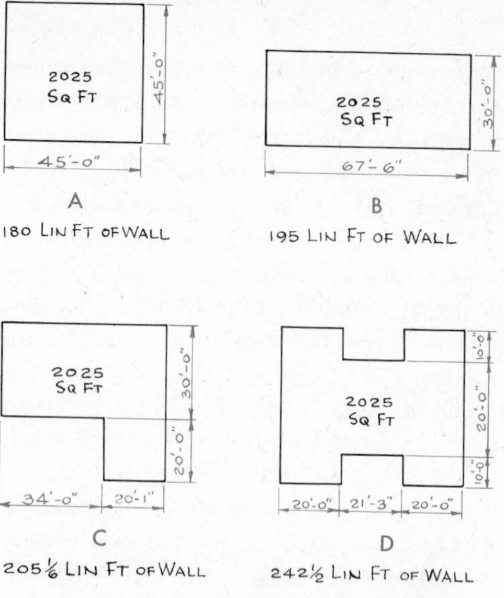

Fig. 4-24. As more off-sets are introduced into the plan, more linear length is needed to give the same square footage. (Notice that a square plan has the smallest perimeter.)

of the lot, additional living area may be added to any of the plan types discussed above (with the exception of basementless houses) by designing an exposed basement as shown in Fig. 4-22. The exposed basement offers added living area at a nominal cost. A portion of the basement may become a family or recreation room, home office, or a bedroom with direct access to the outside terrace, patio, or garden. Some builders construct the basement with its rear or side exposed to a lot which is level. This may create a drainage problem. If a correctly engineered retaining wall and adequate drainage are placed on the lot, this problem will not be encountered.

Plan Shapes

The outline or shape of a plan is determined by the arrangement and size of the rooms. Most house plans may be classified as one of the twelve shapes shown in Fig. 4-23. Each of these plan shapes has its own architectural possibilities, depending on room arrangements, location on the lot, ventilation, lighting, construction, and cost. The more a plan deviates from the basic square or rectangular shape, the more it becomes complicated and disjointed. The cost increases in proportion to the amount of wall surface, roof, number of offsets, etc. It is difficult, however, to estimate the additional cost of a projection on the basic square or rectangular house, even though the square footage may be the same. A simple square footage (total floor area) and a lineal-wall length (total perimeter length of the house) comparison of four plan shapes is shown in Fig. 4-24. Although the general length and depth proportions of each plan may be similar, and the square footage may be equal, the lineal wall footage increases with the number of offsets that are added.

The designer must decide the importance of deviation from the basic square or rectangular plan so that an interesting and attractive exterior design, as well as a functional floor plan, may be created.

Questions and Problems

These questions are based on significant factors of room arrangement in the home.

1. Visit several new homes. Sketch a floor plan based on observed ideas, and compare the livability, room arrangements, adequacy, etc.
2. Members of your family may have special interests and hobbies. What changes could be recommended in your home to accommodate their hobbies and interests?
3. Visit several real estate developments, and note the house and lot sizes, exterior designs, floor plans, proximity to shopping facilities, schools, and transportation. Based on your observations, are any of these homes a good investment?
4. List some of the building restrictions in your community. How do these effect the placement of the house on the lot?
5. Many communities have zoning restrictions; how do these affect a community?
6. What are some disadvantages that occur in sketching plans? Advantages?
7. Develop a floor plan, using any of the methods described in this chapter, for the following two houses.
   a. A basementless ranch-type house containing a combination living room and dining room, kitchen, three bedrooms, bathroom, lavatory, and utility room. The house is to be placed on a lot 70′ × 100′. The short dimension of the lot is parallel to the NW side of a street which runs in a NE direction. The city code specifies a house must be set back a minimum of 35′ from the front lot line and a minimum of 8′ on the sides. The lot is level and a desirable view is due north.
   b. A summer cottage containing a combined living, dining, and kitchen area, 2 bedrooms, bathroom, and a large porch. The lot is 112′ × 250′, the short dimension parallels a lake and faces west. There are no restrictions as to placing the cottage on the lot. The rear ⅓ of the lot is heavily forested with pines and spruce trees, and slopes downward from the rear lot line at a 16 per cent slope.
8. Sketch two different sets of elevations (front and side) for each of the plans developed in problem 7a and 7b above.

UNIVERSITY OF CHICAGO.

Lettering is an ancient art. This tablet from Ur, shown in obverse and reverse, is dated circa 2062 B.C.

Architectural Lettering 5

Lettering is thought to have been one of the earliest means of decoration used in architecture. The Romans, for example, adorned tombs, buildings, and arches with their style of lettering, the **Old Roman** alphabet. Our modern **Roman** alphabet is a direct outgrowth of the Old Roman alphabet. An example of today's use of the Old Roman style alphabet is shown in Fig. 5-1. The proper letter proportions and the relationships of curves to the height of the letters in the Roman alphabet is shown in Fig. 5-2.

Lettering

Architectural drawings require more notes and dimensioning information than drawings from other fields of graphical representation. Good lettering, therefore, is essential on an architectural drawing, and sometimes contributes to "selling" a design. It creates an impression of skilled workmanship. Architectural lettering is one means by which the draftsman or architect may express his individuality. The style of letters he chooses for his drawings should be simple, and his lettering should always be neat. Outstanding lettering depends upon simplicity and neatness.

In architectural lettering, alphabetical characters are formed with the six basic strokes illustrated in Fig. 5-3. These strokes can form every alphabet character, drawn either separately or in combination with each other. Quality lettering is based on the mastery of these six basic strokes.

Architectural lettering is not limited to a specific stroking style. Variation of form and mixing of lettering styles are permissible.

Students frequently remark, "I never could *print,* because my handwriting is poor.", or "I am left-handed and this causes my problems." Many of the finest draftsmen, architects, and engineers who are extremely deft in lettering have poor handwriting or are left-handed. Quality lettering is achieved through constant practice. One cannot study a given style of lettering, make several copying attempts, and then expect good results. Persistent practice, approximately 15 to 20 minutes a day, is necessary until the student has competency in the formation of all the letters, and until he has developed the coordinated finger and hand motions.

Pressure Sensitive Lettering

Individual lettering, however, is not always used on architectural drawings. In

MINORU YAMASAKI AND ASSOCIATES, BIRMINGHAM, MICHIGAN.

Fig. 5-1. Architect Minoru Yamasaki used Old Roman lettering in the design of the McGregor Memorial building at Wayne State University.

McGREGOR
MEMORIAL

WAYNE STATE UNIVERSITY, DETROIT, MICHIGAN.

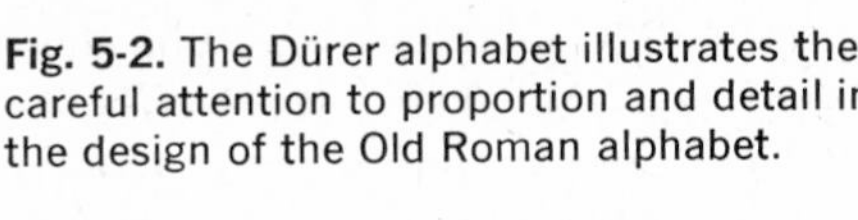

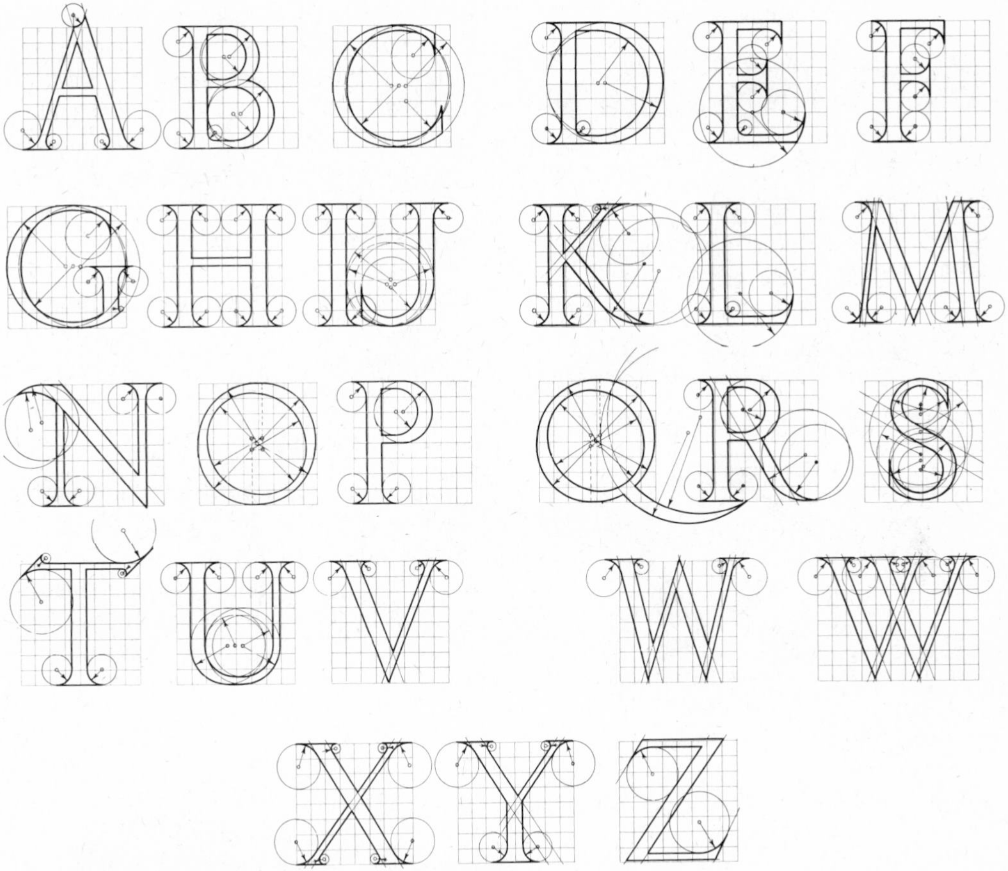

Fig. 5-2. The Dürer alphabet illustrates the careful attention to proportion and detail in the design of the Old Roman alphabet.

some cases (for display or presentation drawings) the designer or illustrator may use manufactured pressure sensitive lettering.

Dry Transfer Lettering. One of the latest innovations in the field of illustrating is the dry transfer method. These transfer letters are arranged on a transparent plastic sheet. Letters are transferred by rubbing over the desired letter with any smooth instrument, such as a ball point pen or soft pencil. Fig. 5-4 illustrates the method of transferring letters. The type sheet is then lifted away leaving the letter on the drawing surface. In circumstances where the illustrations may be handled, the letters may be "fixed" by the application of a clear *acrylic spray*.

Adhesive lettering is similar to the pressure sensitive type of lettering in appearance. The lettering rather than being directly transferred, however, is cut out,

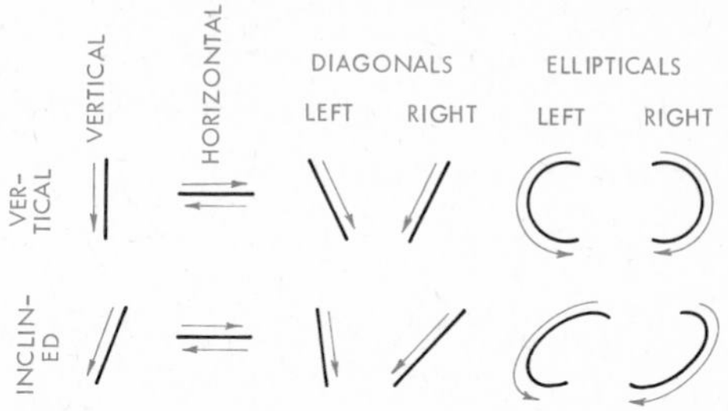

Fig. 5-3. All architectural and engineering lettering may be analyzed into **Six Basic Strokes.**

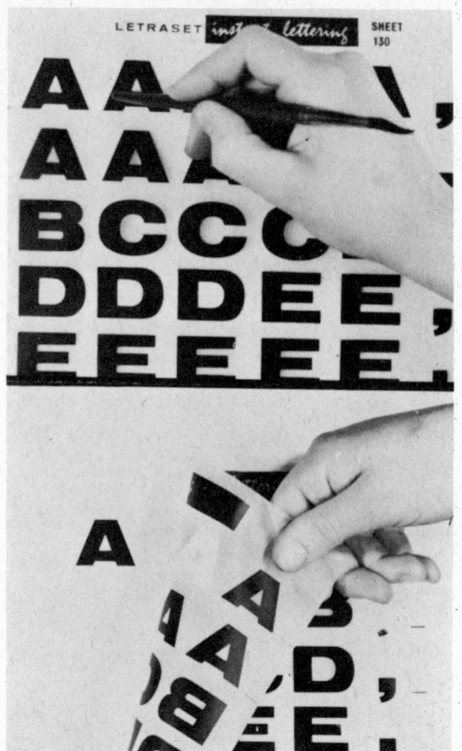

Fig. 5-4. Dry Transfer lettering is easy to apply. Frequently it is used on presentation drawings and architectural models.

placed in the desired position, and rubbed with a smooth instrument. The plastic sheet has an adhesive material on the reverse side which holds the letter securely to the drawing surface.

Lettering Devices

There are several types of lettering devices which are used in the architectural and illustrating fields. The most common and probably the most widely used is the *Varigraph*. This device will produce a wide variety of built-up and single line style letters. Fig. 5-5 illustrates this instrument. A guide pen is moved in the depression on the lettering template. Through an adjustable mechanical linkage the pen (stylus) reproduces the form of the letter on the drawing sheet. The size of the letter (height and width) and angle of depression may be changed by adjusting the controls of the *Varigraph*.

Pencil Selection

A factor not to be overlooked in lettering is selecting the proper grade of pencil. Choosing the right pencil is dependent on several factors: (1) the pressure applied to the pencil, (2) the type of drafting medium used, and (3) the brand (manufacturer) of the pencil.

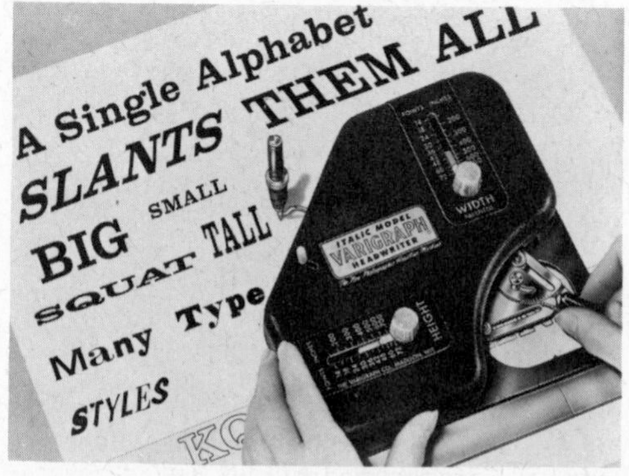

THE VARIGRAPH CO., MADISON, WISCONSIN.

Fig. 5-5. The Varigraph may be used to obtain a wide variety of character styles and sizes, from a single template.

Pressure

Every person applies a different pressure or touch on his pencil. The grade of the pencil to be chosen depends upon the pressure applied on the pencil. One person may choose a 2H grade pencil, while another may prefer to use a pencil grade of H, T, or 3H on the same type of drawing medium to produce the desired dense, black line.

Drawing Medium

The kind and type of drawing medium, such as paper, vellum, cloth, or polyester film, plays an important part in pencil selection. Some mediums, because of their surface finish, are very receptive to hard lead pencil, while others may require a softer lead. Some vellums, pencil cloths, and polyester films are manufactured with a slightly rough surface. This type of surface media is very receptive to a pencil which produces a dense black line with a normal amount of pressure. Roughly surfaced media permits the use of a slightly harder lead pencil to produce the desired line quality.

Brands

Grades of hardness and softness of pencils vary from manufacturer to manufacturer. A 2H grade pencil from one manufacturer may be softer or harder than a 2H grade from another. One reputable brand of pencil should be used. It is not advisable to use mixed brands of pencils.

Guide Lines

Height *guide lines* (very light gray lines)

should be drawn for *all* lettering which appears on a drawing. The most accomplished draftsmen always use guide lines. There are numerous devices available on the market to aid the draftsman or student in drawing guide lines. Among the more popular lettering guide devices are the *Braddock-Rowe Lettering Triangle* and the *Ames Lettering Guide*. These are shown in Fig. 5-6.

Guide lines are drawn to help keep straight the outer edges of letters in a word or sentence. For most lettering, only two guide lines are needed: the base line and the cap (capital) line. However, when upper and lower case letters are used, two other guide lines, the waist and the drop lines, must also be included with the base and the cap lines, as shown in Fig. 5-7. Often, the drop line is omitted. If large and small capital letters are to be made, the four guide lines are used. In addition to these horizontal guide lines, random vertical or inclined lines are also lightly drawn to insure uniform, parallel letters.

Style

The style of lettering, in architectural drawing, is another important factor to be studied. As mentioned earlier, combining the six basic strokes in lettering will produce all the alphabet characters. However, there are some important points to consider when producing an architectural style of lettering. For example, attention must be given to: (1) the design of the letter characters, (2) the spacing of the letter characters within a word, (3) the spacing of words within a sentence or note, and (4) the size of the lettering.

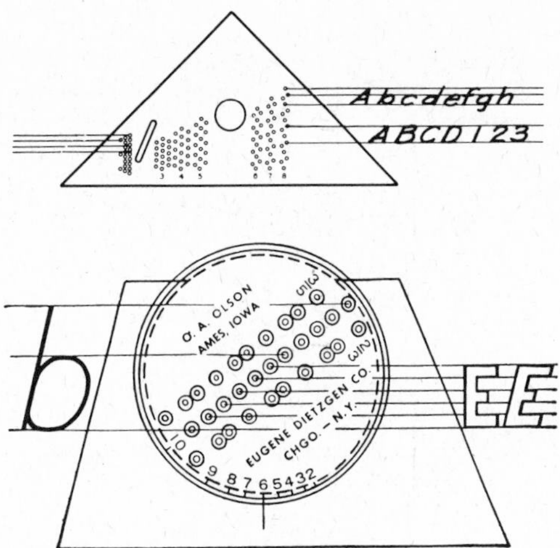

Fig. 5-6. These lettering guides aid the draftsman or student in drawing guide lines.

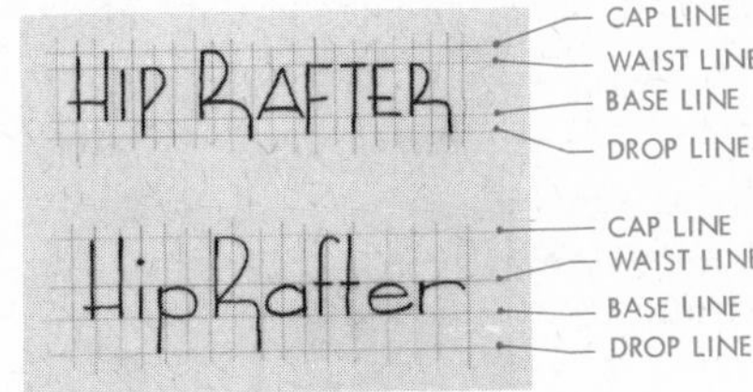

Fig. 5-7. Guide lines are used to maintain uniform character height for caps and lower case.

Letter Design

Virtually all architectural lettering styles are now single stroke (i.e., all the lines and curves of the letter or character have the same line weight or thickness). This single stroke style is similar to the Gothic style lettering used on engineering drawings. Gothic style is similar to the lettering illustrated in Fig. 5-6 (top). The only two probable exceptions are in the lettering of the title line on a presentation drawing or in the reference letters which indicate where a drawing section has been taken. These letters may be of the Old Roman style, or styled to be ornate to attract attention. In the past, architects or draftsmen have often used all caps (capitals or upper case letters) for titles and subtitles, and upper and lower case letters for notes. Today, many architects and draftsmen in architectural firms are switching to all capital letters in the lettering of titles and notes.

In architectural lettering, the alphabet characters are not restricted to a mechanical form such as the lettering generally found in machine, electrical, civil, or other types of engineering drawings. The single stroke Gothic style is required for engineering work. In architectural lettering, the letters may have variations in their form, thus creating a pleasing style. The student is encouraged to study the lettering samples which are illustrated in Figs. 5-8 and 5-9.

The variations in form and design of each

ABCDEFGHIJKLMNO
PQRSTUVWXYZ
1234567890
GERALD KURTZ

ABCDEFGHIJKLMNOPQRSTU
VWXYZ
1234567890
KEN HOMRICH

ABCDEFGHIJKLM
NOPQRSTUVWXYZ
1234567890
GERALD HEETHUIS

ABCDEFGHIJKLMNOP
QRSTUVWXYZ
1234567890
TIIT TELMET

Fig. 5-8. Study these lettering samples. Notice how each draftsman has developed a style which is distinctive.

ABCDEFGHIJKLMNOPQ
RSTUVWXYZ
1234567890
JOHN P. JANDURA

ABCDEFGHIJKLMNO
PQRSTUVWXYZ
1234567890
DOUGLAS GRUNTMAN

ABCDEFGHIJKLMNOPQRS
TUVWXYZ
&1234567890
BOB BOYCE

ABCDEFGHIJKLMN
OPQRSTUVWXYZ
1234567890
RICHARD MONROE

ABCDEFGHIJKLMNOPQRSTU
VWXYZ
&1234567890
ARVID KIANDER

Fig. 5-9. Remember: All lettering must be simple and neat.

letter in architectural lettering are created by the artistic lettering skills of the architect or draftsman. He does not have to conform to any designated form or style of lettering. However, he must design his letters so that they demonstrate his lettering skills, while maintaining an identifiable form for each letter character. The architect or draftsman makes use of *serifs* (short line strokes at the corners on the top and bottom of each letter) in the letters on his presentation drawings, but omits them when speed is more important than ornate lettering.

The variations in style and form are commonly found in the letters, E, F, H, P, R, and B. For example, the center horizontal line of the letter E may be located either above or below the center of this letter, and may be extended a short distance beyond the vertical line on the left and/or beyond the end of the upper or lower horizontal line.

Further attention may be focused on letters if the terminal points of each character are *pointed*. Fig. 5-10 shows several letters which have been pointed. Pointing emphasizes the terminal point of each letter with a slightly heavier pressure than is ordinarily exerted in forming the letter. The top and bottom of each letter that has been pointed is accurately aligned with the cap, waist, base, and drop line. This is a more accurate method than merely stroking the letters, and is usually performed after the character, word, line, or paragraph of lettering is completed.

In all cases, the design of the letters must be consistent with the design of all the other alphabet characters on a drawing. This will produce that artistic quality in architectural lettering which demonstrates the skills of the architect or draftsman.

Letter Spacing

Spacing the letter characters within a word is not difficult once the draftsman is completely familiar with the style of the alphabet. Spacing, or the proper placement of the blank area between the characters, is shown in Fig. 5-11. The spacing between these letters are uniform and are measured visually. However, there are some letter combinations, such as AT, VA, WA, and LT, where the spacing between them is not uniform with the spacing of the other letters. These letters are usually spaced closer together, because the sides of the letters, V, A, and W are sloping, and thus produce a larger space when placed adjacent to such letters as L and T which have space either at the top or at the bottom. Visual judgment is exercised when spacing letters or characters within a word.

Word Spacing

In addition to good spacing of letters within a word, consideration must also be given to spacing words within a sentence, note, or title. Usually, one letter space or the width of the capital letter N or O is used between words. Each word should be a distinct unit spaced well enough apart so the words do not appear to be running together.

Letter Size

The size of lettering is dependent, many times, upon the size of the drawing. Lettering on a complete set of architectural working drawings is usually 3/32″ or 1/8″ high; titles are usually 3/16″ or 1/4″ high. Once the size of the drawing, number of details on the sheet, and the sheet size have been determined, consideration may then be given to the height of the lettering.

Table 5-1 gives the standard sheet sizes. Most architectural drawings are executed on C or D sheets.

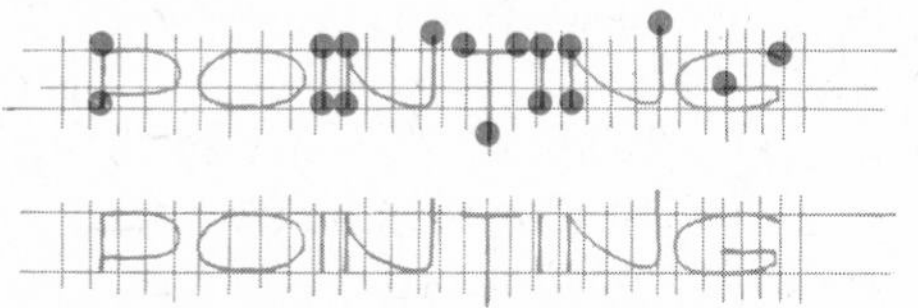

Fig. 5-10. Lettering may be emphasized by **pointing** the terminal portions.

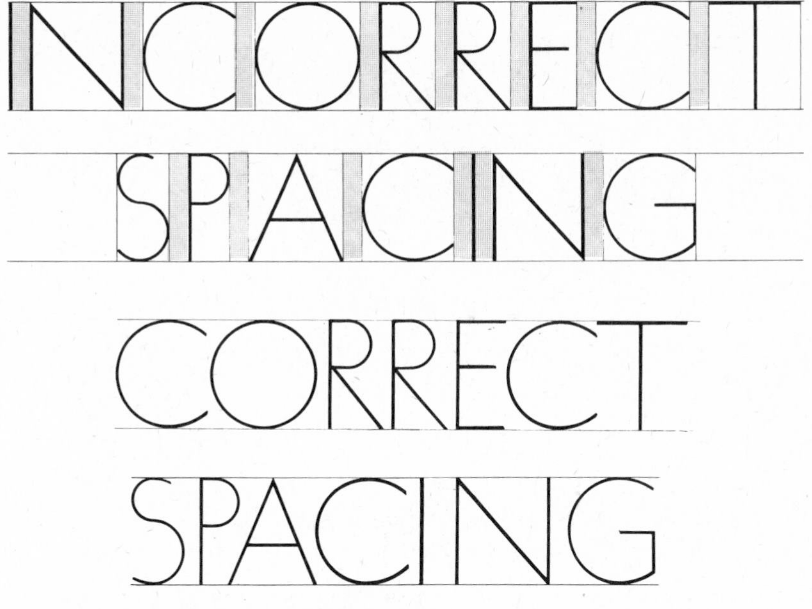

Fig. 5-11. The **visual area** between characters in a work should be approximately equal.

TABLE 5-1
DRAWING SHEET SIZES

A - Size	8 1/2" x 11"	or	9" x 12"
B - Size	11" x 17"	or	12" x 18"
C - Size	17" x 22"	or	18" x 24"
D - Size	22" x 34"	or	24" x 36"
E - Size	34" x 44"	or	36" x 48"

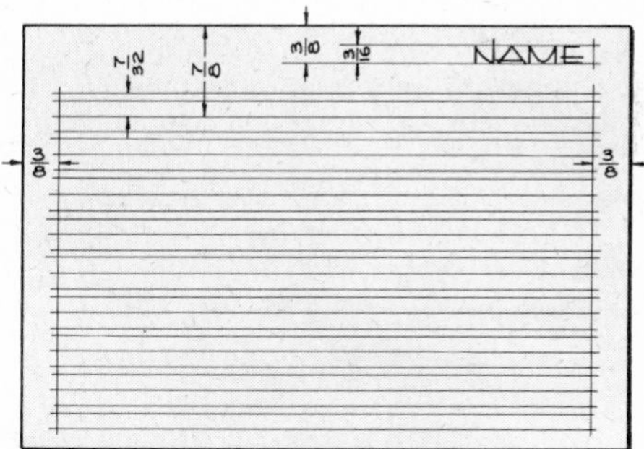

Fig. 5-12. A 4″ by 6″ card layout is used for lettering practice.

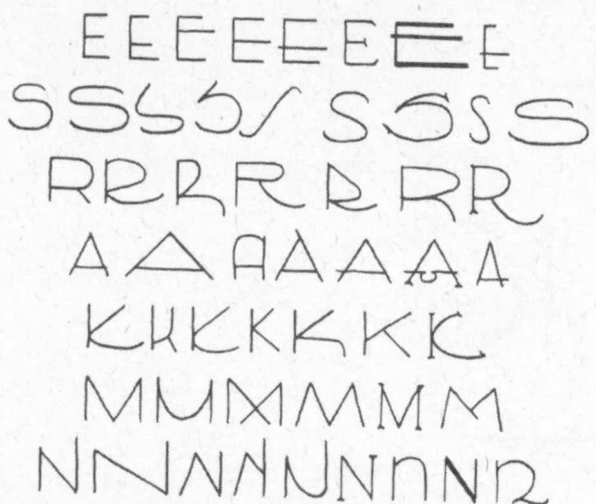

Fig. 5-13. Characters may be modified to suit the individual taste.

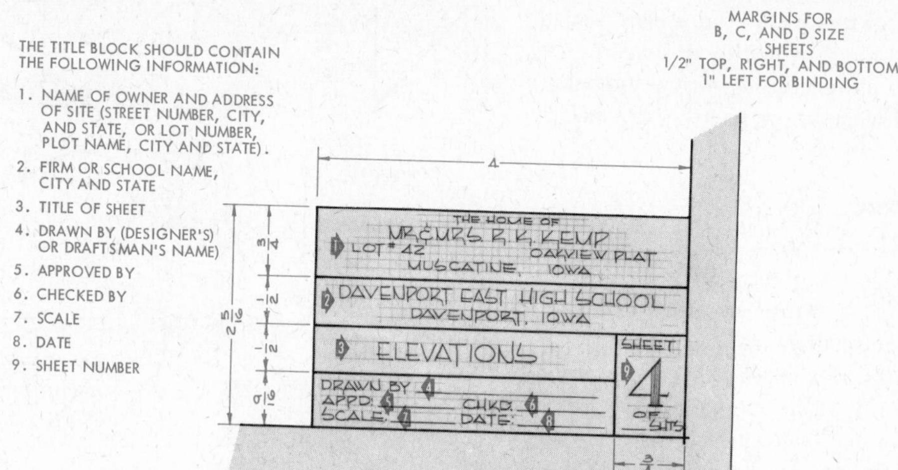

Fig. 5-14A. This title block may be used for architectural working drawings on B, C, or D size sheets.

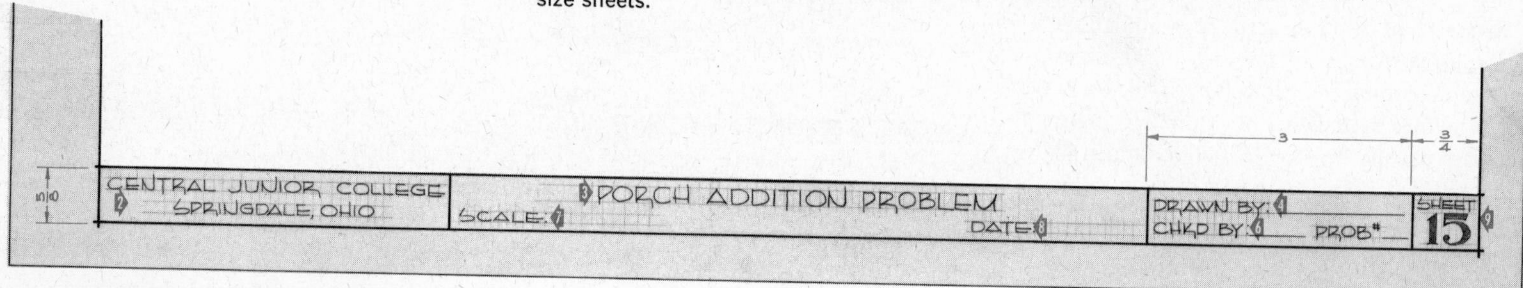

Fig. 5-14B. A file strip may be used for architectural problems on a B size sheet.

G. E. DIEKEMA, AIA, KALAMAZOO, MICHIGAN.

Fig. 5-14C. A title block may be used without border lines. This title block is a plastic applique and may be placed on any size sheet.

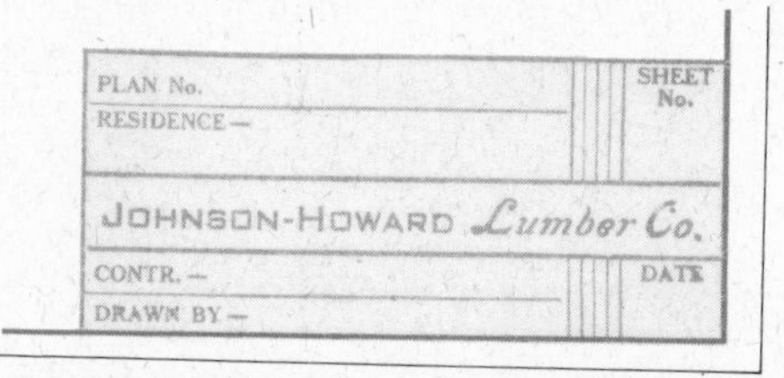

JOHNSON-HOWARD LUMBER CO., KALAMAZOO, MICHIGAN.

Fig. 5-14D. This title block is placed on the vellum sheet by a rubber stamp: border lines are then added. It may be used on any size sheet.

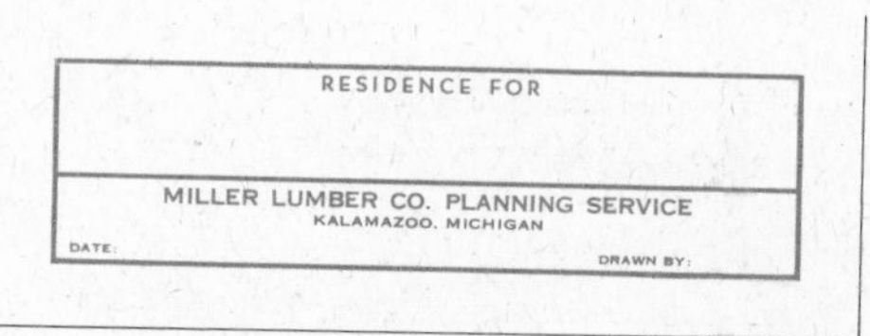

MILLER LUMBER CO., PLANNING SERVICE, KALAMAZOO, MICHIGAN.

Fig. 5-14E. This is a printed title block without border lines.

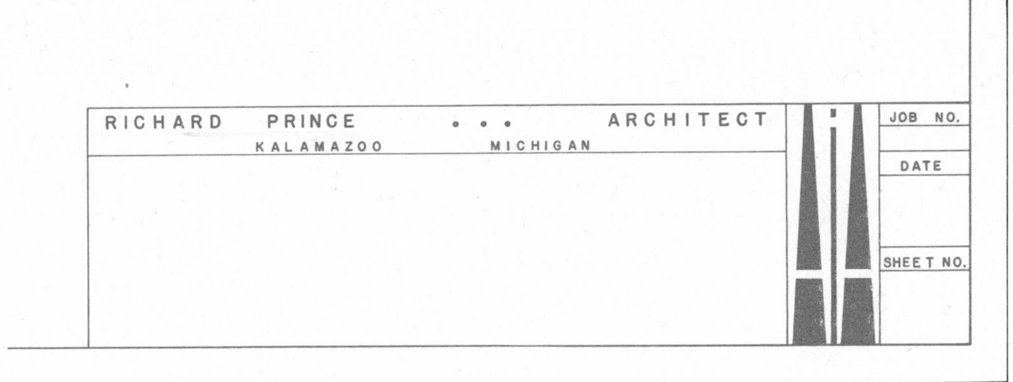

RICHARD PRINCE • • • ARCHITECT
KALAMAZOO MICHIGAN
JOB NO.
DATE
SHEET NO.
RICHARD A. PRINCE, AIA, KALAMAZOO, MICHIGAN.

Fig. 5-14F. This is a sample of a printed title block with border lines. Note the large space allotted for a description and location of the project.

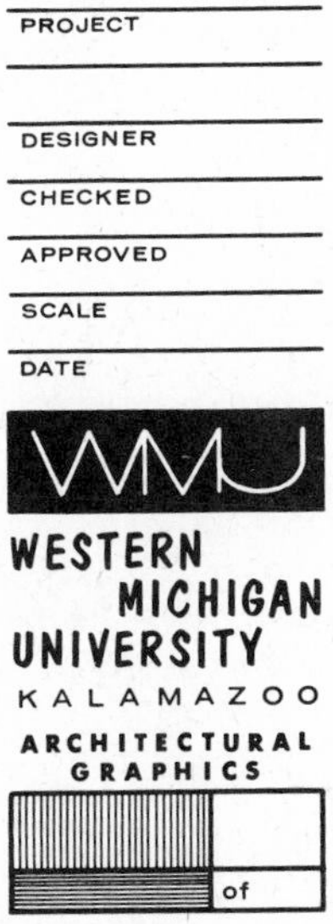

PROJECT
DESIGNER
CHECKED
APPROVED
SCALE
DATE
WMU
WESTERN
MICHIGAN
UNIVERSITY
KALAMAZOO
ARCHITECTURAL
GRAPHICS
of

Fig. 5-14G. This illustrates another style of unbalanced title blocks.

Problems

Obtain three 4″x6″ unruled filing cards, and prepare them with light horizontal guide lines in the same manner as that shown in Fig. 5-12. Select one of the sample sets of alphabets shown in Fig. 5-8 and 5-9. Complete the following on the three cards using all upper case lettering.

1. On the first card, lightly lay out the alphabet set which you have chosen. Modify the letters slightly to suit your taste, as shown in Fig. 5-13. When you have achieved a clear and legible set of letters, darken them on the card and show the card to your instructor for his approval.
2. On the second ruled file card, letter the following in the style you have developed in step no. 1.

   ABCDEFGHIJKLM
   NOPQRSTUVWXYZ
   1 2 3 4 5 6 7 8 9 0 &
   SIMPLICITY, LEGIBILITY,
   SPEED, AND EASE OF
   CHARACTER FORMATION
   ARE PARAMOUNT FACTORS
   IN CHARACTER DESIGN.
3. On the third card, use the same style of lettering as in steps nos. 1 and 2, and copy the following.

   ABCDEFGHIJKLM
   NOPQRSTUVWXYZ
   1 2 3 4 5 6 7 8 9 0 &
   TYPICAL WALL SECTION
   SCALE 1½″ = 1′-0″.
   THE FIELD OF ARCHITEC-
   TURE CHALLENGES MAN'S
   URGE TO CREATE FOR
   THE FUTURE IN A
   FUNCTIONAL FORM.
4. Select a title block from those shown in Fig. 5-14. Lay out the chosen title block on another 4″x6″ unruled filing card. Letter very lightly, making sure that the alphabet characters are all in balance. Darken the letters on the card. This card will serve as a master title block template for all your future tracings. Trace the title block by placing the card under vellum or tracing paper.
5. Copy the first paragraph of this chapter in a clear legible style, and make all the letters about ⅛″ high. Keep the space between letters uniform, and the words about one letter space apart.

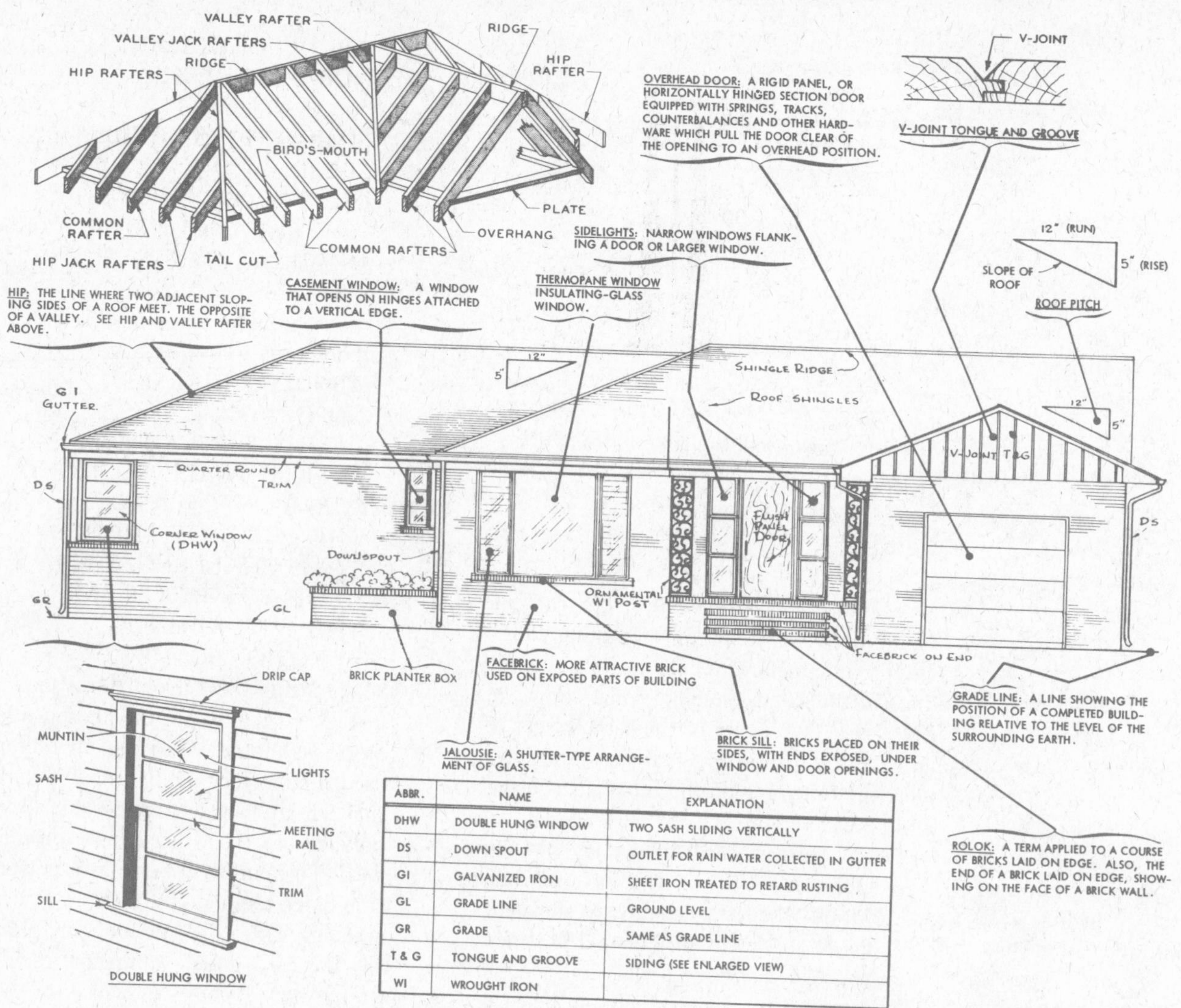

ABBR.	NAME	EXPLANATION
DHW	DOUBLE HUNG WINDOW	TWO SASH SLIDING VERTICALLY
DS	DOWN SPOUT	OUTLET FOR RAIN WATER COLLECTED IN GUTTER
GI	GALVANIZED IRON	SHEET IRON TREATED TO RETARD RUSTING
GL	GRADE LINE	GROUND LEVEL
GR	GRADE	SAME AS GRADE LINE
T & G	TONGUE AND GROOVE	SIDING (SEE ENLARGED VIEW)
WI	WROUGHT IRON	

Symbols and abbreviations are essential to architectural drawings.

Architectural Symbols and Abbreviations 6

The architect's set of drawings for a residence or home is so small (approximately 1/48 actual size when drawn to a scale of ¼″ = 1′-0″) in comparison with the actual home size, that some type of symbolic representation must be used. Each feature of a home cannot be represented on a set of architectural working drawings without the use of symbols or conventions. Almost all symbols and conventions for building materials, walls, floors, window and door openings, electrical and plumbing fixtures, heating and cooling facilities, and duct works have been standardized by the American Standards Association (ASA)[1] and the United States Department of Defense.[2] Standardized symbols eliminate confusion and misunderstanding in architectural drawings.

In residential building construction, most general contractors give copies of the plans and specifications to sub-contractors for their bids on each specialized phase of work, such as plumbing, electrical wiring, sheet metal, heating, etc. Some general contractors are sufficiently large to employ tradesmen specializing in these various phases of work on a full time basis. Each of the specialized contractors necessarily reads and thoroughly understands the drawings and specifications. Thus all bids are predicated on the same basis. In part, this is accomplished through standardized symbols.

1. American Standards Association, Y 32.9, Y32.4, Z 32.2.3, and Z 32.2.4.

2. *Military Standards for General Drawing Practice.*

Symbols and Conventions

Because new materials are constantly being developed in the building industry, new symbols and conventions are also being devised or changed prior to their acceptance or recognition by the ASA. If some material is not covered by ASA conventions, the draftsman or architect devises the symbol and defines the material depicted by such symbol.

To the beginning student, the vast number of symbols may seem confusing. If a symbol is drawn in an area (e.g., kitchen, bathroom, or laundry) where it represents a fixture that is commonly found there, then it is not difficult to recognize. Many symbols resemble the object they represent.

Fig. 6-1 illustrates various types of doors in a floor plan view as they appear in common types of exterior walls. Note that in the 8″ masonry, brick veneer, 10″ cavity, and SCR brick wall, the brick work is re-

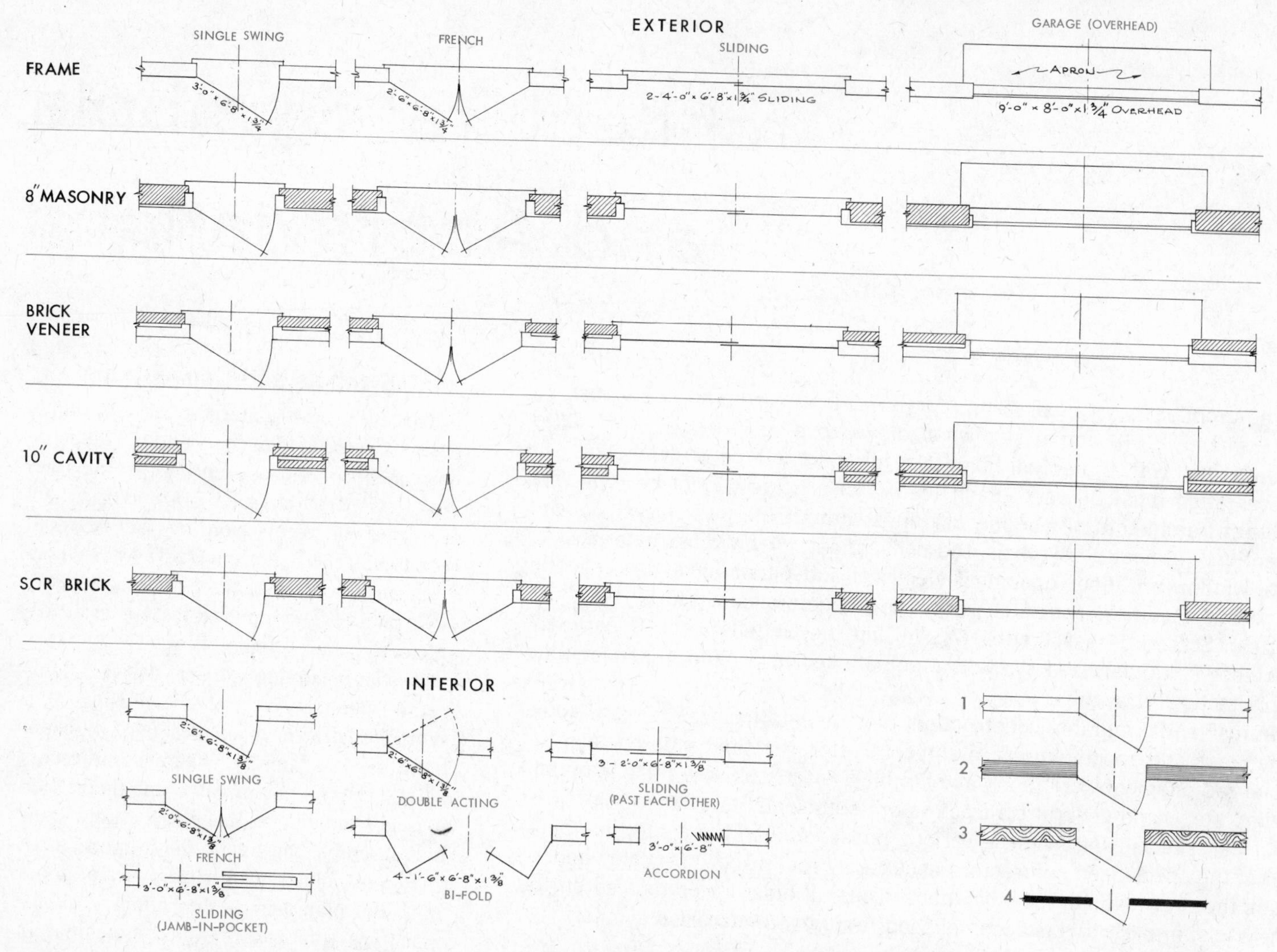

Fig. 6-1. Plan view symbols of several types of exterior doors in several kinds of walls are shown. The symbols for interior doors show the more common types. (Symbols designated 1 through 4 indicate a single swing door in a frame wall. The standard wall convention is shown by symbol 1. Symbols 2 and 3 are occasionally used by architects. Symbol 4 would be used on plans drawn to a very small scale.)

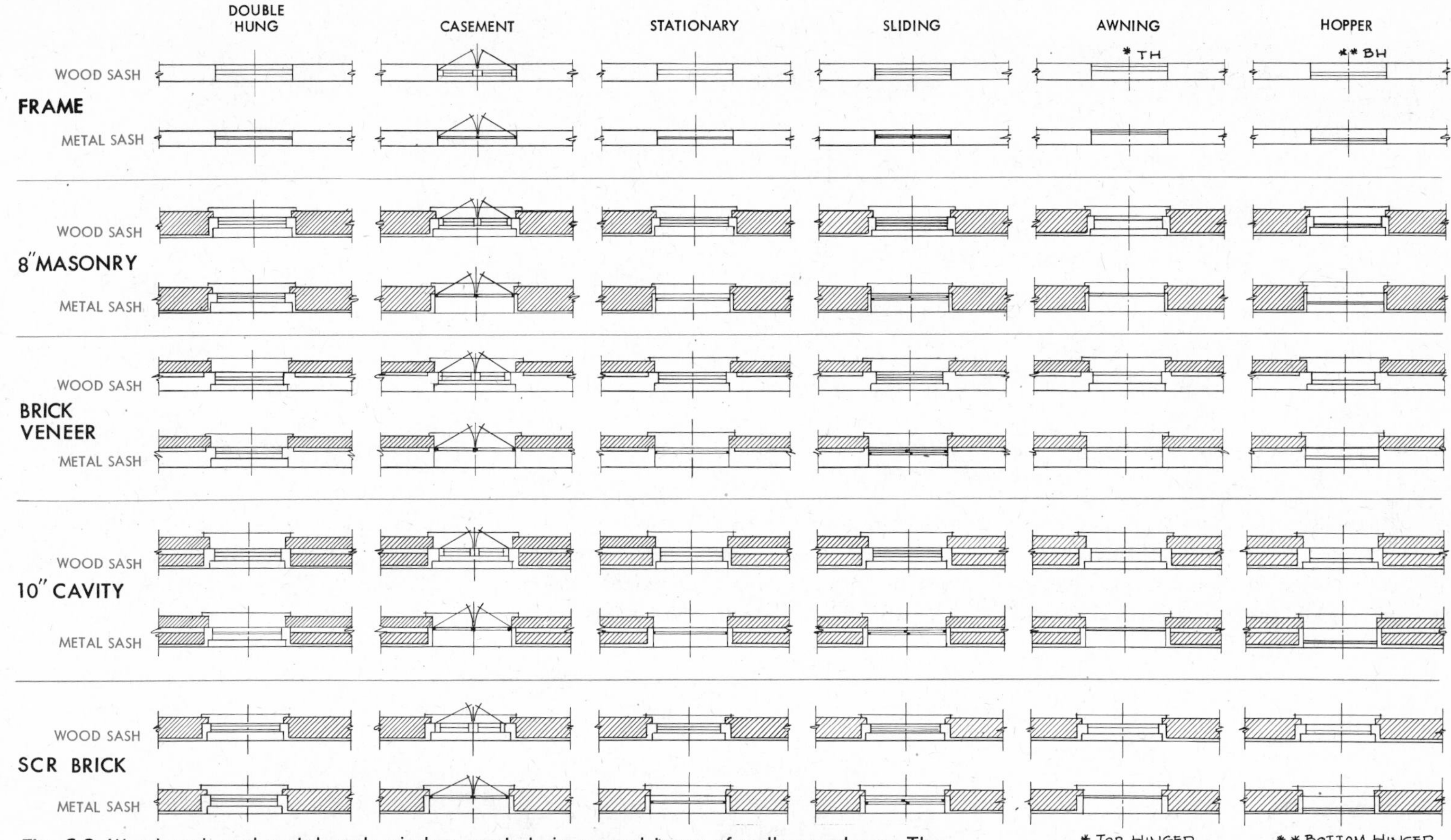

Fig. 6-2. Wood sash and metal sash window symbols in several types of walls are shown. The symbols are related to the actual details of the windows but have been greatly simplified so that they can be drawn at small scale.

lieved (set back) around the door frames. The openings of all doors in masonry and frame walls shown in this illustration are the same, and only the brick work has been relieved. In Fig. 6-1 (lower left) the symbols shown are used to represent different interior residential doors. Both interior and exterior doors are represented in the same manner. The only difference is that interior doors do not require a sill to be shown; the sill is shown for exterior doors. The four symbols shown in Fig. 6-1 (lower right) indicate a single swing door in a frame wall. Symbol 1 is the standard convention for a frame wall or partition. Symbols 2 and 3 are also used to designate a frame wall. Symbol 4, in which the wall is indicated by a single very heavy line, may be used on very small scale drawings.

Fig. 6-2 points out the symbols used for showing windows in a plan view. Note

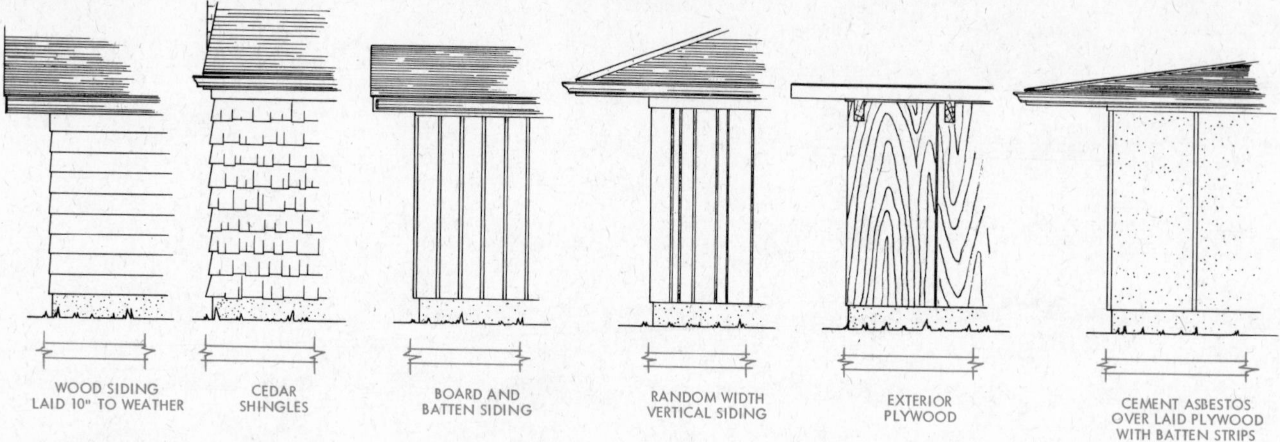

Fig. 6-3. These elevations and plan section symbols are used for various exterior wood building materials.

the representational similarity of the metal and wood windows. Each opening has a different symbolic treatment, depending on the type of wall represented. Windows in all types of masonry walls, regardless of the sash material used (such as metal or wood) must be drawn with a sill. Representation given to windows in masonry walls is the same as that given to exterior doors (i.e., the brick work is relieved around the window frames). The window opening, as it is drawn on the plan view, is the sash open-

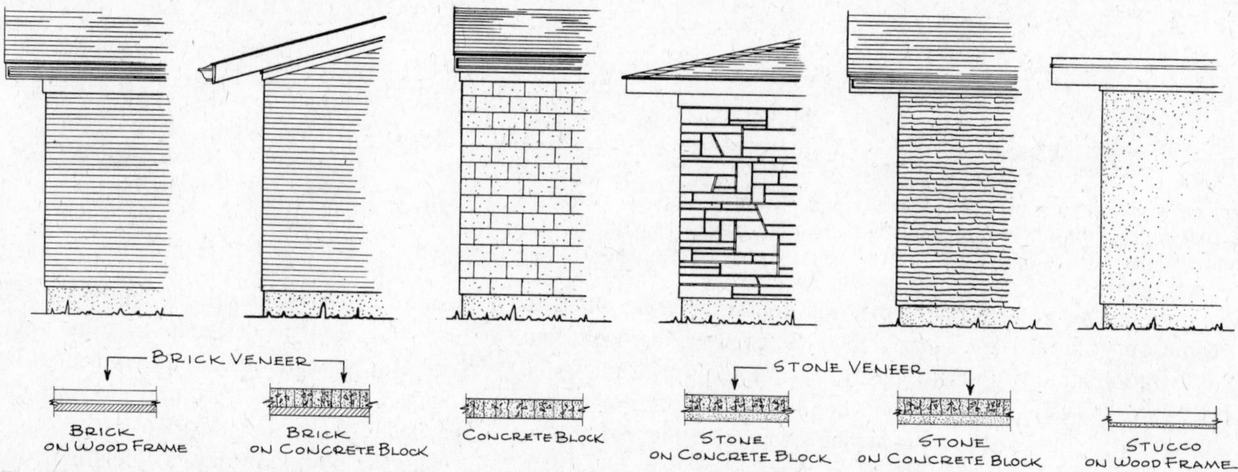

Fig. 6-4. These elevation and plan section symbols are used for various masonry building materials.

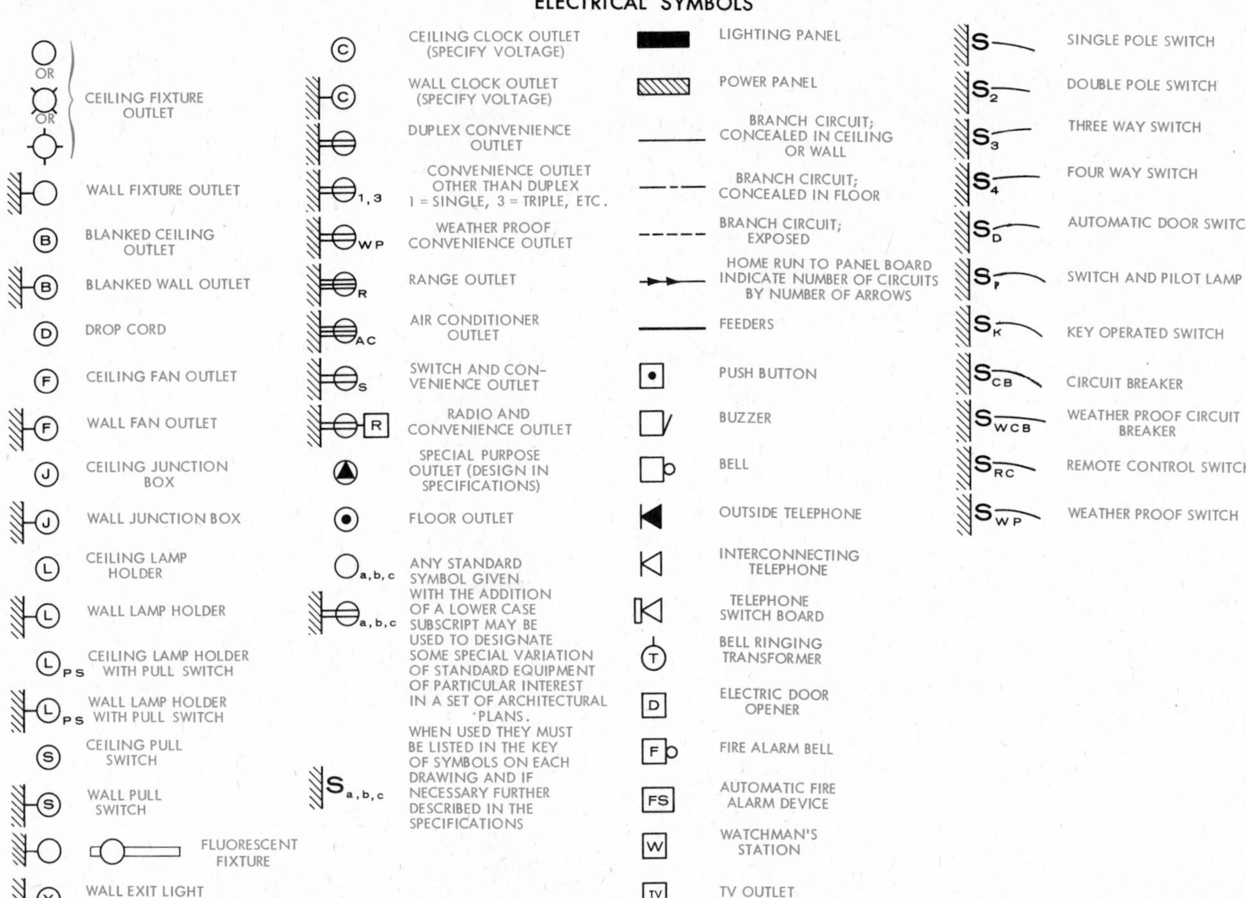

Fig. 6-5. Standard electrical symbols simplify the work of the electrical contractor as he works out the details of wiring the house.

ing. Usually, all window sizes show three basic dimensions: (1) rough opening—the size which must be allowed by the builder to permit placement of the window in the wall (the distance between the inner faces of the *studs* and the distance between the *header* and the sill); (2) sash opening—the width and height of the sash; and (3) glass size—the size of the glass placed in the sash.

Numerous exterior building materials are shown in Figs. 6-3 and 6-4. These figures show the standard symbols in elevation and plan view. (It should be pointed out that each brick or roof shingle represented in elevation is not drawn completely, this would be too time consuming).

Symbols play a more extensive role in the electrical area of the building trades than in other areas. This is because there are many different types of general, con-

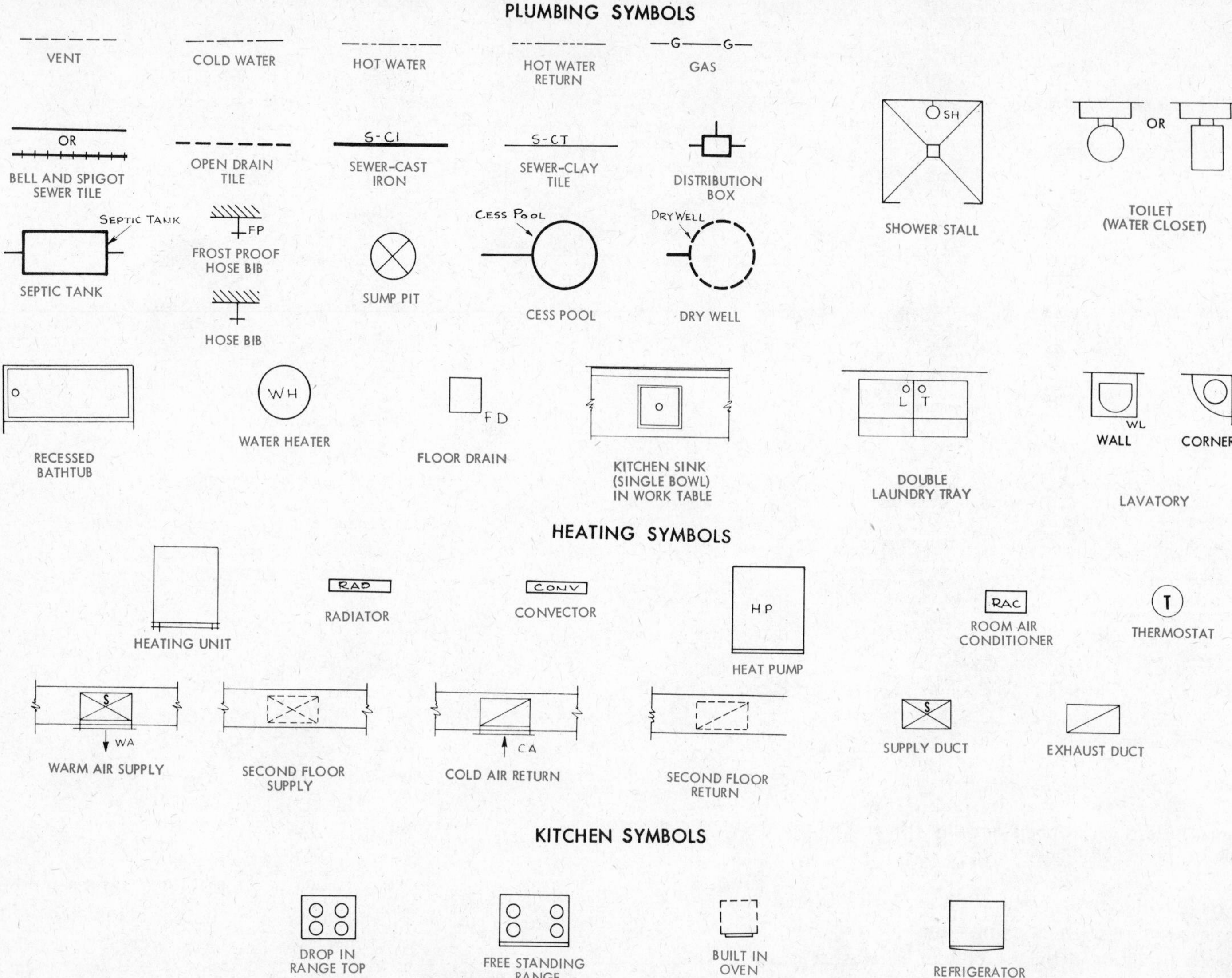

Fig. 6-6. Plumbing, heating, and kitchen symbols are essential to the designer as he plans the arrangement of facilities and leaves room for them. Some of the symbols are arbitrary in form, others resemble the object they represent.

MATERIAL	PLAN	ELEVATION	SECTION
BRICK	COMMON FACE FIREBRICK	SAME AS COMMON BRICK SAME AS ABOVE	SAME AS PLAN VIEW
STONE	CUT STONE RUBBLE CAST STONE (CONCRETE)	CUT STONE RUBBLE	SAME AS PLAN VIEW
CONCRETE	CONCRETE OR CONCRETE BLOCK	CONCRETE CONCRETE BLOCK	SAME AS PLAN VIEW
STRUCTURAL STEEL	OR OR	NONE	OR
INTERIOR PARTITIONS	STUDS, LATH AND PLASTER SOLID PLASTER WALL		SAME AS PLAN VIEW
GLASS		OR	SMALL SCALE LARGE SCALE
INSULATION	LOOSE FILL, OR BATTS BOARD AND QUILT SOLID AND CORK	NONE	SAME AS PLAN VIEW
WOOD	FLOOR AREAS LEFT BLANK NOTE INDICATES KIND OF WOOD USED	SIDING PANEL	END OF BOARD (EXCEPT TRIM) TRIM

MATERIAL	PLAN	ELEVATION	SECTION
SHEET METAL FLASHING	INDICATE BY NOTE		HEAVY LINE SHAPED TO CONFORM
EARTH	NONE	NONE	
ROCK	NONE	NONE	
SAND	NONE	NONE	
GRAVEL OR CINDERS	NONE	NONE	
FLOOR AND WALL TILE			
SOUNDPROOF WALL		NONE	NONE
PLASTERED ARCH		DESIGN VARIES	SAME AS ELEVATION VIEW
GLASS BLOCK IN BRICK WALL			SAME AS ELEVATION VIEW
BRICK VENEER	OR ON FRAME	SAME AS BRICK	SAME AS PLAN VIEW
CUT STONE VENEER	OR ON BRICK ON CONCRETE BLOCK	SAME AS CUT STONE	SAME AS PLAN VIEW
RUBBLE STONE VENEER	OR ON FRAME ON BRICK ON CONCRETE BLOCK	SAME AS RUBBLE	SAME AS PLAN VIEW

Fig. 6-7. The symbols for common materials encountered in building construction help the designer to pass on information to contractors without having to designate every material used. The student should memorize these conventions.

venience, and switch outlets, as well as components of auxiliary electrical systems. Fig. 6-5 shows some general electrical symbols.

Plumbing and heating symbols have their shape similar to the objects they represent. Some of the more common plumbing and heating fixtures are illustrated in Fig. 6-6. Depending upon the accepted practices in various localities, the *cold air returns* and *heat registers* may or may not be indicated by the designer. The location of heating ducts and registers is often worked out with the advice of the heating contractor.

Fig. 6-7 gives the symbols for common building materials.

It should be pointed out that not all of the symbols have been illustrated within this chapter. Any symbol not illustrated in the text will be found, in all probability, in *Architectural Graphic Standards*.[3]

Abbreviations

Because of the multiplicity of items which must be represented on a single sheet of drawings, abbreviations for materials, construction procedures, equipment, etc., are necessary so the drawings will not appear too crowded. Many words have several abbreviations, and some words have the same abbreviation. Therefore, care must be exercised in reading or lettering a note so there will be no misunderstanding. The following is a list of the more frequently used *standard* abbreviations found on architectural drawings.

Access Door	AD
Acoustic or Acoustical	ACST
Alarm	ALM
Alternating Current	AC or a-c
Altitude	ALT
Aluminum	AL
Anchor Bolt	AB
Angle	
Area Drain	AD
Asbestos	ASB
Asphalt	ASPH
Asphalt Tile	AT
At	@
Avenue	AVE
Basement	BSMT
Bath Tub	BT
Bench Mark	BM
Better	BTR or Btr
Between	BET.
Blocking	BLKG
Board	BD or bd
Boiler	BLR
British Thermal Units	BTU or Btu
By	×
Cabinet	CAB.
Cast Concrete	C CONC
Cast Iron	CI
Catch Basin	CB
Ceiling	CLG or Clg
Cement	CEM
Center	CTR
Center Line	℄ OR CL
Center Matched	CM
Center to Center	C to C or c to c
Cinder Block	CIN BL
Circuit Breaker	CIR BKR
Cleanout	CO
Cleanout Door	COD
Clear	CLR or Clr
Closet	C, CL, or CLO
Cold Rolled Steel	CRS
Cold Water	CW
Column	COL
Common	COM or Com
Concrete	CONC
Concrete Block	CONC B
Conductor	COND
Construction	CONST
Contractor	CONTR
Cubic	CU or cu
Cubic Yard	CU YD or cu yd
Damper	DMPR
Dampproofing	DP
Detail	DET
Diameter	DIA or diam
Dimension	DIM or dim
Dishwasher	DW
Ditto	DO. or ″
Double Hung	DH
Douglas Fir	Df
Down	DN or D
Drain	D or DR
Dressed & Matched	D & M

3. Charles G. Ramsey and Harold R. Sleeper, *Architectural Graphic Standards*, 5th ed. (John Wiley & Sons, Inc., 1956).

Each	EA
East	E
Elevation	EL or el
Entrance	ENT
Estimate	EST
Excavate	EXC
Expansion Joint	EXP JT
Exterior	EXT
Extra Heavy	XH or X HVY
Feet	FT, ′, or ft
Finish	FIN.
Firebrick	FBRK
Fireplace	FP
Fixture	FIX.
Flashing	FL
Flat Grain	FG
Floor	FL
Floor Drain	FD
Flooring	FLG or Flg
Foot	FT, ft, or ′
Footing	FTG
Full Size	FS
Galvanized Iron	GI
Glass	GL
Glass Block	GL BL
Glaze	GL
Grade	GR
Grade Line	GL
Guard	GD
Gypsum	GYP
Hardware	HDW
Hardwood	HDWD or Hdwd

Head	HD
Height	HT, H, or HGT
Horizontal	HOR
Hose Faucet or Bib	HF or HB
Hot Water	HW
Hot Water Heater	HWH or WH
House	HSE
I Beam	I
Inch	IN, in, or ″
Insulate or Insulation	INS
Interior	INT
Joint	JT
Kilowatt Hour	KWH or kwhr
Kitchen	K
Knocked Down	KD or k.d.
Laundry	LAU
Laundry Chute	LC
Left Hand	LH
Length	LG, L, or lgth
Light	LT
Limestone	LS
Linen Closet	L CL
Living Room	LR
Louver	LV
Louver Opening	LVO or L
Louvered Door	LVD
Lumber	LBR or lbr
Manufacturing	Mfg
Masonry Opening	MO

Medicine Cabinet	MC
Moulding	MLDG or Mldg
North	N
Number	NO., #, or No
On Center	OC
Opening	OPNG
Outlet	OUT
1000 Board Feet	MBM
Over Head	OVHD
Partition	PTN
Penny (Nail)	d
Per	/
Plaster	PL or PLAS
Plate Glass	PL GL
Pound	LB, #, or lb
Pounds Per Square Foot	LB / FT^2, #/□′, or PSF
Pull Chain	PC or P
Radius	R or r
Random Length	R/L
Range	R
Rectangular	Rect
Refrigerator	REF
Register	REG
Register, Bottom	BR
Register, Ceiling	CR
Register, Center	CR
Register, Top	TR
Regulator	REG
Re-sawn	RES
Revolutions Per Minute	RPM or rpm

Revision	REV
Right Hand	RH
Riser	R
Roof	RF
Roof Drain	RD
Roofing	RFG or Rfg
Round	RD or rnd
Scale	SC
Schedule	SCH
Section	SECT
Sheathing	SHTHG
Ship Lap	S/Lap
Shower	SH
Siding	SDG or Sdg
Sink	S or SK
Socket	SOC
Softwood	sftwd
South	S
Square Foot	sq ft or □′
Square Inch	sq in or □″
Stained	STN or stnd
Stainless Steel	SST
Storage	STG
Sump Pit	SP
Surface Area	A or S
Surface 1 Side 1 Edge	S1S1E
Surface 4 Sides	S4S
Suspended Ceiling	SUSP CEIL
Tee	T
Telephone	TEL
Terrazzo	TER
Terra Cotta	TC
Thermostat	THERMO
Thick or Thickness	THK or T
Thousand	M
Toenail	TN
Toilet	T
Tongue & Groove	T & G
Tread	T or TR
Typical	TYP
Vapor Proof	VAP PRF
Vent	V
Vent Duct	VD
Vent Pipe	VP
Vent Stack	VS
Ventilator	V
Vertical	VERT
Volume	VOL or V
Wall Cabinet	W CAB
Wall Vent	WV
Washing Machine	WM
Water Closet	WC
Water Proofing	WP
Watertight	WT
Weather Stripping	WS
Weatherproof	WP
Weephole	WH
Weight	WT or wt
West	W
White Pine	W P
Width	W or Wth
Window	WDW
Wood	WD
Wood Door	WD
Wood Frame	WF
Wrought Iron	WI
Yard	YD or yd
Yellow Pine	YP

Questions and Problems

1. Copy a floor plan of a 5 or 6 room house at the scale of ¼″ = 1 foot. Sketch in the symbols on the floor plan which will show the following:
   a. A masonry wall on the front of the house only; the sides and rear walls are frame covered with siding. The interior partitions are of frame construction.
   b. Casement windows in the kitchen, ribbon sliding windows in the bedrooms, and double-hung windows in the rest of the rooms of the plan.
   c. Front and rear entrance doors, a double acting door between the kitchen and dining room, bi-fold or accordion doors for the closets, and a plastered arch if the plan requires one.
   d. Draw plumbing fixtures on the plan.
   e. Locate electrical fixtures, outlets, and switches on the plan.
2. Identify the following symbols by a sketch:
   a. Electric range outlet (plan)
   b. Outside electric outlet (plan)
   c. 4-way switch (plan)
   d. Metal flashing (elevation)
   e. Stone (elevation)
   f. 2″ × 4″ dimensioned lumber (section)
   g. ¾″ × 3½″ casing (section)

h. Sliding door (interior wall plan)
i. Sliding door (exterior wall plan)

3. Study the first floor plan of a set of plans found in this text. List 20 to 25 items of information found on the plan which are shown by symbols.
4. Study the elevations of the set of plans found in problem 3 above, and list 15 or more items of information which are shown by symbols.
5. Why is there a need for symbols?
6. What organizations concern themselves with the standardization of symbols?
7. What are three distinct kinds of architectural drawings which use symbols?
8. Sketch a floor plan of a log cabin located in the north woods at the scale of ¼" = 1 foot. Using symbols, show at least three doors, some windows, a fireplace, an open porch, some built in furniture, and a bath.
9. Copy a plan from a magazine, make the outside walls either frame or masonry, with the interior partitions of wood at the scale of ¼" = 1 foot. Indicate on this plan, by proper symbols, two different kinds of appropriate windows and doors, stairs, cabinets, plumbing fixtures, and chimney.

An understanding of basic construction detail is a prerequisite for good house design.

Construction Details: Foundations and Main Structure 7

Almost everyone who builds or buys a house is interested in obtaining the most for his dollar. Frequently, it is difficult to distinguish those items which are absolutely required from those which are desired but not necessary. Too often good construction is slighted for built-in conveniences which could have been added or installed later.

The best way to evaluate any home would be to examine the materials and workmanship during the actual construction. Usually, however, the buyer does not have this opportunity. Even if he saw the structure being erected, he might not recognize sound construction practices or honest use of materials. This chapter offers information essential to the basic understanding of building materials and construction. A sound grasp of these basics is a prerequisite for good house design.

Footings and Foundations

The old adage, "A chain is no stronger than its weakest link," is particularly appropriate when discussing one of the most essential elements of residential structure. An adequate foundation must be designed to support the house. Quality materials must be used for construction. By so doing, many settlement cracks will be eliminated, and the house will better withstand the ravages of time.

Footings

A footing is an enlarged projection at the base of the foundation walls. The primary purpose of the footing is to distribute the building's weight over a greater soil area. By using footings the building will have more resistance to settlement. Footings are used under every part of the structure which will support an appreciable amount of weight (e.g., foundation, porch, stoop, columns, fireplace, chimney, etc.).

The function of the footing may be easily visualized by the analogy shown in Fig. 7-1. In Fig. 7-1 (top) relatively little pressure would be required to push the *pointed* stake into dry sand. By comparison, however, if an *unpointed* stake, Fig. 7-1 (bottom), were pushed into the same mound of dry sand, more pressure would be required to penetrate the sand. The unpointed stake has more bearing area, thereby offering more resistance. In the same manner, increased width at the lower portion of the foundation wall gives more bearing area and retards uneven settlement. Unequal settling causes cracks and other defects, not only in the footing and foundation, but in the walls as well.

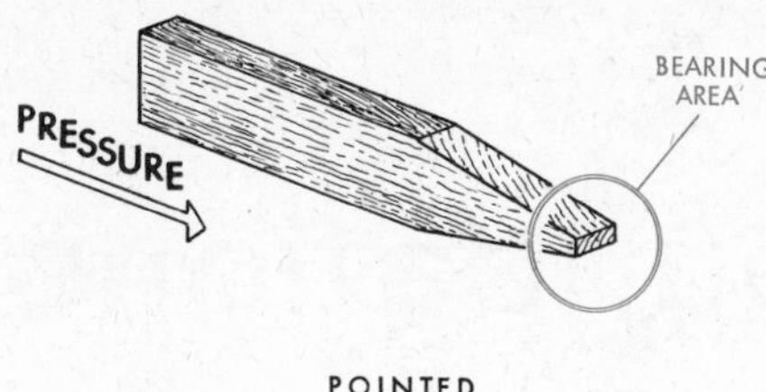

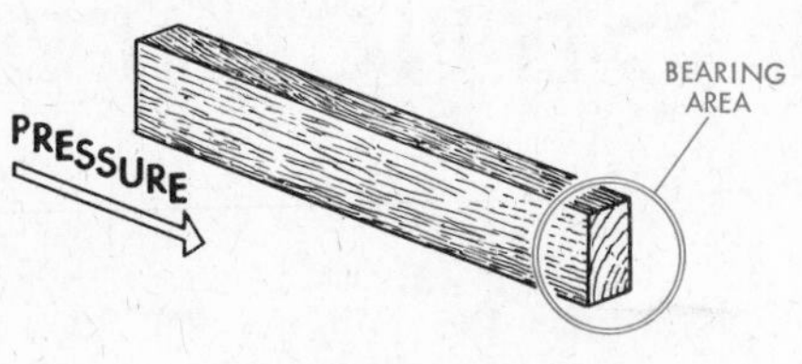

Fig. 7-1. A larger bearing area offers increased resistance to pressure.

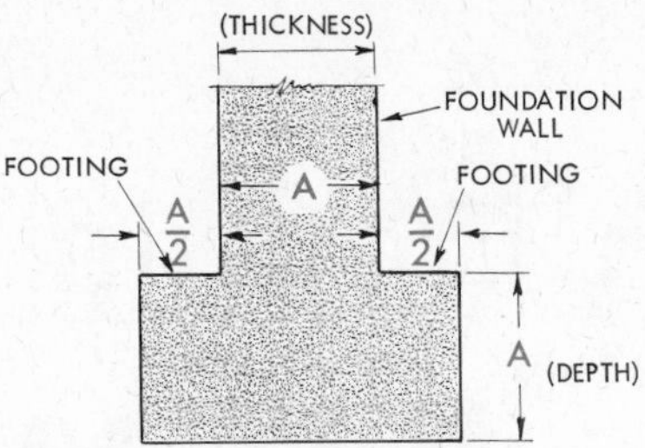

Fig. 7-2. The footings may have a depth equal to the thickness of the foundation wall.

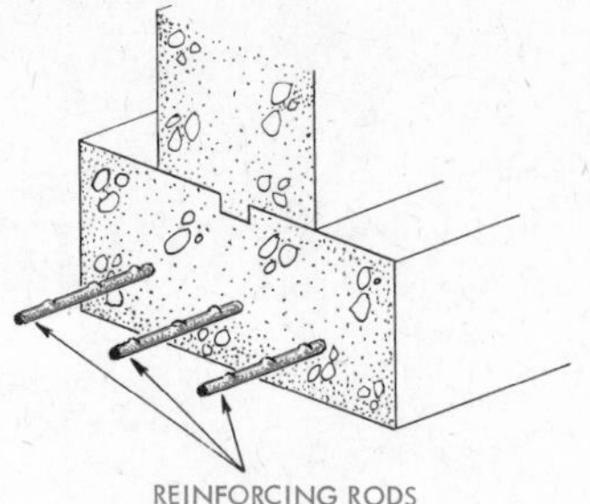

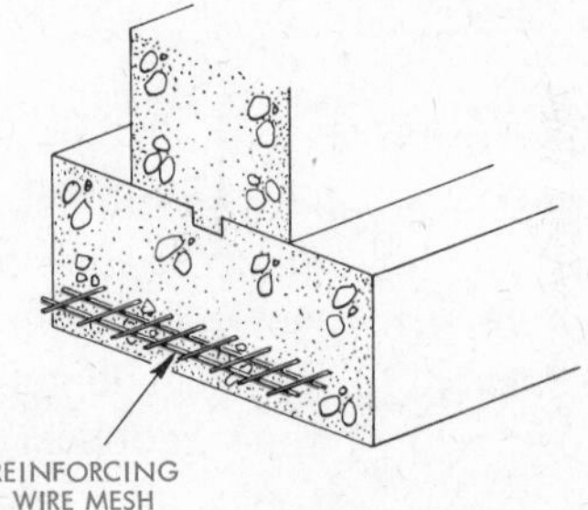

Fig. 7-4. Reinforcing rods or mesh may be placed in the footings for extra strength.

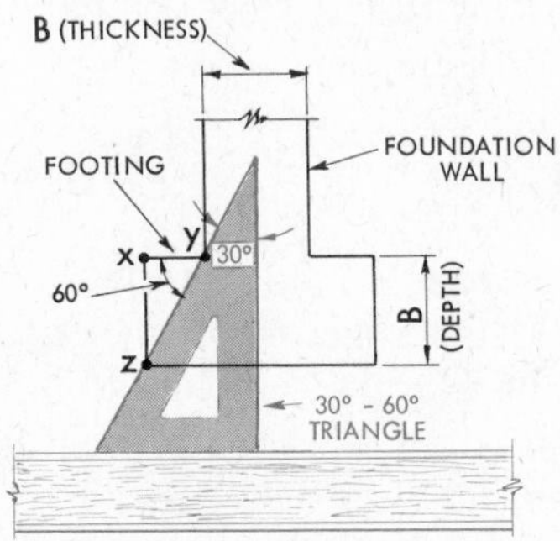

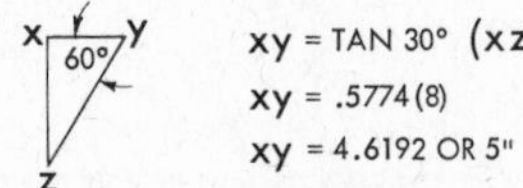

Fig. 7-3. A 60° angle drawn away from the base of the foundation wall (point Y) and extended to the depth of the footing (point Z) will give graphically the footing projection.

Footing Design and Detail

Footings, in both type and size, should be suitable to the soil conditions and the type of structure. Poured concrete footings are more dependable than those made of other materials and are recommended for use in residential foundations and footings. Building codes in most cities specify the footing size in relation to the structure type, height, and general soil conditions. In the absence of a code, however, the general practice is to design and construct residential footings with a depth equal to the thickness of the foundation wall (not less than 12″). The footings should project out on either side a distance of one-half the foundation wall thickness (not less than 6″). See Fig. 7-2.

Another formula for light residential footing design is shown in Fig. 7-3. The depth of this footing is equivalent to the thickness of the foundation wall. If a 60° line is drawn from the intersection of the foundation wall and footing to the depth of the footing, as in Fig. 7-3, it will graphically give the correct amount of footing projection. Apply the same amount to the other side of the foundation wall.

Reinforcing is frequently used to add strength and alleviate stresses in the footing. Reinforcing rods or mesh are shown only in the detail sectional view of the footing, as in Fig. 7-4, and are listed in the written specifications as to their size, type, and spacing.

Stepped Footings. If the foundation is at two different depths (as in the case of a split-level dwelling), or if the house is to be built on sloping ground, the footings will of necessity be stepped as in Fig. 7-5. The purpose

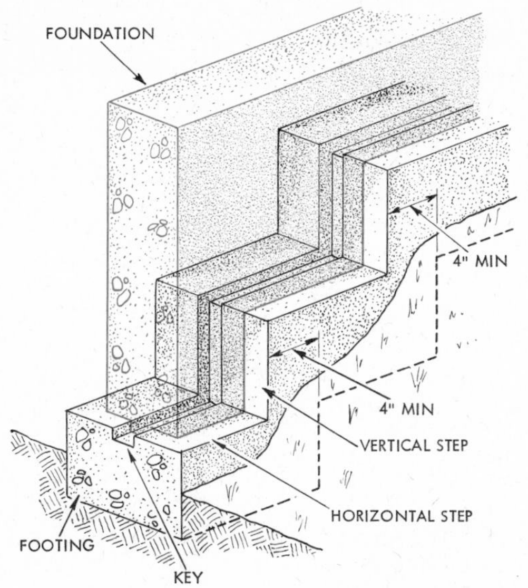

Fig. 7-5. Stepped footings are designed to give horizontal support when the ground is uneven or the house levels are not on the same plane.

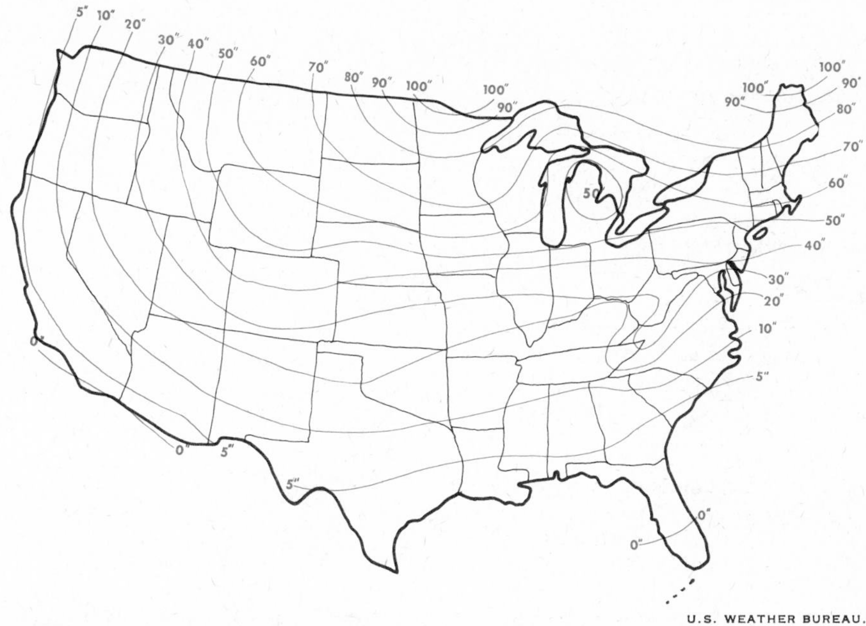

U.S. WEATHER BUREAU.

Fig. 7-6. This map shows maximum frost penetration in United States.

TABLE 7-1
FOOTING DEPTHS AS REQUIRED BY REPRESENTATIVE CITY CODES

CITY		CITY	
MILWAUKEE, WISCONSIN	5'-0"	BALTIMORE, MARYLAND	3'-0"
CHICAGO, ILLINOIS	4'-0"	KANSAS CITY, MISSOURI	3'-0"
ST. PAUL, MINNESOTA	4'-0"	PHILADELPHIA, PA.	3'-0"
BOSTON, MASSACHUSETTS	4'-0"	LOUISVILLE, KENTUCKY	2'-6"
HALIFAX, NOVA SCOTIA	4'-0"	ST. LOUIS, MISSOURI	2'-6"
NEW YORK CITY, N.Y.	4'-0"	DENVER, COLORADO	1'-6"
DETROIT, MICHIGAN	3'-6"	SEATTLE, WASHINGTON	1'-6"
		JACKSONVILLE, FLORIDA	1'-0"

is to permit the slope of the footing to be composed of a number of horizontal surfaces. The horizontal surfaces should be as long as possible to derive the greatest benefit from the structural value of the concrete. This also prevents a sliding action by the footing and foundation.

Frost Line

The effect of freezing and thawing is much greater upon soil than upon other materials, such as brick or concrete. Footings should be carried below the *frost line* (the depth that frost penetrates below the grade). Many building codes require the footing to be carried one foot below the frost line. If the footings are above the frost line they are likely to *heave* (move) as a result of soil pressures caused by extreme temperature change. It is evident from the map shown in Fig. 7-6 that the maximum frost penetration differs in various sections of the United States. Local building codes usually specify the footing depth. Depths below grade are determined by the general drainage conditions and extreme temperatures in a locality. Table 7-1 shows footing depths based on the frost line as required by building codes in representative cities in the United States.

Foundation Walls

In all structural work, proper support is essential to good construction. Foundation walls should be designed to provide adequate support to the main structure, and to prevent any moisture from entering the basement or crawl space. No building of any type or size will be sound unless it is built on a good, well designed foundation.

Foundation Thickness

Most cities publish building codes detailing exact specifications for foundation design. In this case the architect indicates on the plans that the foundations are to be built in accordance with existing regulations. If a code does not exist, however, the architect must calculate the foundation thickness and height and show these dimensions.

Foundation thickness is primarily dependent upon the type of exterior walls and the height (number of floors) above grade. There are, however, no generally accepted rules for the design of concrete block, brick, or stone foundations. The type of block or brick must be taken into consideration, along with the quality of mortar. Generally, block and brick foundations should be at least as thick as the walls they support. Experience has shown stone foundations for residence should be 16″ or 18″ thick (if laid in Portland cement mortar).

TABLE 7-2
CONCRETE FOUNDATION THICKNESS

Construction	One Story	Two Story
WOOD FRAME (without basement)	a 6" Minimum	————
WOOD FRAME (with basement)	a 8" Minimum	a 10" if not more than 7'-0" below grade.
	b 10" Minimum if longer than 20'-0".	b 12" if more than 7'-0" below grade.
SOLID MASONRY (with basement)	a As thick as the walls they support.	a As thick as walls they support if not more than 7'-0" below grade.
		b 12" if more than 7'-0" below grade
BRICK OR STONE VENEER (with frame backing)	a 8" if veneer does not extend beyond 1 1/4" of foundation.	a 10" if not more than 7'-0" below grade
	b Increase thickness so that veneer does not extend beyond 1 1/4".	b 12" minimum if more than 7'-0" below grade

Concrete foundation thickness may be roughly calculated by using Table 7-2. These "rules of thumb" are applicable to small home construction.

Some exterior house designs utilize a combination of brick and siding. The front elevation of the house may be brick or stone veneer, and the sides and rear may be *drop siding*. In such cases the thickness of the foundation wall beneath the brick should be 10″, and the walls beneath the frame should be 8″. It would be an unnecessary expense for the home builder to have a 10″ foundation wall completely around the house.

Basements

Poured concrete is usually used in forming a full basement. This has the advantage of being one solid piece of concrete, thus assuring a firm and continuous support of the house with less possibility of settlement. Fig. 7-7 illustrates a typical full basement constructed of concrete. Fig. 7-8 gives details of the garage and main foundations (Fig. 7-7, section A-A). Note that footings are not used for the garage foundations. This is true also of the porch and areaway foundations. The exterior stair well however, does use a small footing to prevent possible settlement. Exterior stair wells and areaways are usually provided with a drain connected to the house sewer.

Concrete block or brick is also used for basement foundations. Care must be taken to form waterproof joints. Waterproof wall coatings should also be used.

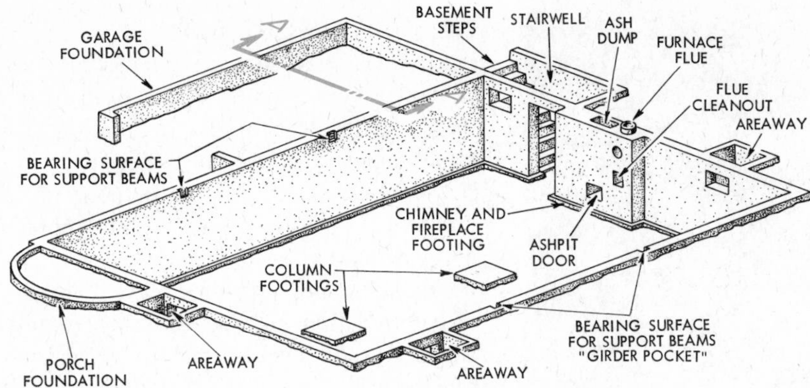

Fig. 7-7. Poured concrete forms a strong full basement without any breaks. Footings are required under the main wall and the stairwell wall.

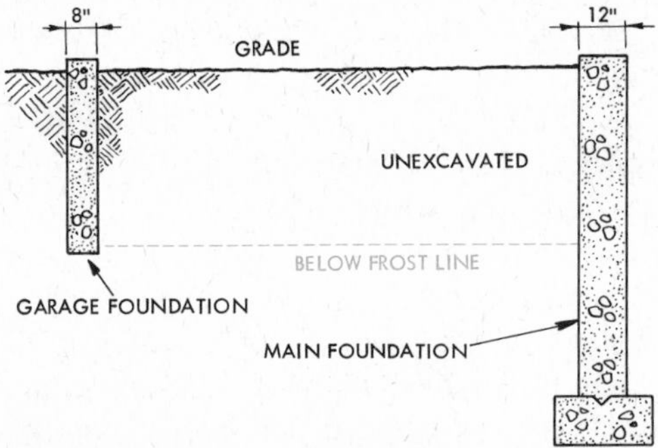

Fig. 7-8. Footings are not used for the garage foundation. (Section A-A of the foundation shown in Fig. 7-7.)

Basementless Houses

Foundations for basementless houses with the slabs on grade may be in either of two general classifications: (1) *perimeter wall foundations* or (2) *floating slab foundations*. Perimeter wall foundations derive their name from the fact that the foundation is carried to the frost line, thus creating a "wall" completely around the outside of the house. This type of foundation is sometimes referred to as a *rim wall*. The floating slab foundation is just as its name indicates—it rests on the ground; there is no "wall" beneath the slab. This type of foundation is predominately used in the warmer climates where no frost problem is encountered.

Perimeter Wall Foundation. A common perimeter wall foundation used in northern areas of the United States is shown in Fig. 7-9. Note the use of perimeter insulation extending 2′ or more under the floor. This prevents heat loss and moisture penetration.

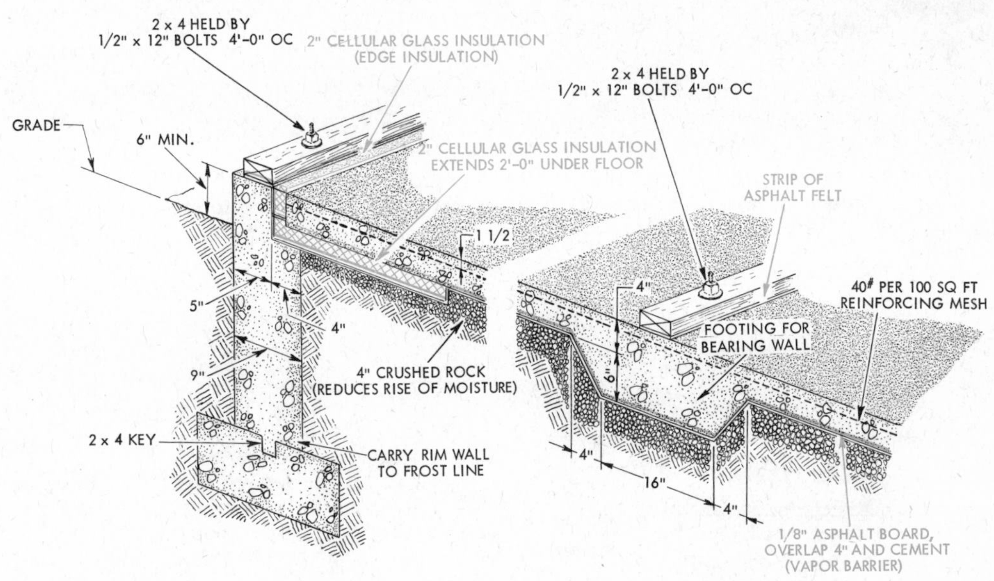

Fig. 7-9. In northern areas the perimeter wall in a basementless house extends two feet under the floor to prevent heat loss and moisture penetration. Note the insulation at the perimeter of the slab.

NATIONAL GYPSUM CO., BUFFALO, NEW YORK.

Fig. 7-10. Perimeter cellular glass insulation and polyethylene film is used to prevent heat loss and moisture penetration in slab houses.

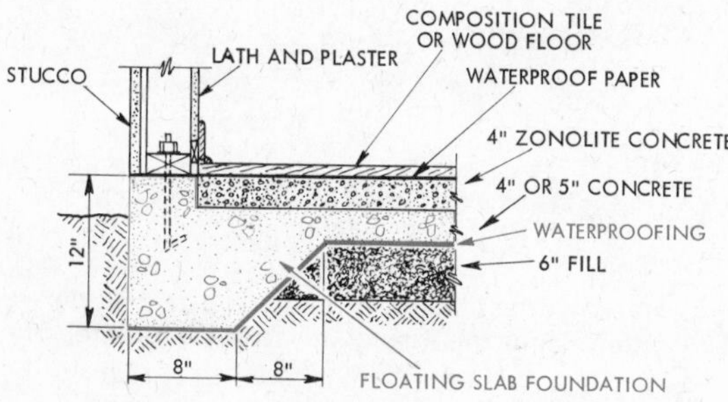

Fig. 7-11. In southern areas a floating slab foundation for a basementless house is used. Note how the foundation splays inward to give additional support.

Fig. 7-10 shows the perimeter insulation and polyethylene film prior to pouring the concrete slab. Observe that in both figures the upper surface of the foundation is a minimum of 6″ above finished grade.

Floating Slab Foundation. In the southern areas where frost penetration is not appreciable or common, and where the soil is predominately hard and/or rocky, a floating slab foundation may be used successfully. Usually, when a concrete slab rests directly on the earth, there is an excellent chance for moisture and cold to penetrate the concrete. This is prevented by using *membrane waterproofing* topped by 4″ of concrete and 4″ of *Zonolite concrete*. Since the foundation is not carried to any extensive depth, it is splayed inward to give additional bearing surface, thereby distributing the weight over a wider area. See Fig. 7-11.

In slab houses space must be provided in the concrete for electrical conduit, water pipes, and heat ducts. If ordinary duct and register heating is not used, radiant heating may be desired. Radiant heating systems usually have pipe coils imbedded in the concrete.

Crawl Spaces. Fig. 7-12 illustrates a foundation used in many of the northern areas of the United States. This foundation is designed to have a crawl space of 18″ to 36″ to lessen the effects of moisture and cold on the floor framing materials. In addition, this crawl space provides an area for plumbing, electrical conduit, and heating ducts. Even though an air space is provided between the earth and floor joists, further insurance

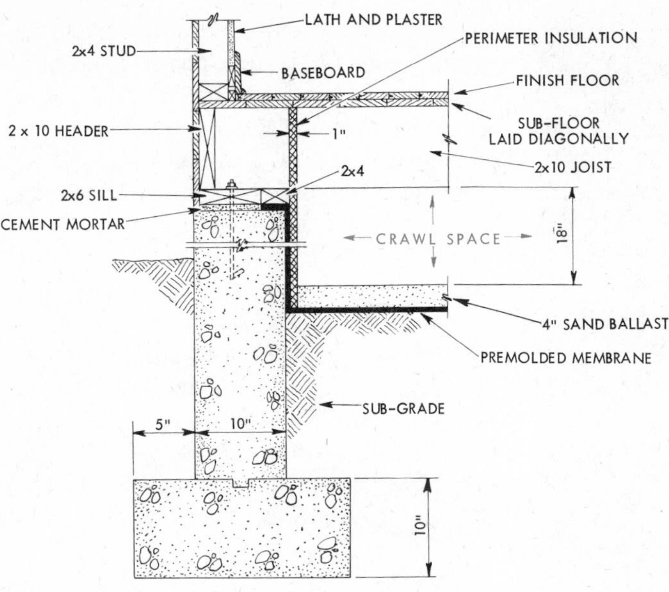

Fig. 7-12. Basementless houses are sometimes built with a crawl space.

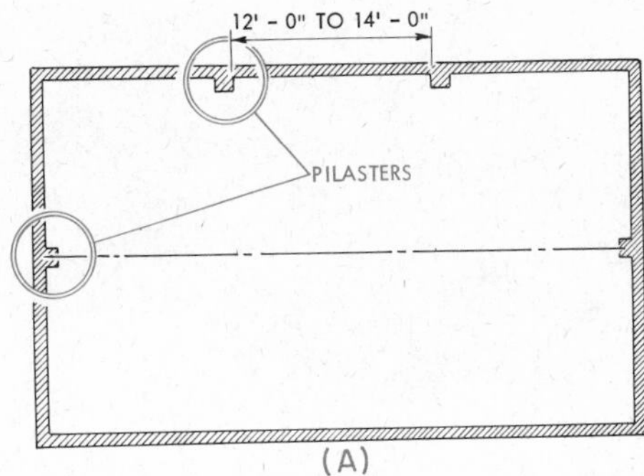

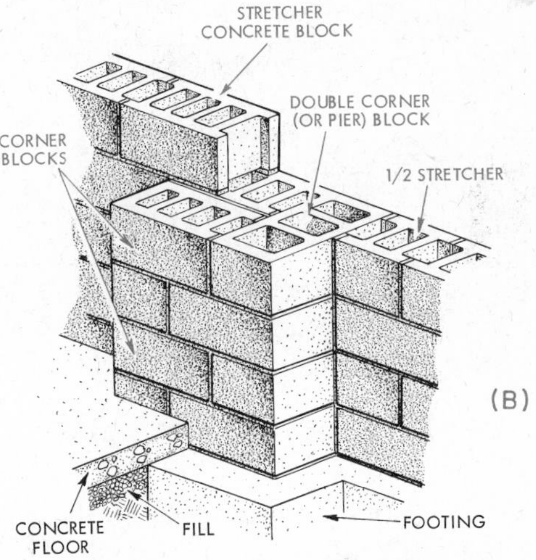

Fig. 7-13. Pilasters are added to basement walls to provide increased strength. When pilasters are used with concrete block they are tied into the wall by alternating the pattern on each level.

against heat loss and moisture penetration must be furnished. A means of preventing heat loss is vertical insulation board. This is nailed to the sill and carried down to the pre-molded membrane. Pre-molded membrane or polyethylene film may be installed as a moisture seal. See Fig. 7-12.

Foundation Reinforcement

Pilasters. Poured concrete foundations for residences seldom require any stiffening unless they are very high and over 20′ long. Exceptionally high concrete foundations are subject to considerable soil pressures. To resist this, *pilasters* are added for extra strength. Pilasters may also be added to support beams which are to carry extraordinarily heavy loads. This gives an increased bearing area.

Frequently, pilasters are used in concrete-block foundation walls (Fig. 7-13) to provide increased rigidity in long runs of the wall. These, together with some type of horizontal joint reinforcement, provide extra wall strength. Pilasters are usually placed from 13′ to 14′ apart.

Horizontal Joint Reinforcement. When the foundation wall is constructed with concrete block, horizontal joint reinforcement should be used to prevent any sheer forces from pushing in the wall. See Fig. 7-14. Horizontal joint reinforcement usually runs 20″ apart, or every other or third block

DUR-O-WAL PRODUCTS, INC., CEDAR RAPIDS, IOWA.

Fig. 7-14. Horizontal joint reinforcement provides added lateral strength for a concrete block foundation wall.

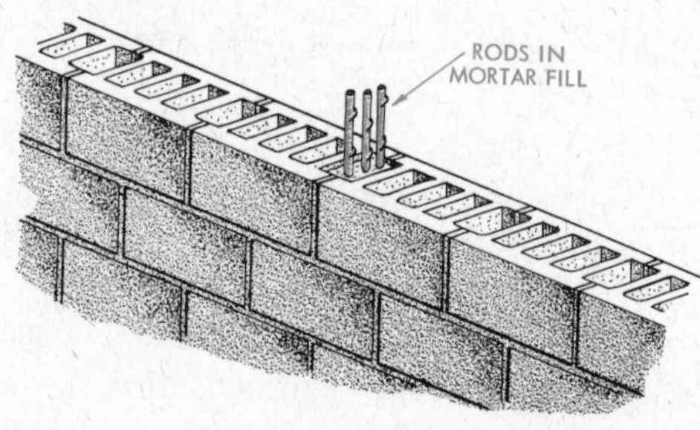

Fig. 7-15. Vertical wall stiffening is accomplished by "rodding" the cores. The rods extend through several block levels.

course. If the blocks are carefully laid, they make a good foundation, and in some cases (dependent upon labor and material costs), are more economical than poured concrete.

Steel Rods. Steel rods (round or square) are sometimes placed in poured cement for extra strength. The rods provide a "bone structure" which gives strength to the concrete.

Concrete block walls may also be strengthened by steel rods. Several ½″ diameter by 8′ long reinforcing rods are run vertically through the block cores of several courses. The cores are then filled with mortar. This is called "rodding the cores." *Rodded cores* are shown in Fig. 7-15.

Foundation Drainage

Drain Tile. Every foundation should be

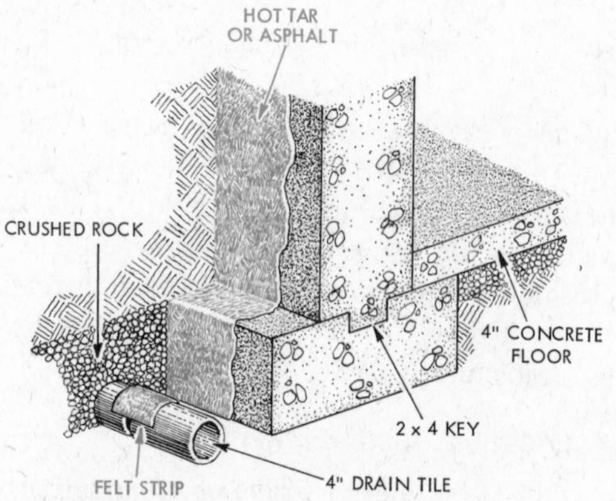

Fig. 7-16. Drain tile is laid around foundations to remove water. For waterproofing, tar or asphalt is applied to the foundation wall and footings. The felt strip prevents the open tile joints from filling up.

constructed with an adequate drainage system to remove any water which may accumulate. Drain tile is laid around the outside of the footing with open joints. This is covered with coarse stone or gravel to a depth of at least one foot. (The coarse stone or gravel allows the water to seep to the tile.) A piece of impregnated felt is laid on top of the open tile joints to prevent these spaces from becoming clogged with stone or soil. See Fig. 7-16. The tile is laid with a slight slope to drain the water away from the house.

Waterproofing. Foundations may also be protected by waterproofing. The method most generally used for residences with poured concrete foundations is to cover the wall and footings with several applications of asphalt or tar, sometimes called "blackjack." See Fig. 7-16. Concrete block foundation walls are usually covered (parged) with a rich cement grout, ¾″ thick, and several coats of asphalt or tar (Fig. 7-17).

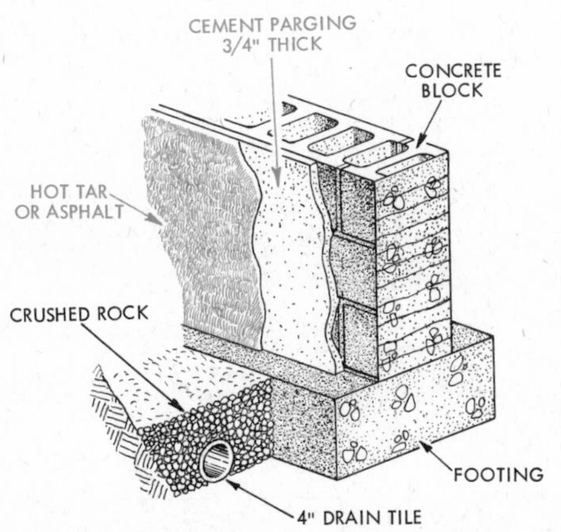

Fig. 7-17. Cement parging covered with tar or asphalt is applied to concrete block foundation walls on the outside.

Extremely damp soil conditions may require the foundation wall to be membrane waterproofed. Fig. 7-18 shows membrane waterproofing applied to the concrete wall and footings. This type of waterproofing employs several layers of fabric which are cemented together with asphalt. Often, the membrane waterproofing is covered with a protective wall of brick or concrete. This adds protection against ground water damage and damage that may be incurred in backfilling.

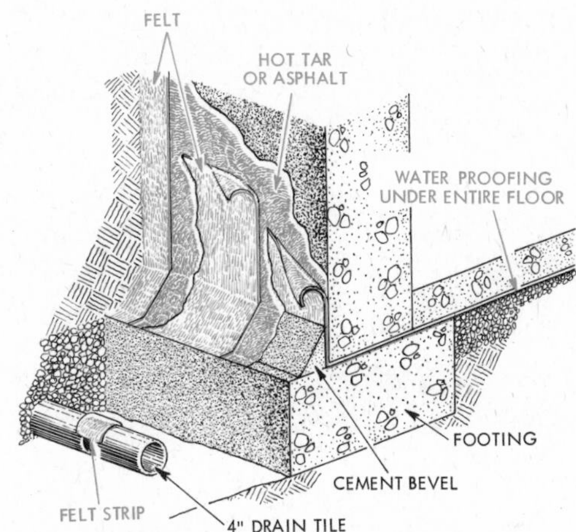

Fig. 7-18. Membrane waterproofing uses several layers of felt cemented together with tar or asphalt.

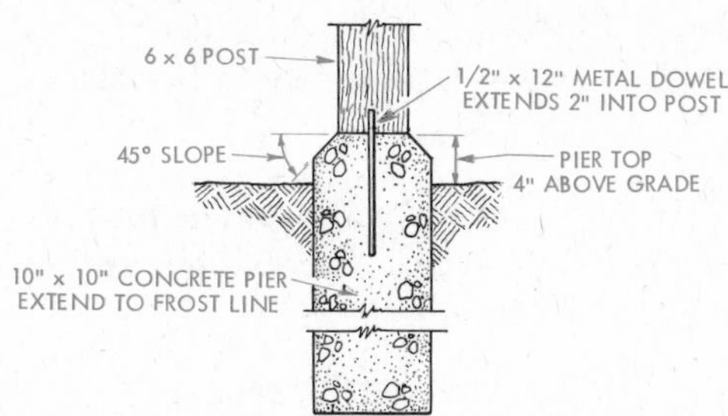

Fig. 7-19. A concrete pier is set into the ground to support a porch or decking column.

Secondary Foundations

Up to this point the discussion has centered around foundations and footings beneath the main building—no mention has been made of detached or semi-detached structures. Porches, garages, and other structures also require foundation planning.

Porches: A common concrete pier, in essence a footing, is used for porches which are exposed beneath the flooring, or for decks (floors) which extend from the house. Fig. 7-19 shows a common concrete pier. If support for the porch or deck is made of wood, the top of the concrete pier should be sloped (preferably at a 45° angle) to shed water. However, if a *lally column* (concrete-filled pipe) or a *pipe column* is used in place of a wood post, the top of the pier needs no

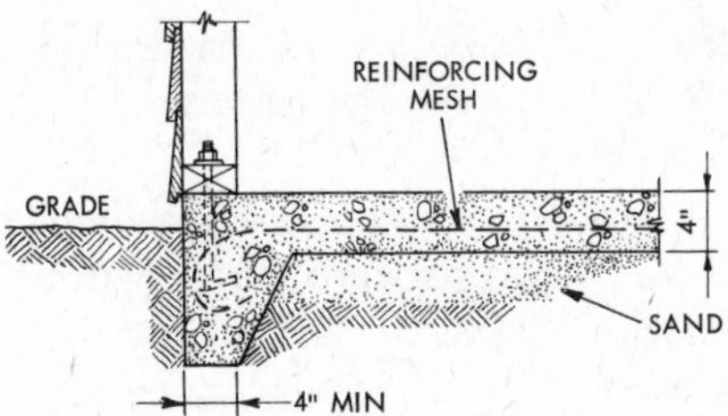

Fig. 7-20. A floating slab may be used for a detached garage foundation. The foundation is **above** the frost line.

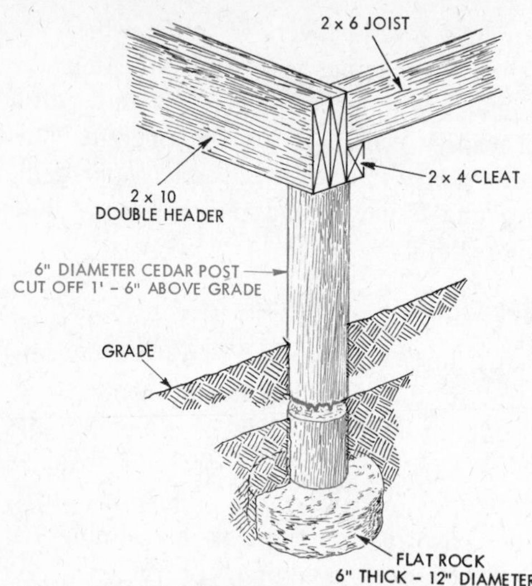

Fig. 7-21. A wooden post set on a flat rock may be used for temporary foundations. The posts must be treated to prevent termite damage and rot.

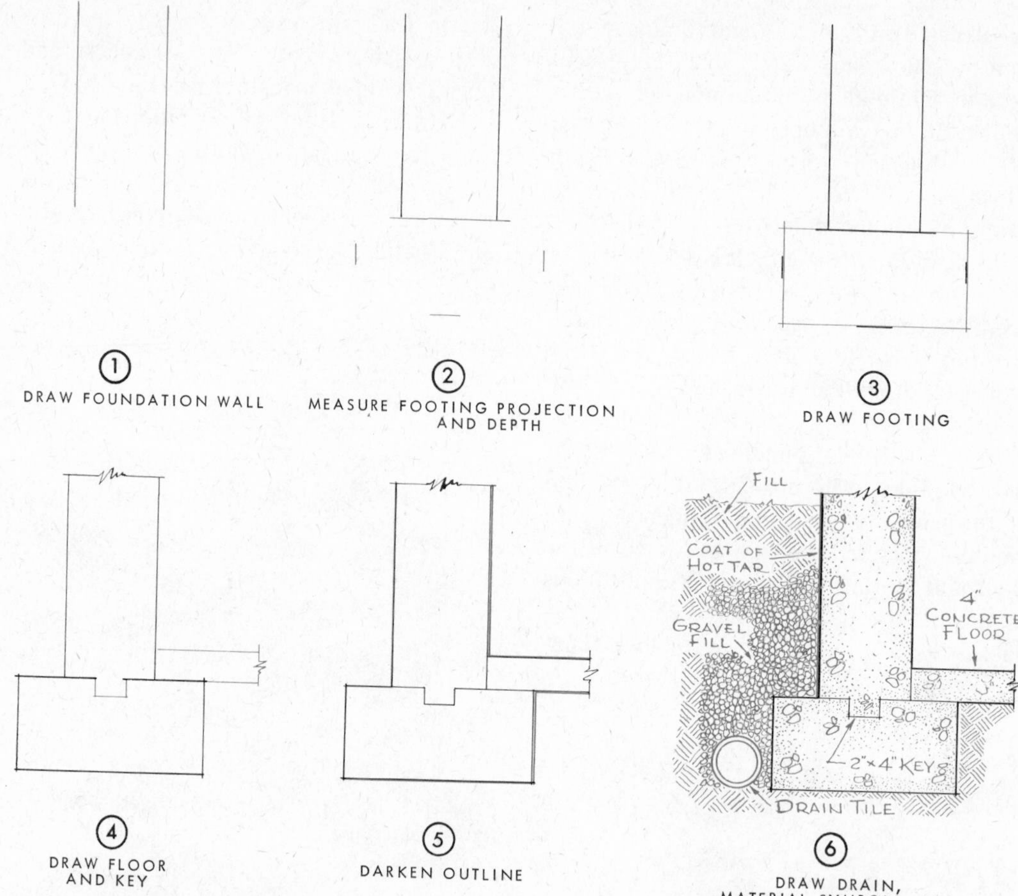

Fig. 7-22. Follow this step-by-step procedure in drawing a foundation wall.

slope. A metal *dowel,* similar to that shown in Fig. 7-19, should be imbedded in the pier and extended 2″ into the post to prevent movement.

Garages. The foundation wall for garages does not require footings to be carried to the frost line. Fig. 7-20 shows a common design for a detached garage foundation. Usually, the depth of the rim wall is between 12″ to 16″ below grade.

Temporary Structures. Occasionally the home owner desires to erect a temporary structure such as a shed, small summer cottage, or cabin. A wooden post set on a flat rock for the footing is frequently used because of the economy and ease of construction (Fig. 7-21). The post should be thoroughly saturated with creosote or other preservative to retard deterioration and to guard against termites.

Step-By-Step Drawing Procedure: Footings and Foundation Walls

Drawing any footing and foundation wall is not complicated if the step-by-step procedure shown in Fig. 7-22 is followed.

Frame Construction

Nine out of ten homes built since 1940 in the United States may be categorized as *wood frame houses.* This statement may seem rash since every day we see houses made of brick, stucco, concrete asbestos shingle, stone, and imitation brick or stone. Regardless of the exterior covering, however, these houses are in the general classification of wood frame construction if there is a wooden frame structure behind the covering.

Wood frame houses may be preferred for two basic reasons. First, frame construction is usually less expensive than solid masonry or steel. Secondly, wood frame construction,

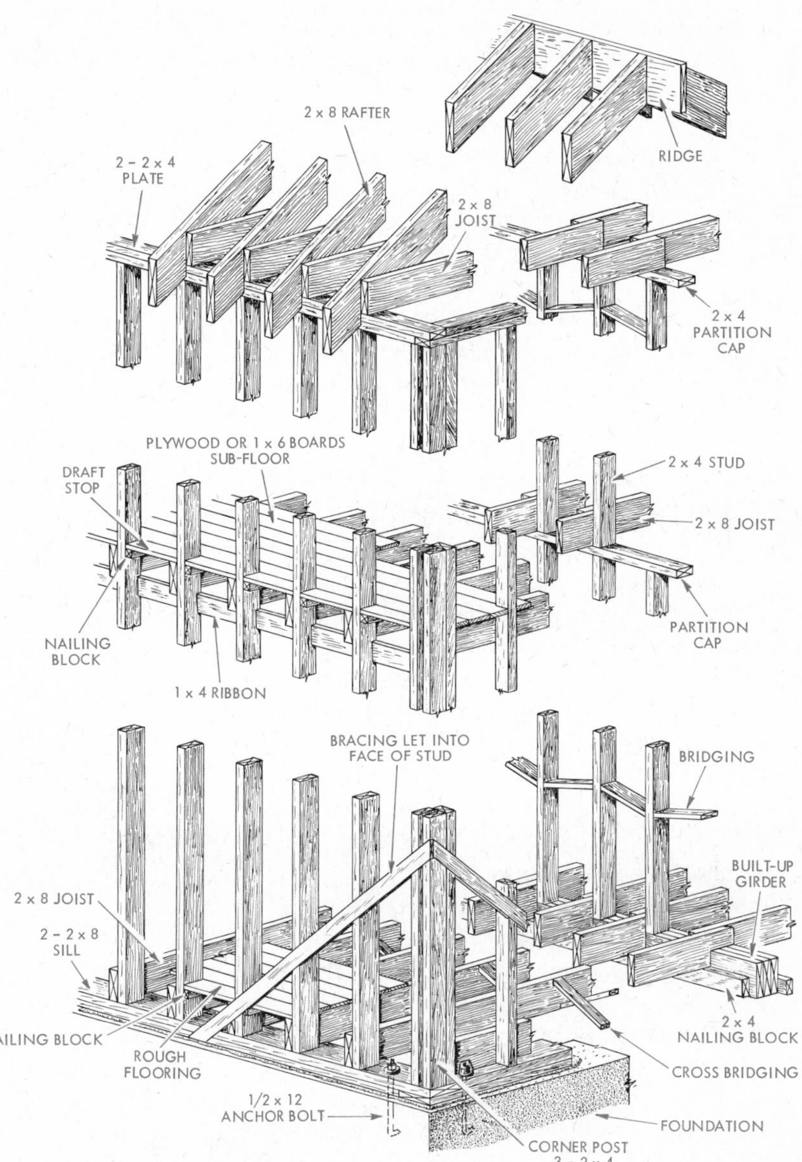

Fig. 7-23. Balloon Framing. Balloon framing is widely used for two-story and masonry veneer houses. Note that the studs are continuous between floors: shrinkage is at a minimum.

if properly designed and built, provides better insulation. A frame house is an extremely durable structure. Some of the oldest existing buildings in the United States (dating back to 1660) are of this type.

Framing may be placed in three categories: *balloon, western* or *platform,* and *braced*. The two framing systems which are most used are the balloon and western. The third type, the braced frame, has rarely been used in contemporary construction because of the size of many framing members and the cost of labor involved in erecting the structure.

Balloon Frame

The balloon frame (Fig. 7-23) is probably most widely used for two-story houses. The exterior studs of this frame are continuous from sill to plate. The second-floor joists rest on a 1″ × 4″ or 1″ × 6″ *ribbon* or *ledger board* recessed into the face of the studs. The advantage of balloon framing is that very little shrinkage occurs. This makes it ideal for a masonry veneer.

Western or Platform Frame

The western or platform frame is comparable to a layer cake, where one layer or level is placed on the other. Each level is independent: studding is separate for each level or floor. This type of framing is preferred for one-story buildings, although it is also used for multilevel structures. The western frame permits uniform shrinkage and settlement on the outside and inside of the walls.

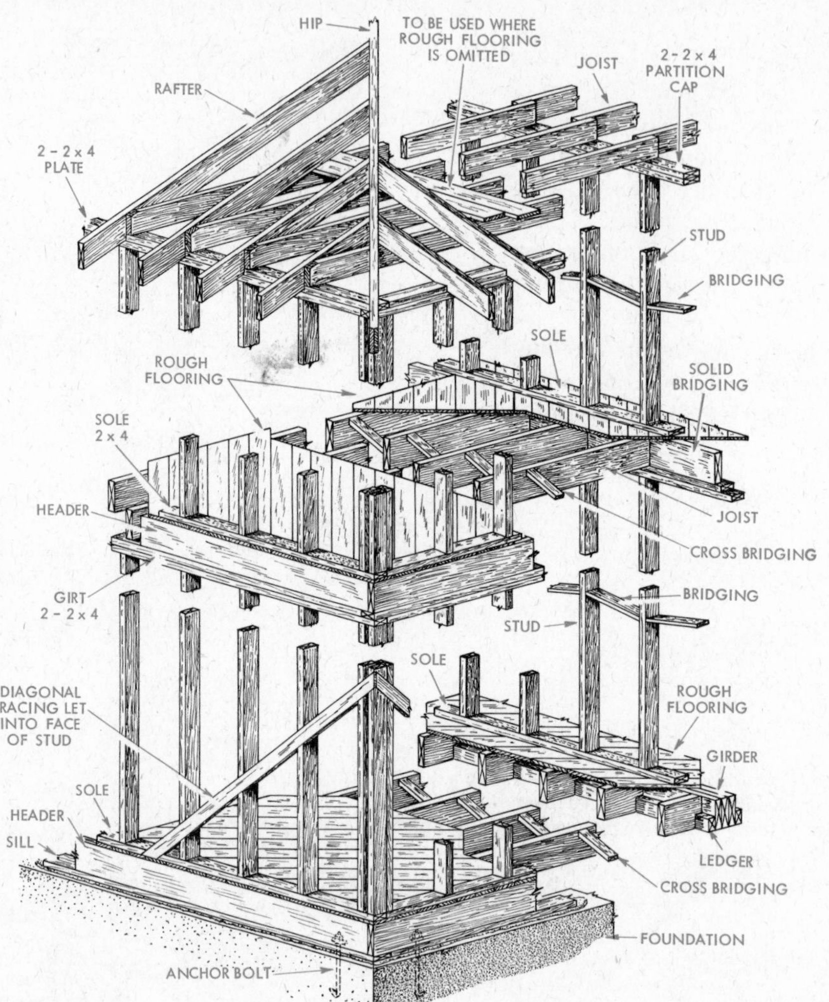

Fig. 7-24. Western Framing. The western or platform frame is built on levels; it is preferred for one-story buildings. Note that studs are **not** continuous between floors: shrinkage is equalized.

Fig. 7-24 shows a typical western framed house. Note that the studs extend through the height of one story *only,* and rest on the *sole* which is nailed to the top of the rough floor. The second floor joists are carried on a double 2″ × 4″ *girt* (sometimes called a *cap plate*) which is placed at the top of the first floor studding. On the second floor, a *header* (the same size as the second floor joists) is carried around the structure. At the first floor level the header rests on a sill which is fastened to the masonry foundation walls.

Braced Frame

Many of the oldest frame structures, dating back to colonial times, use braced frame construction. Originally, this type of construction was imported from Europe. The modern adaptation of the braced frame type of construction is shown in Fig. 7-25. The

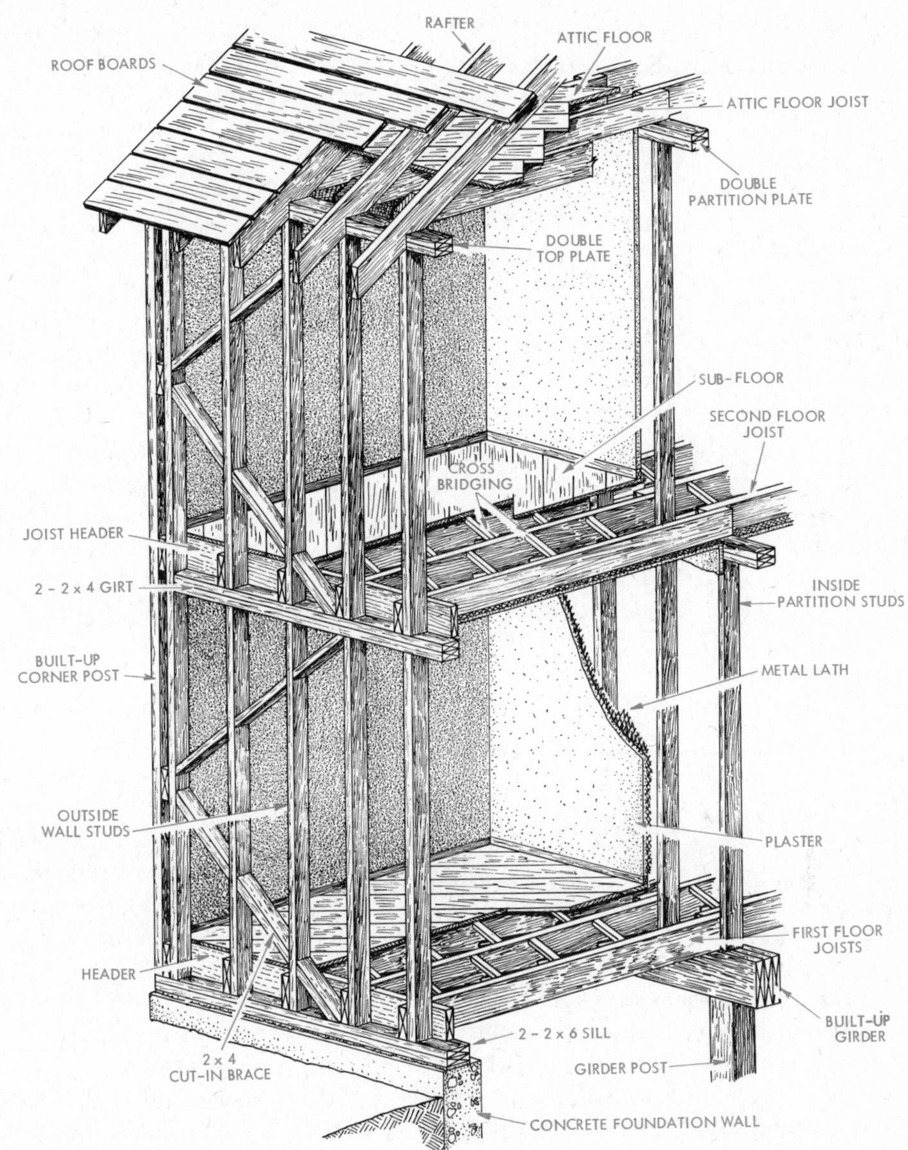

Fig. 7-25. Braced Framing. Braced frame construction is extremely rigid but it is seldom used because of the size of the framing members and the cost involved. This modified braced framing is very satisfactory where strong winds are encountered. Notice the girt at the second floor.

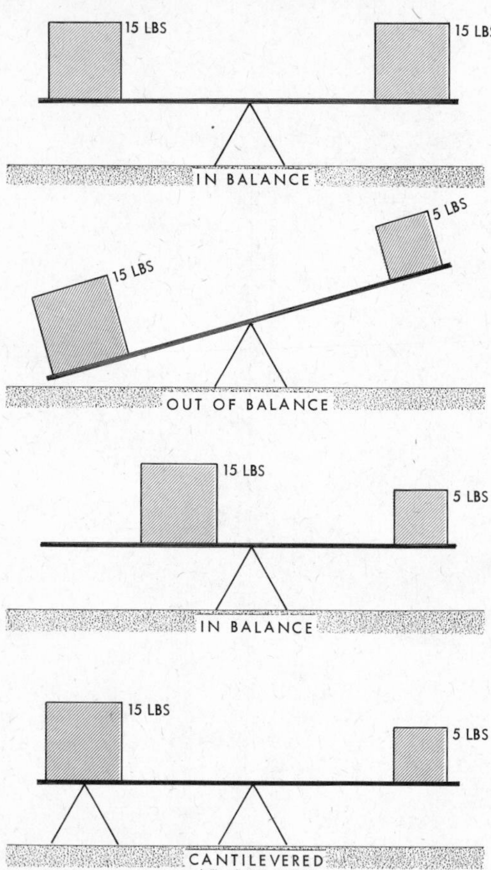

Fig. 7-26. The cantilever is a combination of the fulcrum and counter balance.

braced frame, as the name implies, is a very rigid construction. Stud walls extend only between floors and are topped by a 4″ × 4″ or a 4″ × 6″ girt (modern design uses a false girth of two 2″ × 4s″). The girt forms a sill for the joists. Corner posts, girts, sills, and girders are heavier than those used in either the balloon or western type of framing. Modern braced framing uses a built-up post, sill, and girder. These were solid in older designs.

Cantilever

The cantilever may be defined as a member that is supported only on one end. The principle of the cantilever is similar to a combination of the fulcrum and counterweight. Fig. 7-26 illustrates this concept. The weights on either side of the fulcrum are unequal, but the member is kept from moving since the load imposed on one side is heavier than the other. When the side of the member that carries the heavier load is firmly anchored, the projecting member may then be subjected to a change in forces without damage to the anchoring elements on the heavy side of the fulcrum. Heavy weights and/or extreme lengths that must be carried by the cantilevered member are difficult to calculate. However, the small cantilevered overhang of a roof, bay window, or small balcony may be successfully designed by the student. For example, some buildings are constructed so the second floor or level projects over the first floor or level, as in the case of the split-level house. If the second floor joists are parallel to the overhang dimension, the joists may be extended to the length of the projection. If, however, the joists are perpendicular to the overhang dimension, short joists may be cantilevered (see Fig. 7-27) from a double joist. Note that the short joists must be notched for a 2″ × 4″ ledger strip nailed to the double joist. The same method of cantilevering is used for bay windows, as well as for the long overhang on gable ends of roofs.

Floor Support

Beams and Girders

Floor joists require some type of support to adequately carry the load created by the weight of the interior partitions, floor (s), and roof. Steel I-beams or wood girders are usually placed under the first floor joists for this purpose. The beam or wood girder is normally supported every 8′ to 12′ by a lally column, wood post, or I-beam column. See Fig. 7-28.

Joists

Floors are generally supported by joists placed on edge and spaced 12″, 16″, or 24″ *on center* (abbreviated OC or O.C.). ("On center" is measured from the center of one member to the center of another.) The usual and most common joist spacing is 16″ O.C. The joists are supported at the outer ends by a sill bolted to a masonry wall. When openings are cut in the floor framing for a fireplace, chimney, stairs, etc., the joists must be doubled around these openings to maintain the structural value. Fig. 7-29 illustrates this practice. Those joists which are doubled and run parallel to the regular joists are commonly referred to as *double trimmers*. Those joists doubled and run perpendicular to the regular joists are usually called *headers*.

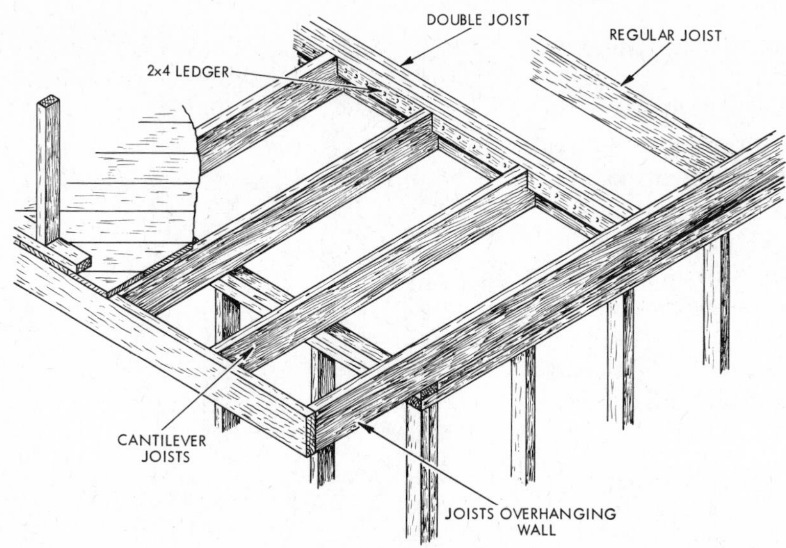

Fig. 7-27. Where regular joists do not extend over the wall, short cantilevered joists may be used. Cantilever joists rest on the wall plate and are fastened to a double joist and ledger.

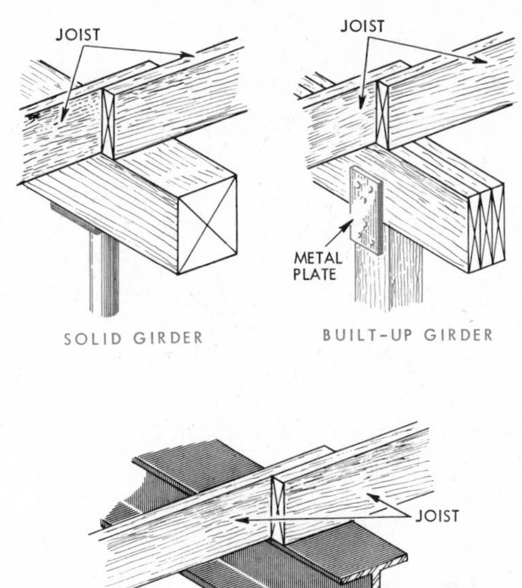

Fig. 7-28. Various supports are used for the beams and girders under the floor joists.

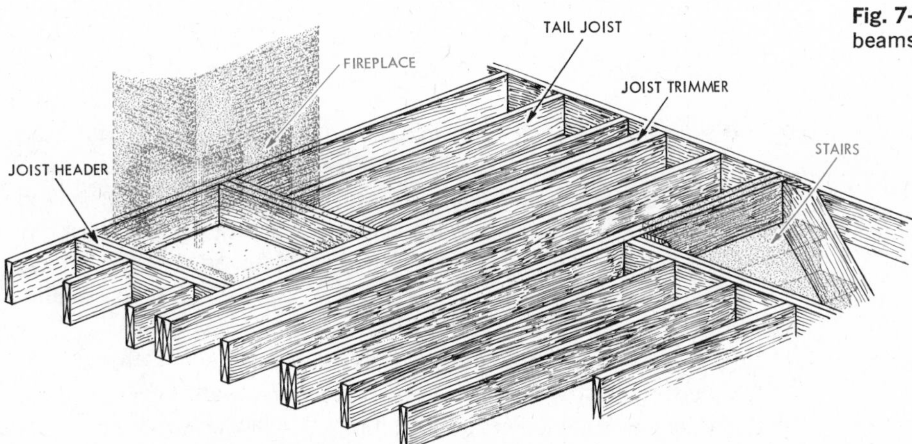

Fig. 7-29. Floor joists should be doubled around openings.

Joist Bridging

All floor joists should be braced with bridging. (Refer to Fig. 7-24.) Bridging may take the form of: (1) cross bridging with 1″ × 2″, 2″ × 2″, or 2″ × 4″ pieces of wood (Fig. 7-30, top left); (2) solid bridging the same size as the joists (Fig. 7-30, top right); or (3) metal cross bridging (Fig. 7-30, bottom). Wood cross bridging is nailed *only* to the top edge of the joist prior to laying the sub-floor. After the sub-floor has been laid, the bottom may then be nailed to the opposite joist. Solid wood bridging and metal cross bridging is placed between the joists *after* the sub-floor has been laid. This prevents settlement strain.

Bridging helps maintain the joists in an upright position and stiffens the floor to eliminate movement. It also strengthens the floor by distributing the load over a large area. To be most effective, the rows of bridging should run in a straight line across the floor. If the joist span does not exceed 14′, one row of bridging is sufficient. Any span greater than 14′ necessitates two rows of bridging. The rows of bridging are normally placed 7′ apart.

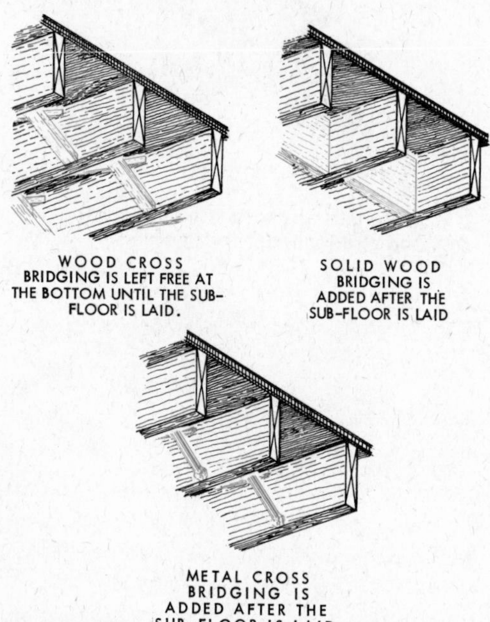

Fig. 7-30. Various types of bridging are used to strengthen floors and distribute the load.

Outside Walls

Outside or exterior walls are usually formed of 2″ × 4″ studs spaced 16″ O.C. Since the outside walls bear a large amount (sometimes all) of the weight of the house, care should be exercised in their design and construction. Outside walls are referred to as load bearing walls. As with the case with floors, all openings should be doubled.

Stud Bracing

Sometimes light wooden braces are "*let into*" (notched into) the outside wall studs of balloon and western type framing. (Refer to Figs. 7-23 and 7-24.) Frequently, however, metal cross bridging, as shown in Fig. 7-31, is used rather than *inlet* (recessed) bracing. This type of bracing is installed rapidly and eliminates all hand work that would ordinarily be involved. Metal cross bridging may be used as bracing in both the western and balloon type framing.

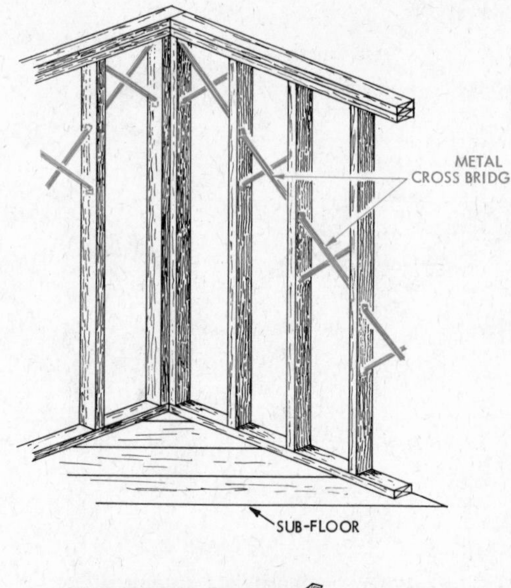

Fig. 7-31. Metal cross bridging may be used in place of bracing inlet into the face of the studs.

Sheathing

When a frame building is erected, it is customary to first cover the outside faces of the stud wall with wood sheathing, fabricated fiberboard, or plywood. Sheathing adds an extra protective surface; serves as an insulating material; strengthens the structure; and, when wood sheathing or plywood is used, forms a nailing base for exterior finishing materials. Wood sheathing may have edges that are square, tongue and grooved, or shiplapped. See Fig. 7-32. By placing wood sheathing at a 45° angle, as in Fig. 7-33, increased strength may be obtained in the framing.

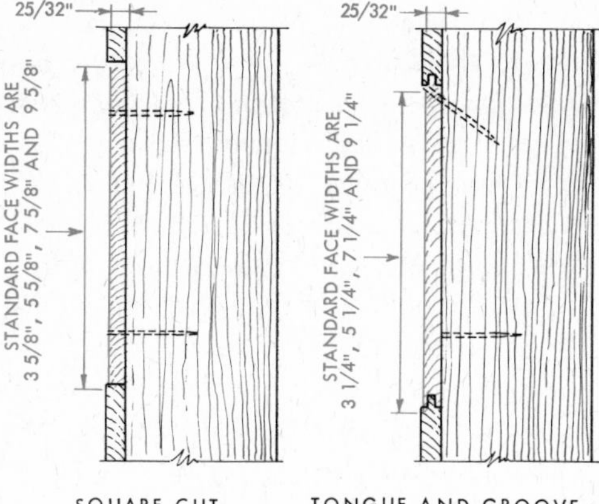

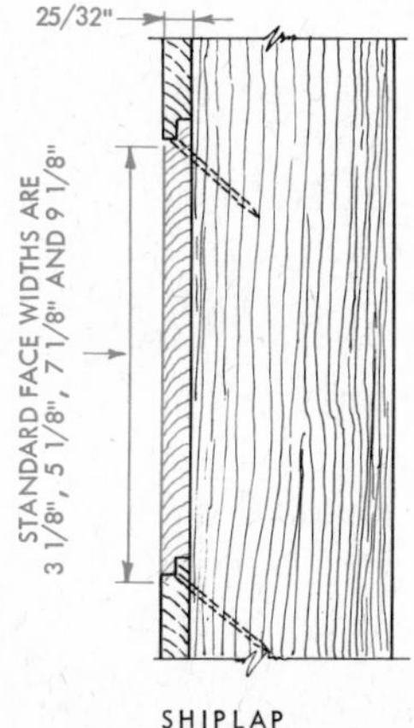

Fig. 7-32. Three basic types of sheathing edges are used for walls, sub-floors, and roofs.

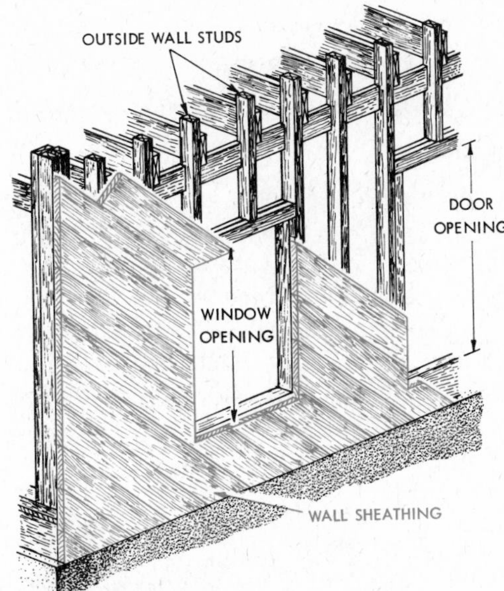

Fig. 7-33. Wall sheathing may be applied diagonally (45°) to increase the strength of the framing.

Contractors in many areas do not use wood sheathing because of the increased expense for material and labor. To reduce the cost of erection, many now use fabricated fiberboard (composition board) or plywood sheathing. These sheets of fiberboard or plywood sheathing may be placed vertically or horizontally. The thickness of fiberboard is 25/32″; width, 4′-0″; and lengths, 6′-0″, 7′-0″, 8′-0″, and 9′-0″. Any exterior siding materials placed over the fiberboard must be nailed to the studs or to special *furring strips* since this type of sheathing does not provide sufficient anchorage for nails. The usual thickness of plywood sheathing is either ½″ or ⅝″; width, 4′-0″; length, 8′-0″. If the studs are 16 inches O.C., ½″ plywood may be used; if the studs are 24″ O.C., ⅝″ may be used. Fiberboard and plywood are both more advantageous than wood sheathing because the wall units tend to be stronger and considerably more airtight.

The roof rafters and floor joists are covered in the same manner as the exterior walls, with *either* 1″ × 6″ wood sheathing or plywood.

Building Paper

Building paper is placed over the sheathing material to seal all joints and cracks from drafts. Building paper is not a vapor or moisture barrier. *If waterproof paper were used, this would prevent the escape of moisture on the inside of the wall in cold weather.*

The wall must breathe to prevent condensation. Polyethylene film or a similar type plastic film may be placed around window and door openings prior to setting the frames to insure a weather-tight seal.

Siding

The outside walls are finished with shingles, siding, plywood, stucco, etc. Shingles may be either wood (usually cedar) or cement asbestos. Wood shingles are often impregnated with creosote to prevent decay. The width of wood shingles vary, but they are usually 16″ or 18″ long. Depending upon the desired effect, wood shingles may be laid with either 8″ or 10″ *to the weather* (amount exposed). The overlap prevents wind, rain, or snow from entering. Fig. 7-34 shows a section through an exterior wall covered with wood shingles. The first course of shingles directly above the foundation is doubled and at the butt end is backed by a ⅜″ *batten.*

Siding is usually laid horizontally, but if a tight fit is possible (such as the tongue and groove joint) a vertical lay may be used.

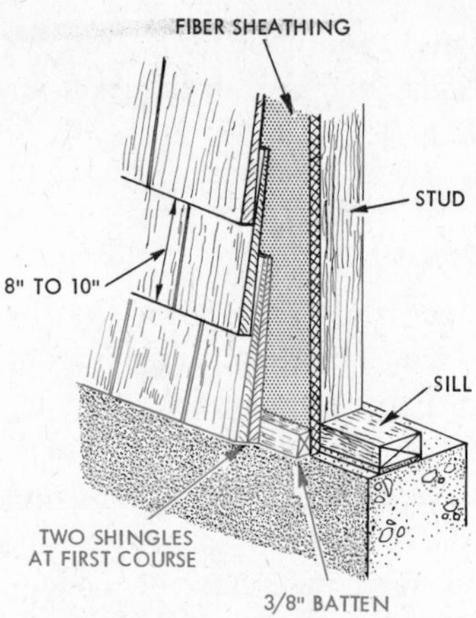

Fig. 7-34. Wood shingles on a frame wall are laid 8″ to 10″ to weather.

Board and batten or board on board, as in Fig. 7-35, is also used vertically. Aluminum siding also comes in either horizontal or vertical panels.

Exterior grade plywood panels with variously textured surfaces may be chosen in place of siding. The long dimension of these panels will be cut (routed) in a shiplap joint to create a continuous pattern. These plywood sheets come in standard 4′ widths, with either 8′ or 10′ lengths. They run both vertically and horizontally. Plywood panels may be joined with a special vinyl weatherproof paint.

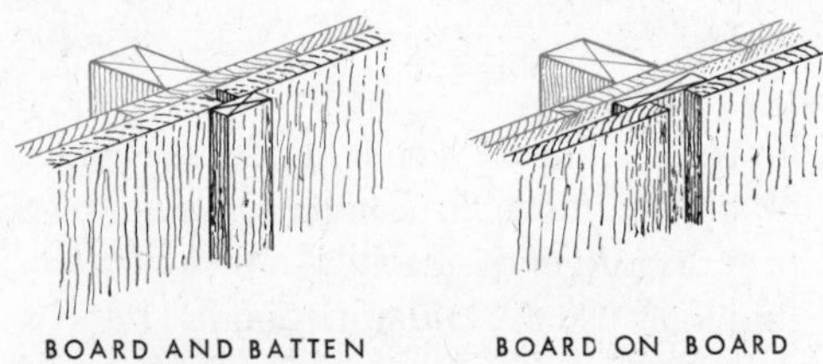

Fig. 7-35. Siding may be applied vertically with battens over joints or boards on boards.

Insulation

Almost all residences are insulated with some type of thermal barrier. Usually exterior walls of new construction will have *blanket* or *batt* insulation between the studs. The same material is used for the attic floor (if the attic space is unheated) and the ground floor (if there is no basement). See Fig. 7-36. The mineral wood blankets or batts are encased in paper to facilitate easy installation. Further reduction in heat loss may be realized if the blanket or batt insulation is covered with a metallic foil which serves to reflect much of the heat. The reflective surface is placed adjacent to the interior plaster or gypsum wall covering. Complete insulation of the exterior walls and roof or ceiling will be a direct advantage to the home owner in fuel consumption. In mild areas this is not so important. In the southern areas insulation is used to keep heat from entering the house.

Existing structures may be insulated with *loose* or *fill* insulation. Mineral wool or pellets are poured or blown between the outside wall studs and joists in attic areas.

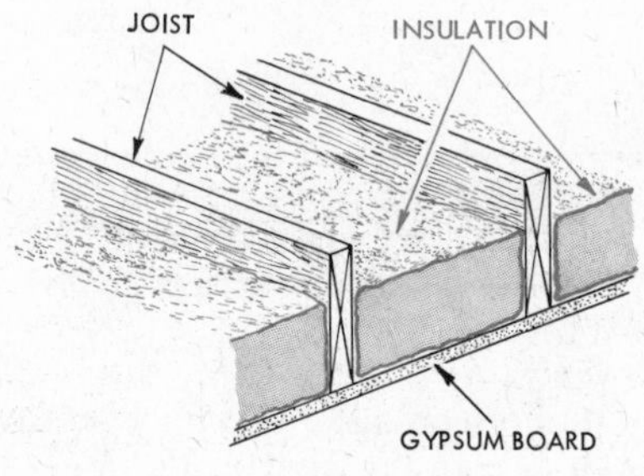

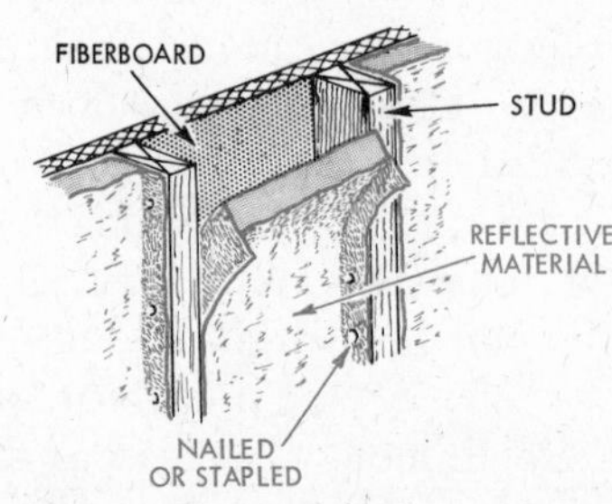

Fig. 7-36. Blanket or batt insulation is placed between studs and joists.

Partitions

Partitions (interior walls) within the structure are usually fabricated from 2″ × 4″ studs, with either lath and plaster or gypsum board (dry wall) covering the framing members. These partitions may be either *bearing* or *non-bearing*. Bearing partitions, like the outside walls, carry the load of the joists and the wall of the floor above. A non-bearing partition forms the walls of a room but does not carry any load. The top and bottom (sole and top plate) of these walls have 2 × 4's spiked to them. When a partition runs parallel to a floor joist, those joists directly under the wall should be doubled to carry the increased load placed on that joist. This is also true in the case of heavy equipment or fixtures (such as the bathtub).

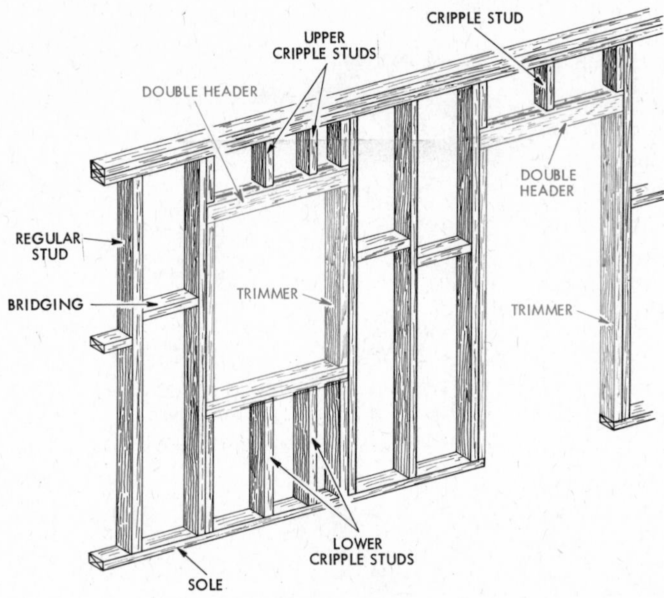

Fig. 7-37. Members around openings in frame walls are usually doubled.

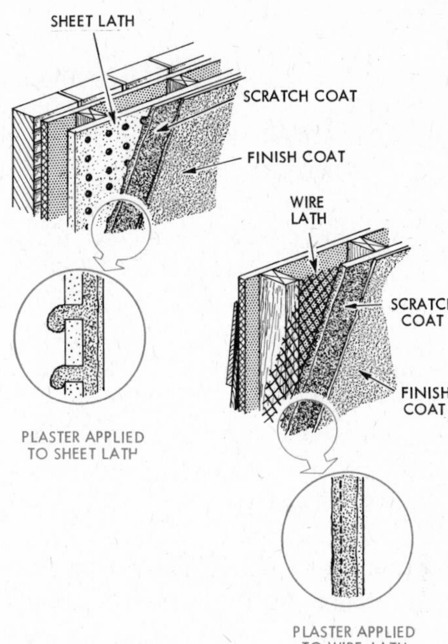

Fig. 7-38. Plaster is applied to sheet and wire lath.

Bearing Partitions

Any openings designed in a bearing partition (or in a bearing wall) should (as in the case of floor joists) be doubled at the sides, top and bottom to increase the strength of the framing members which have been cut. (Fig. 7-37 shows an opening for a window and door in a bearing wall.)

In recent years emphasis has been placed on subdividing the basement into separate rooms. In this case, a bearing partition, usually masonry, may replace the post and girder and serve as the main dividing member. A bearing partition in the basement of either concrete block or 2″ × 6″ studs will adequately carry the imposed load. It is necessary that a footing be placed under this wall.

Stack Walls

In many areas the local building code requires that walls housing the soil pipe (waste pipe) be constructed of 2″ × 6″ or 2″ × 8″ studs. This allows adequate space for the pipe. This wall is commonly referred to as a *stack wall* or *stack partition.*

Closet Walls

Closets which have a common wall may be made of 2″ × 4″ studs positioned so the 4″ dimension is parallel to the plaster or dry wall rather than perpendicular. This will produce a thinner wall.

Interior Wall Finishes

In recent years interior wall finishes have become more diversified. Originally, plaster was considered as the main interior finishing material; however, dry wall covering has been on a steady increase. Plaster is applied to a base of metal lath, rock lath, gypsum, or fiberboard. (Wood lath has all but been discontinued. This is due primarily to the fire hazard and time required for installation.) Fig. 7-38 illustrates two different types of lathing with plaster applications. *Sheet lath* is shown in Fig. 7-38 (top left) with a scratch coat (rough base) and a finish coat of plaster. Each piece of sheet lath has a series of holes so that when the scratch coat is applied, the plaster is forced into the holes, thereby bonding it to the lath. Sheet lath is either ⅜" or ½" thick. *Wire lath,* shown in Fig. 7-38 (bottom right), serves the same function as sheet lath, only the wire lath becomes an integral part of the plaster. The main disadvantage of plaster is that it requires a drying period which may halt construction. Dry wall is easier and faster to work with. However, it is not considered to be as soundproof or as durable.

There are many different kinds of dry wall construction materials, but the type most widely used is *sheetrock* (or *gypsum board*). Sheetrock comes in standard 4′-0″ × 8′-0″ sheets with thicknesses of ⅜", ½", or ⅝" and is nailed directly to the studs. Sheetrock joints are cemented and covered with a paper tape. When the joints have thoroughly dried, they are sanded smooth and flush. Sheetrock has the appearance of a plastered wall, yet is less expensive.

Dry wall construction may also use insulating board, manufactured in a wide variety of shapes and sizes, in place of plaster and sheetrock. Sometimes regular rigid insulation (wallboard) is used beneath the insulating board. Plywood, V-grooved boards, hardboard paneling, plastic laminates (these are available in wood grain and solid colors), planks, and other forms of wood are used for decorative effects.

Wood Trim

On plastered walls, wood trim, such as baseboards, window casings, door frames, and moldings, are fastened to a *nailing ground* (Fig. 7-39). The trim conceals the joint between the plaster and nailing ground to give a finished appearance. Mill work companies and building supply companies have catalogs showing various shapes of trim, base, shoe, etc. The nailing ground is the same thickness as the plaster and is fastened to the framing member, i.e., a stud or joist. Dry wall construction does not require the use of nailing grounds since there is relatively little danger of cracking.

Finish Floor

A wood *finish floor* is laid after the plaster is dry or the *taping* on the dry wall has been sanded. To insure a soundproofing quality to floors and to prevent heat loss, sometimes the finished floor is nailed to *furring strips* placed 16″ O.C. over the sub-flooring which has been previously covered with building paper. See Fig. 7-40. This serves as a good base for the finish flooring. The finished flooring, however, is usually nailed directly to the sub-flooring that has been covered with building paper. All finish flooring and floor boards are tongue and grooved and are *blind nailed* (nail driven diagonally in the upper angle formed by the tongue). Finish flooring varies in thickness from ⅜" to $^{13}/_{16}$" and in width from 1¼" to 3¼".

Asphalt, rubber, or vinyl tile may be used in place of wood finish flooring. *Particle board* (or plywood) then must be placed over the sub-floor (see Fig. 7-41) to create the same thickness where tile is used (kitchen, bathroom, etc.), as where wood flooring is used (living room, halls, etc.).

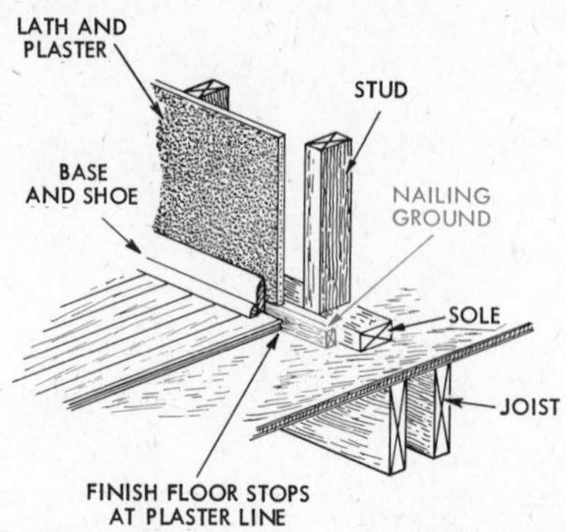

Fig. 7-39. A nailing ground serves as an anchor for the trim. (It also serves to indicate the desired thickness of the plaster.)

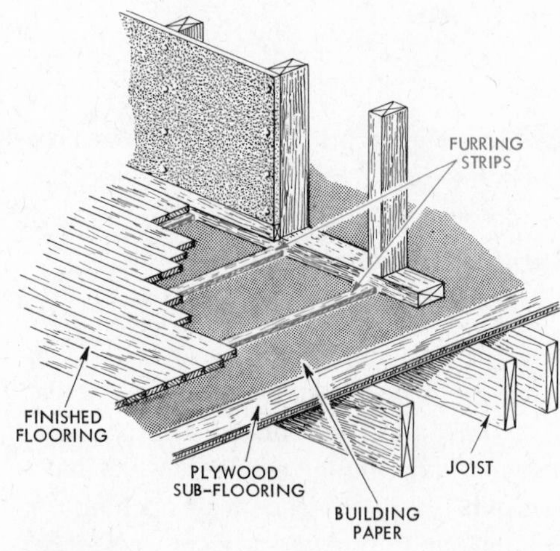

Fig. 7-40. Furring strips are frequently used beneath the finish floor.

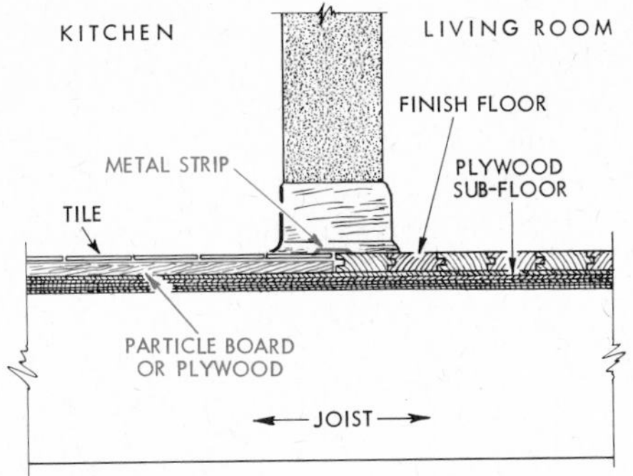

Fig. 7-41. Particle board or plywood is used beneath linoleum or tile floors to maintain the same level as a wood finished floor.

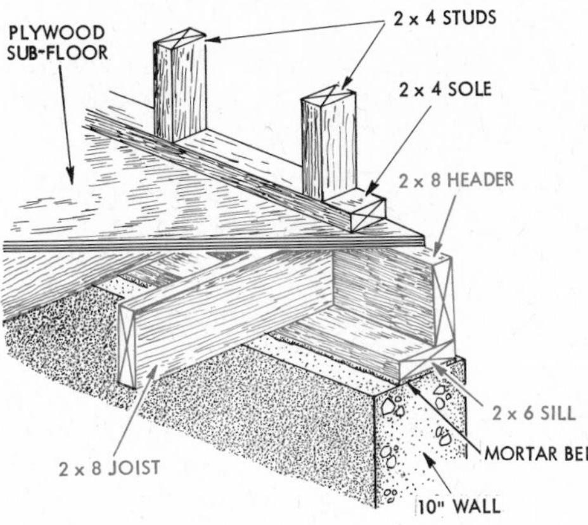

Fig. 7-42. Box sill construction is commonly used for western framing. Note: joists and headers are spiked to the sill; the flooring, sole, and studs are spiked to the joists and headers.

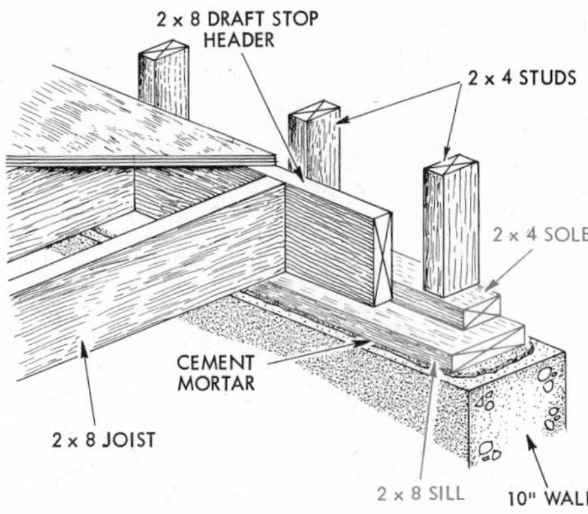

Fig. 7-44. T-sill construction with a sole beneath the studs is also used for balloon framing. Note: joists bear directly on the sill; studs on the sole.

Sills

It would seem logical to discuss sill construction immediately following footings and foundations since the sill is the first segment of framing to be constructed. The sill extends around the perimeter of the foundation and provides a base for framing members. Sills, however, cannot be intelligently discussed without some knowledge of basic types of framing and their specific purposes.

Box Sills

Western framing commonly uses the *box sill* (Fig. 7-42). This type of sill consists of a 2″ × 6″ sill plate anchored to the foundation to support the joists and headers. The joists and headers are then spiked to the sill. Some contractors may omit the header joist to reduce costs, but this is false economy from the standpoint of sound construction. The header provides better nailing ground for rough flooring and wall sheathing. It also helps as a fire stop (draft stop).

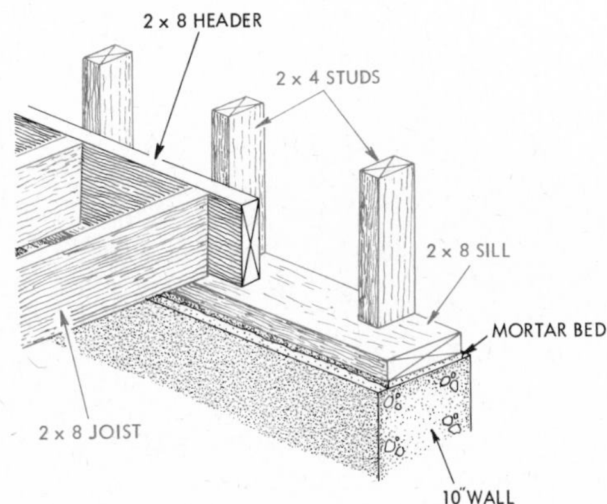

Fig. 7-43. T-sill construction without a sole beneath the studs is used for balloon framing. Note: joists and studs bear directly on the sill.

T-Sills

The T-sill is commonly used with the balloon framing. The studs and joists in the T-sill may bear directly on the sill plate as in Fig. 7-43, or may be spiked to a 2″ × 4″ sole nailed to the sill as in Fig. 7-44. Again the header serves as a draft stop.

Eastern Sills

Another sill variation used for balloon construction is the *eastern sill* (Fig. 7-45). The structural qualities are comparative to the T-sill. Blocks equivalent to a header and serving as fire stops are cut to fit and are placed between the joists. Both the T-sill and the eastern sill have the advantage of less potential shrinkage, thus making them ideal for stucco, brick, and stone veneer residences.

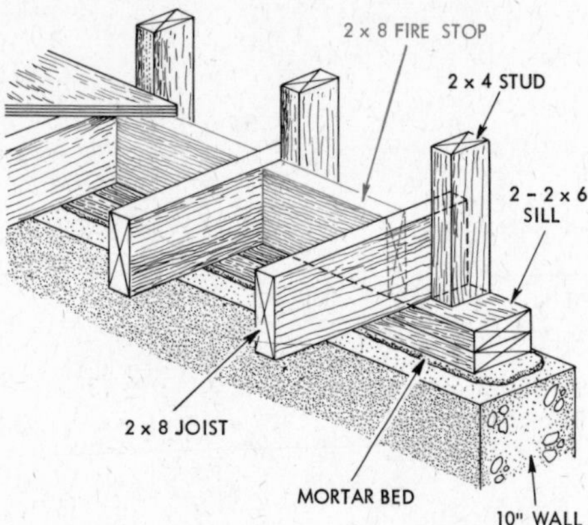

Fig. 7-45. The eastern sill offers an alternate type of sill construction for balloon framing. Note: the header is cut and placed between the joists; joists are nailed against the studs.

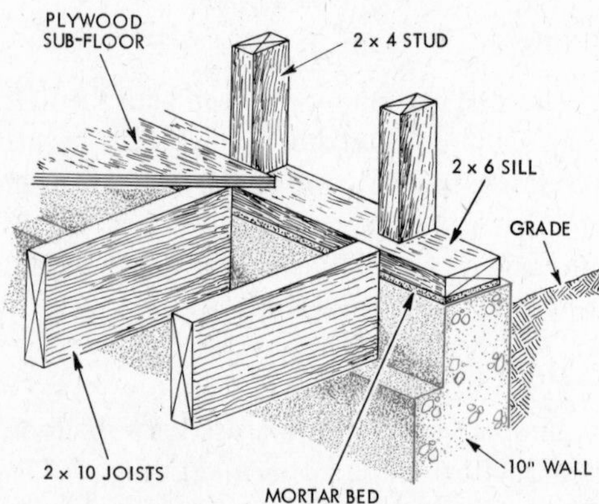

Fig. 7-46. A recess along the top of the foundation wall allows the joists to be partly or completely below grade.

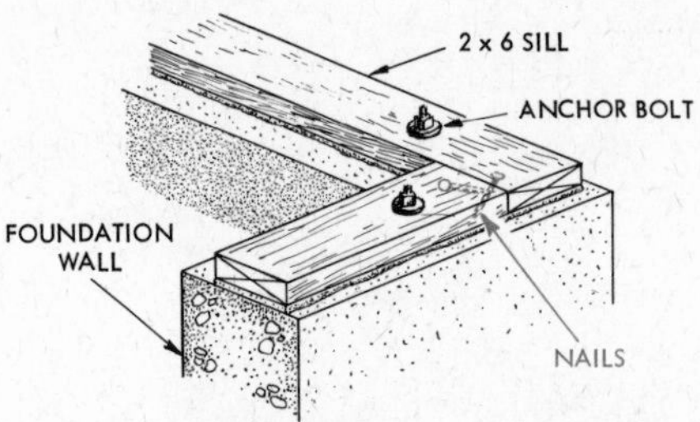

Fig. 7-47. Sill members are secured by anchor bolts and "toenailed" at corners.

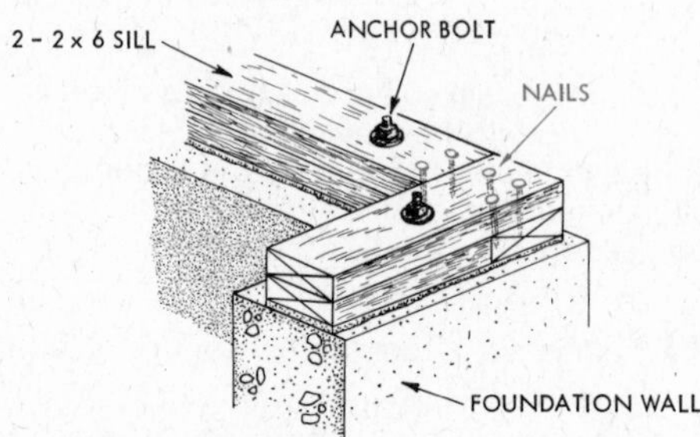

Fig. 7-48. Built-up sills are lapped at the corners and nailed.

Under most conditions, a 2″ × 6″ sill plate provides sufficient nail anchorage. A double or 4″ sill plate is desirable for the two-story home and for the home built in a locality subjected to high wind velocities.

Lowered Sill. To achieve certain architectural effects in designing a house to the topography of a given lot, it may be necessary to bring the level of the floor closer to the finished grade. In this case, the joists may be lowered completely or partly below the grade by providing a recess along the top of the foundation wall (Fig. 7-46). This type of construction is often not as strong as those previously discussed due to the decreased bearing area for the joists.

Sill Bedding. Figs. 7-42 through 7-46 illustrate sill plates that have been bedded in mortar. A ½″ to ¾″ layer of mortar is spread on top of the foundation and the sill is placed over this and leveled before the mortar has set. This provides an even bearing surface and prevents air leakage. Mineral wool or pliable plastic material is sometimes used in place of mortar as a bedding material. This will be compressed when the sill is drawn tight by the anchor bolts and/or by the weight of the structure. Sometimes the sill is placed directly on the foundation and wood shingles are driven between the foundation and sill to fill any voids. Eventually these shingles may work loose, providing an opportunity for cracks to occur.

Anchor Bolts. It is imperative that the sill be fastened to the foundation wall. Anchor bolts, ½″ to ¾″ diameter by 16″ to 18″ long, are used for this purpose. Anchor bolts are set in the foundation every 4′ to 8′ O.C.; one bolt should be placed near each corner. Holes are drilled in the sill to fit the bolt spacing.

Sill Joints. When a single sill is joined at the corner of the building the ends are *toenailed* together as in Fig. 7-47. When a built-up or double sill, or sill with sole is required, the components are lapped and nailed at the corner as in Fig. 7-48.

Termite Protection. Protection against termites (subterranean, non-subterranean, or dry wood types) should not be overlooked in sill design. The subterranean termite is found in almost every area of the United States. To eliminate the possibility of termites burrowing into lower framing mem-

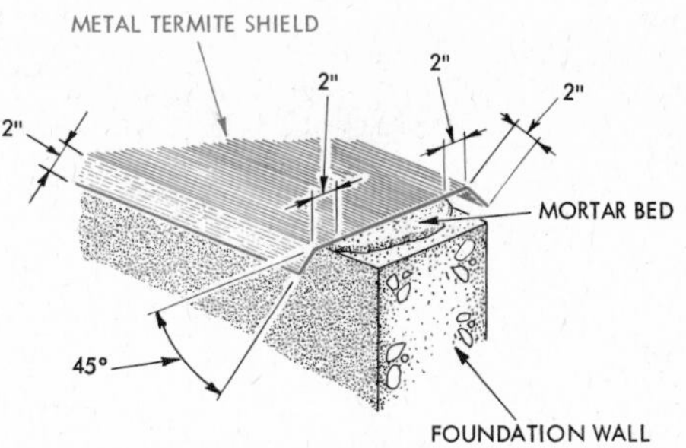

Fig. 7-49. A galvanized iron or copper termite shield extends without break around the top of the foundation wall.

bers, a termite shield may be used as shown in Fig. 7-49. These rust proof metal shields extend completely around the top of the foundation wall and are bedded in mortar. They should project on both sides of the wall. Creosote or other chemicals may be used to treat wood members so they will not be attacked by termites.

Step-By-Step Drawing Procedure: Sills

Fig. 7-50 illustrates the step-by-step procedure for drawing any type of sill.

Brick Masonry

Brick has been used as a building material for the last 6,000 years and ranks as one of man's greatest inventions. It is only one, however, of several kinds of materials used in masonry construction. Masonry building units include brick, stone, hollow tile, and concrete block.

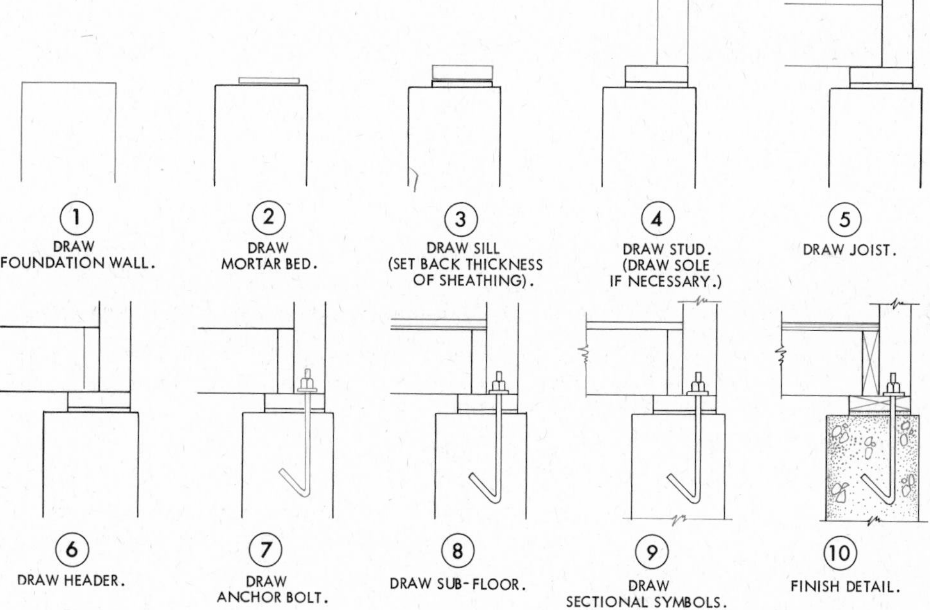

Fig. 7-50. The step-by-step drawing procedure for sills roughly follows the order of construction.

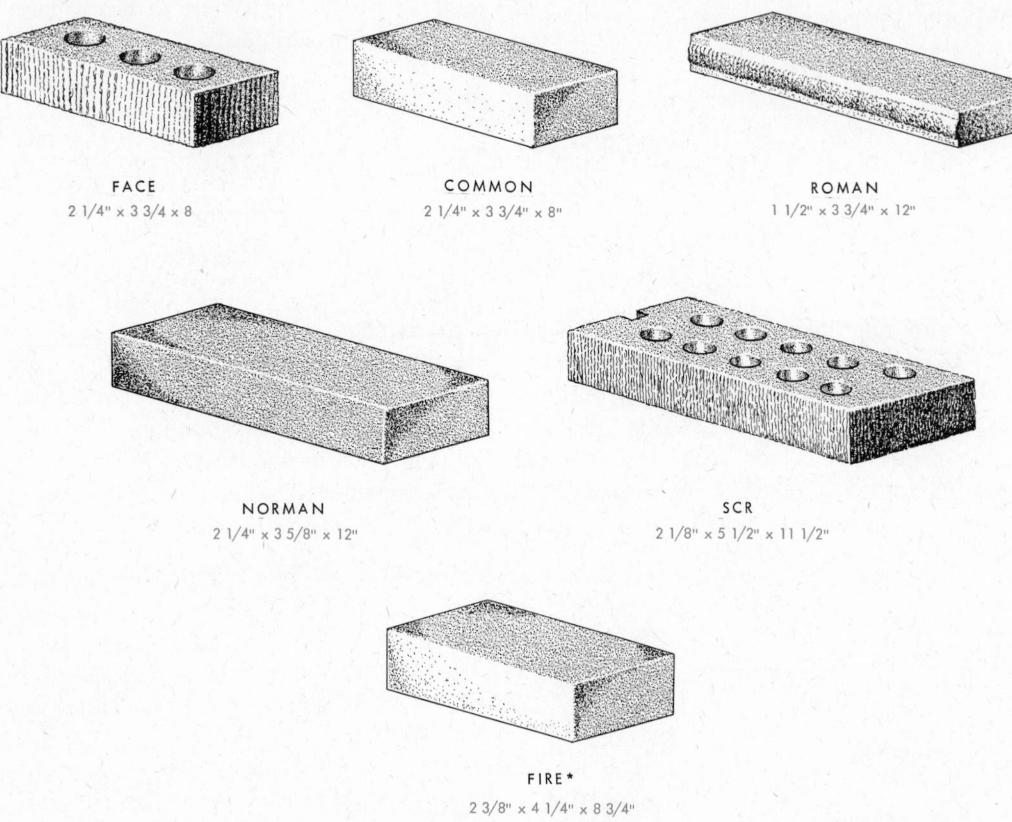

Fig. 7-51. These six standard brick types are used in residential construction.

Brick Sizes

Brick sizes are standardized just as lumber is standardized. In residential construction, standard brick, either face or common, is usually used. Fig. 7-51 shows the sizes of the most widely used types of brick.

Mortar Joints

Sound, watertight joints are necessary for a strong wall. Mortar joints should not be less than ¼" nor more than ½" in thickness. Thicker joints are sometimes used for decoration but they are structurally weak. Joints are either left flush with the brick face, or formed with a *pointing tool*. See Fig. 7-52. The concave or rodded joint is the most common shape used. The main purpose of treating the joints is to force the edges of the mortar into firm contact with the brick so water cannot penetrate. The shape of the joints may also play an aesthetic role by giving different shadow effects to the wall.

Brick Bond

The strength of any masonry wall depends to a great extent upon the *bond* used in erecting the wall. A bond refers to the arrangement of brick or stone in the wall. The arrangements are designed to prevent

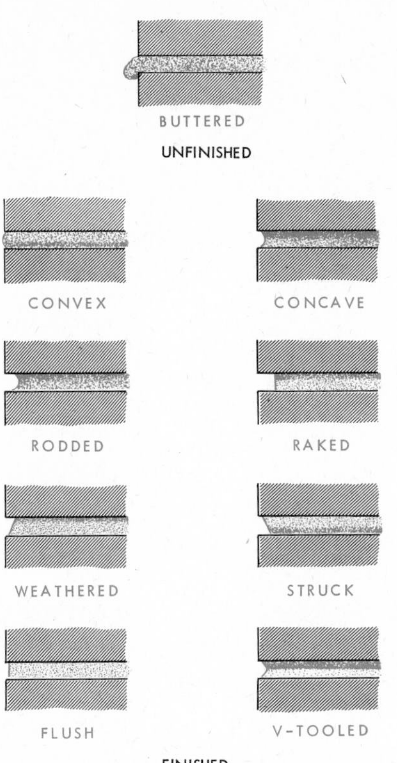

Fig. 7-52. The various types of finished mortar joints are designed to force the mortar into contact with the brick. Note the unfinished "buttered" joint.

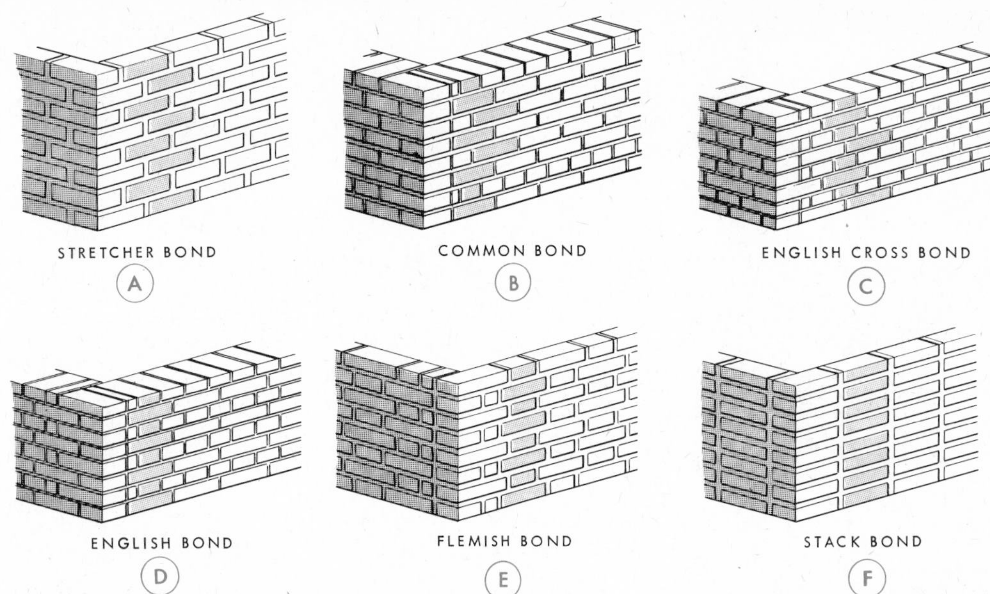

Fig. 7-53. The variations between brick bonds depend upon the distribution of stretchers and headers in various courses.

the vertical joints between the masonry units from being directly above each other. There are many patterns for placing brick which will produce a structurally sound wall. The variation between bonds is brought about by the distribution of *stretchers* (the length of the brick laid parallel with the face of the wall) and *headers* (laid with the length at right angles to the face of the wall) laid in various *courses* (rows).

The following paragraphs list some of the basic bonds used in brick work.

Running or Stretcher Bond. (See Fig. 7-53A.) This bond uses stretcher courses with the joints breaking at the center of each brick immediately above and below. Face, common, Roman, or SCR brick is used for this bond.

Common Bond. (See Fig. 7-53B.) The common bond, or American bond as it is sometimes called, is a variation of the running bond, with a header course every 5th, 6th, or 7th course. This ties the wall to the backing masonry material. The header courses are centered on each other. Face or common brick is usually used in the common bond.

English Cross or Dutch Bond. (See Fig. 7-53C.) This bond uses alternate header and stretcher courses. The joints of the stretchers center on the stretchers two courses above and below; headers center on headers. This bond is usually common or face brick.

English Bond. (See Fig. 7-53D.) Alternate courses of headers and stretchers are laid so that the joints between stretchers are centered on the headers. Stretchers are centered on stretchers; headers on headers. Face or common brick is usually used for the English bond.

Flemish Bond. (See Fig. 7-53E.) Alternate headers and stretchers are in each course. The headers in one course are cen-

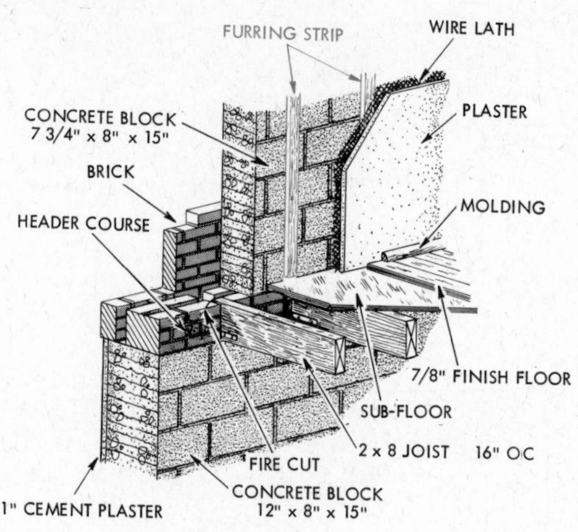

Fig. 7-54. A brick veneer is often used over concrete block. Note the furring strips.

tered above and below the stretchers in the other course. Face or common brick is used for this bond.

Stack Bond. (See Fig. 7-53F.) All courses are stretchers and all joints are in line. This is used primarily for aesthetic purposes—it has relatively little structural value. The most effective brick for this type of bond is Roman.

Many of the more ornamental bonds have been excluded from this discussion — they are seldom used because of the cost.

Masonry Walls

Masonry walls are porous and after a driving rain or period of severe cold, moisture may condense on the inside of the wall. To prevent this, the inner wall covering (covered with lath and plaster or other finish) is separated from the back-up masonry by *furring* or *furring strips* as in Fig. 7-54. This air space will stop any moisture transfer. Furring is adjusted to compensate for irregularities in the masonry wall and provides a nailing base for the wall covering. Furring may be either light steel channels or 1″ × 2″, 1″ × 3″, or 2″ × 2″ wood strips. These are positioned vertically and nailed to the inside face of the masonry unit. The spacing of the furring strips is determined by the type of interior wall covering. For example, if sheet rock is used, furring strips should be placed 16″ or 24″ O.C. to maintain the module of the standard size sheet (4′ × 8′). Placing the furring strips at a greater distance O.C. would cause too much flexibility when pressure was applied. The furring serves as a base for the interior finish: lath and plaster, dry wall, gypsum board, paneling, plywood, etc.

Brick Walls. With mortar the standard brick width is roughly 4″. Therefore, brick walls are normally constructed in multiples of 4″: that is, in widths of 4″, 8″, 12″, and 16″. A residential building less than 35′ high normally uses an 8″ wall. A 12″ wall is recommended if there are high winds or earthquakes. Usually the outside layer of brick is backed-up by an inside layer with a lesser grade of brick. Sometimes the outside brick wall is backed up by concrete blocks or hollow tiles. A brick veneer (one brick thick) may also be built over wood framing.

Concrete Block Walls. The most widely used size of concrete block is 7⅝″ × 7⅝″ × 15⅝″. If these are laid in a single wall thickness, they will produce roughly an 8″ thick wall. Block are also available in 4″, 10″, and 12″ widths, as well as other shapes, as shown in Fig. 7-55. The names given to each block are indicative of their use in construction.

The face of a concrete block wall will take

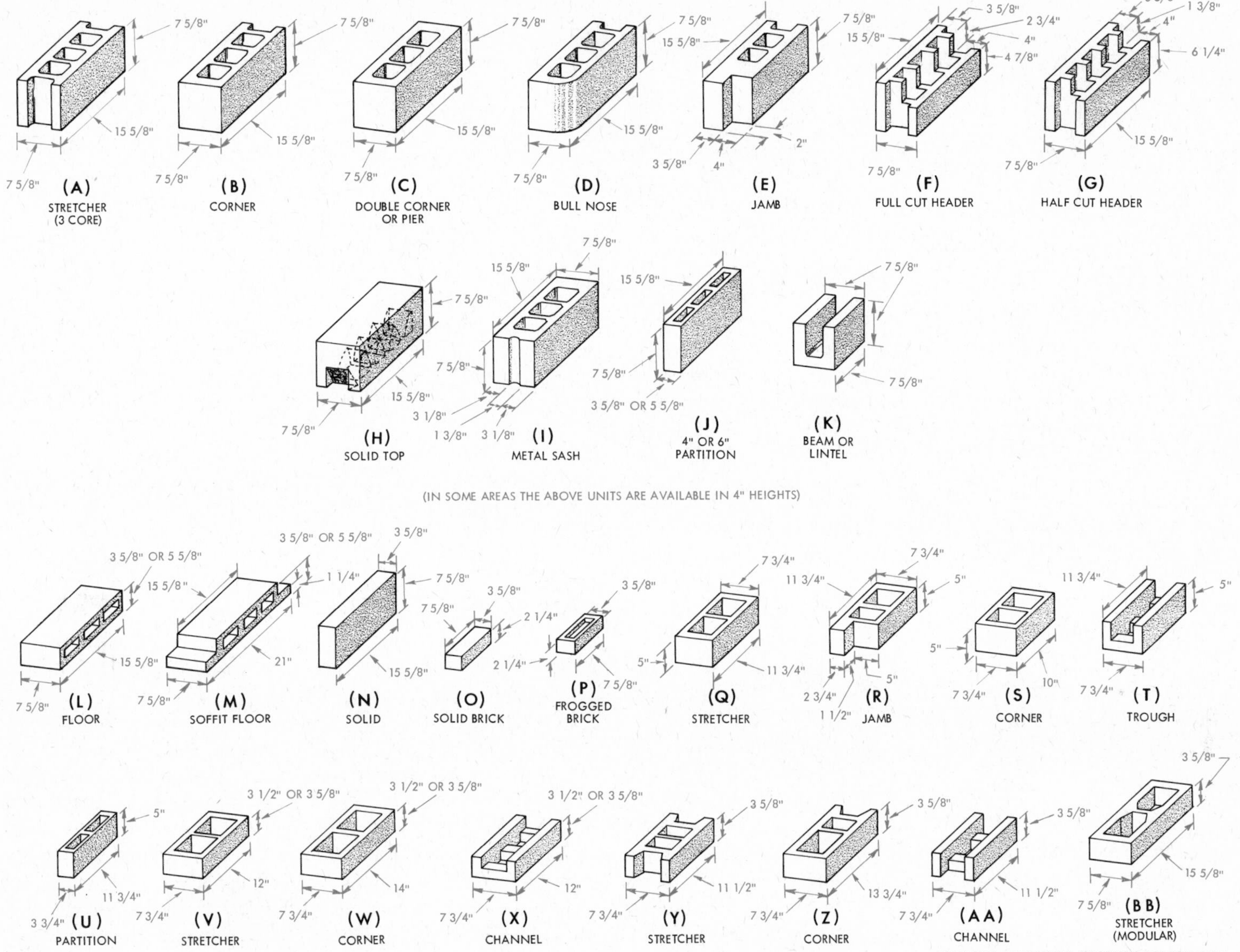

Fig. 7-55. Concrete blocks come in various shapes and sizes to serve many purposes. (Actual not nominal sizes are given.)

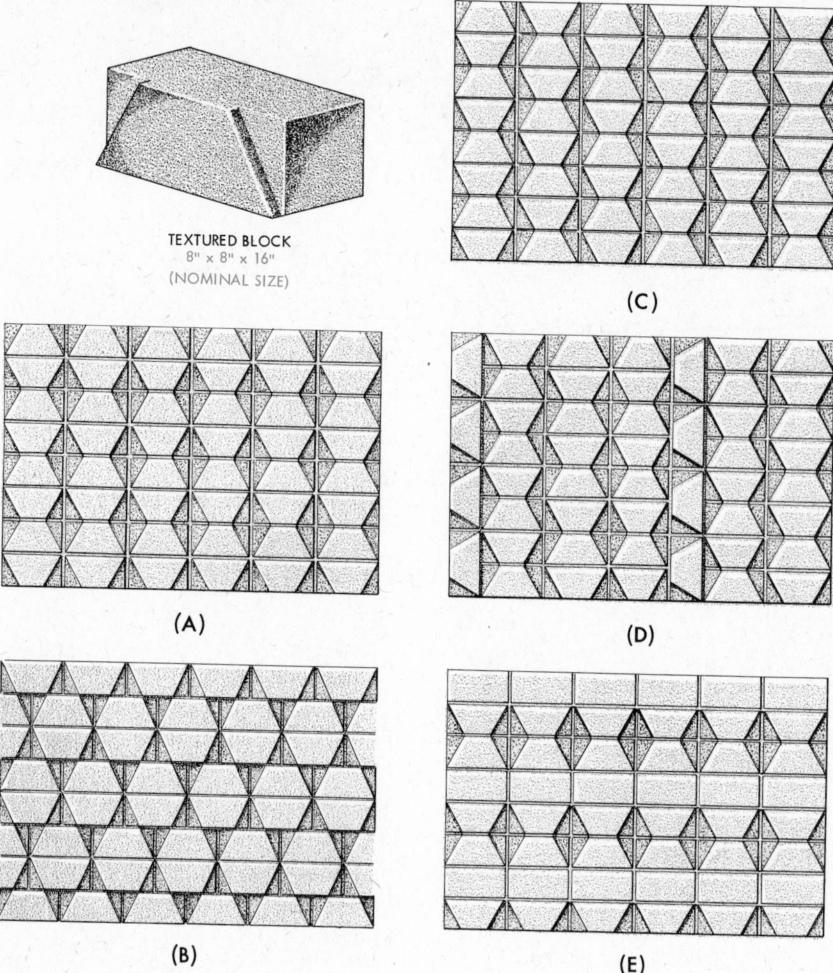

Fig. 7-56. Textured or shadow masonry block add beauty and variety to interior and exterior walls.

on a new depth when laid with *textured blocks* (sometimes called shadow blocks). These may be randomly placed with plain blocks or used together to develop a pattern as in Fig. 7-56. Textured block may be used on both interior and exterior walls. A combination of blocks may produce an attractive interior wall as shown in Fig. 7-57.

Hollow Tile Walls. Hollow tile (sometimes called building tile) is composed of the same ingredients as brick. The thickness of the shell is ¾″. Hollow tile are available in numerous sizes and shapes; selection is dependent upon its intended use (masonry wall backing unit, a wall, etc.).

SCR Brick Walls. In recent years the SCR (Structural Clay Products Research) brick wall has been introduced into the masonry

Fig. 7-57. An attractive interior partition has been produced with a combination of stretchers and core blocks.

PORTLAND CEMENT ASSOC., CHICAGO, ILLINOIS.

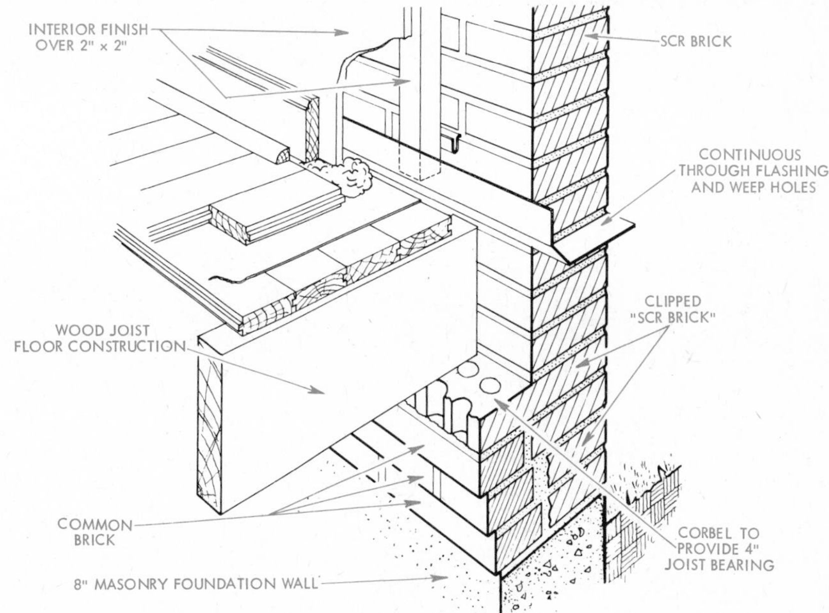

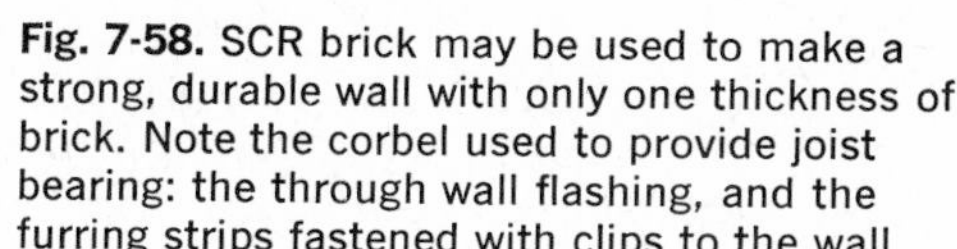

Fig. 7-58. SCR brick may be used to make a strong, durable wall with only one thickness of brick. Note the corbel used to provide joist bearing: the through wall flashing, and the furring strips fastened with clips to the wall.

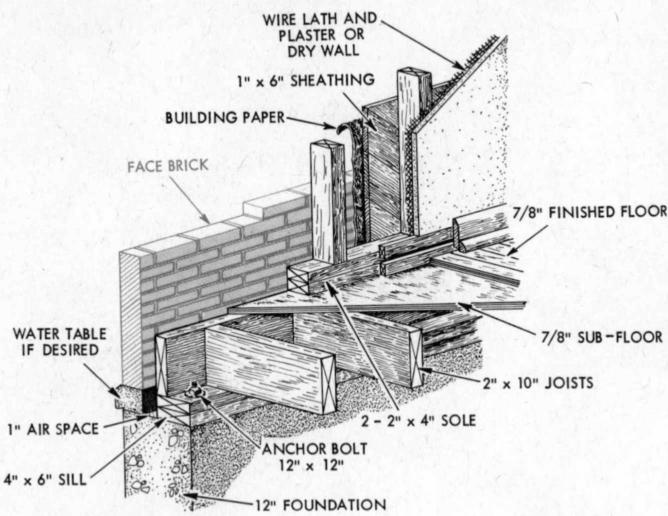

Fig. 7-59. Brick veneer construction is popular because it provides a brick exterior with the interior flexibility of frame construction.

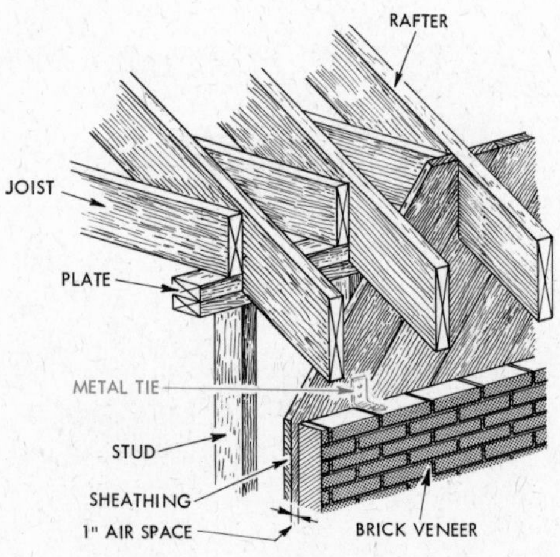

Fig. 7-60. Metal ties are used to hold the masonry wall to the frame superstructure.

construction field. This wall was designed primarily to compete with the frame wall. It has met with success in many areas. Fig. 7-58 shows a typical SCR brick wall. The wall is one unit or brick thick. A jamb slot or notched cut is made into one end of every brick to accommodate metal or wood windows. It is necessary with the SCR brick wall to use furring strips to provide a cavity for the installation of wiring and insulation. Attachment of the 2″ × 2″ furring strip is made by a patented clip which fits into the masonry joint.

Brick Veneer Walls. Brick veneer is commonly considered as a skin of brick over a frame house. See Fig. 7-59. The foundation wall must be wide enough to accommodate a course of brick and also the sill for the frame wall. Allowance must be made for ¾″ sheathing on the frame wall and 1″ air space. Balloon frame construction lends itself to this type of wall because there is a minimum of vertical shrinkage. Corrugated galvanized metal strips or wires are used to tie the brick wall to the frame construction. One end is nailed to the sheathing and the other end is embedded in the mortar joint. See Fig. 7-60. The ties are placed every fifth course and spaced 2′-0″ O.C. horizontally. The masonry veneer part of the wall usually is not load bearing. The roof, floor, and ceiling joists are supported by the frame wall.

Stone Walls. The oldest example of masonry houses in America are represented by the brick and stone buildings of colonial days. Stones in a wall must overlap so that joints are not directly above each other. The

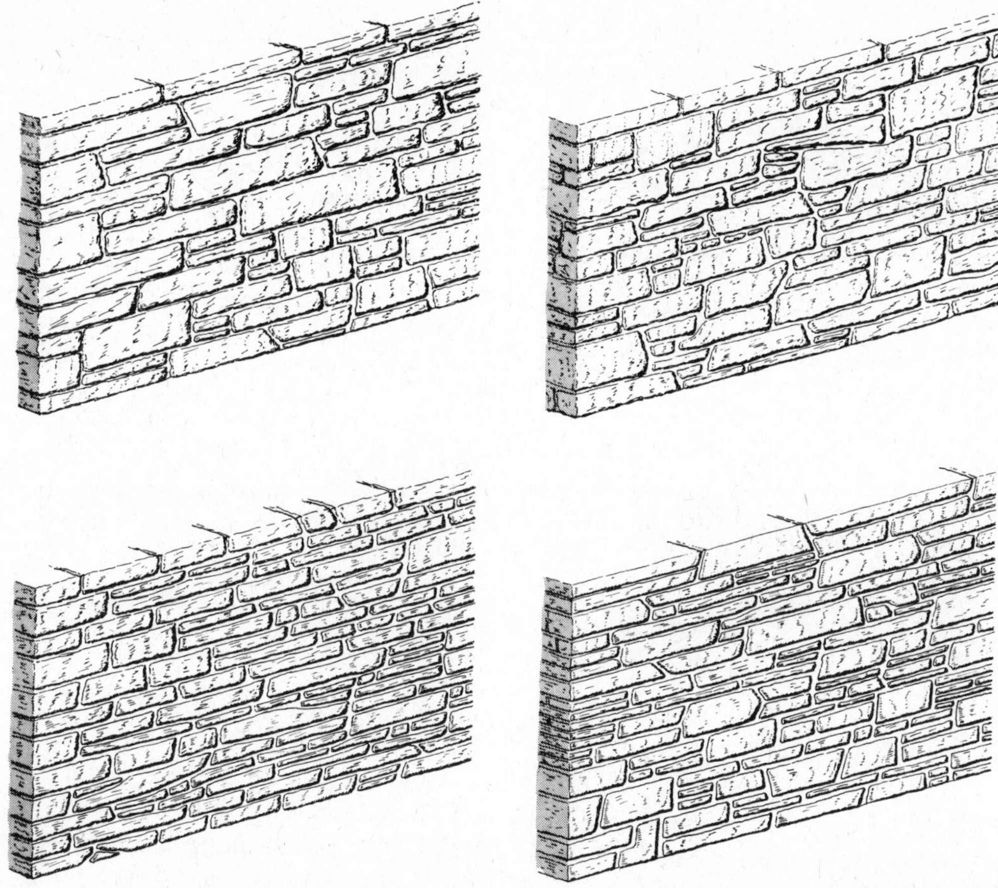

Fig. 7-61. Split stone may be used to form an attractive wall. Stones must be laid so that no vertical cracks can develop.

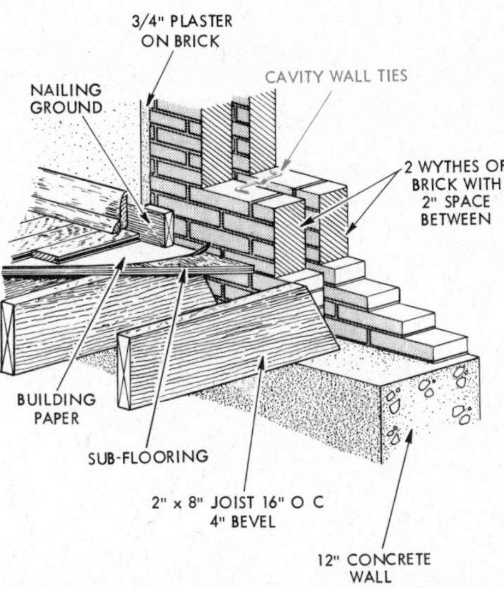

Fig. 7-62. A 10″ cavity wall is formed of two 4″ walls plus a 2″ cavity. Note the metal ties used for support.

size and shape of the stone used, in addition to the color and texture, will determine how it will be laid in the wall. Today, almost all stone homes are veneered. The wall section will be essentially the same as brick veneer. The only difference is that stone replaces the brick, and the numerous types and cuts of stone produce many patterns. A few of the more common stone-work combinations are displayed in Fig. 7-61.

Cavity walls are used to produce a watertight wall with good thermal and sound insulation. These are made up of two 4″ walls normally separated by a 2″ air space. These are tied together by ¼″ metal ties placed in every 5th course and not more than 3′ apart horizontally. See Fig. 7-62. Cavity walls should not exceed 25′ in height. Since the cavity wall prevents the penetration of heat and cold, it is important that the air space be kept free of mortar drippings or other obstructions.

A cavity wall with an interior plaster finish would need no furring strips, since the void between the outside brick and the back-up brick serves the same purpose as furring strips. In other words, a dead air space is provided. Plaster, therefore, may be

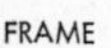

Fig. 7-63. Flashing, either plastic or metal, is required wherever water may seep into the building.

applied directly to the brick work, or the masonry may remain exposed for its aesthetic value. Metal or wire lath is not necessary if plaster is to be used, since the rough surface will readily accept the scratch coat of plaster.

Flashing is placed wherever water may seep into a building, such as under windows and at the base of a wall. It is a continuous piece (usually metal) shaped to prevent moisture from entering the wall. See Fig. 7-63.

Wall Ventilation

Some type of ventilation must be supplied to the solid masonry or masonry veneer wall to drain off any moisture which may

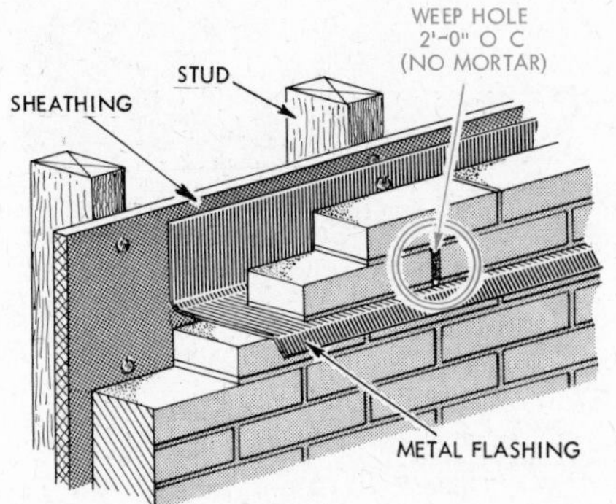

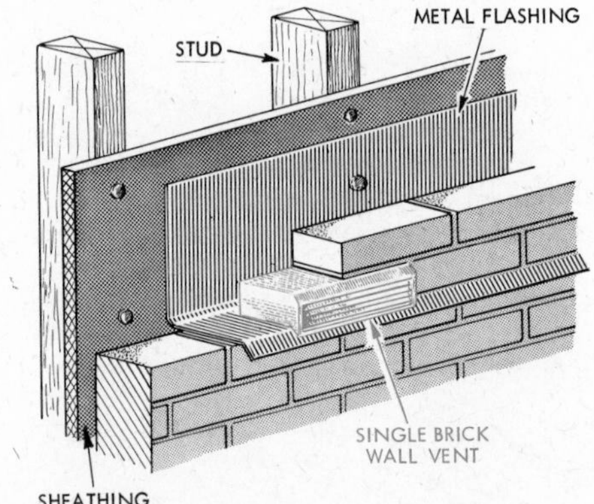

Fig. 7-64. Brick walls must be vented by weep holes or wall vents.

form. Ventilation in a solid or veneer masonry wall (Fig. 7-64) may be produced by either: (1) weepholes placed every 2′ O.C.; or (2) cavity ventilators spaced according to size and manufacturers specifications. Either method of ventilating should be placed immediately above the flashing at the base of

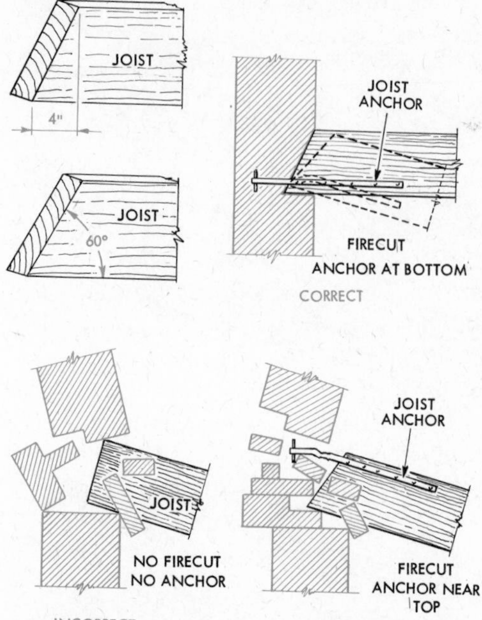

Fig. 7-65. A fire cut is used on joints in solid masonry walls. A joist anchor prevents the building from falling outward in the event of fire.

the wall, over flashing on the second story, and over openings.

Structural Details

Joists that fit into masonry walls are cut on a 60° angle, or with a 4″ bevel (Fig. 7-65, top left). This angular cut is called a *fire cut*. In the event of fire, without a fire cut the falling joist could create a lever action causing the wall to topple outward (Fig. 7-65, bottom left) with hazard to life and property. In addition to the fire cut joist, anchors are usually required by city building codes. It is also necessary to anchor floors and roofs to walls because of possible high winds. Joists are secured to walls at the ends by metal anchors which are embedded in the masonry walls. These are fastened near the bottom of every 5th or 6th joist. See Fig. 7-65 (top right). Anchors are fastened to the bottom of the joists to prevent wall damage if the joist falls (Fig. 7-65, bottom right). Joists parallel to walls, as shown in Fig. 7-66, may be fastened by means of an anchor strip nailed across the top of 2 or 3 joists. The metal strip, for most small dwellings, is placed in the middle of the joist span and anchored to the masonry wall.

Anchor Bolts and Plates. To provide anchorage for roof rafters or trusses, a plate must be fastened to the top of the masonry wall. Bolts, ½″ to ¾″ in diameter, 12″ to 16″ long, are set in mortar every 5′ to 6′ O.C. A ¼″ diameter, 2″ × 6″ steel plate, is welded to the bottom of the bolt. See Fig. 7-67.

Stud partition ends are fastened in a similar manner.

Lintels. Masonry over the tops of windows and doors must be supported by *lintels*. Angle or channel iron is usually used in brick veneer; reinforced concrete is usually used in concrete block walls. Wood is very seldom used as a lintel due to shrinkage which causes cracks in the masonry wall and eventual decay. The lintel in residential construction should have a 4″ bearing on each side of the opening. This is sufficient in most

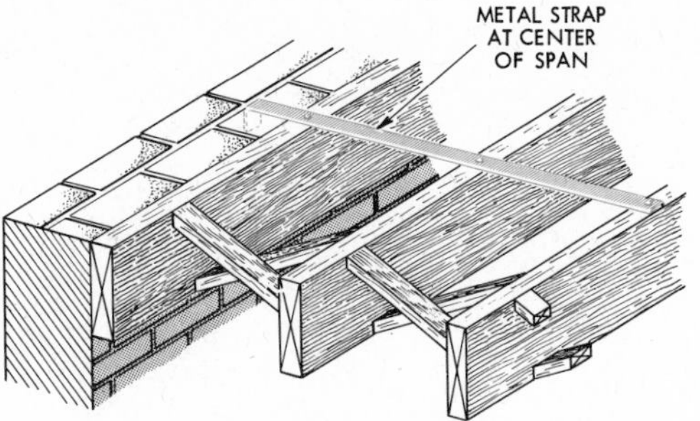

Fig. 7-66. Joists may be fastened to walls by a metal strip at the center of the span.

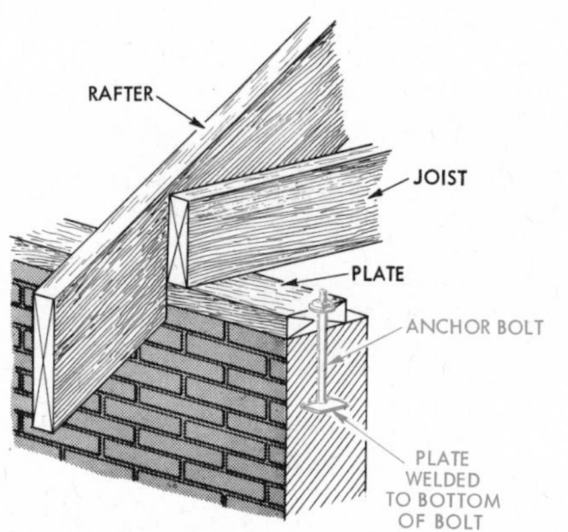

Fig. 7-67. Anchor bolts are used to secure the plate to the brick wall and to hold down the roof in the case of high winds.

cases. If the opening is extremely wide, the size of the angle iron will have to be increased. Fig. 7-68 shows angle iron used as a lintel in brick veneer construction. Note the use of the laminated 4″ × 4″ header. Since the frame wall is not carrying the weight of the exterior wall, a 4″ × 4″ header is sufficient.

Fig. 7-69 illustrates a solid, reinforced, precast, concrete lintel in a brick veneer wall with concrete block backing. Greater strength is given to the lintel by placing the

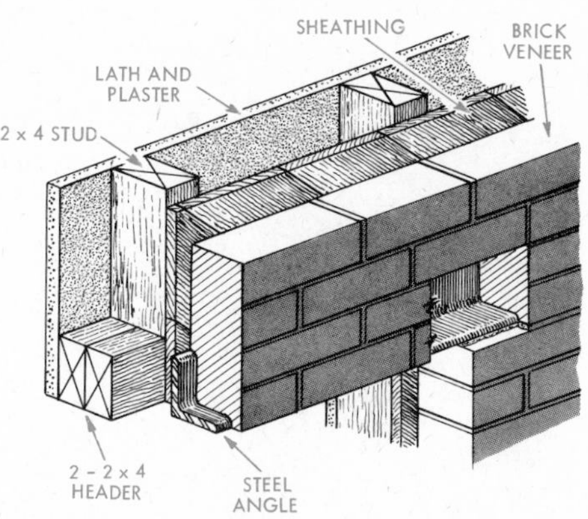

Fig. 7-68. An angle iron or steel angle is used as a lintel in brick veneer walls. Note the 2—2x4's used to support the frame.

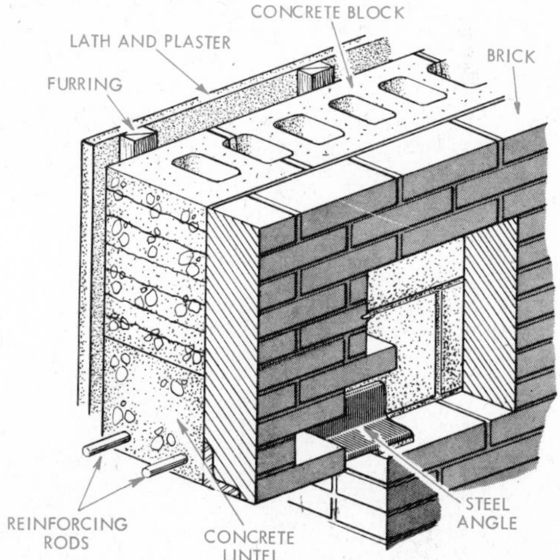

Fig. 7-69. A precast reinforced concrete lintel is used over the concrete block part of this brick veneer wall. Note the angle iron lintel used to support the bricks over the opening.

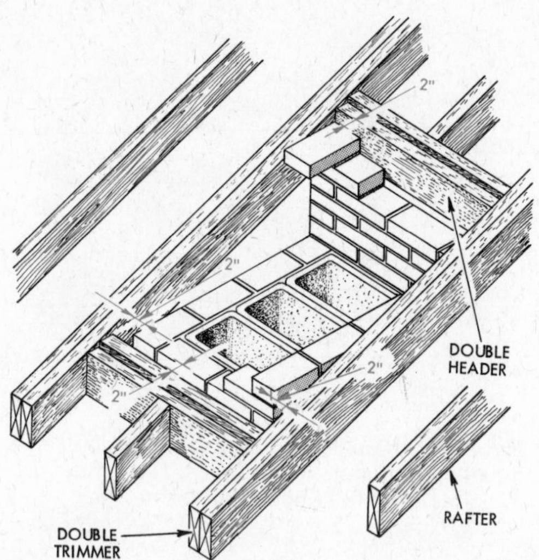

Fig. 7-70. A 2" clearance must be provided between the chimney and the roof framing members. This space is filled with non-combustible material.

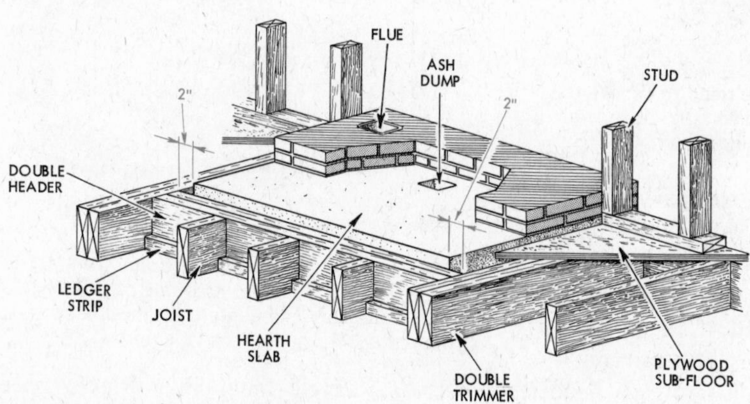

Fig. 7-71. A 2" clearance must also be provided around the sides of the fireplace.

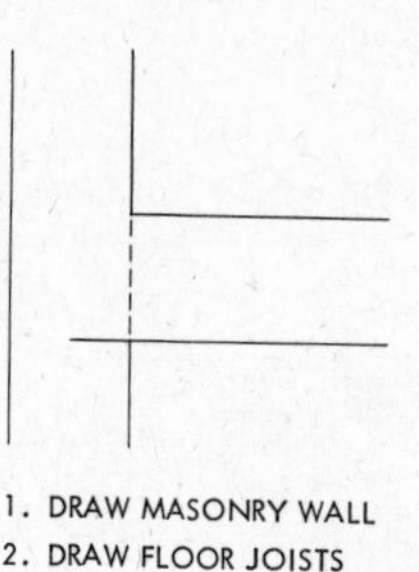

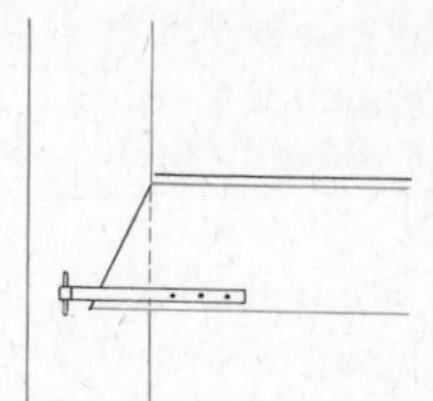

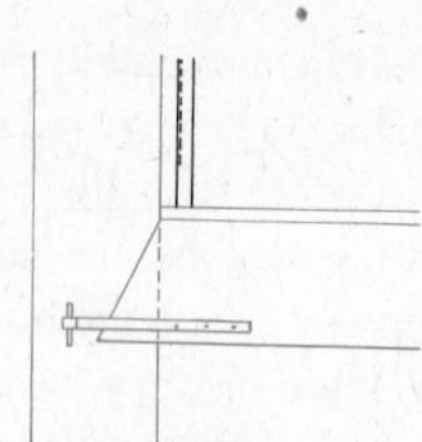

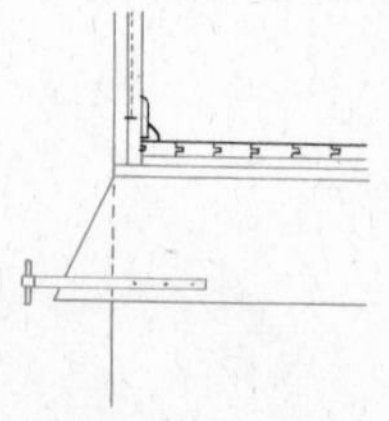

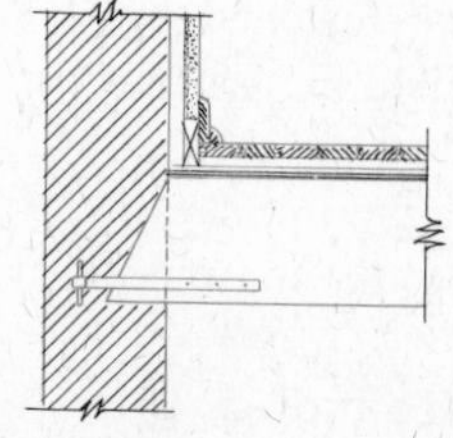

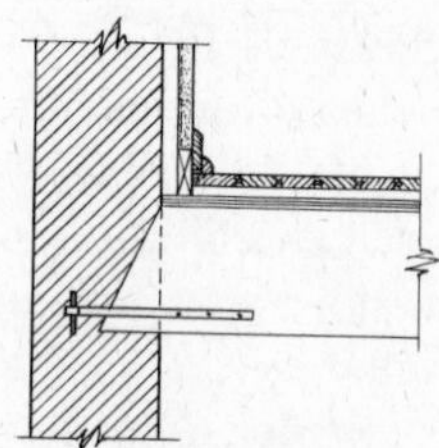

Fig. 7-72. Follow this step-by-step procedure for drawing a masonry wall.

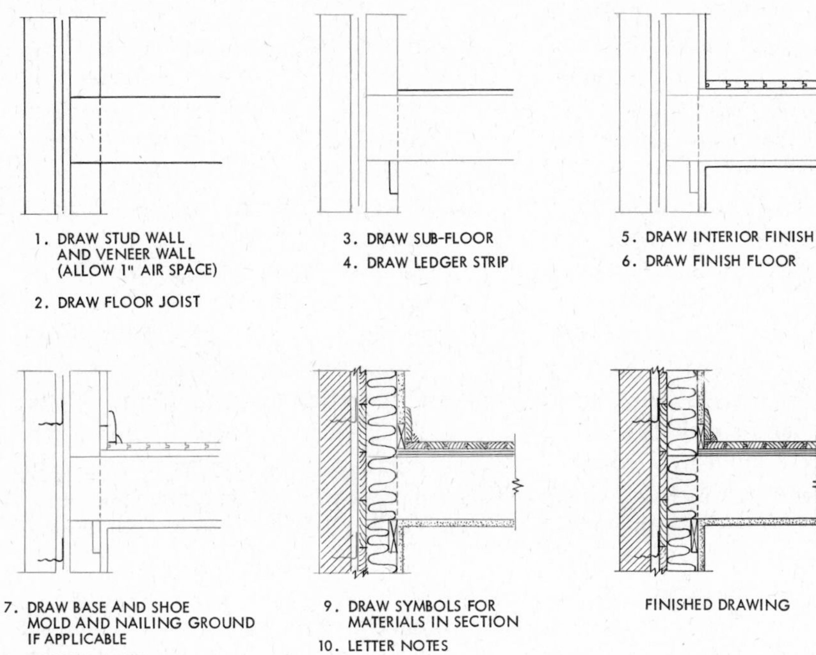

Fig. 7-73. Follow this step-by-step procedure for drawing a masonry veneer wall. (For simplicity the fire stops have been omitted.)

reinforcing rods close to the bottom edge of the lintel. Most "pure forms" of traditional or period residential architecture will use a precast or cut stone lintel in lieu of an angle or channel iron lintel. However, modern adaptations (of the colonial for example) will employ an angle iron lintel. A cast concrete, cut stone, or brick *rowlock* course sill (course of bricks laid on edge) is placed at a slight angle below *all* window and door openings to shed water.

Chimneys and Fireplaces. Floor, roof, wall, or partition framing members must be kept free of the masonry chimney or fireplace. Figs. 7-70 and 7-71 show the headers and trimmers around a chimney and fireplace at a minimum distance of 2″. This space between the masonry and structural members must be filled with non-combustible insulation. Mineral or glass wool is frequently used for this purpose.

Step-By-Step Drawing Procedure: Masonry Walls

Fig. 7-72 illustrates the step-by-step procedure used in drawing any masonry wall section.

Fig. 7-73 illustrates the step-by-step procedure in drawing a masonry veneer wall. A frame wall is similar to the masonry wall; however, siding is used in place of brick.

Questions and Problems

1. What is the basic purpose of a footing?
2. Does a difference exist between the local building code specification for a residential footing and the footing design shown in Fig. 7-2? Does the building code recommend different size footings for the varying types of soil that may be common in the area?
3. According to the map shown in Fig. 7-6 (maximum frost penetration), does a difference exist between that figure and the frost line in your community?
4. Is the bottommost portion of the footing placed at the frost line or slightly below?
5. Design a foundation wall and footing for a single-story frame, ranch-type dwelling on a flat site. Assume the site is located in your community.
6. What is the maximum frost penetration in the area in which you live? Does this differ from the depth used by most builders or specified by the local building code? If a difference does exist, is this an "error"?
7. Make a quick sketch of two sections taken through the foundation and footing of a single-story house. The house has brick veneer on the front and frame on the other three sides. Take one section through the front foundation wall and the other through the rear wall. Dimension each section.
8. What methods may be used to insure a dry basement?
9. Which type of frame superstructure is best suited for a masonry veneer exterior finish? How thick will the foundation wall be?
10. What purpose does bridging serve between (a) floor joists or (b) studs.
11. Why is it recommended that 1″ × 6″ wood sheathing be nailed diagonally on the studs of an exterior wall?
12. When an exterior wall is covered with shingles, why should the lowermost course of shingles be doubled and backed with a batten strip?
13. Take a section through a floor composed of 2″ × 10″ joists, ¾″ plywood sub-floor, building paper, and ¾ (finish oak flooring. This is to be a detail section. Scale 1½″ = 1′-0″. Use the proper symbols in the section. Call out all materials and sizes. Draw another detail section through a kitchen floor that is covered with vinyl tile having a particle board underlayment.
14. Draw a detail section of four different types of sills as specified by the instructor. Place a different inside and outside wall covering on each sill. Carry each covering 1″ below top of foundation wall. Use ½″ × 12″ anchor bolts, 8′-0″ O.C. Place the finished grade line 6″ to 8″ below the top of the foundation wall. Draw all building materials *actual* size. Use a ½″ mortar bed under all wood sills. Place a termite shield under all sills.
15. What purpose does the fire stop serve? Is it necessary in both the balloon and platform types of construction?
16. Must a termite shield be used on all sills?
17. What other type of material may be

used for sill bedding other than mortar?

18. Relative to brick walls, what do the terms stretcher, header, and course mean?
19. Explain the purpose of weep holes in a masonry wall. How far apart and how far above the foundation wall are they placed?
20. Is it necessary to place vents in an exterior wall covered with wood siding?
21. How can an SCR brick wall be distinguished from a common or face brick wall?

Well planned roofing and supports create a sound structure.

Construction Details: Roofs and Structural Openings 8

This chapter continues the examination of house construction begun in Chapter 7. The following sections give detailed information essential to understanding the construction and design of roofs and structural openings. Structural openings include windows, doors, fireplaces and chimneys, and stairs. Step-by-step drawing procedures are given for the main structural details.

Roofs

In quality home construction a good roof is as essential as a properly designed and well-built foundation. The obvious primary purpose of the roof is to shed water and prevent leakage. The most common type of roof material is shingles. Shingles are lapped and their joints *broken* (staggered) to give as much protection as possible from the weather. Shingles may be of wood, cement asbestos, asphalt composition, slate, tile, or metal. Generally the first course or row of shingles is doubled to cover the joints of the under course and to give added protection. The portion of the shingle which is exposed is said to be *laid to the weather*.

Roofs with a slight slope or low pitch must have a tight, sealed covering. If sheet metal is used as a roofing material, the bonds are lapped and soldered. If asphalt composition (rolled roofing) is used, the bonds must be made watertight by asphalt or other similar types of cement. On nearly all flat roofs, tar and gravel is applied over the surface of several *plies* (layers) of roofing felt. (The layers of roofing felt are bound to each other with tar or asphalt.)

The rafters are the structural framing members that support the roof and are covered by roof boards or plywood. This sheathing serves as a base for the roofing material.

Roof Types

There are many kinds of roofs—all having an almost infinite number of slopes. The most common types of roofs are depicted in Fig. 8-1.

Shed or lean-to roofs (Fig. 8-1A) are the simplest roof form and have a single pitch or slope. They are used on small temporary buildings, porches, and places where appearance may not be a primary factor.

Gable roofs (Fig. 8-1B) are the most common roof type. Next to the shed roof, they are the simplest in design and construction. They have two slopes meeting at the *ridge* or center.

Hip roofs (Fig. 8-1C) consist of four

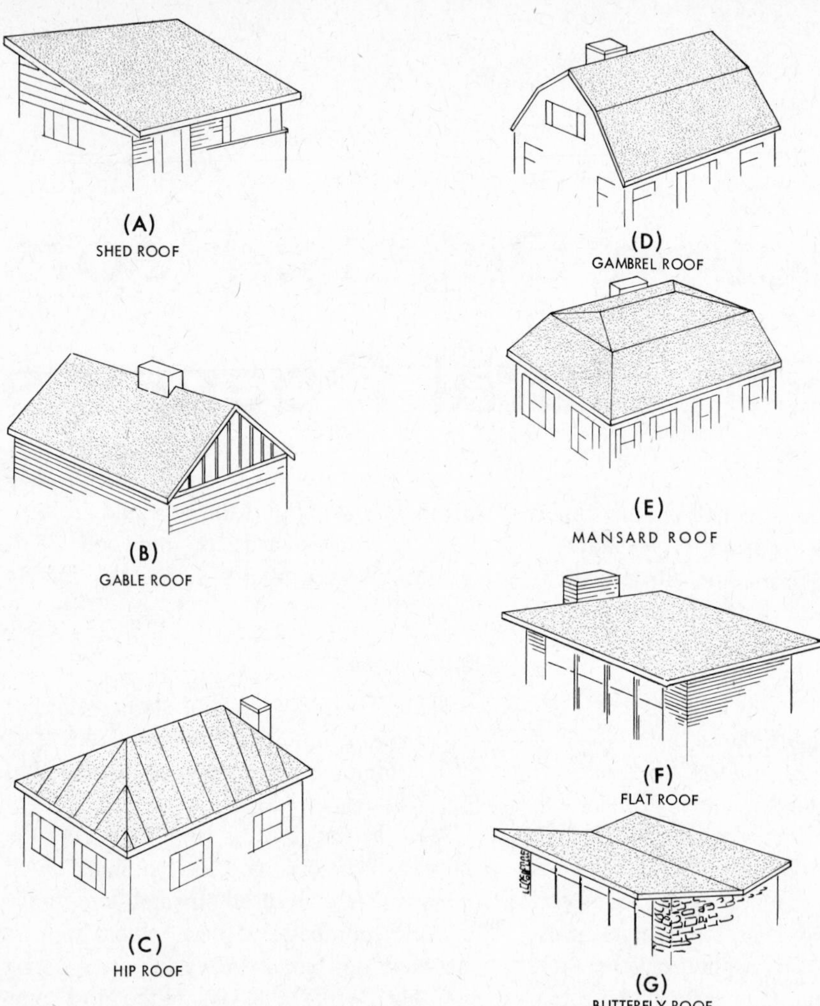

Fig. 8-1. These seven basic roof types are used in residential construction.

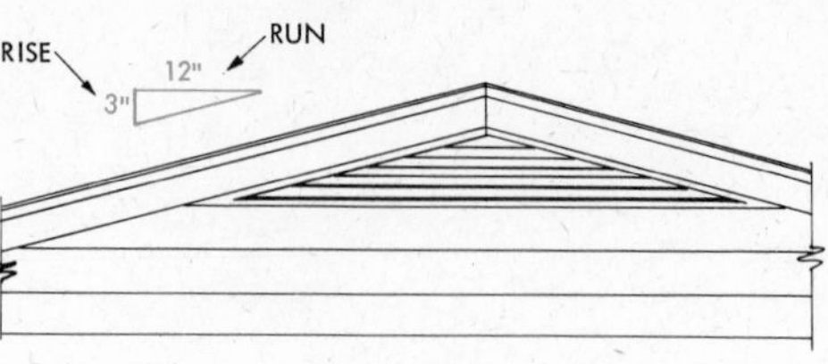

Fig. 8-2. The pitch triangle denotes the angle of the roof in terms of rise and run.

slopes, all sloping in the same angle toward the center of the building.

Gambrel roofs (Fig. 8-1D) are formed by two slopes of unequal pitch on each side. This type of roof allows more space directly below the roof surface.

Mansard roofs (Fig. 8-1E) are a modification of the gambrel roof. The upper slope has considerably less slant than the lower. It slopes on *all four sides*. Both the gambrel and the mansard roof are beginning to regain popularity.

Flat roofs (Fig. 8-1F) are generally pitched just enough so that they will provide for adequate water run-off.

Butterfly roofs (Fig. 8-1G) have two roofs sloping inward—generally each has a slight pitch. The butterfly roof is the opposite of the gable roof.

Roof Pitch

The angle of the roof is referred to as *pitch* or *slope* and may be expressed as x″ of *rise* in 12″ of *run*. This is denoted by a pitch triangle adjacent to the roof line (Fig. 8-2).

Pitch may also be referred to in fractional form, such as ⅓, ¼, ⅕, etc. To determine pitch by the fractional method, divide the *rise* of the roof by the *span*. This fraction (rise divided by span) is then reduced to its lowest terms.

Fig. 8-3 illustrates the various parts of the roof. *Rise* is the vertical distance measured from the top of the plate to the intersection of the "center" lines of the rafters.

"Center" lines (sometimes called base lines or measuring lines) originate from the juncture of the seat and cheek cut (see Fig. 8-3, detail) and run parallel to the rafter sides. This line (Fig. 8-3, A or C) is called "line of the bird's mouth." The *bird's mouth* (seat and cheek cut) provides a bearing surface for the rafter on the wall plate. *Span* is the horizontal distance from outside of one stud wall to the outside of the opposite stud wall. *Run* is one-half of the span.

Using the dimensions given in Fig. 8-3 (rise 7′ and span 28′), the fractional expression would be 7/28, or a ¼ pitch. Using the triangle method (x″ rise in 12″ of run), this roof would have a 6″ rise in 12″ of run. This is found by converting the span (28′) to the run (one-half of the span, thus 14′). The rise to run is found by a simple proportion formula (X : 12 :: 7 : 14, thus X = 6).

Some of the more commonly used pitches are ¾, ⅝, ½, 5⁄12, ⅓, ¼, and ⅙. The design is not limited to these pitches—any pitch may be used which will enhance the appearance of the finished home. In contemporary design the pitch is usually kept low.

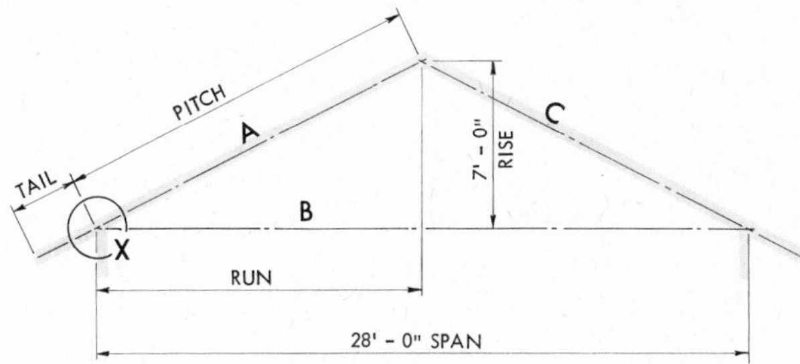

Fig. 8-3. This figure gives the basic rafter terminology.

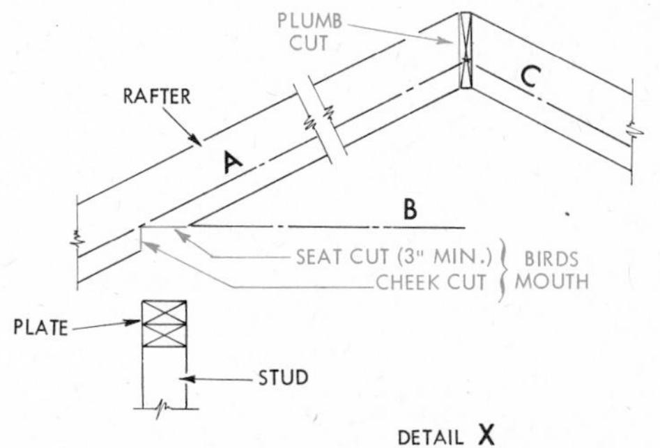

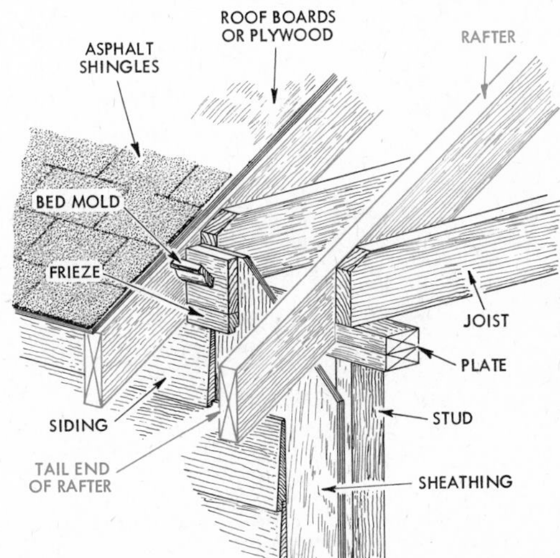

Fig. 8-4. In the open cornice the rafter ends are exposed. Note the frieze is cut to fit the space between rafters.

Cornice

The cornice or overhang is used on the top exterior of the wall as a protection and also as ornamentation. The amount of overhang designed for a cornice depends upon the style of the house and the designer.

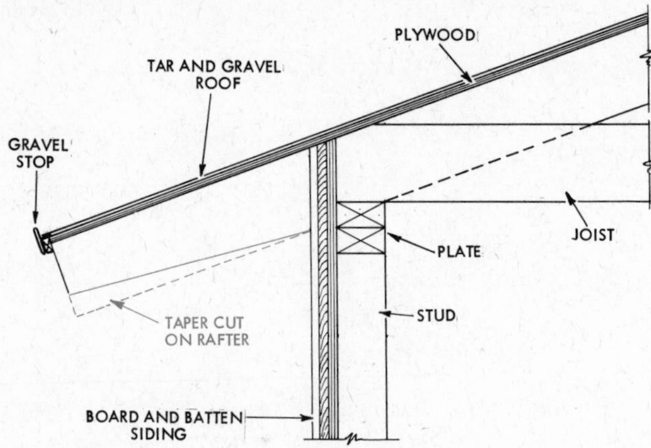

Fig. 8-5. Open cornices for low pitched roofs often have a taper cut on the rafter ends.

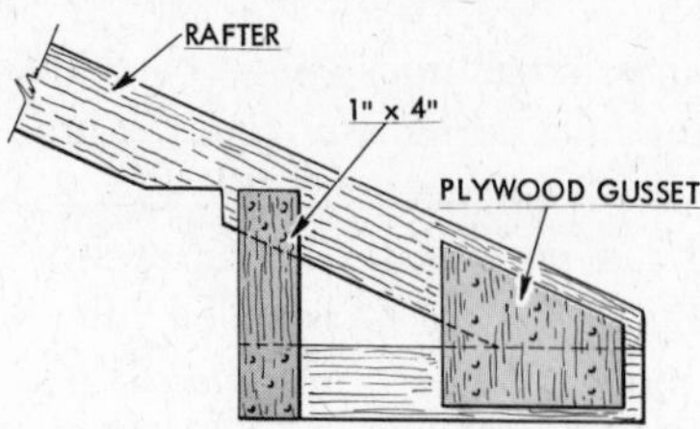

Fig. 8-7. A plywood gusset and 1″ x 4″ piece can be used in constructing the box cornice.

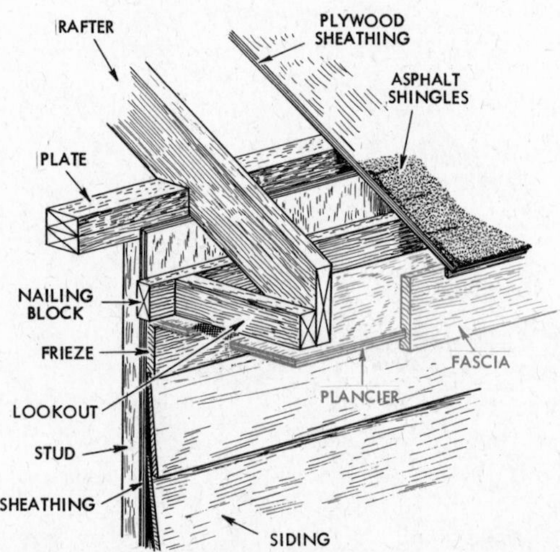

Fig. 8-6. In the box or closed cornice the pancier and fascia conceal the rafter end. (Note the soffit screen in the pancier to ventilate the cornice.)

Houses having steep pitched roofs, such as a Cape Cod, require very little overhang. Houses with low pitched roofs, such as ranch homes, usually require wide overhang. The type or style cannot always be the guide in determining the amount of overhang. Houses designed and built on the ranch pattern, for example, may use a colonial exterior. The cornices in this instance could be either wide or narrow depending on the illusion desired by the designer.

Cornices may be categorized into two general types: the open cornice and the box cornice.

Open Cornice

The open cornice has visible rafter ends. The space between the rafters is closed by an upward extension of the *frieze*. See Fig. 8-4. Fig. 8-5 is another example of the open cornice which is used frequently in contemporary houses that require low pitched roofs with wide overhang. The tail portion of the rafter may be tapered to prevent an extremely heavy or bulky appearance.

Box Cornice

The box cornice has the tail portion and the underside of the rafters entirely closed with a *fascia* and *plancier* (Fig. 8-6). The plancier may be nailed directly to the underside of the rafter, extending from the wall plate to the fascia. Frequently the plancier is level rather than being nailed directly to the underside of the rafter. In this type of box cornice a *lookout* is nailed to the tail of the rafter and carried level to the wall. Note (Fig. 8-6) that the lookout is nailed to a 2″ × 4″ *nailing block* at the wall. An alternate method of attaching lookouts (Fig. 8-7) is by the means of plywood gusset plates. In either case, the fascia is dropped ⅜″ to ¾″ below the plancier to act as a drip mold and to prevent water from entering the cornice interior.

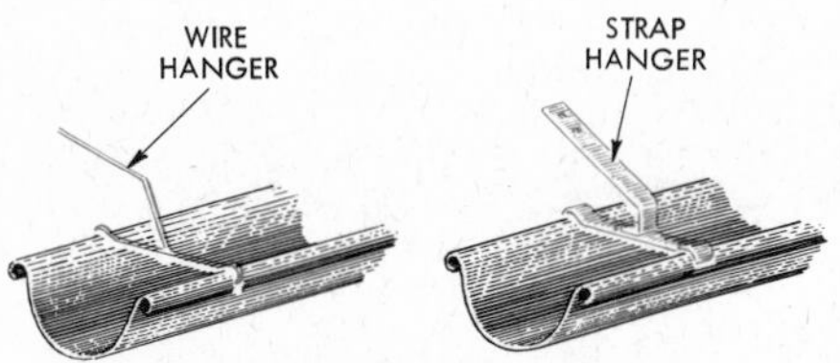

Fig. 8-8. The half round hanging gutter is the simplest in construction.

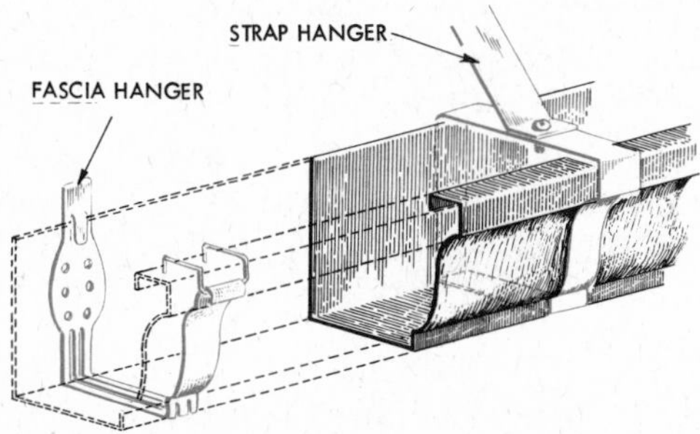

Fig. 8-9. The OG metal gutter is probably the most common.

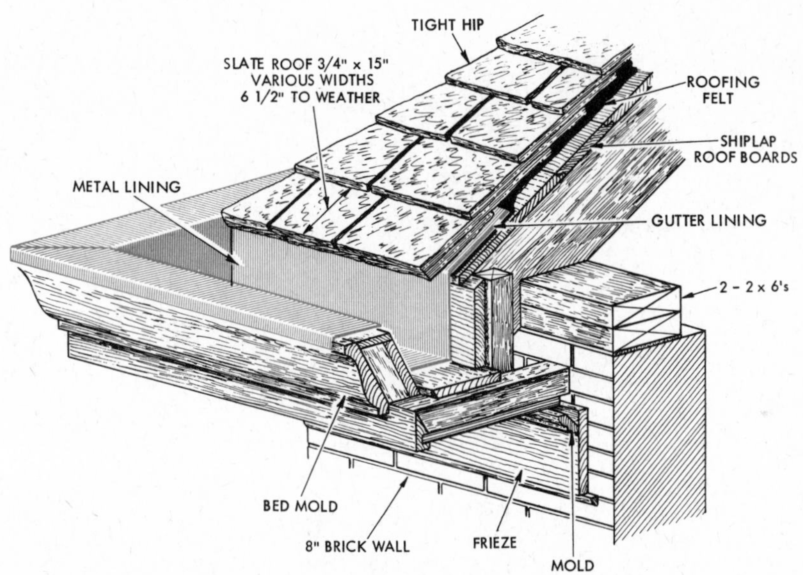

Fig. 8-10. The box gutter is used in traditional architecture. Special care must be taken to make the gutter lining waterproof.

Gutters

To prohibit water from running directly off of the eaves, it is collected in gutters and directed to an outlet. Gutters are pitched 1″ to 1¼″ in every 20′ to provide an even flowage. If this pitch is increased, the obvious angle of the gutter will detract from building design. Gutters may be either metal (galvanized iron, aluminum, or copper) or wood. Various types of gutters are available in standard sizes.

Half Round Hanging Gutters. The hanging gutter is semicircular in shape and is suspended from the roof by wire or strap hangers (Fig. 8-8). This is the simplest form of gutter; however, it is not used extensively on new construction.

OG metal gutters are probably the most common. This gutter has a molded face (Fig. 8-9) and is called the OG. The illustration shows two methods of hanging the gutter: either by a strap or by a fascia hanger. Regardless of the type of gutter or method of hanging, the gutter should be slightly below the roof line. On steep pitched roofs the outermost portion of the gutter should be approximately ¼″ below the roof line, on medium pitched roofs (7″ in 12″) approximately ½″, and on low pitched roofs (5″ in 12″) approximately ¾″. This allows the snow to slide clear of the gutter.

Box gutters, illustrated in Fig. 8-10, are built up using a series of lookouts which are nailed together to form a framework for the built-up gutter. The metal lining extends from beneath the roof covering to the bed molding. The box gutter is generally used on traditional houses. It is relatively expensive and more difficult to waterproof than other types of gutters.

Wood gutters of straight grain fir, redwood, or cypress have long been noted for their durability. The face of the wood gutter is similar to that of the metal molded OG gutter. Fig. 8-11 shows a wooden gutter with various dimensions.

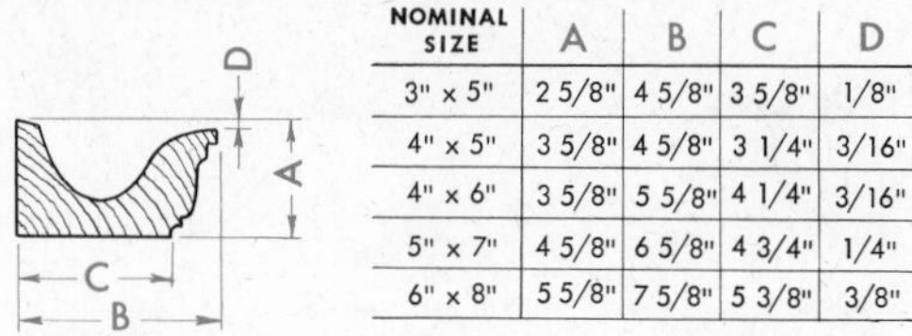

NOMINAL SIZE	A	B	C	D
3" x 5"	2 5/8"	4 5/8"	3 5/8"	1/8"
4" x 5"	3 5/8"	4 5/8"	3 1/4"	3/16"
4" x 6"	3 5/8"	5 5/8"	4 1/4"	3/16"
5" x 7"	4 5/8"	6 5/8"	4 3/4"	1/4"
6" x 8"	5 5/8"	7 5/8"	5 3/8"	3/8"

Fig. 8-11. Wood gutters (redwood or fir) come in various dimensions.

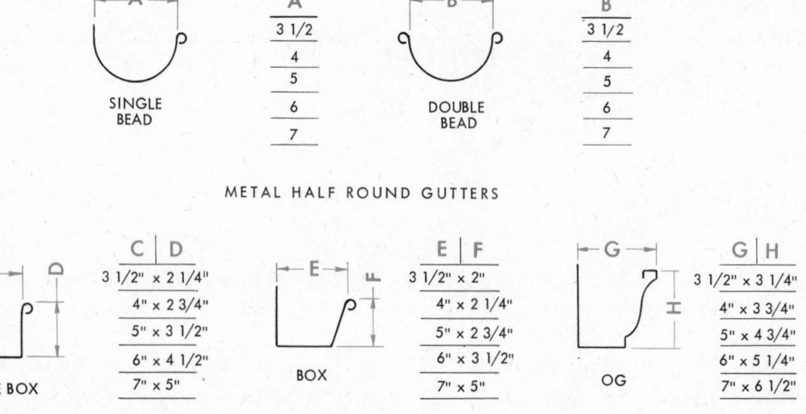

Fig. 8-12. Metal gutters come in various sizes and shapes.

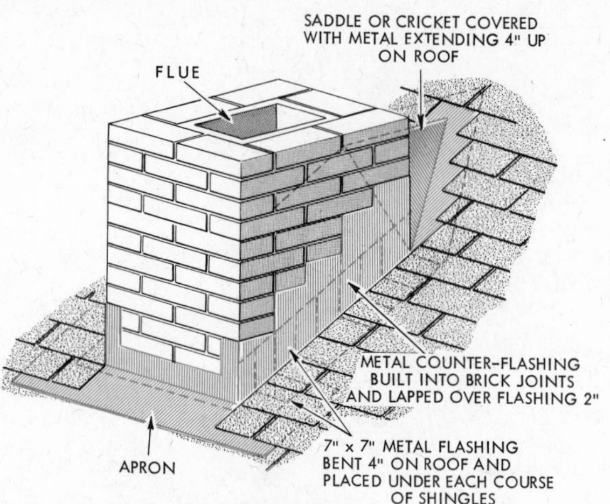

Fig. 8-13. Flashing around a chimney is turned into the mortar joints and carried under the shingles for 4″.

Various standard sizes and shapes of gutters are shown in Fig. 8-12.

Leaders

Water is drained from the gutters by *leaders* or *conductor pipes* which are usually placed at the ends of the gutter and/or intersecting cornices. Leaders, just as gutters, may be galvanized iron, aluminum, or copper. They may be either round or rectangular, plain or corrugated. Round leaders, either plain or corrugated, range in size from 2″ to 6″ in diameter. Plain or corrugated rectangular leaders are available in the following standard nominal sizes: 1¾″ × 2¼″, 2″ × 3″, 2″ × 4″, and 3″ × 4″. The leader is fastened to the wall and may turn out at the bottom and discharge the water on a concrete splash block, or the leader may be connected by field tile to a dry well or storm sewer. (Note: many cities prohibit draining the run-off into the storm sewer.) One square inch of conductor pipe should be required for every 100 square feet of roof area to be drained.

Flashing

Where surfaces meet (as between chimney and roof or dormer and roof) the juncture must be made watertight. The most practical method is to use wide strips of rustproof metal, such as galvanized iron, copper, and sometimes lead. These metal strips are called *flashing*. Unequal expansion of adjoining material, particularly when they are continually exposed to the elements, will cause shrinkage and leakage. For this reason the flashing must be worked in beneath the adjacent exterior covering materials. Flashing is required over the foundation and over and under all openings for windows and doors.

The flashing around a chimney is turned into the mortar joints, as in Fig. 8-13, and carried under the shingles for 4″. Frequently the garage roof butts against the main wall (Fig. 8-14). In this case, flashing must be carried over the siding and under the shingles to insure a watertight joint.

Step-by-Step Drawing Procedure: Cornices

Fig. 8-15 points out the step-by-step procedures used in developing the cornice detail. These basic principles may also be applied to an open cornice just as they have been illustrated for a closed or box cornice.

Wood Trussed Roofs

A roof can be more than a protection against the sun and rain. It can affect virtually every function of the rooms below. Few innovations have done more to change the orthodox pattern of home building than

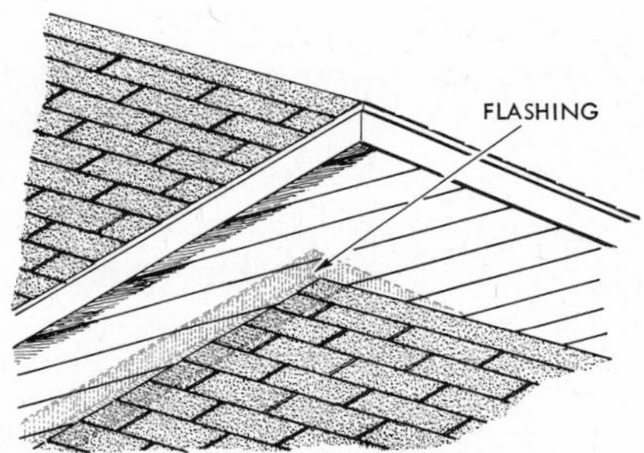

Fig. 8-14. Flashing must be installed at roof and wall junctures.

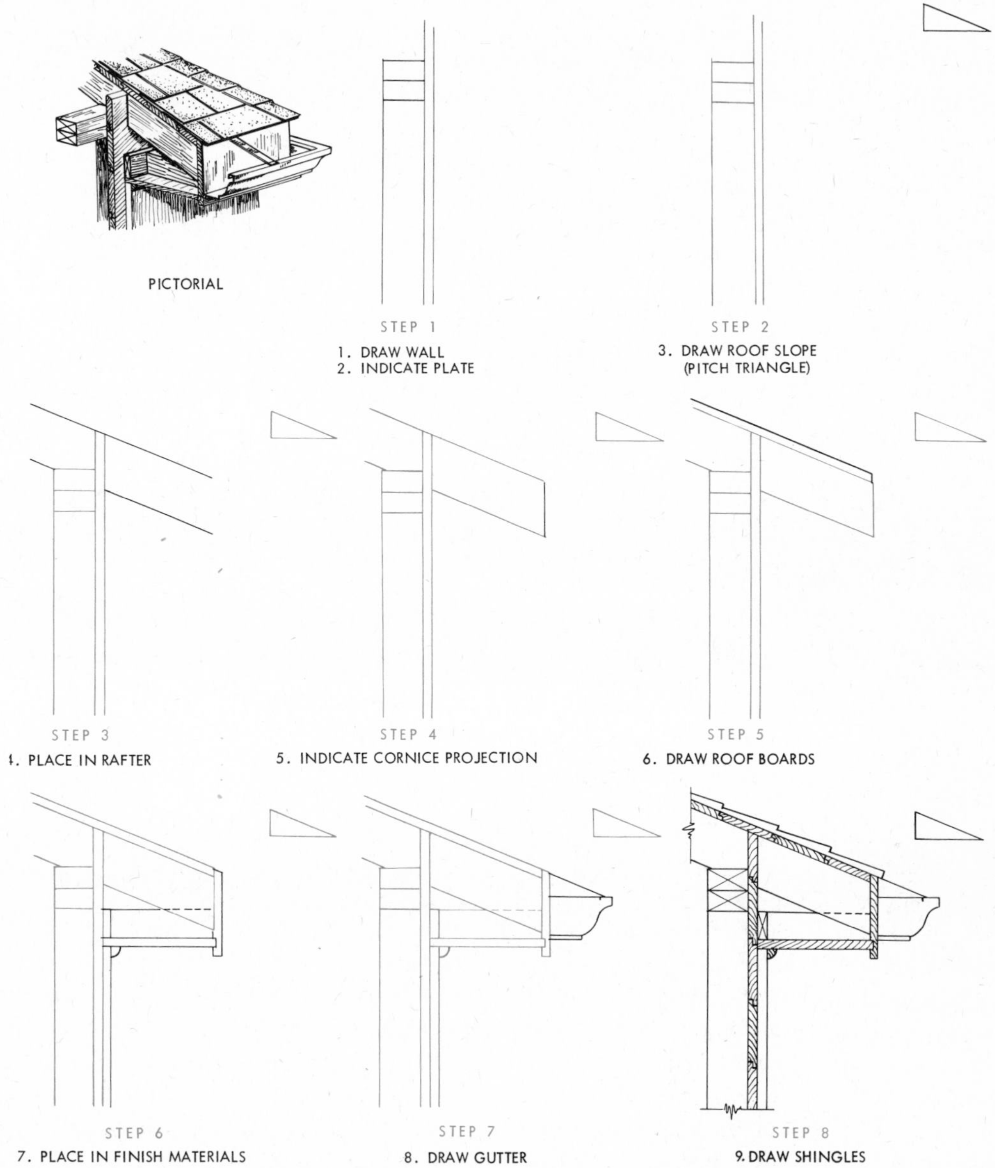

PICTORIAL

STEP 1
1. DRAW WALL
2. INDICATE PLATE

STEP 2
3. DRAW ROOF SLOPE (PITCH TRIANGLE)

STEP 3
4. PLACE IN RAFTER

STEP 4
5. INDICATE CORNICE PROJECTION

STEP 5
6. DRAW ROOF BOARDS

STEP 6
7. PLACE IN FINISH MATERIALS

STEP 7
8. DRAW GUTTER

STEP 8
9. DRAW SHINGLES

Fig. 8-15. Follow this step-by-step procedure in drafting the cornice detail.

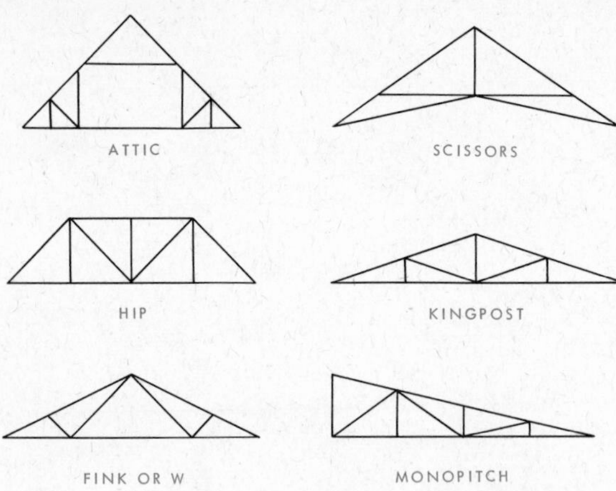

Fig. 8-16. The trussed roof rafter has several basic shapes each designed for a particular purpose.

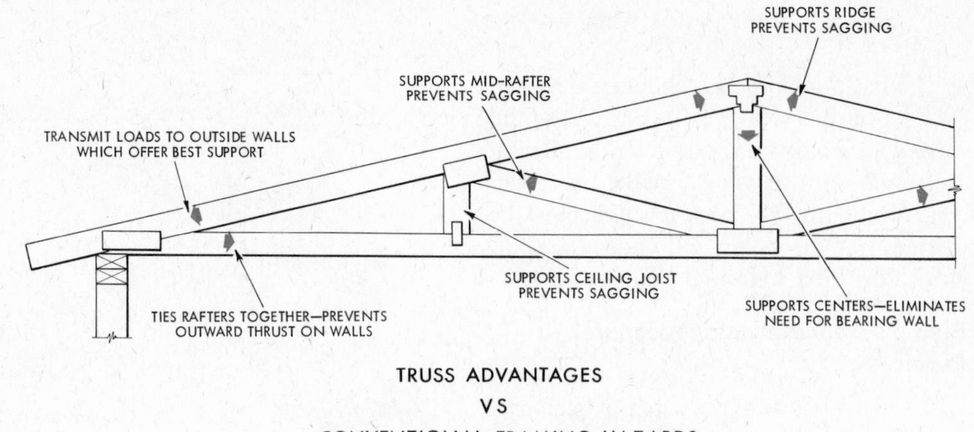

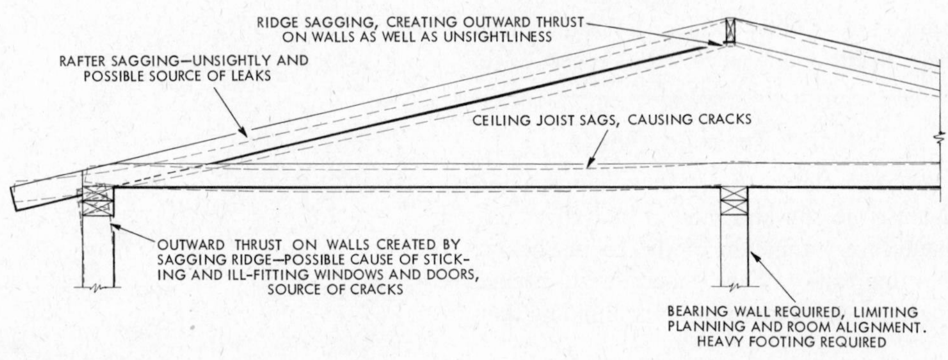

Fig. 8-17. This comparison of trussed and conventional roof framing illustrates the advantage of the truss.

the wood trussed rafter. The trussed rafter (Fig. 8-16) is usually triangular in form and is supported internally by framing. The slanted sides of the triangle form the slopes of the roof. The chord or base of the triangle "clear spans" the entire width of the house and therefore requires no support. On the other hand, conventional roof framing requires a bearing wall approximately in the center of the structure to act as a support for the imposed load of the roof. The truss requires vertical support only at the outer walls. Load-bearing partitions are eliminated, thus permitting larger rooms and greater variations in planning. Fig. 8-17 graphically compares the trussed roof with the conventional framing method.

Trusses are usually spaced 24″ O.C. (16″ O.C. is common for conventional roof framing members). Interior finishing materials, such as lath and plaster, sheet rock, or fiberboard, are fastened directly to the underside of the bottom chord.

Trussed roofs, when properly designed, are stronger than conventionally framed roofs. Depending on the type of truss, a material savings up to 30 per cent may be realized. Both erection costs and lumber costs (smaller dimensioned lumber is used) are more economical.

Trusses may be constructed in the shop or at the building site. For residential homes, they are usually fabricated in the contractor's shop or purchased commercially and delivered to the site. The trusses may be erected, fastened, and then sheathed rapidly. This permits the house to be "under roof" or "closed in" in a fraction of the time required when using conventional framing methods. See Fig. 8-18.

Frequently it is assumed that the trussed roof is limited to those homes having a low pitched gable roof. This is not true. Trusses may be designed for any roof type.

Truss Connectors

Trussed rafters are usually assembled with either *split rings* or *truss plates (clip connectors).*

Split rings (Fig. 8-19) may be used to assemble clear spans ranging from 20′ to 250′. The split ring is placed in a specially cut groove in the overlapping members. Maximum strength is developed at the joint by distributing the stress over a greater area. The wedge shape of the split ring insures a tight fitting joint when the ring is fully seated in the conforming groove. The 2½″ diameter ring which is used for residential trusses utilizes 2″ lumber.

Truss plates or clip connections (Fig. 8-20) have a strength comparable to the split ring connector. Depending upon the size of the connector, each clip has an effective holding power of 20 to 60 nails. One of the advantages in using a plate or clip connector (as compared with the split rings) is the constant thickness of the truss. The web members of a truss assembled with split rings must be bolted to the sides of the chord giving a thickness of 6½″, whereas the plate or clip connector method of fabrication pro-

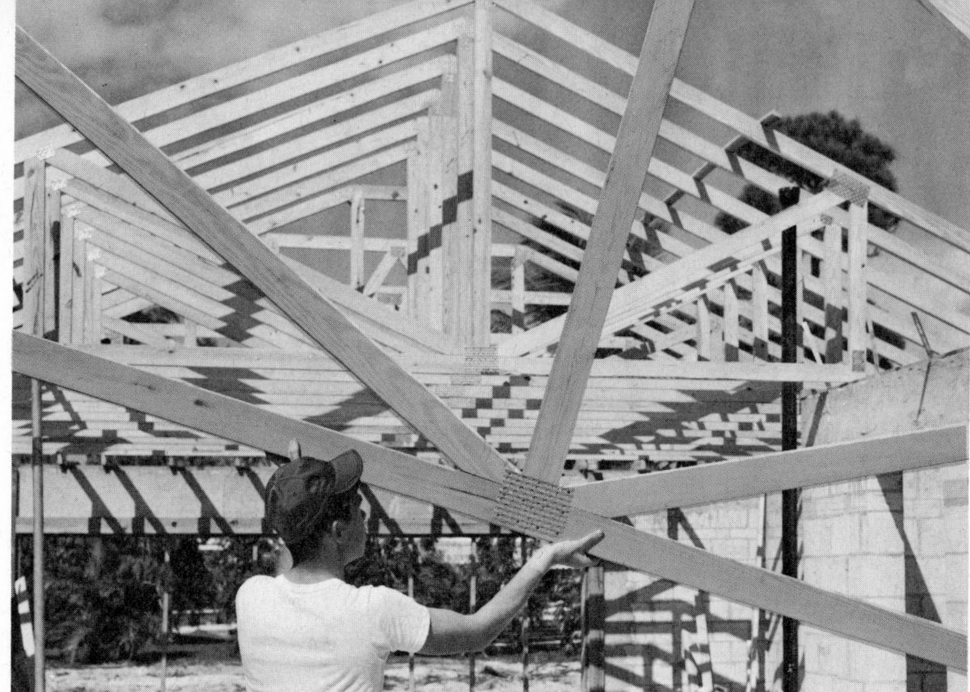

SANFORD TRUSS, INC., INDIANAPOLIS, INDIANA.

Fig. 8-18. In this photograph a kingpost trussed rafter roof is being erected. Note the hip trusses in the background.

TIMBER ENGINEERING CO., WASHINGTON, D.C.

Fig. 8-19. Split ring connectors give strength by distributing the stress over a greater area.

Fig. 8-20. Truss clips have an effective holding power of 20 to 60 nails.

PANEL CLIP CO.; FARMINGTON, MICHIGAN.

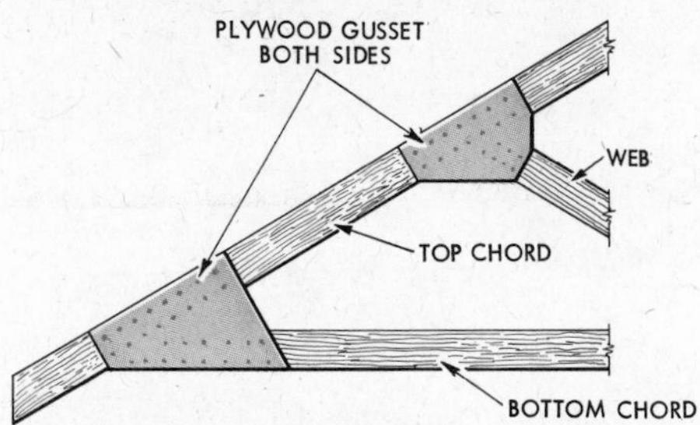

Fig. 8-21. Plywood gussets glued and nailed in place serve to make strong, lightweight trusses.

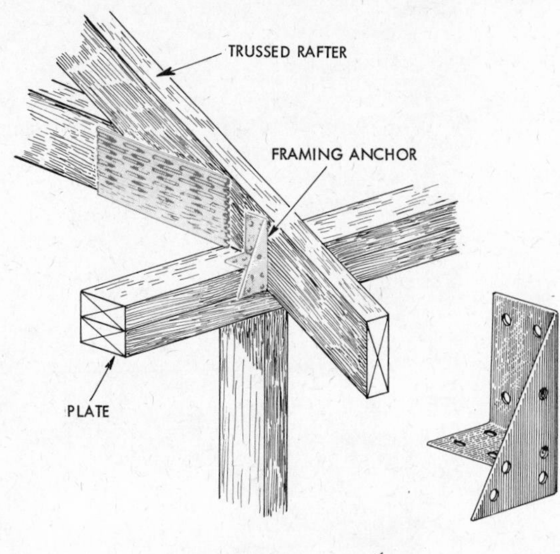

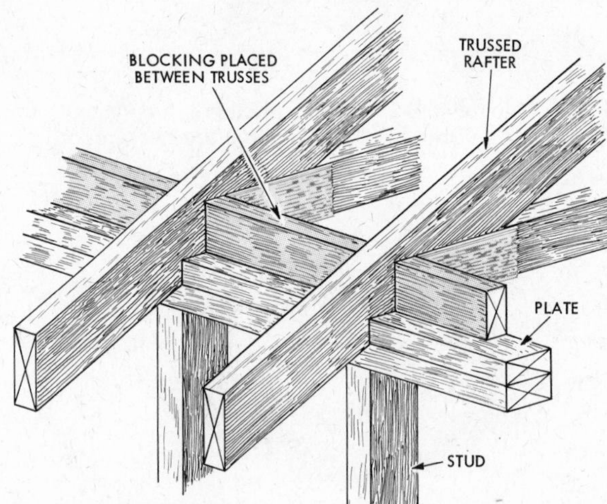

Fig. 8-22. Either a framing anchor or blocking may be used to secure roof trusses.

duces a truss 1⅝″ thick (actual size of nominal 2″ lumber) plus the minimal thickness of the plates. Truss plates are either galvanized (zinc coated) to prevent rusting or they are made from a non-rusting material.

Plywood Connector Plates. Truss designs may *also* be fastened with plywood gussets (Fig. 8-21) glued and nailed or stapled to the chords and webs. Each plate must have a specific number of nails or staples depending upon the pitch and clear span of the truss as well as the imposed load. One of the problems, however, with the plywood gusset is that pressure must be applied if they are glued; also a specific amount of curing time is required for the glue to set. The plywood gusset is slowly being replaced by the clip type connector (Fig. 8-20).

Truss Anchors

Trussed rafters may be fastened to the plate by either a framing anchor (Fig. 8-22, top) or spacing blocks (Fig. 8-22, bottom). The framing anchor will produce a joint comparable to the usual toenail method. The framing anchor type of connection, however, is usually stronger and more efficient. All anchors are either galvanized or made from rust-proof material. The spacing block allows the rafter to be spiked to the block; the block, in turn, is toenailed to the plate.

Fink Truss

The Fink truss design is probably the most common design used in residential

Fig. 8-23. The Fink truss is probably the most common design used in residential construction. Note that split rings are used. (The figures shown here will give a safe live and dead load of 35 lbs. per sq. ft. and a dead ceiling load of 10 lbs. per sq. ft. with trusses spaced 2'-0" OC.)

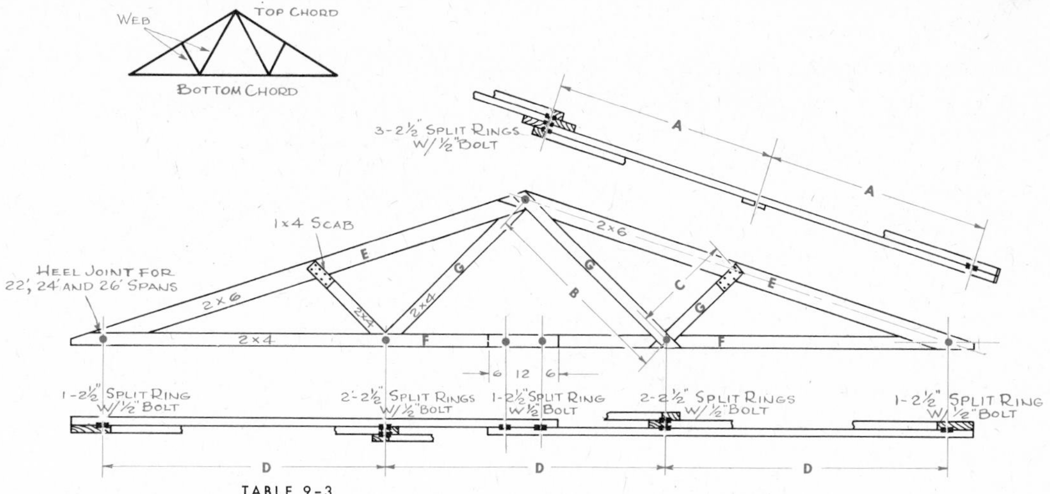

TABLE 9-3

FINK TRUSS SIZING WITH DRYWALL CEILING

SLOPE	LENGTH OF SPAN	DIMENSIONS A	B	C	D	LUMBER SIZE (TWO LENGTHS NEEDED) 2×8	2×6	2×4
	20	5'-3 1/4"	4'-8 3/16"	2'-3 13/16"	6'-8"		E (12'-0")	F (12'-0") G (8'-0")
	22	5'-9 9/16"	5'-1 7/8"	2'-6 3/4"	7'-4"		E (14'-0")	F (14'-0") G (10'-0")
	24	6'-3 7/8"	5'-7 1/2"	2'-9 9/16"	8'-0"		E (14'-0")	F (14'-0") G (10'-0")
	26	6'-10 3/16"	6'-1 3/16"	3'-0 7/16"	8'-8"		E (16'-0")	F (16'-0") G (10'-0")
	28	7'-4 9/16"	6'-6 13/16"	3'-3 1/4"	9'-4"	E (16'-0")	F * (16'-0")	F (16'-0") G (12'-0")
	30	7'-10 7/8"	7'-0 1/2"	3'-6 1/16"	10'-0"	E (18'-0")	F * (18'-0")	F (18'-0") G (12'-0")
	32	8'-5 3/16"	7'-6 3/16"	3'-8 7/8"	10'-8"	E (18'-0")	F * (18'-0")	F (18'-0") G (12'-0")
	20	5'-5"	5'-3 5/8"	2'-7 5/8"	6'-8"		E (12'-0")	F (12'-0") G (10'-0")
	22	5'-11 1/2"	5'-10 1/16"	2'-10 13/16"	7'-4"		E (14'-0")	F (14'-0") G (10'-0")
	24	6'-6"	6'-4 7/16"	3'-2"	8'-0"		E (14'-0")	F (14'-0") G (12'-0")
	26	7'-0 1/2"	6'-10 7/8"	3'-5 1/4"	8'-8"		E (16'-0")	F (16'-0") G (12'-0")
	28	7'-7"	7'-5 1/4"	3'-8 7/16"	9'-4"		E,F * (16'-0")	F (16'-0") G (12'-0")
	30	8'-1 1/2"	7'-11 11/16"	3'-11 5/8"	10'-0"		E,F * (18'-0")	F (18'-0") G (14'-0")
	32	8'-8"	8'-6 1/16"	4'-2 13/16"	10'-8"		E (20'-0") F * (18'-0")	F (18'-0") G (14'-0")
	20	5'-7 1/16"	5'-11 11/16"	2'-11 5/8"	6'-8"		E (12'-0")	F (12'-0") G (10'-0")
	22	6'-1 13/16"	6'-6 7/8"	3'-3 1/4"	7'-4"		E (14'-0")	F (14'-0") G (12'-0")
	24	6'-8 1/2"	7'-2 1/8"	3'-6 7/8"	8'-0"		E (16'-0")	F (14'-0") G (12'-0")
	26	7'-3 3/16"	7'-9 5/16"	3'-10 7/16"	8'-8"		E (16'-0")	F (16'-0") G (12'-0")
	28	7'-9 15/16"	8'-4 9/16"	4'-2 1/16"	9'-4"		E (18'-0") F * (16'-0")	F (16'-0") G (14'-0")
	30	8'-4 5/8"	8'-11 3/4"	4'-5 11/16"	10'-0"		E,F * (18'-0")	F (18'-0") G (16'-0")
	32	8'-11 5/16"	9'-6 13/16"	4'-9 1/4"	10'-8"		E (20'-0") F * (18'-0")	F (18'-0") G (16'-0")
	20	5'-9 7/16"	6'-8 3/16"	3'-3 7/8"	6'-8"		E (14'-0")	F,G (12'-0")
	22	6'-4 7/16"	7'-4 1/4"	3'-7 15/16"	7'-4"		E (14'-0")	F (14'-0") G (12'-0")
	24	6'-11 5/8"	8'-0 5/16"	3'-11 15/16"	8'-0"		E (16'-0")	F,G (14'-0")
	26	7'-6 5/16"	8'-8 3/8"	4'-4"	8'-8"		E (16'-0")	F (16'-0") G (14'-0")
	28	8'-1 1/4"	9'-4 7/16"	4'-8"	9'-4"		E (18'-0") F * (16'-0")	F,G (16'-0")
	30	8'-8 3/16"	10'-0 1/2"	5'-0 1/16"	10'-0"		E (20'-0") F * (18'-0")	F (18'-0") G (16'-0")
	32	9'-3 1/8"	10'-8 9/16"	5'-4 1/16"	10'-8"		E (20'-0") F * (18'-0")	F,G (18'-0")

* BOTTOM CHORD SIZES FOR PLASTER CEILING

LIVE LOAD, 35 LBS PER SQUARE FT; DEAD CEILING LOAD, 10 LBS PER SQUARE FT; SPACED 2'-0" OC

TIMBER ENGINEERING CO., WASHINGTON, D.C.

construction. Framing for a gable roof, assembled with split rings, is shown in Fig. 8-23. Web and chord dimensions are given for roofs having 4″, 5″, 6″, and 7″ rises in 12″ of run.[1] Note that dimensions are given for the maximum clear spans within each slope.

As an example, assume that a Fink truss fabricated with split rings is to be used on a house having a clear span of 30′-0″ and a ⅙ slope roof (4″ rise in 12″ run). Using Fig. 8-23, the dimensions for the chords and webs may be determined. The lumber sizes and lengths are also given. For a 30′-0″ span (4″ in 12″), dimension A is 7′-10⅞″, B is 7′-0½″, C is 3′-6$\frac{1}{16}$″. The lumber for the two top chords (E) will be 2″ × 8″ × 18′-0″. The bottom chord (F) will require two 2″ × 6″ × 18′-0″ lengths if the ceiling is to be plastered *or* two 2″ × 4″ × 18′-0″ lengths if the ceiling is to be dry wall. Two 2″ × 4″ × 12′-0″ lumber lengths will be needed to construct the webs (G). Note that the measurements for chords are given *along* and *between* the ℄ of the members and that the shorter of the webs is fastened to the top chord with a 1″ × 4″ scab.

Fink truss designs fabricated with Truss Clips (a patented clip connector) are shown in Fig. 8-24. The design of the Fink truss assembled with clip connectors is the same as that with split rings. If, for instance, a home is designed 42′-4″ in length and 28′-11″ deep and a Fink truss rafter having

1. Designs for other types of trusses for residential construction may be obtained from Timber Engineering Co., Washington, D.C.

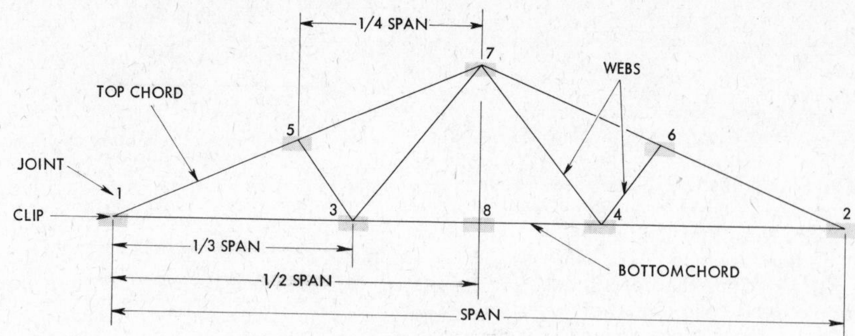

PITCH	CLIPS FOR JOINTS*					CHORD SIZE		WEB SIZE
	1 and 2	3 and 4	5 and 6	7	8	TOP	BOTTOM	
4, 5 and 6 in 12 spans to 28' - 0"	M spans to 24' - 8" N spans 24' - 9" to 28' - 8"	K	D	L or M	K spans to 26' - 8" L spans 26' - 9" to 28' - 8"	2 x 4	2 x 4	2 x 4
4 in 12 spans to 36' - 0"	N spans to 32' - 8" O spans 32' - 9" to 36' - 8"	L	J	M	L	2 x 6	2 x 4	2 x 4
3 in 12 spans to 28' - 0"	N spans to 24' - 8" O spans 24' - 9" to 28' - 8"	L	J	N	L spans to 24' - 8" M spans 24' - 9" to 28' - 8"	2 x 4	2 x 4	2 x 4
3 in 12 spans to 34' - 0"	P	M	J	D** and N	M spans to 31' - 5" N spans 31' - 9" to 34' - 8"	2 x 6	2 x 4	2 x 4
7 in 12 Spans to 27' - 0"	P	M	J	O	M spans to 22' - 8" N spans 22' - 9" to 27' - 8"	2 x 4	2 x 4	2 x 4

* ALL CLIPS PLACED ON BOTH SIDES TO TRUSS
** CLIP PLACED ON ONE SIDE OF TRUSS

CLIP SIZES

LETTER	SIZE	LETTER	SIZE
D	1 7/16 x 4 5/8	M	3 5/8 x 9 27/32
J	3 5/8 x 3 15/16	N	3 5/8 x 11 15/16
K	3 5/8 x 5 29/32	O	5 5/8 x 13 25/32
L	3 5/8 x 7 7/8	P	3 5/8 x 19 11/16

PANEL CLIP CO.; FARMINGTON, MICHIGAN.

Fig. 8-24. Truss clips may also be used with the Fink truss.

a ⅛ pitch is going to be used to support the roof, from the information given in Fig. 8-24 the top chords will be cut from 2″ × 6″ lumber and the bottom chord and webs will require 2″ × 4″ lumber. A "P" truss clip will be used at the intersection of top and bottom chord at joints 1 and 2; the "M" clip will be used to secure the juncture of the 2 webs and bottom chord; the "J" clip will be used at joints 5 and 6; the top chords will be joined with an "N" clip and a "D" clip placed on only one side of the truss; and, since the clear span of the house is *less than* 31′-5″, an "M" clip will be used to splice the two bottom chords together.

Trussed Roof Cornice

The cornice for the trussed roof, just as with a conventionally framed roof, may be either open or closed. The same principles of design for cornice construction apply to both kinds of roofs.

Roof Ventilating

An attic that is improperly vented is the most frequent cause of waterspots on the ceiling, frost at the junction of the wall and ceiling, and ice dams in the gutters. To eliminate damp areas and frost, fresh air in sufficient quantities must circulate through the attic. Areas in the attic that are not directly vented usually do not have circulating air. For example, if the roof is vented only with louvers on the gable ends, the areas at the extremities of the attic will have little or no circulating air. When the air has an opportunity to circulate, the warm moist air that leaks into the attic will not have sufficient time to condense and form water. Adequate circulation will eliminate the condensation problem during the winter months. It will also eliminate heat build-up during the summer months, thus making the house much cooler.

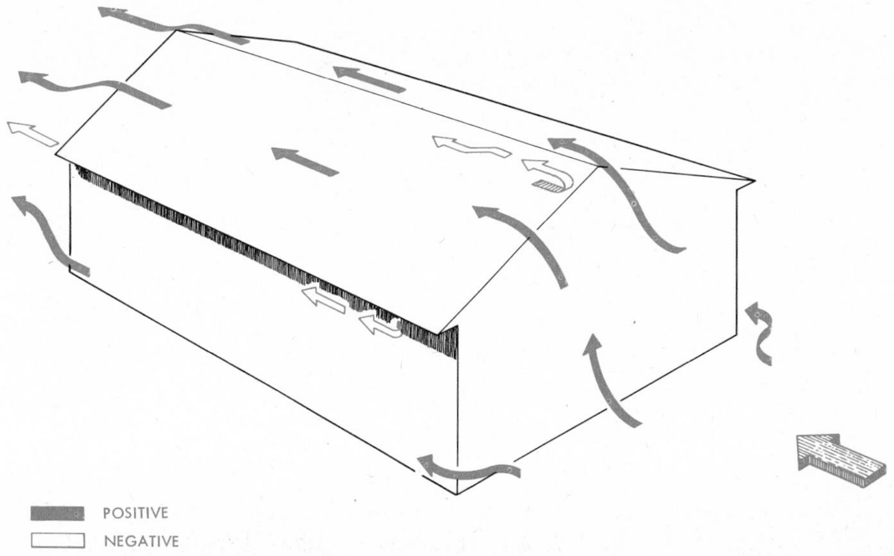

Fig. 8-25. External air flow creates negative pressures (vacuums) and positive pressures on the roof, sides, and ends of a building.

Attics

Until recently little regard was given to attic ventilation. Houses were extremely hot in summer and condensation formed during the winter. As more information was obtained about home insulation and new and more economical insulative materials were available, heat loss was no longer a problem. Vents were placed in the roof or gable ends to provide ventilation.

The direction and velocity of the wind will definitely affect the movement of air in the attic. As the air flows around a residence (Fig. 8-25), areas of negative pressure and positive pressure are created on various parts of the sides and roof. The areas of positive and negative pressure will vary with the direction and velocity of the wind. The variations of pressure will affect the air movement within the attic.

An adequately ventilated attic must have a reasonably uniform flow of air through *all parts of the attic* under all ranges of wind velocity and direction.

FIXED PITCH TRIANGULAR GABLE END LOUVER

ADJUSTABLE TRIANGULAR GABLE END LOUVER

CUPOLA VENTILATOR

PITCHED ROOF VENTILATORS

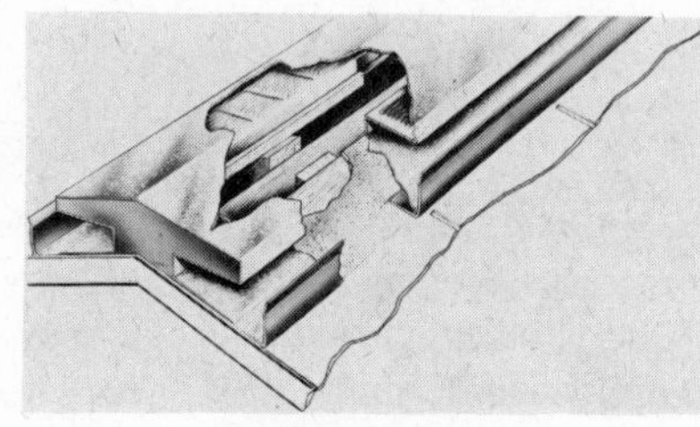

RIDGE VENTILATOR

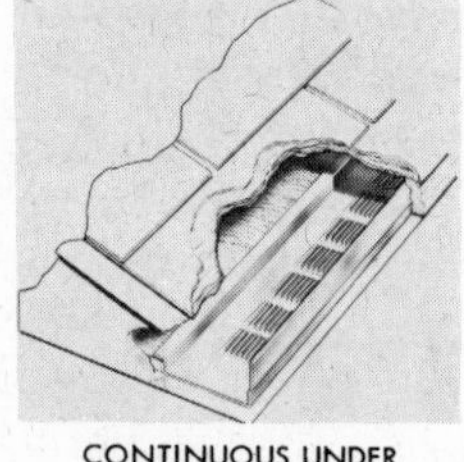

CONTINUOUS UNDER EAVE VENTILATOR

H.C. PRODUCTS CO.; PRINCEVILLE, ILLINOIS.

Fig. 8-26. Various devices are used to vent the attic.

Gutters

In some areas ice dams along gutters pose maintenance problems. Ice dams are caused by appreciable differences in attic and outside temperatures. By maintaining an attic temperature similar to the outside, snow melting from the roof will not refreeze on the overhang and gutters. By maintaining an adequate air flow *through all parts* of the attic, this problem can be eliminated.

Venting Devices

Obviously the amount of air permitted to enter and leave the attic is dependent upon the number, size, and type of venting devices. Fig. 8-26 shows six different types of venting devices. Frequently two of these are used in combination, such as the ridge ventilator and the continuous under-the-eave (soffit) ventilator. The air flow through any vent is dependent on the *placement* and the *total free ventilating area* relative to the positive and negative pressure areas. Winds frequently shift direction as much as 30° and occasionally as much as 90° in a short period of time. These changes in wind direction will effect the air flow within the attic. Recent research has shown that the total volume of air flowing through an attic is not sufficient basis to indicate the quality of ventilation. In certain circumstances, most of the air may flow through one portion of the attic leaving other portions with minor air movement.

Vent System Requirements

H. C. Product's research has brought out several ventilating factors:[2]

1. Roof louvers, either when used alone or in combination with soffit vents, contribute very little to effective air flow through the attic.
2. Gable end louvers are dependent upon favorable winds, either perpendicular or diagonal to the louver face. With such favorable winds the effective air flow is approximately 1/6 of the total air flow through the louver. This fractional air flow is not appreciably increased when the gable end louver is combined with continuous soffit vents. Gable end louvers provide very limited attic ventilation when the winds are perpendicular to the ridge (parallel to the louver face). Under *these* conditions, the addition of a continuous soffit vent will increase the effective air flow by 50 per cent.
3. Continuous ridge vent when used alone has the important characteristic that effective air flow remains approximately the same at zero wind velocity as at 10 m.p.h. This type of vent provides air flow due to temperature differences.

TABLE 8-1

VENT SYSTEM REQUIREMENTS FOR ADEQUATE Air Flow in the Attic (5 mph winds)

VENTING DEVICE(S)	Square Inches of Net Free Area Needed per Square Foot of Ceiling Area
ROOF LOUVERS ONLY	11.0
GABLE END LOUVERS ONLY	8.2
CONTINUOUS RIDGE VENT ONLY	7.3
ROOF LOUVERS AND CONTINUOUS SOFFIT VENT	6.9
CONTINUOUS SOFFIT VENT ONLY	6.4
GABLE END LOUVERS AND CONTINUOUS SOFFIT VENTS	5.5
CONTINUOUS RIDGE AND SOFFIT VENTS	1.2

From: H. C. Hinrichs, Comparative Study of the Effectiveness of Fixed Ventilating Louvers (Princeville, Illinois: H. C. Products Co., 1961).

4. Continuous soffit vents produce substantial air flow proportional to wind velocity regardless of wind direction. The major portion of the air flow remains near the attic floor with the result that effective air flow is approximately 1/5 of the total air movement.
5. Combination of continuous ridge and soffit vents provide a steady flow of air through the attic regardless of wind direction and velocity. Utilizing both a soffit and ridge vent will provide an *effective* air flow 3 to 5 times as great as any other combination of fixed venting equipment, i.e., roof and soffit vent, gable end louvers and roof vent, ridge and roof vent, etc.
6. Prevailing wind direction has a limited value as a basis for the design of an attic ventilating system.
7. Control of moisture condensation requires a minimum effective *air flow of 0.8 cubic feet per minute per square foot of ceiling area* during winter.

Various figures may be located which enable the designer to *approximately* calculate proper attic ventilation. Most existing tables have proven to be *too low to adequately control* condensation during the winter and reduce attic temperatures in summer. The figures shown in Table 8-1 give the correct net free areas in square inches for a non-mechanical venting systems per square foot of ceiling area. This will give a system which will provide an air flow of 0.8 cubic feet per square foot of ceiling area at 5 m.p.h. winds. (Free net areas for venting systems are given in manufacturers specifications.)

For example, given a total ceiling area of 1200 sq. ft., a venting system using only a continuous ridge vent would need a net free area of 8760 sq. in. (7.3 × 1200). If a con-

2. H. S. Hinrichs. *Comparative Study of the Effectiveness of Fixed Ventilating Louvers* (Princeville, Illinois: H. C. Products Co., 1961).

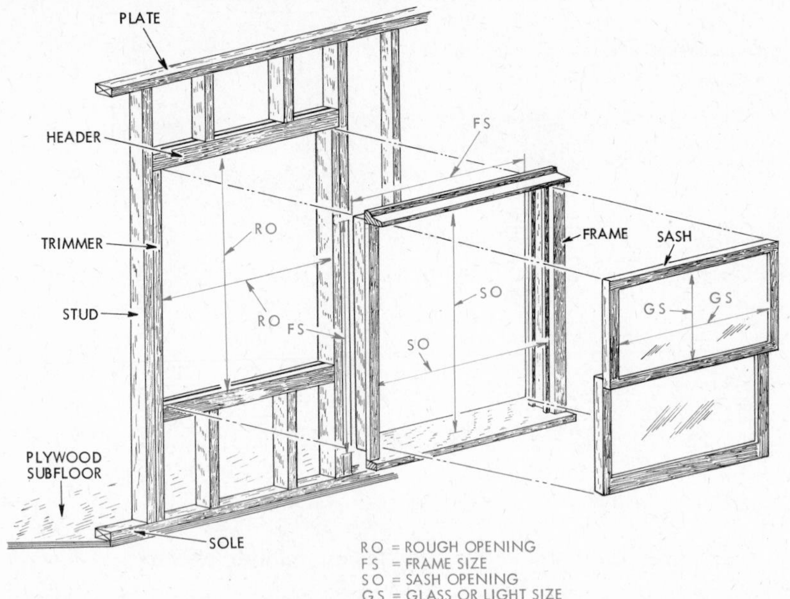

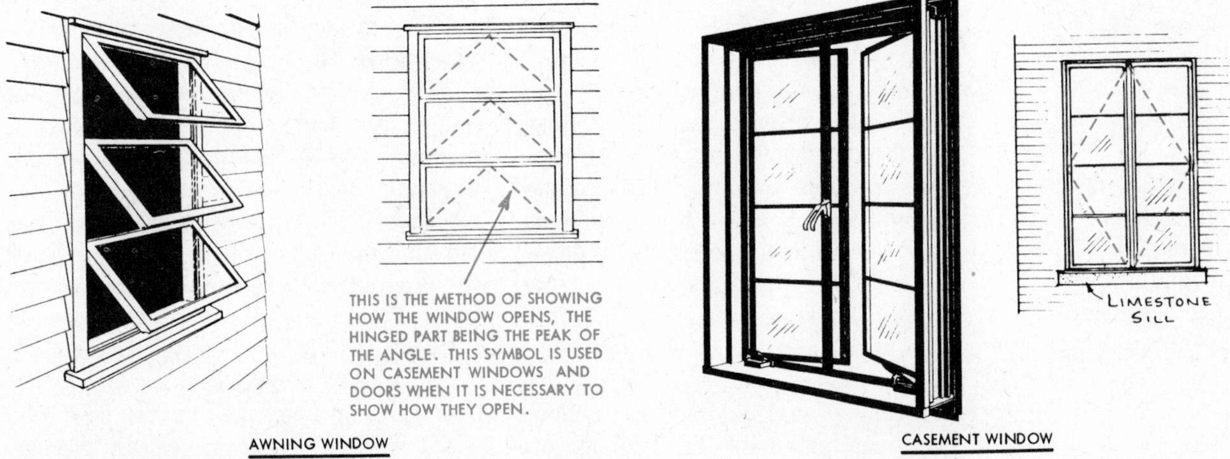

Fig. 8-27. These illustrations give window framing details and show the manner of depicting the hinge swing.

tinuous ridge *and* soffit vents were used, only 1440 sq. in. (1.2 × 1200) would be needed in the system.

Windows

The first window was also a door. The cave dweller had one all-purpose door-window for access, light, and air. As man's abode increased in complexity, separate openings for light and ventilation were inserted into the exterior walls. The Egyptians, as early as 5000 B. C., used simple windows with sculptured frames. At that period in history, the window was elevated from its location near the floor and placed higher in the wall for light and ventilation; the sill was placed below the opening. Later, transparent material was inserted in the openings to afford protection from the weather. Better control of ventilation was instituted by the hinged casement window. Other forms of protection were developed: shutters (for winter warmth, summer coolness, and protection against intruders), curtains, blinds, insect screens, awnings, and jalousie windows. In France, during the 18th Century, an improved type of window, having a vertically sliding sash, was developed. This was nick-named *Fenetre Guillotine*. We know it today as the common double-hung window.

Fig. 8-27 (top) graphically depicts the relationship between the rough opening, frame, sash, and window panes. The vertical sides of the sash are called *stiles*. The horizontal members of the sash (top and bottom) are called *rails*. The two vertical sides of the frame and the top piece are called the *jamb*. The exposed vertical pieces on the outside are called the *trim* and the piece at the top is called the *drip cap*. The bottom of the frame is called the *sill*. Glass panes are called *lights*. Dimensions of the glass panes or lights are given in inches. The width is given first, the height second: 26″ × 14″ *or* 26⁄14. Fig. 8-27 (bottom) illustrates the correct manner of showing the direction of swing.

Window Styles

The home designer is no longer limited to a few styles of windows. There is now a wide selection from which to choose. Fig. 8-28 illustrates windows which are currently used in small home construction.

Double-hung windows (Fig. 8-28A) are one of the most popular types of windows since they provide excellent ventilation. This is facilitated by raising the lower sash and lowering the upper sash to permit continual air circulation; however, only 50 per cent of the window may be opened. The double-hung window was originally held in its open position by spring-loaded pins in the sash. Later, the sashes were counterbalanced by cords, pulleys, and weights. Virtually all double-hung windows now are fitted with spring loaded balances or friction holding devices. Very little maintenance is required for the new models of double-hung windows. They are easy to clean since many manufacturers are now building windows so that each sash may be removed from the frame. The double-hung window placed in a frame wall is essentially the same as the double-hung placed in a masonry wall. The difference in wall construction will require different details in the opening.

"Sliders" or horizontal sliding windows (Fig. 8-28B) operate just as double-hung windows only they are placed on their side. Sliders were designed primarily for the modern ranch style home. There are a minimum number of working parts—usually only nylon rollers since no counter-balancing or holding device is needed. Sliding windows are made so that either both sashes slide or only one sash slides with the other fixed. Some manufacturers have designed the movable sash with a spring tension device to allow removal of the sash for painting and cleaning. This type of window is placed 3′-6″ to 4′-6″ above the floor and creates extra wall space that would otherwise be used by a double hung window.

Awning or projected windows (Fig. 8-28C) are top hinged and open to the outside. This type of window may be used either as a single unit or as a multiple unit with several windows placed in a vertical or horizontal line. They may be used in combination with fixed sash units, i.e., those that do not open. When awning windows are placed together, side by side, they are called *ribbon* windows. When fully opened, the awning window gives 100% ventilation. Most units are operated by a geared crank, thus making opening, closing, and locking easier. The top hinging feature of the awning window permits opening for ventilation during rain.

Hopper windows (Fig. 8-28D) are a variation of the awning window. The difference is that they are hinged at the bottom and open to the inside. Frequently, single hopper units are used as basement windows. These, similar to the awning window, may also be used in combination with fixed sash units. Either singly or in combination with fixed glass units they are often used high on the wall for bedroom windows. The hopper-type window provides draft-free ventilation since it deflects the incoming air upwards.

Casement windows (Fig. 8-28E) are hinged to the frame on either side and swing outward for ventilation. The projecting sashes act as scoops to bring in any available breezes. It is difficult, however, to make the casement window completely weather-tight. To overcome this situation a drip molding is placed along the bottom rail to prevent water from entering at the sill. Metal

ANDERSON CORP., BAYPORT, MINNESOTA.

A. Double-Hung Window.

ANDERSON CORP., BAYPORT, MINNESOTA.

B. Horizontal Sliding Window or "Slider"

ANDERSON CORP., BAYPORT, MINNESOTA.

C. Awning Window.

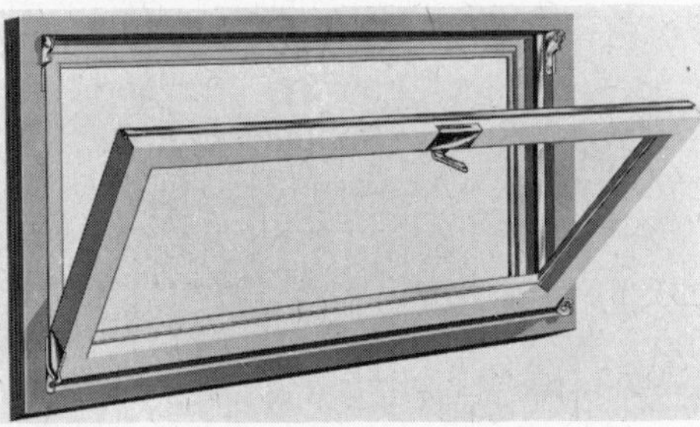

ANDERSON CORP., BAYPORT, MINNESOTA.

D. Hopper Window.

ANDERSON CORP., BAYPORT, MINNESOTA.

E. Casement Window.

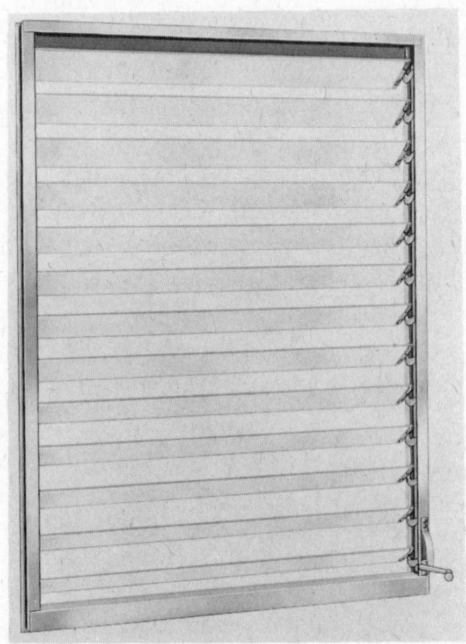

F. Jalousie Window.

Fig. 8-28. Various window styles are used in home construction.

casements may be set in a mastic (bituminous) cement to insure a complete seal around the frame. These windows may be used singly, in multiple units, or in combination with a fixed window unit. When open, the casement window provides 100 percent ventilation.

Jalousie windows (Fig. 8-28F) are a comparatively recent development in the window manufacturing field. They operate on the principle of a venetian blind. The jalousie is similar to a series of glass louvers, each louver being 2′ to 6′ wide. They also provide 100 percent ventilation when open. These louvers are activated by means of a geared crank. Generally, jalousies are located in living areas which are used in mild, seasonal weather.

Picture windows are large, stationary windows which provide no ventilation since the sash is fixed. These windows are usually installed with welded insulating glass (two layers of glass separated by a sealed air space) which requires a thicker sash. Fig. 8-29 shows insulating glass in a sash. This type of *glazing* (i.e., glass installed in the sash) allows for a large glass area with a small amount of heat loss. Picture windows are ventilated by double hung, casement, hopper, or awning windows at either side. Louvered openings or hopper windows are used at the bottom. Some designers, however, use picture windows which are carried to the floor.

Lights

The glass in the sashes of the double hung and casement windows may be divided into *lights*. These are small squares or horizontal sections of glass separated by *muntins* (slender bars of wood or metal). Small lights are used primarily in traditional Cape Cod, colonial, and early American style houses. Windows using small lights or divided sash are not limited to the special architectural types just mentioned—they may also be used in the contemporary ranch-type home.

Two or more windows may be placed together in a common frame to form a multiple window. The vertical member separating the windows is called a *mullion*. (Note: do not confuse *mullions* with *muntins*, defined above.)

Metal Windows

Windows have traditionally been constructed with a wood frame and sash. Many windows are now made of steel or aluminum structural components or a combination of metal and wood. As an insulator, however, wood remains the most efficient.

Window Samples

The great majority of windows are completely assembled at the factory or mill with hardware, glazing, weather stripping, and screens. The architectural designer or architectural draftsman does not design the windows as was the practice years ago. Today he selects the windows from a wide range of styles and sizes listed in catalogs.

ANDERSON CORP., BAYPORT, MINNESOTA.

Fig. 8-29. Insulating glass (two layers of sealed glass) is one of the most efficient methods of insulating a window.

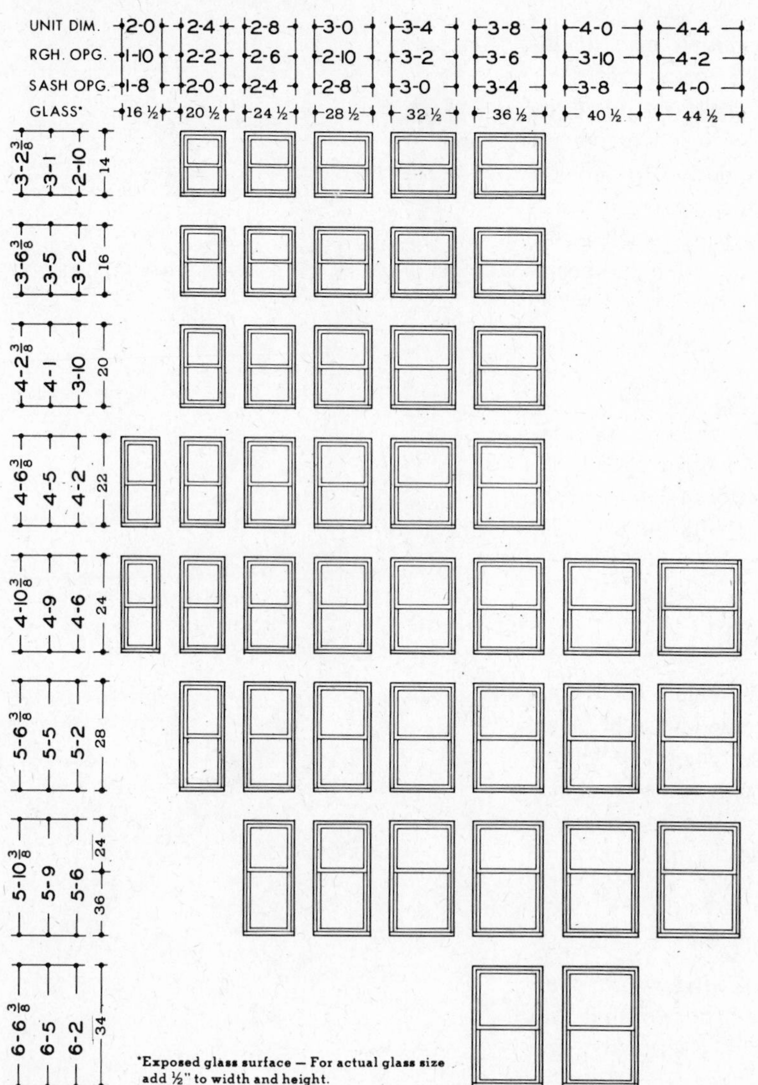

Fig. 8-30. Standard Double-Hung Window Sizes.

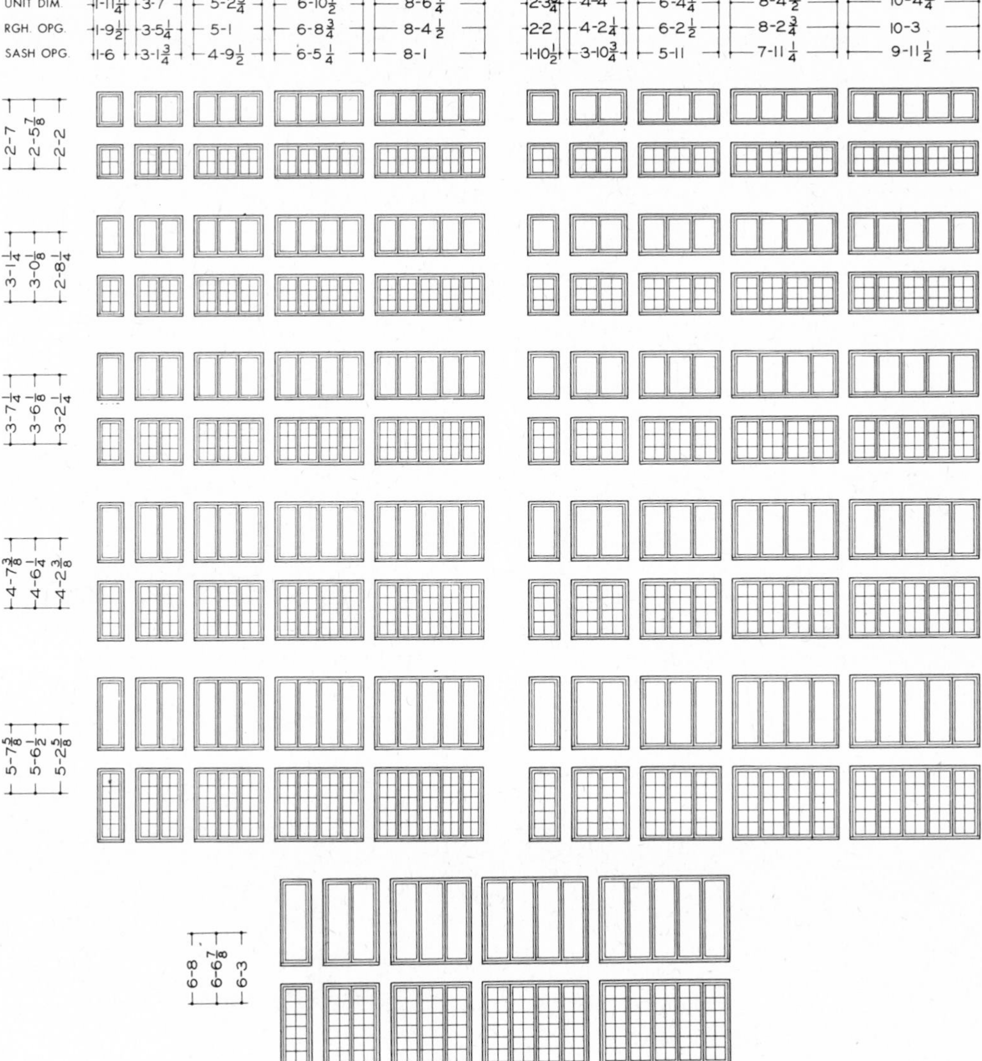

Fig. 8-31. Standard Single and Combination Casement Window Sizes.

Fig. 8-30, 8-31, 8-32, and 8-33 are samples from manufacturers' catalogs. The sash opening or light size must always be specified on the drawing.

Almost all window manufacturers' catalogs indicate the rough opening size, sash size, and light size. Some, however, list only the rough opening and frame size. The size of the rough opening is slightly larger than the actual window frame. This extra space provides sufficient room between the frame and opening for leveling and blocking in the window.

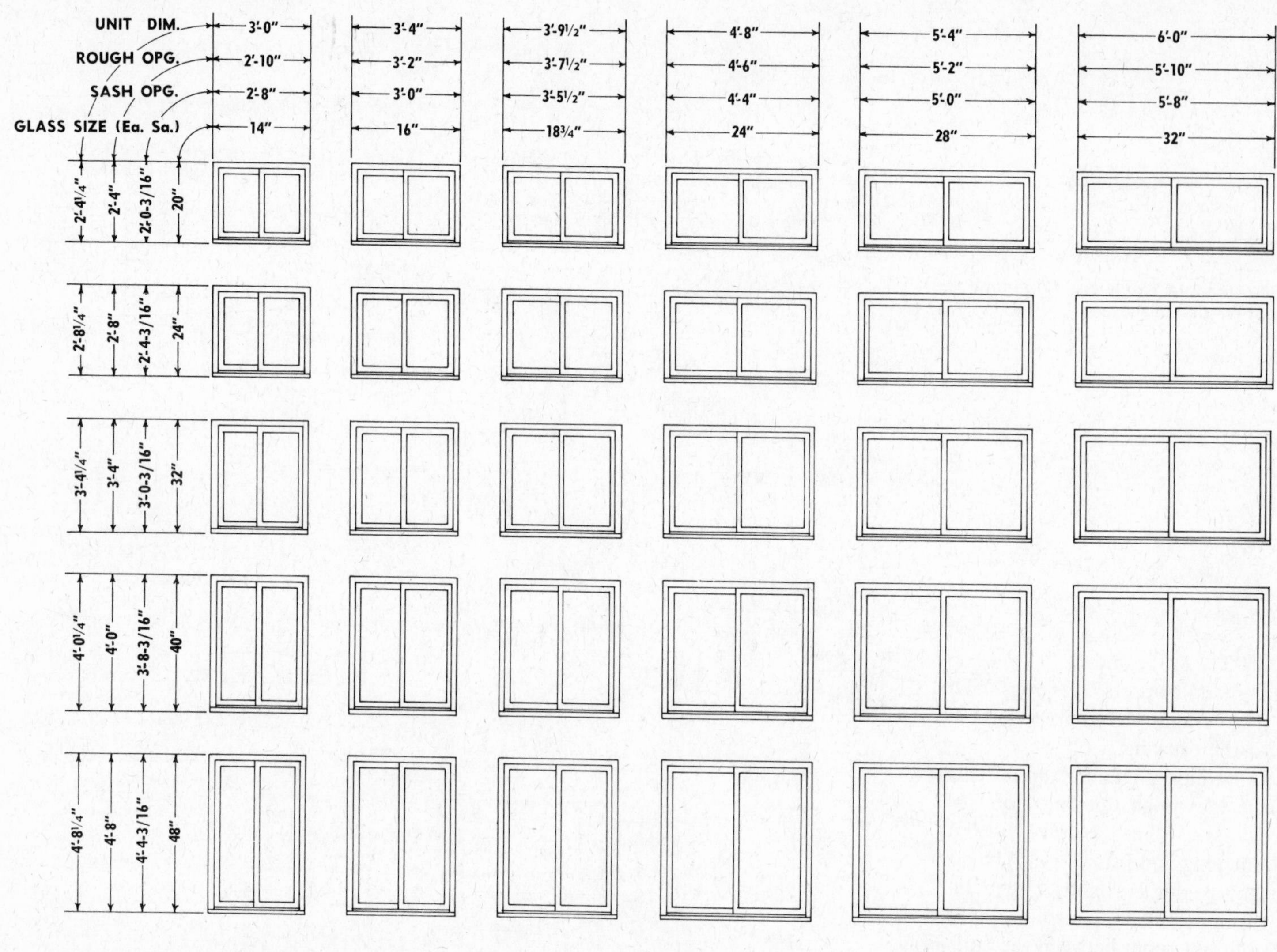

Fig. 8-32. Standard Horizontal Sliding Window Sizes.

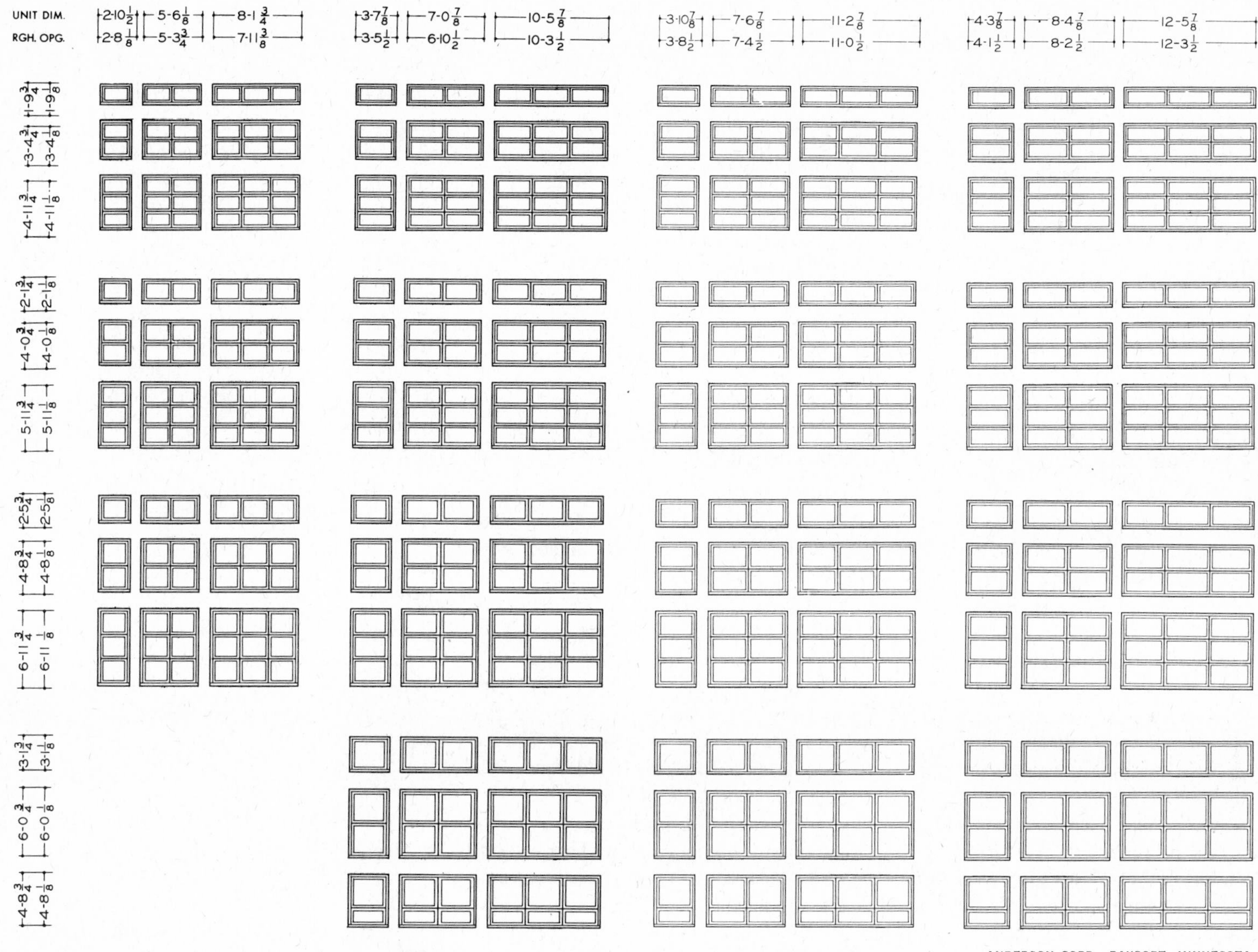

ANDERSON CORP., BAYPORT, MINNESOTA.

Fig. 8-33. Standard Awning and Hopper Window Sizes. (Note that any of the compound units may be designated as awning, hopper, or fixed.)

WINDOW SCHEDULE						
SYMBOL	QUANTITY	TYPE	ROUGH OPENING	SASH SIZE	MFG NO	REMARKS
1	3	AWNING, 1 LT	3'-1½" x 2'-0¼"	3'-0" x 1'-8"	1-36-20	OBSCURE GL IN ONE SASH
2	2	CASEMENT, 4LTS	5'-2" x 4'-6⅜"	1'-6" x 4'-2⅜"	6434	MIDDLE SASH FIXED
3	1	" "	6'-9¾" x 4'-6⅜"	1'-6 & 3'-3" x 4'-2⅜"	342	" " "
4	3	" 3LTS	3'-6¼" x 4'-6⅜"	1'-6" x 3'-6¼"	4323	—
5	2	FIXED SASH, 3LTS	3'-10½" x 6'-10½"	3'-8" x 6'-8"	—	CENTER SASH IN SPACE SHOWN
6	3	" " 1LT	4'-3⅜" x 7'-3⅜"	SEE REMARKS	—	4'-0" x 7'-0" x ¼" PLATE GLASS
7	4	" " "	5'-0⅜" x 7-3⅜"	" "	—	4'-9" x 7'-0" x ¼" PLATE GLASS
8	1	CASEMENT, 3LTS	1'-10½" x 3'-0¼"	1'-6" x 2'-8 3/16"	23103	OBSCURE GLASS
9	1	" 4LTS	3'-6¼" x 4'-6⅜	1'-6" x 4'-2⅜"	4424	—

Schedule A.

Window Schedules

For convenience and clarity the draftsman usually puts important information concerning windows in a table. This table, referred to as a *window schedule,* is usually located on the elevation drawings. Window schedules (as well as door and room finish schedules) may also be placed on the first or second floor drawings. Sometimes a single sheet is used for all the schedules. A symbol (number or letter) is given to each type of window. This code symbol is placed on the work drawing by each particular window. The quantity, type, rough opening dimensions, sash size, and the manufacturer's number are also placed in the window schedule. A remarks column gives information unique to each window type, such as the kind of glass, etc. Schedule A gives an example of a typical window schedule.

Window Detail

It is not necessary on the elevation drawings to completely draw each window. One window of each type may be detailed (with schedule symbol indicated); others of the same type are indicated by the symbol only. An elevation detail shows the sill, stiles, rails, trim, lintel or dripcap, muntins, and mullions. Many designers do not detail windows since it is a time consuming process. Special windows must, of course, be detailed for special manufacture. In addition to the normal window details which may be drawn on an elevation, the direction of window swing should also be shown. This is done by dashed lines converging to the hinge side of the window. Fig. 8-27B illustrates how window swing is shown.

Sometimes, to show detailed construction, sectional details are drawn.

Window-section details will show (1) *a section through the head* (a vertical cut taken through the top of the frame and adjacent header); (2) *a section through the sill* (a vertical cut taken through the bottom of the frame and adjacent header); and (3) *a section through the jamb* (a horizontal cut taken through the side of the frame and adjacent studs). These three sections are shown pictorially (outside and inside) in Fig. 8-34. Two typical details of a double-hung window showing sections through the head, jamb, and sill are illustrated in Fig. 8-35. Fig. 8-35 (left) shows a detail of a window in a frame wall. Fig. 8-35 (right) shows a detail of a window in a frame wall with brick veneer. The framing around the window, in either frame or brick veneer construction, would be the same for *any* type of window.

Step-by-Step Drawing Procedure: Windows

Fig. 8-36 shows the step-by-step procedure for drawing the window in section. With slight modifications this same sequence of steps may be used for drawing the jamb section.

Doors

Doors are one of the most critical aspects in the exterior appearance of the house. Doors (along with windows) are major focal points that influence the opinion of the design. The design of the main entry door should blend well with the architectural style.

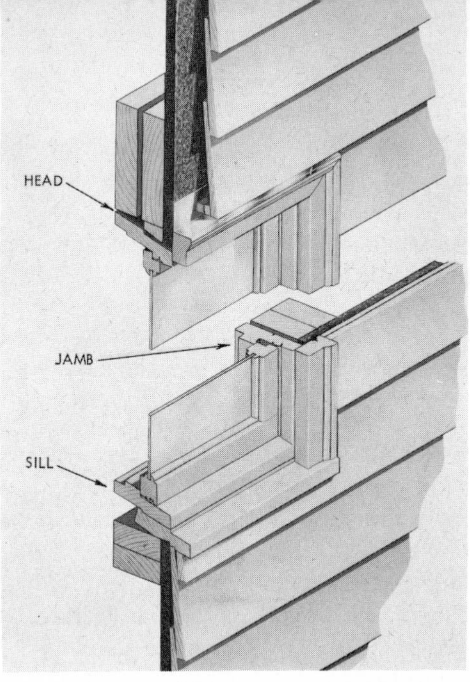

ANDERSON CORP., BAYPORT, MINNESOTA.

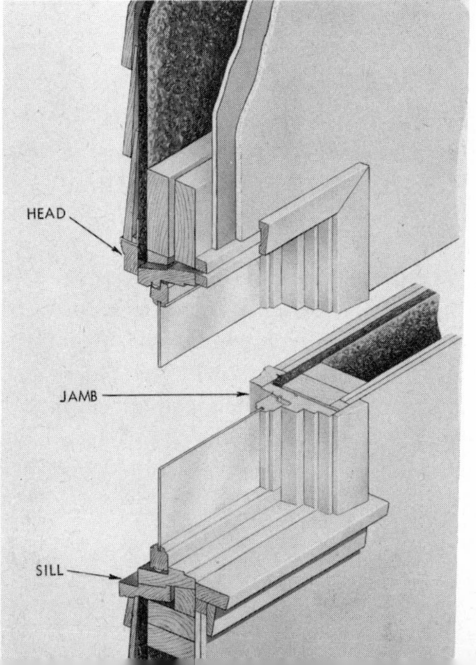

Fig. 8-34. These pictorial views, one taken from the inside and one from the outside, show where the cuts are taken when drawing a section through a window. This is an awning type window.

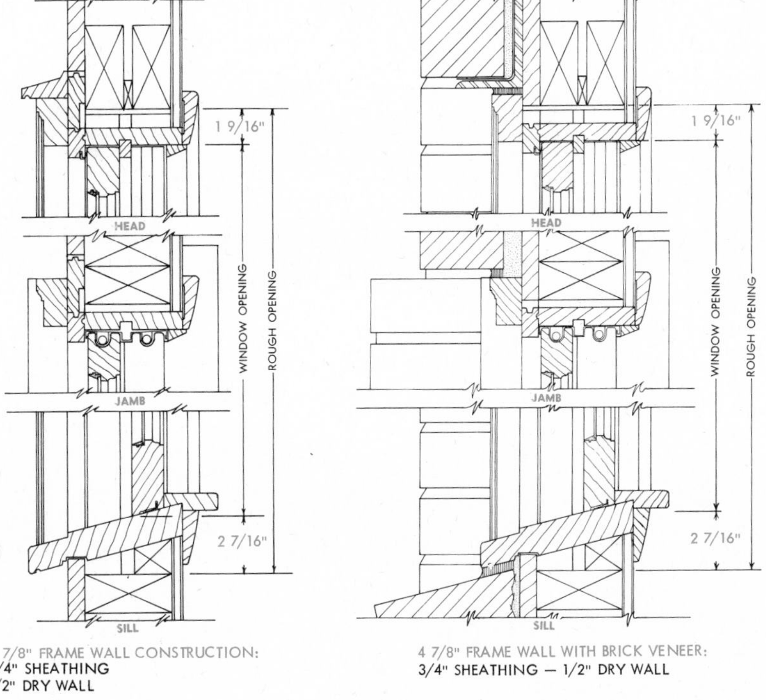

ROCK ISLAND MILLWORK CO., ROCK ISLAND, ILLINOIS.

Fig. 8-35. This typical window detail drawing shows sections through the head and sill and a section through the jamb turned into position so that sash, trim, etc., line up.

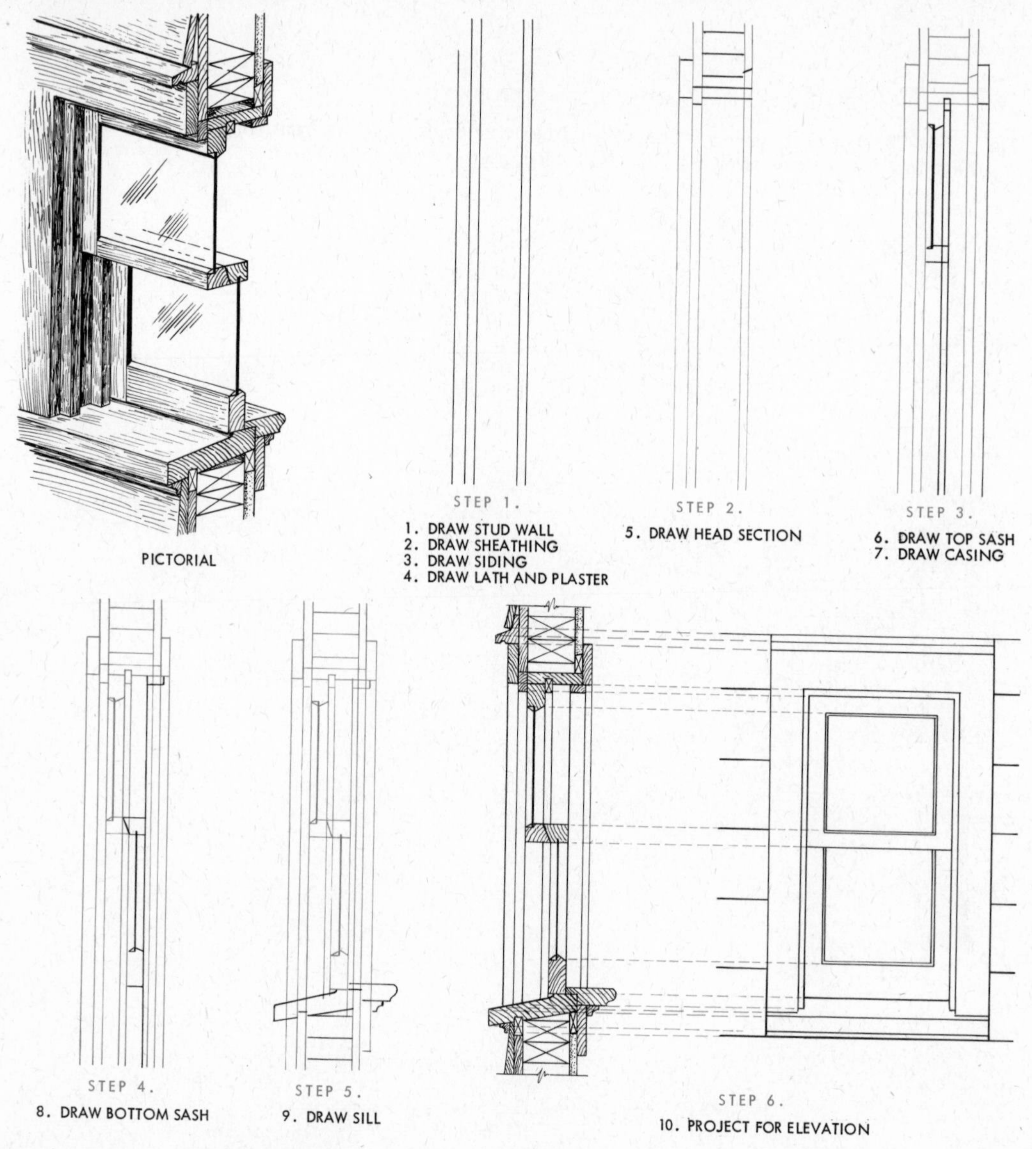

Fig. 8-36. Follow this step-by-step procedure in drawing a window section.

Doors are no longer designed by the architect but are selected from standard designs offered in millwork catalogs. Doors, like windows, have many designs and sizes for various styles of dwellings.

Door Types

Doors may be classified according to appearance, use, or construction. The two basic types are panel and flush doors used for both interior and exterior applications. Louver, accordion, French, double acting, sliding (pocket and bi-pass), and folding doors have special construction features or use. They are used as interior doors.

Panel doors (Fig. 8-37) consist of *stiles* (vertical members) and *rails* (horizontal members) which are generally *mortised and tenoned* together: grooves on the inside edge of the stiles and rails accommodate the panels (thin boards). Glazing may replace the upper panels. The rails and stiles may be made of solid pieces of wood or they may have a built-up core of small pieces of soft wood covered with an oak, birch, mahogany, etc., veneer.

Flush doors (sometimes called slab doors) are perfectly flat, i.e., the surface is unbroken by panels or moldings. There are two types of flush doors. The *solid core door* (Fig. 8-38) consists of small pieces of wood in varied combinations which are covered on both sides with veneer. The *hollow core door* (Fig. 8-39) is similar in appearance to the solid core flush door, but it is constructed with built-up rails, stiles, and lock

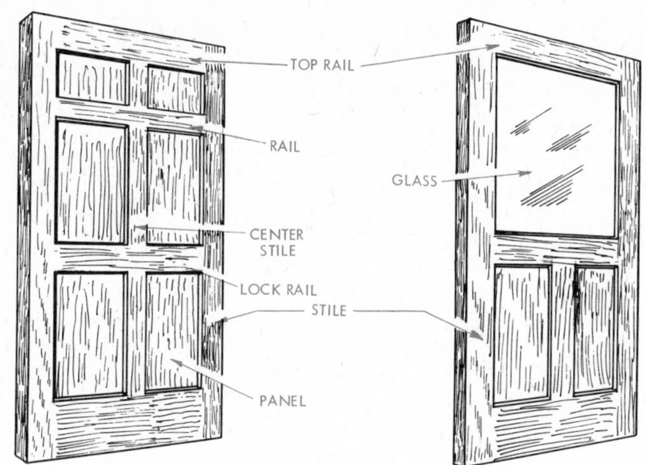

Fig. 8-37. Panel Doors—Six Panel and Two Panel Glazed.

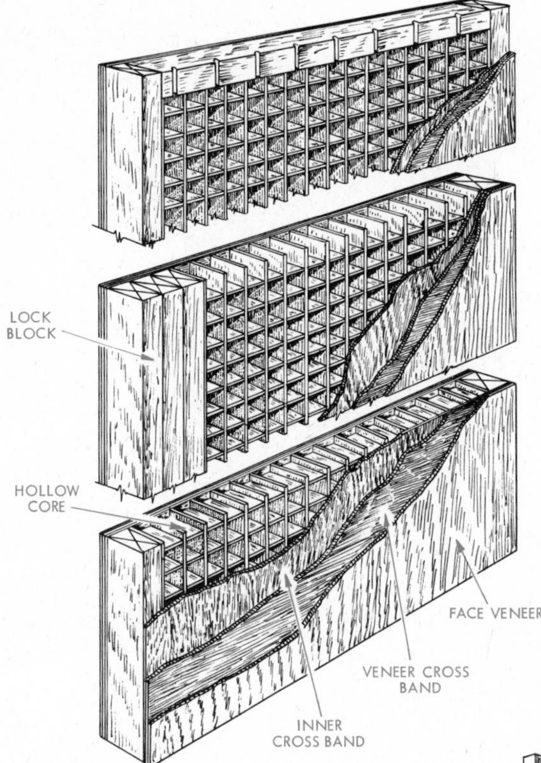

Fig. 8-39. Hollow Core Flush Door.

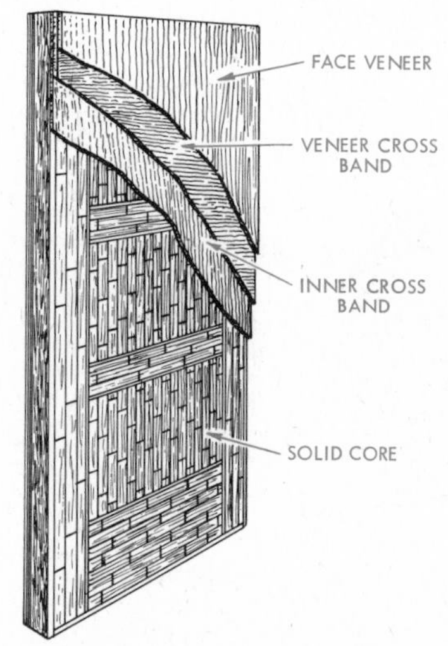

Fig. 8-38. Solid Core Flush Door.

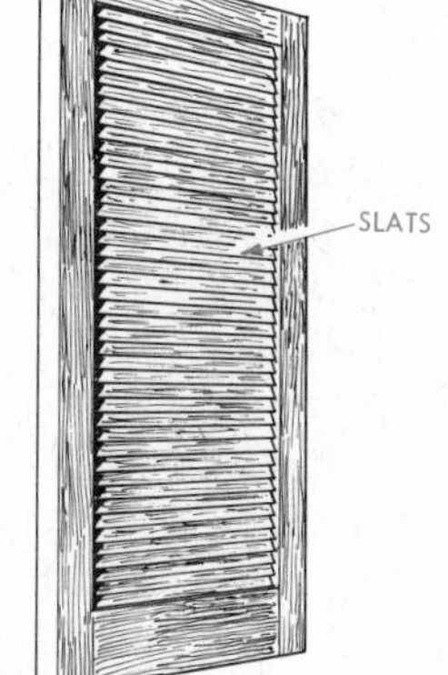

Fig. 8-40. Louvered or Slatted Door.

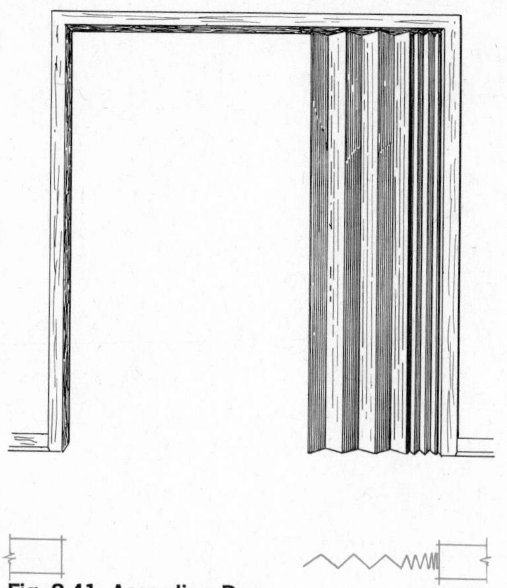

Fig. 8-41. Accordion Door.

Fig. 8-42. French Door.

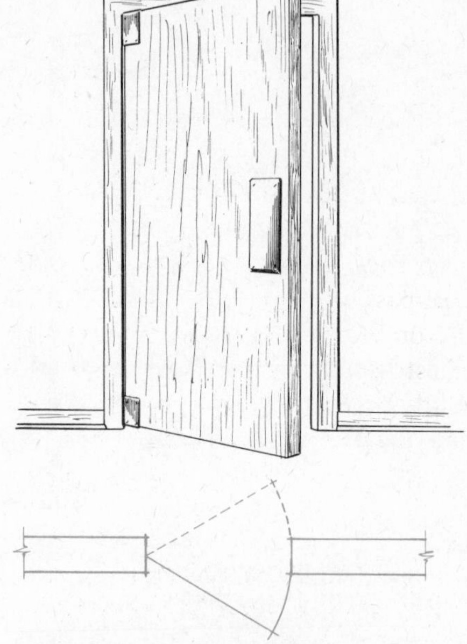

Fig. 8-43. Double Acting Door.

block. The space between the door members in the hollow core door is filled with a grid of crossed struts; the exterior is covered with two-ply veneer. This makes a door that is light, serviceable, and strong.

Louvered or slat doors (Fig. 8-40) have an outside frame of rails and stiles holding a series of horizontal slats set at an angle to provide ventilation.

Accordion doors are a relatively recent development in the building field. The folding portion of the door is made of narrow strips of wood (4″ to 8″ wide) hinged or fastened with fabric or plastic material. Other types are made from vinyl plastic hung from a track and hanging device. The folding portion may use either an accordian fold or a scissors linkage—both permit the "door" to "fold flat" or "stack" against the jamb. Fig. 8-41 shows a cloth or plastic accordion door with a scissors linkage.

French style doors (Fig. 8-42) are similar to panel doors except that they have glass from top to bottom rails and from stile to stile. The glass is usually divided by muntins. These may be used between rooms or where the room opens onto a terrace.

Double acting doors may be panelled, flush, or louvered. The door is hinged in such a manner that it will swing in either direction (Fig. 8-43). This is an ideal door when there is a great deal of travel between

Fig. 8-44. Bi-Pass Sliding Door.

rooms, and it is desirable to have the door closed most of the time.

Sliding doors may be either *bi-pass* or *pocket*. Sliding doors are hung from a track mounted on the head of the door and either slide past each other, as bi-pass doors (Fig. 8-44), or slide into a wall pocket (Fig. 8-45). Bi-pass doors are used almost exclusively on closets; the pocket door finds its greatest use as a door between rooms, particularly between the kitchen and dining or living areas. Unless sliding doors are properly sealed and finished they may warp and scrape the adjacent door or pocket. The flush door is usually used for the sliding or pocket door. If it is desired, however, a panel door may be specified. Sliding doors do not require a swing radius and do not interfere with furniture or other doors.

Folding doors (Fig. 8-46) may be flush, louvered, or a combination of both; they are hinged in the center of each section so they may be folded back against the jamb. Folding doors are ideal for wide closet entrances. This type of door may also be fabricated of metal. (Some home owners object to the folding door since it does not have a "solid" sound when opened or closed.)

Door Size

The inside opening dimension of the door frame is normally ¼″ larger than the door; the rough opening in the framing is made a total of 1″ to 1½″ larger than the outside dimension of the frame.

Exterior doors are usually 1¾″ thick; sometimes they are only 1⅜″ thick. The

Fig. 8-45. Pocket Sliding Door.

Fig. 8-46. Folding Doors.

TABLE 8-2
STANDARD SIZES OF INTERIOR AND EXTERIOR PANEL (P) AND FLUSH (F) DOORS

	EXTERIOR						INTERIOR			
	Thickness 1⅜″		Thickness 1¾″				Thickness 1⅜″			
	Height		Height				Height			
Width	6′-8″	7′-0″	6′-0″	6′-6″	6′-8″	7′-0″	6′-0″	6′-6″	6′-8″	7′-0″
1′-6″				F	F			P	P	
2′-0″			F	F	F	F			P	
2′-4″			F	F	F	F	P	P	P	P
2′-6″	P		F	F	P, F	F			P	
2′-8″	P	P	F	F	P, F	P, F			P	P
3′-0″	P				P, F	P, F			P	P
3′-4″					P, F	P, F				

width of the main exterior door is usually 3′-0″, while other exterior doors, such as rear and service doors, are 2′-10″ or 2′-8″. Manufacturers' catalogs list stock doors in heights of 6′-6″, 6′-8″, and 7′-0″.

Interior doors are more simply constructed than exterior doors. The common thickness for an interior door is 1⅜″; sometimes closet doors or narrow doors may be only 1⅛″ thick. Stock door sizes vary in height between 6′-6″ and 7′-0″ but are usually 6′-8″. Most interior doors are 2′-4″, 2′-6″, and 2′-8″ wide. Small closet doors may be as narrow as 1′-4″.

Table 8-2 gives basic standard sizes for interior and exterior panel and flush doors. Doors with other than stock sizes are usually available on special order. It is advisable to follow standard sizes as much as possible to eliminate extra cost.

Package Units

Emphasis is now being placed on labor saving methods, new materials, etc. This, of course, helps to reduce building and maintenance costs. Many mills and manufacturers now "package" the door and frame as a unit, with the door "pre-hung" (i.e., the door is fitted and hinged to the frame). The entire unit is placed in the rough opening, eliminating the steps of fitting the frame, hanging the door, etc. Packaged units are available for both interior and exterior doors.

Metal Doors

Metal clad wood doors are seldom used

DOOR SCHEDULE						
SYMBOL	QUANTITY	TYPE	ROUGH OPENING	DOOR SIZE	MFG NO	REMARKS
(A)	2	STANDARD	3′-2½″ × 6′-9¼″	3′-0″ × 6′-8″	——	BIRCH, FLUSH
(B)	1	″	2′-10½″ × 6′-9¼″	2′-8″ × 6′-8″	——	″ ″
(C)	2	″	2′-8½″ × 6′-9¼″	2′-6″ × 6′-8″	——	″ ″
(D)	1	FOLDING	—— ——	6′-0″ × 6′-8″	——	——
(E)	4	SLIDING	2′-10½″ × 6′-9¼″	2′-8″ × 6′-8″	52A	BIRCH, FLUSH
(F)	1	CANOPY	SEE MFG INSTRUC	16′-0″ × 7′-0″	1670	STEEL (PRIMED)

Schedule B.

in residential construction. Some building codes, however, require that the door opening into the garage from the dwelling be covered on the garage side with galvanized iron or tin plate for fire protection.

Glass Doors

Complete glass doors are rarely used in the main entryway in residential construction. Sliding glass doors, however, are frequently used in living areas opening onto a patio, terrace, or garden area. These glass doors have a wood frame, aluminum frame, or steel reinforced wood frame and are not, in the true sense, a glass door.

Door Schedules

Door schedules, like window schedules, are usually located on elevation drawings. They may also be located on the first or second floor plans, or on a separate sheet with window and room finish schedules. As with window schedules, door schedule code symbols are placed on the plans and elevations by each particular door. The door schedule also gives the quantity, type, rough opening dimensions, door size, manufacturer's number, and information unique to each door, such as type of wood, etc. Schedule B gives an example of a typical door schedule.

Door Sections

Fig. 8-47 shows the standard section taken through the door frame to detail the construction. Sections A, B, and C through the *head* (top member), *jamb* (vertical member at the side), and *threshold* or *saddle* (lower member) respectively show the door frame in a frame wall. Sections D, E, and F show the same detail-section treatment in a brick veneer wall.

An interior door frame has *only* a jamb and head. It is framed in an identical manner to the exterior door. Fig. 8-48 shows pictorial sections through the head and jamb. Note the use of a metal plaster casing around the head and jamb, and the use of wood casing over dry wall finish.

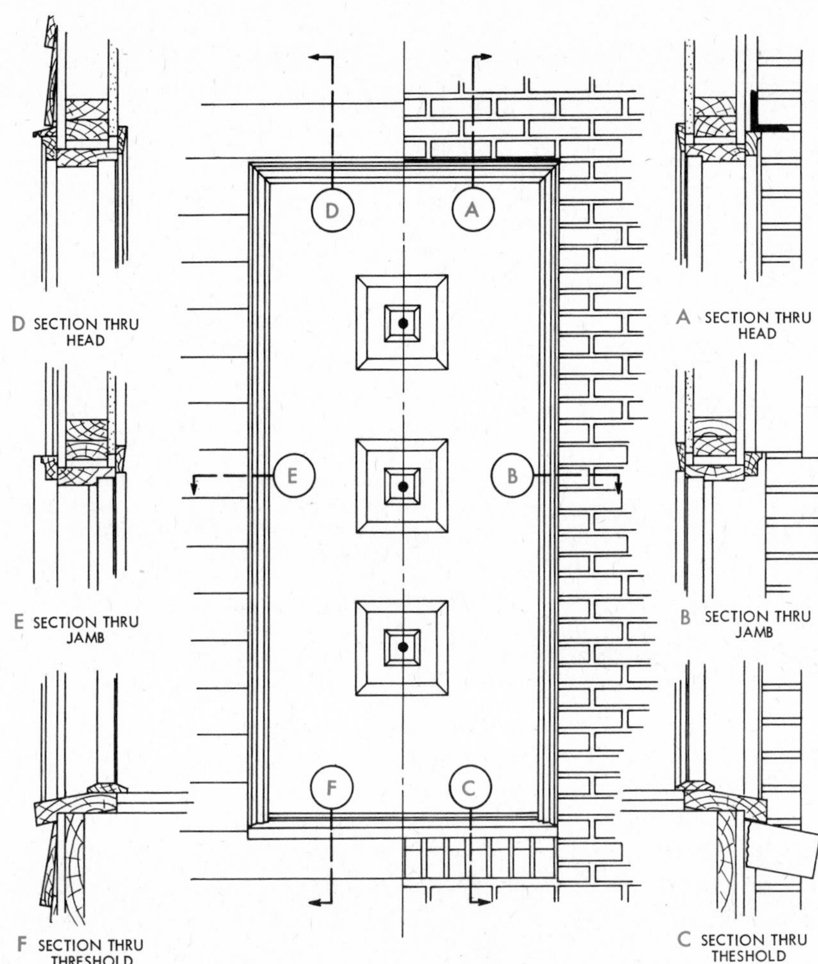

Fig. 8-47. This figure shows typical sections through the head, jamb, and threshold of an exterior door in a frame and in a brick veneer wall.

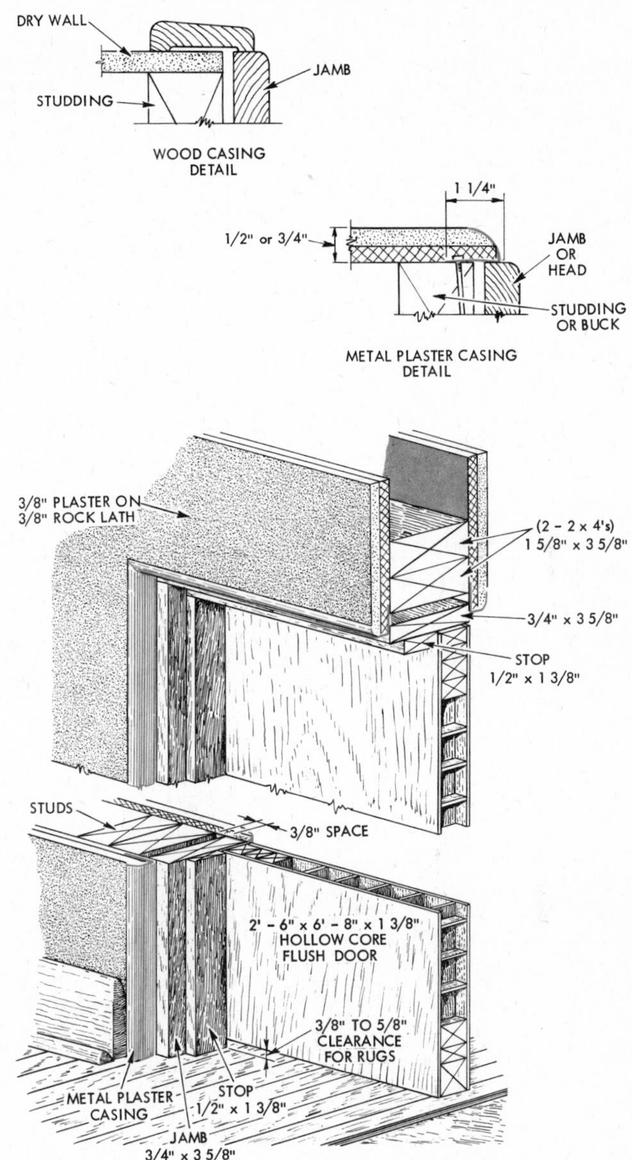

Fig. 8-48. This figure shows details for an interior door.

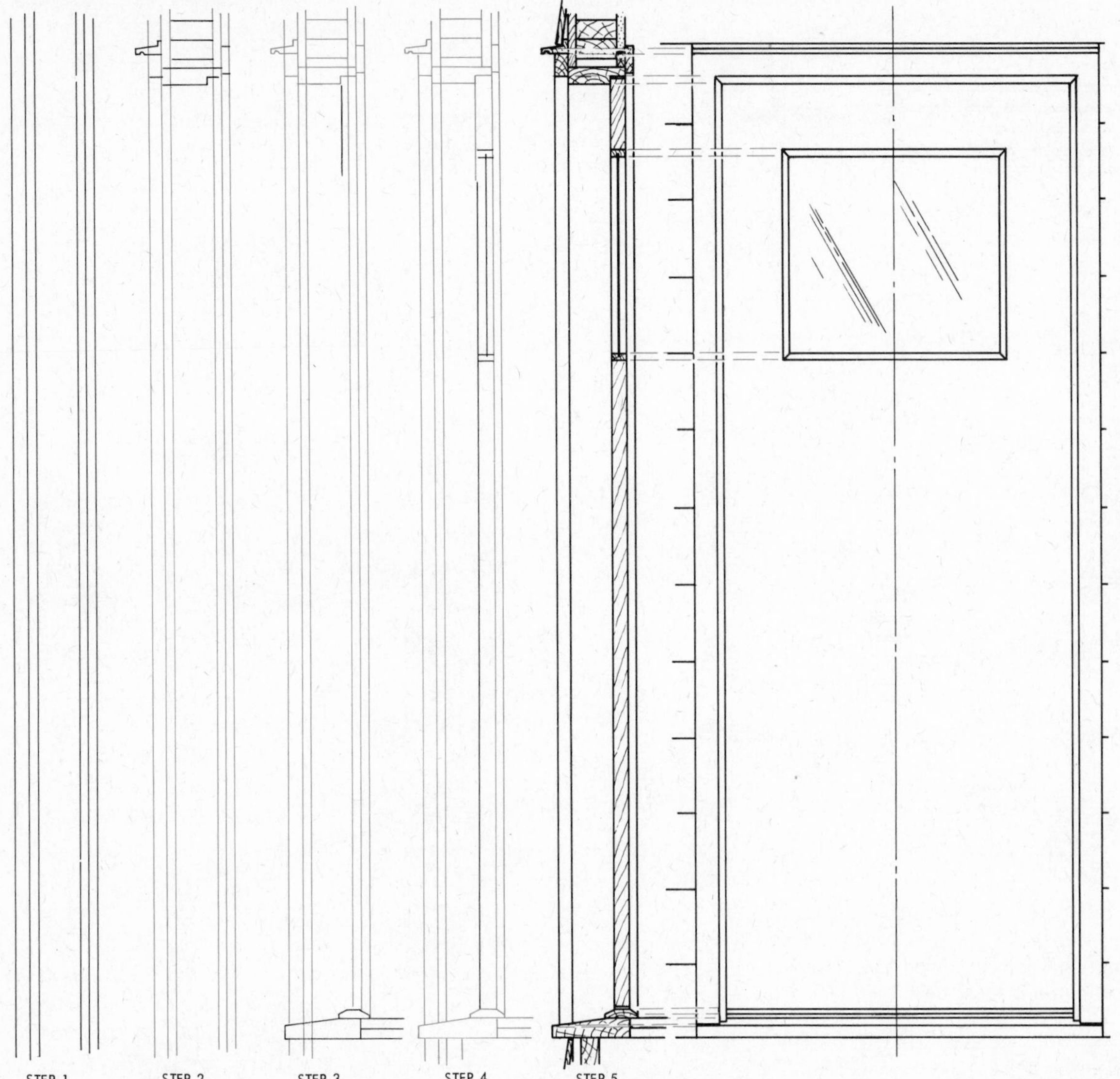

Fig. 8-49. Follow this step-by-step procedure in drawing exterior door framing and door in elevation. **Step. 1.** Draw vertical lines representing: stud wall, sheathing, plaster and lath, inside casing, and outside casing. **Step 2.** Draw head section. **Step 3.** Measure height of door; draw sill section. **Step 4.** Draw door. **Step 5.** Erase surplus lines and project for elevation.

Fig. 8-50. A prefabricated free-standing fireplace may add interest in the contemporary home.

Fig. 8-51. A spherical free-standing fireplace is ideal for a family room, cottage, or week end lodge.

Step-by-Step Drawing Procedure: Doors

Fig. 8-49 shows the step-by-step procedure for drawing all doors.

Fireplaces

A fireplace may be considered a luxury when compared with the cost of the house and the *total number of hours the fireplace is used per year*. Tradition, however, makes the fireplace a desired feature. Pre-historic man met around the fire for warmth and fellowship; in the rush of today's society we still derive solace and cheer from a warm glowing fire.

New locations and designs for fireplaces have evolved with recent innovations in contemporary architecture. The fireplace is no longer necessarily thought of as a brick covered enclosure with a mantel above the opening. Creative design may turn the fireplace into a piece of dynamic furniture. Modern fireplaces may be free standing and have three dimensional geometric shapes, such as those in Figs. 8-50 and 8-51.

Correct fireplace design is based on three principles. First, the proper proportional relationship of width, height, and depth for the fire chamber must be maintained. Second, the flue must be sized in relation to the fireplace opening. Third, the chimney must be carried 2′-6″ above the roof ridge or above the highest point to eliminate a smoky fireplace.

Hearth and Fire Chamber

The front hearth serves as a floor protection against sparks. This area may be shortened to 6″ if a fireplace screen is installed. The hearth rests on a hearth slab which is supported by a 2″ × 4″ cleat attached to the double trimmer and header. Fig. 8-52 shows the hearth in relationship to the rest of the fireplace. The hearth may be elevated above or recessed in the floor.

The back hearth, the surface on which the fire is built, is lined with firebrick using fire clay joints. (Fire clay is a mortar-like material used to bond the firebrick.) Also note that the sides and back of the opening are *laid up* with firebrick and fire clay. Common brick and mortar is not used because they will not withstand heat. Frequently, an ash dump is installed in the center of the back hearth. This leads to an ash pit below. The interior walls of the fire chamber (Fig. 8-53) are inclined to reflect the heat into the room. (Note: wood trim should be placed no closer than 6″ around the sides and top of the fireplace opening.)

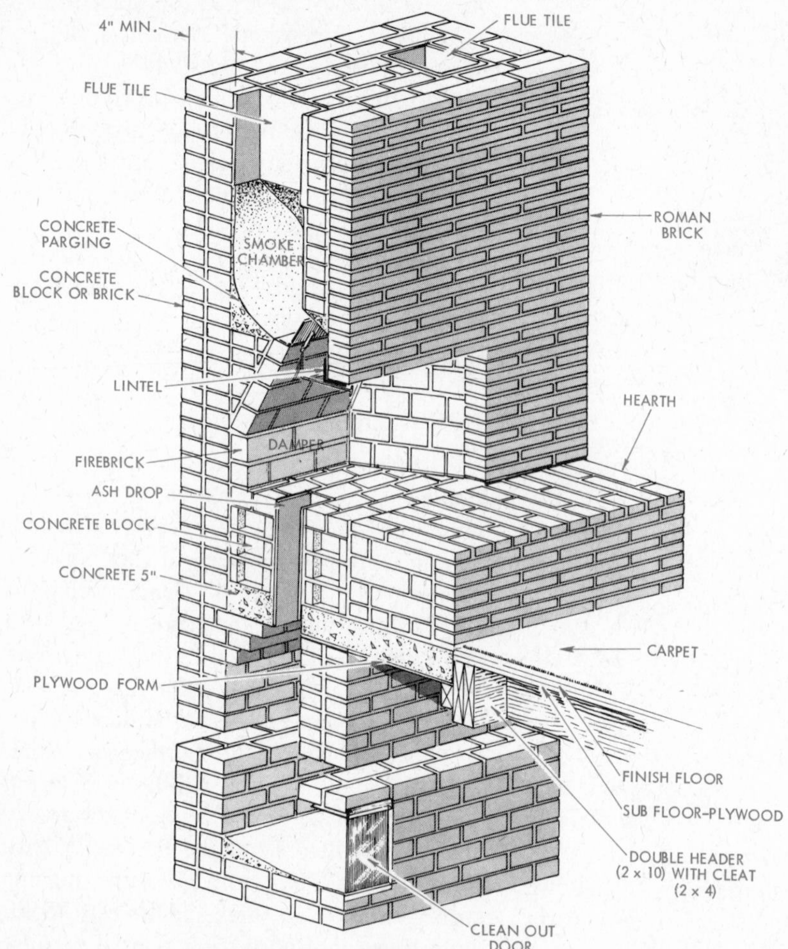

Fig. 8-52. Fireplace Details and Nomenclature.

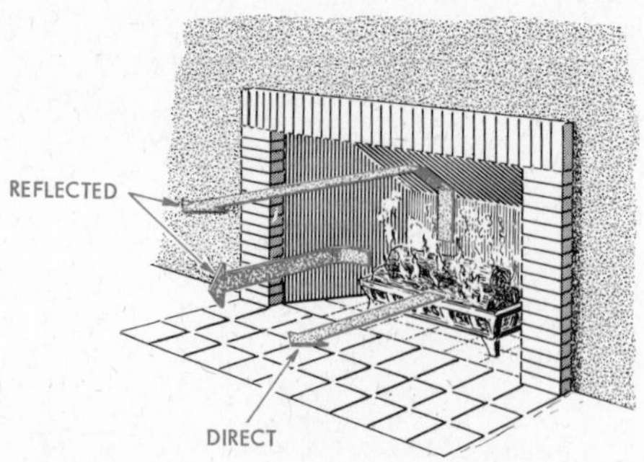

Fig. 8-53. Proper design of the fire chamber increases the reflected heat.

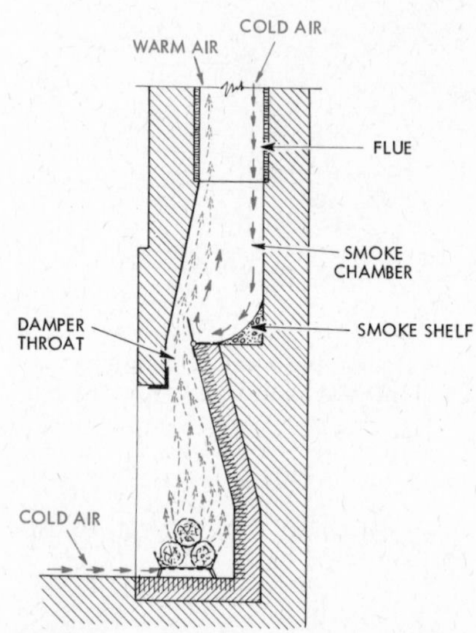

Fig. 8-54. The smoke shelf directs the cold air toward the warm rising air.

Damper and Smoke Chamber

A cast iron or sheet steel damper is located in the *throat* (between the fire area and smoke shelf) to regulate the draft. The damper is the same length as the fireplace opening and is adjustable so the down drafts are deflected up the chimney. (The square inch area of the damper *should not* be less than that of the flue.) The smoke chamber is pyrimidal in shape, connecting the damper with the flue. The curved surface of the smoke shelf, in addition to the angle of the damper prevents the downrushing air currents from forcing the smoke into the room. See Fig. 8-54. If the draft should be shut off temporarily by the wind, the smoke chamber will hold any accumulated gases. The damper is closed to prevent cold air flow when the fireplace is not in use.

Flue

The chimney flue begins at the top of the smoke chamber and extends up the chimney. Clay flue linings are almost universally used to satisfy building codes and the recommendations of the National Fire Underwriters. The flue tile lining, for safety reasons, should be backed up with a minimum 4″ of brick. If the flue tile lining is omitted in a chimney, the thickness of brick around the opening should be 8″.

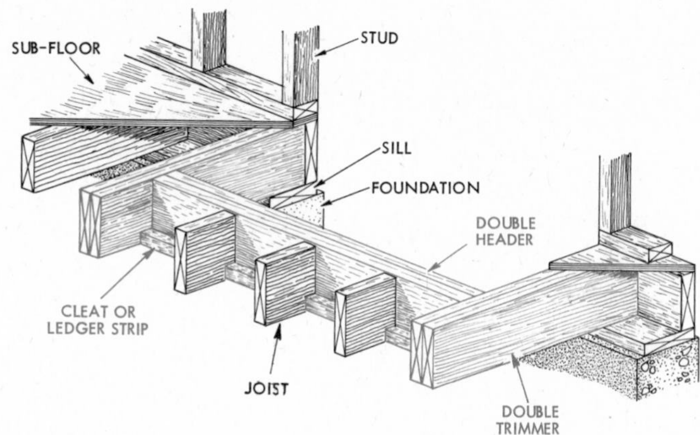

Fig. 8-57. Framing is doubled around a chimney placed on an outside wall.

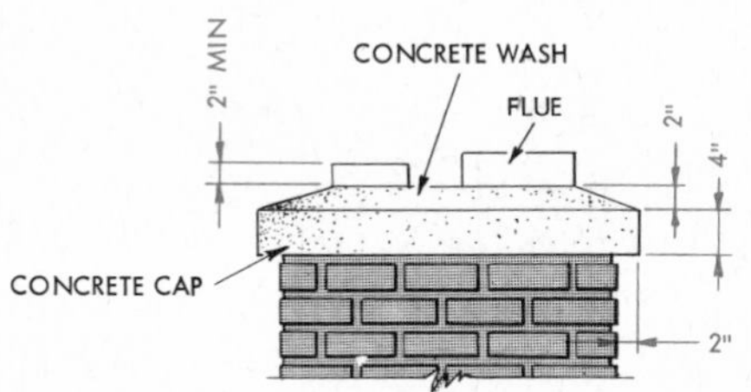

Fig. 8-55. The flue lining projects 2″ above the concrete cap.

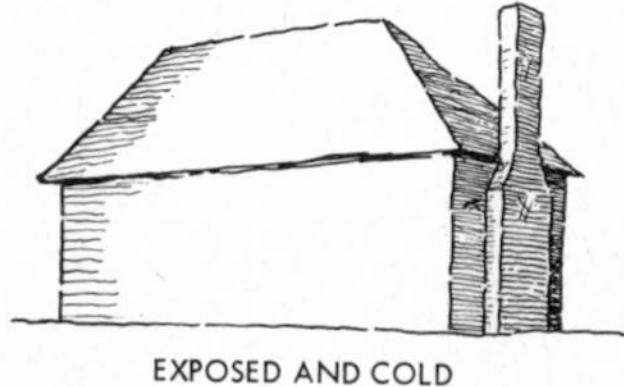

Fig. 8-56. Location of the chimney on an interior wall promotes greater efficiency.

Chimney

Chimneys should project above the highest point on the roof to provide for an adequate draft. If the chimney is *on* the sloping portion of the roof and not at the ridge, the chimney is extended 2′-6″ above the ridge. A chimney *at* the ridge is projected 2′-0″ above the ridge. In the case of a flat roof, the chimney extends 3′-0″ above the roof line. The flue lining projects 2″ above the concrete cap. Fig. 8-55 gives details of concrete cap. If a single chimney houses several flues, these flues should be carried to different heights above the cap. If the flue linings project above the cap equally, a down draft from interior suction may pull the smoke from the top of one flue down into an adjoining flue.

Greater fireplace efficiency may be obtained if the chimney is placed within the structure rather than on an outside wall as in Fig. 8-56. Frequently however, due to space limitations, the fireplace must be placed on an outside wall.

A single chimney is used to house several flues. *Separate* flues are needed to allow for proper draft. A chimney would have three separate flues to accommodate, as an example, a fireplace, a furnace, and an incinerator. Fig. 8-52 shows an example of a two flue chimney.

Heating devices for single family residential dwellings should have a minimum effective flue area as follows:

Small special stoves and heaters 28 sq.in.

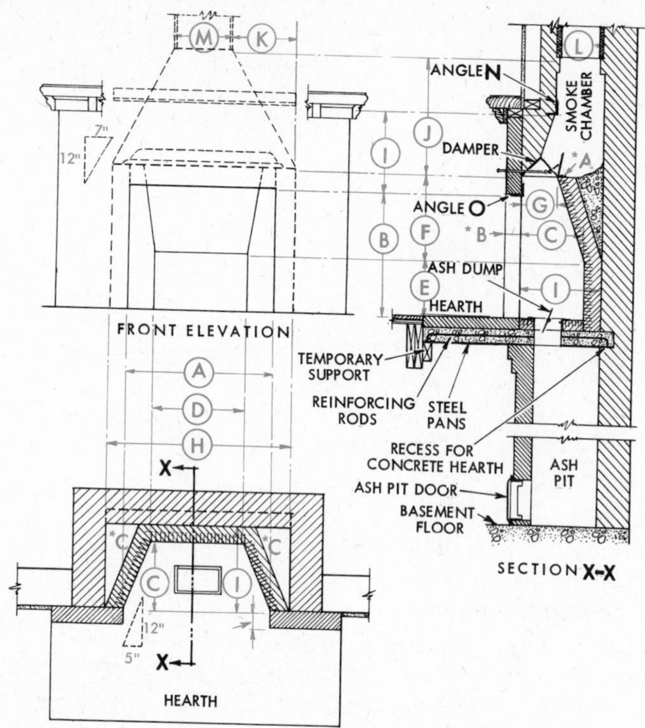

TABLE OF FIREPLACE DIMENSIONS

Finished Fireplace Opening										Rough Brick Work and Flue Size					Equipment		
										New Flue Sizes**		Round	Old Flue Sizes		Ash Pit Door	Steel Angles*	
A	B	C	D	E	F	G	H	I	J	K	L M		K	L M		N	O
24	24	16	11	14	15	8¾	32	20	19	10	8x12	8	11¾	8½x 8½	12x8	A-36	A-36
26	24	16	13	14	15	8¾	34	20	21	11	8x12	8	12¾	8½x 8½	12x8	A-36	A-36
28	24	16	15	14	15	8¾	36	20	21	12	8x12	10	11½	8½x13	12x8	A-36	A-36
30	29	16	17	14	21	8¾	38	20	24	13	12x12	10	12½	8½x13	12x8	A-42	A-36
32	29	16	19	14	21	8¾	40	20	24	14	12x12	10	13½	8½x13	12x8	A-42	A-42
36	29	16	23	14	21	8¾	44	20	27	16	12x12	12	15½	13 x13	12x8	A-48	A-42
40	29	16	27	14	21	8¾	48	20	29	16	12x16	12	17½	13 x13	12x8	A-48	A-48
42	32	16	29	14	23	8¾	50	20	32	17	16x16	12	18½	13 x13	12x8	B-54	A-48
48	32	18	33	14	23	8¾	56	22	37	20	16x16	15	21½	13 x13	12x8	B-60	B-54
54	37	20	37	16	27	13	68	24	45	26	16x16	15	25	13 x18	12x8	B-72	B-60
60	37	22	42	16	27	13	72	27	45	26	16x20	15	27	13 x18	12x8	B-72	B-66
60	40	22	42	16	29	13	72	27	45	26	16x20	18	27	18 x18	12x8	B-72	B-66
72	40	22	54	16	29	13	84	27	56	32	20x20	18	33	18 x18	12x8	C-84	C-84
84	40	24	64	20	26	13	96	29	61	36	20x24	20	36.	20 x20	12x8	C-96	C-96
96	40	24	76	20	26	13	108	29	75	42	20x24	22	42	24 x24	12x8	C-108	C-108

*ANGLE SIZES· A-3 x 3 x 3/16, B-3 1/2 x 3 x 1/4, C-5 x 3 1/2 x 5/16.
**NEW FLUE SIZES—CONFORM TO NEW MODULAR DIMENSIONAL SYSTEM. SIZES SHOWN ARE NOMINAL. ACTUAL SIZE IS 1/2 IN. LESS EACH DIMENSION.

DONLEY BROS. CO., CLEVELAND, OHIO.

Fig. 8-58. With these standard dimensions the student may design a conventional, opening fireplace.

Coal or wood stoves, ranges and room heaters — 40 sq. in.
Fireplaces—at least 1/12 of the fireplace opening — 50 sq. in.
Warm air furnaces, steam and hot water boilers (gas, oil, or coal fired) — 70 sq. in.

Fireplace Framing

Framing members, flooring, roof members, and walls must be free of the chimney. A minimum space of 2″ must always be provided. Non-combustible insulation is inserted between the framing members and the chimney masonry. The fireplace itself always has a 2″ clearance with insulation on both sides and the back. If the exterior covering of the dwelling is wood siding, shingles, etc., the junction of the wood and brick must be caulked.

Framing around the chimney placed on an exterior wall is accomplished by two double trimmers resting on the wall plate (Fig. 8-57). A double header is spiked between the trimmers to carry the regular floor joists. A 2″ clearance with insulation is provided only on the sides of an exterior fireplace.

The opening in the roof is framed in a similar manner with double rafters and trimmers. (Note: Fig. 7-70 in the preceding chapter shows roof framing details around the chimney.)

Fireplace Proportions

Few experiences can be more disappointing to the home owner than an ill-functioning fireplace. Mistakes in fireplace construction are inexcusable considering the amount invested in this home feature. The successfully operating fireplace is based on simple principles of design. Standard proportions for the conventional single opening fireplace are shown in Fig. 8-58. Probably the most important construction features of the single opening fireplace are: (1) the relation of the width, height, and depth dimensions of the fire chamber to the inclined faces in the rear of the chamber, and (2) the proper flue, damper, and smoke chamber size in relation to the fireplace opening. An attractive, well sized, single-opening fireplace made from split 4″ concrete block is shown in Fig. 8-59.

NATIONAL CONCRETE MASONRY ASSOC., WASHINGTON, D.C.

Fig. 8-59. A fire adds warmth and beauty to a room.

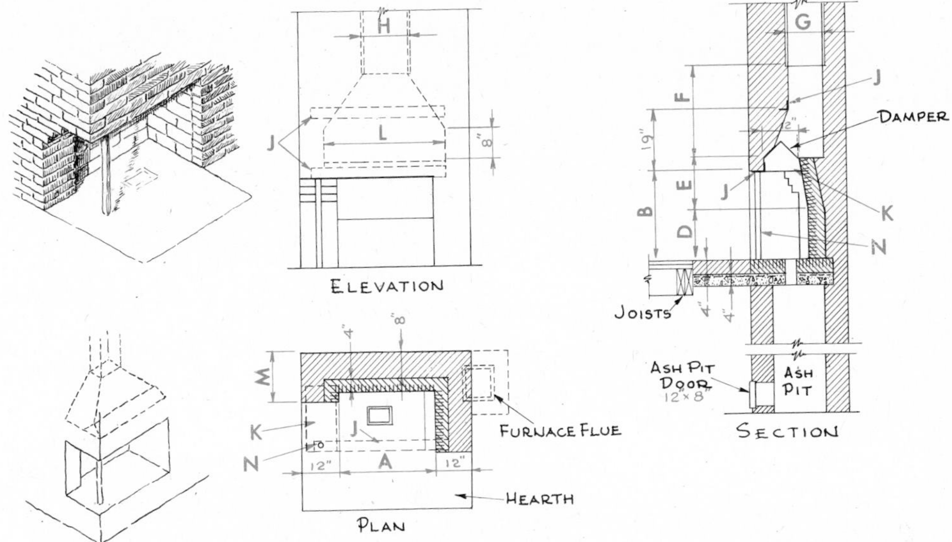

TABLE OF DIMENSIONS AND EQUIPMENT (IN INCHES)

A	B	C	D	E	F	Old Flue Sizes G IN	G OUT	H IN	H OUT	New Flue Sizes G IN	G OUT	H IN	H OUT	L	M	Steel Angle J*	Plate Lintel K	Corner Post N
28	26½	20	14	20	29¼	11¼	13	11¼	13	10¼	12	10¼	12	36	16	*A-36	11×16	3ϕ×26½
32	26½	20	14	20	32	11¼	13	11¼	13	10¼	12	13½	16	40	16	*A-42	11×16	3ϕ×26½
36	26½	20	14	20	35	11¼	13	11¼	13	10¼	12	13½	16	44	16	*A-48	11×16	3ϕ×26½
40	29	20	14	20	35	11¼	13	15¾	18	13½	16	13½	16	48	16	*B-54	11×16	3ϕ×29
48	29	24	14	24	43	11¼	13	15¾	18	13½	16	13½	16	56	20	*B-60	11×16	3ϕ×29

* ANGLE SIZES *A 3×3×3/16 *B 3½×3½×¼

DONLEY BROS. CO., CLEVELAND, OHIO.

Fig. 8-60. A projecting fireplace may be designed using these dimensions.

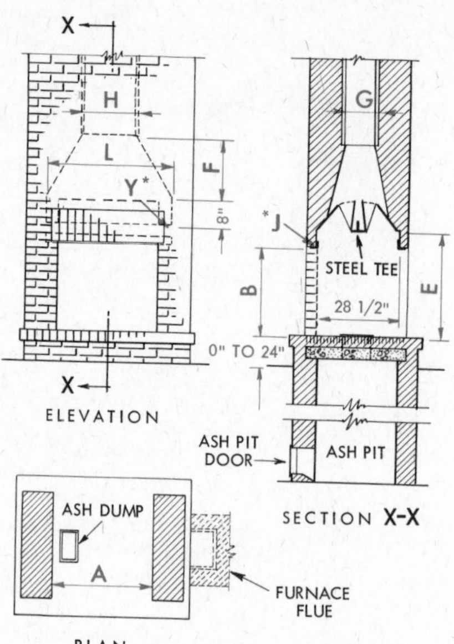

TABLE OF DIMENSIONS AND EQUIPMENT (IN INCHES)

Width of Opening	Height of Opening	Damper Height	Smoke Chamber	Old Flue Size		New Flue Size		Angle 2 req'd		Tee	Ash Dump	Ash-Pit Door
A	B	E	F	G	H	G	H	*J	L			
28	24	30	19	13	13	12	16	A-36	36	35	58	12 x 8
32	29	35	21	13	18	16	16	A-40	40	39	58	12 x 8
36	29	35	21	13	18	16	20	A-42	44	43	58	12 x 8
40	29	35	27	18	18	16	20	A-48	48	47	58	12 x 8
48	32	37	32	18	18	20	20	B-54	56	55	58	12 x 8

*ANGLE SIZES: A-3 x 3 x 3/16"; B-3 - 1/2 x 3 1/4".
NOTE Y—THE DAMPER AND THE STEEL T SHOULD NOT BE BUILT IN SOLID AT THE ENDS BUT GIVEN FREEDOM TO EXPAND WITH HEAT.

DONLEY BROS. CO., CLEVELAND, OHIO

Fig. 8-61. A two-way or double fireplace may be designed using these dimensions.

Two- and Three-Way Fireplaces

Fireplaces are no longer limited to a one-way opening. In recent years novel variations in basic fireplace design have taken place. This change is in part due to the popularity of large living areas. Sometimes the fireplace design assumes the role of a room divider. The projecting corner fireplace (Fig. 8-60) has the opening visible on the side and front. Where a partition separates two rooms, a two-way fireplace (Fig. 8-61) will serve both areas. A three-way fireplace (Fig. 8-62) may project a sufficient distance into the room to form a semi-partition between two living areas.

Metal Circulating Fireplaces

The heating capacity of a fireplace can be increased considerably by using metal built-in circulating units, such as shown in Fig. 8-63. These units are efficient and easily installed. Firebrick lining is not necessary in the fire chamber since the entire unit is fabricated of heavy sheet metal. A double wall surrounds the fire chamber so that cold air entering near the bottom (through ducts) is warmed by passing over the hot sides. The heated air then rises and is discharged into the room through outlet ducts. These pre-formed units include the firebox, heat chamber, damper, smoke shelf, throat, and smoke chamber. All that needs to be provided is a hearth slab, brick work to cover the unit, flue tile, and the chimney. Most manufacturers of circulating fireplaces have units designed similar to the conventional fireplaces discussed above.

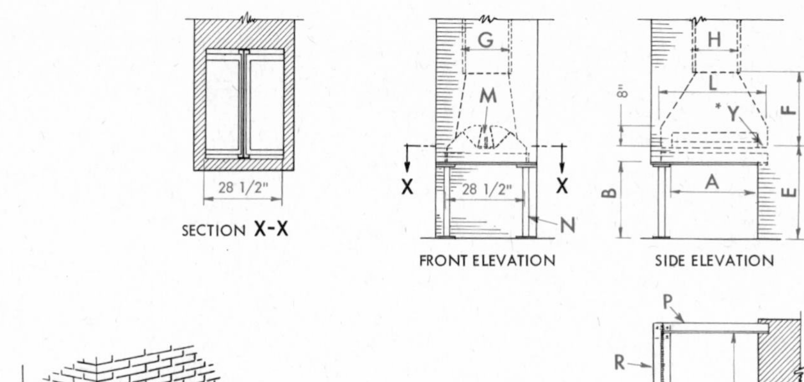

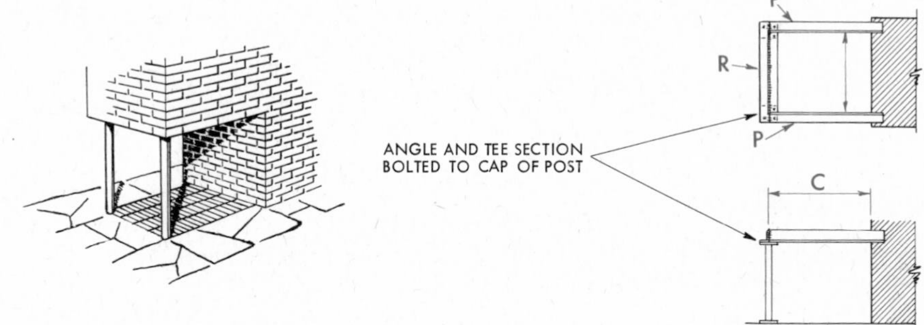

Fig. 8-62. Using these dimensions three-way fireplaces may be designed.

TABLE OF DIMENSIONS AND EQUIPMENT (IN INCHES)

A	B	C	E	F	Old Flue Size		New Flue Size		L	Steel Tee	Post Height 2 req'd	Drilled Angle 2 req'd	Special Welded Tee
					G	H	G	H		M	N	P	R
28	26½	32	32	24	18	18	16	20	36	35	26½	36	34
32	26½	36	32	27	18	18	20	20	40	39	26½	40	34
36	26½	40	32	32	18	18	20	20	44	43	26½	44	34
40	26½	44	32	35	18	18	20	20	48	47	26½	48	34
48	26½	52	32	35	20	20	20	24	56	55	26½	56	34

*Y —DAMPER AND STEEL T SHOULD NOT BE BUILT IN SOLID AT THE ENDS BUT GIVEN FREEDOM TO EXPAND WITH HEAT

DONLEY BROS. CO., CLEVELAND, OHIO.

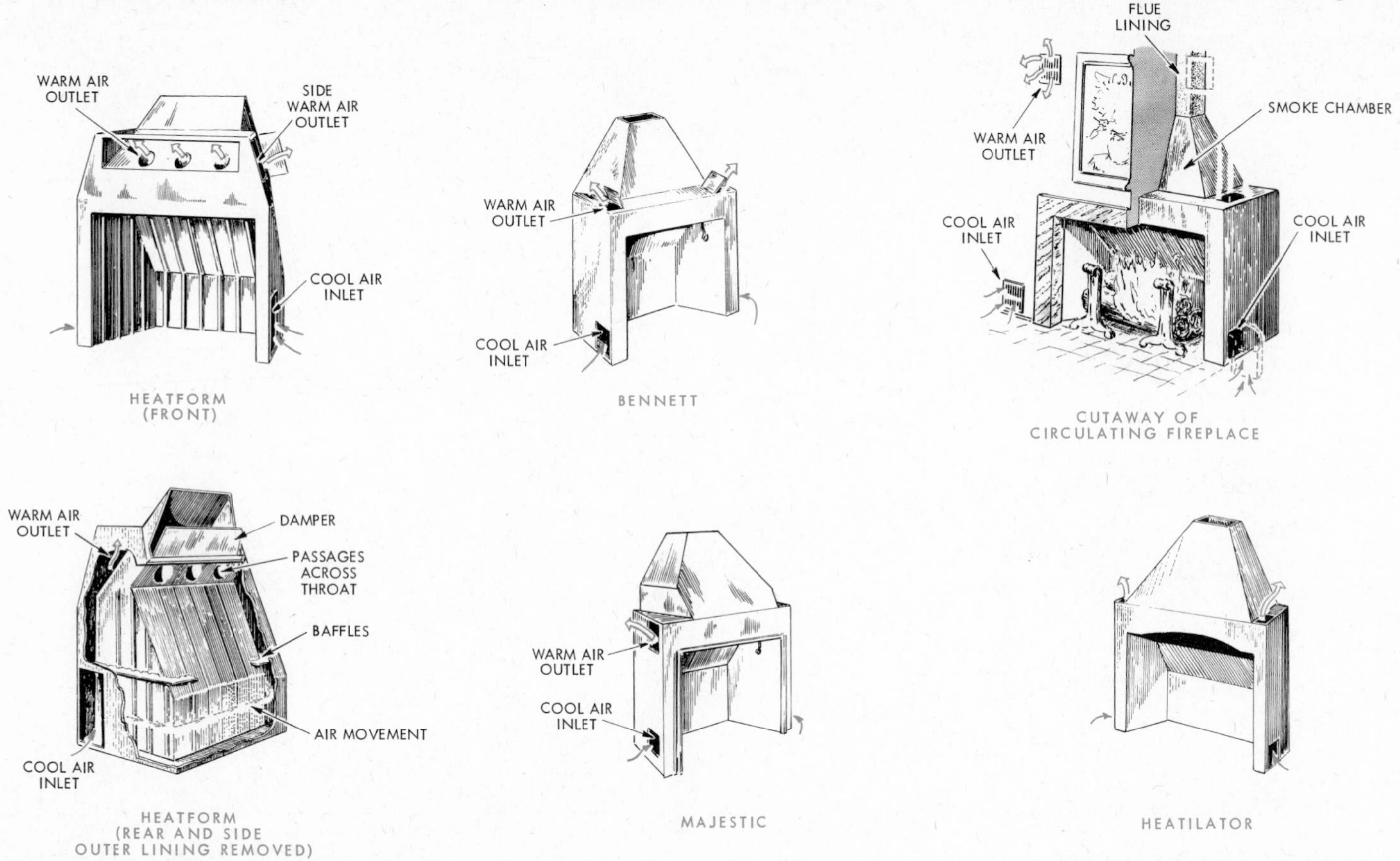
WARM AIR OUTLET
SIDE WARM AIR OUTLET
COOL AIR INLET
HEATFORM (FRONT)
WARM AIR OUTLET
COOL AIR INLET
BENNETT
FLUE LINING
WARM AIR OUTLET
SMOKE CHAMBER
COOL AIR INLET
COOL AIR INLET
CUTAWAY OF CIRCULATING FIREPLACE
WARM AIR OUTLET
DAMPER
PASSAGES ACROSS THROAT
BAFFLES
AIR MOVEMENT
COOL AIR INLET
HEATFORM (REAR AND SIDE OUTER LINING REMOVED)
WARM AIR OUTLET
COOL AIR INLET
MAJESTIC
HEATILATOR

Fig. 8-63. Metal, built-in circulating fireplaces increase the heating efficiency by permitting air to circulate around the fire chamber.

Free Standing Prefabricated Fireplaces

Small, free-standing prefabricated fireplaces are becoming more popular. These units are complete in themselves: the hood, damper, chimney pipe, hearth, base, grate, and screen are included. No masonry work is required since these fireplaces attach to wall or stand free. See Figs. 8-64 and 8-65.

THE MAJESTIC CO.; HUNTINGTON, INDIANA.

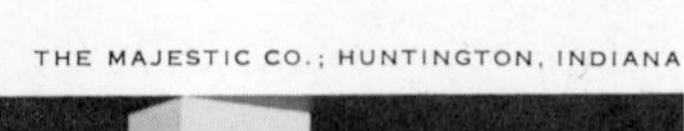

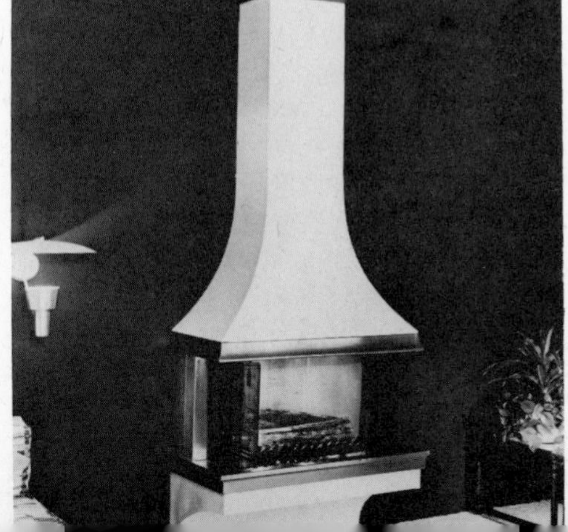

Fig. 8-64. A free-standing fireplace may compliment the décor of the room.

VEGA INDUSTRIES, INC., SYRACUSE, NEW YORK.

Fig. 8-65. Free-standing fireplaces are a simple and inexpensive way to provide heat.

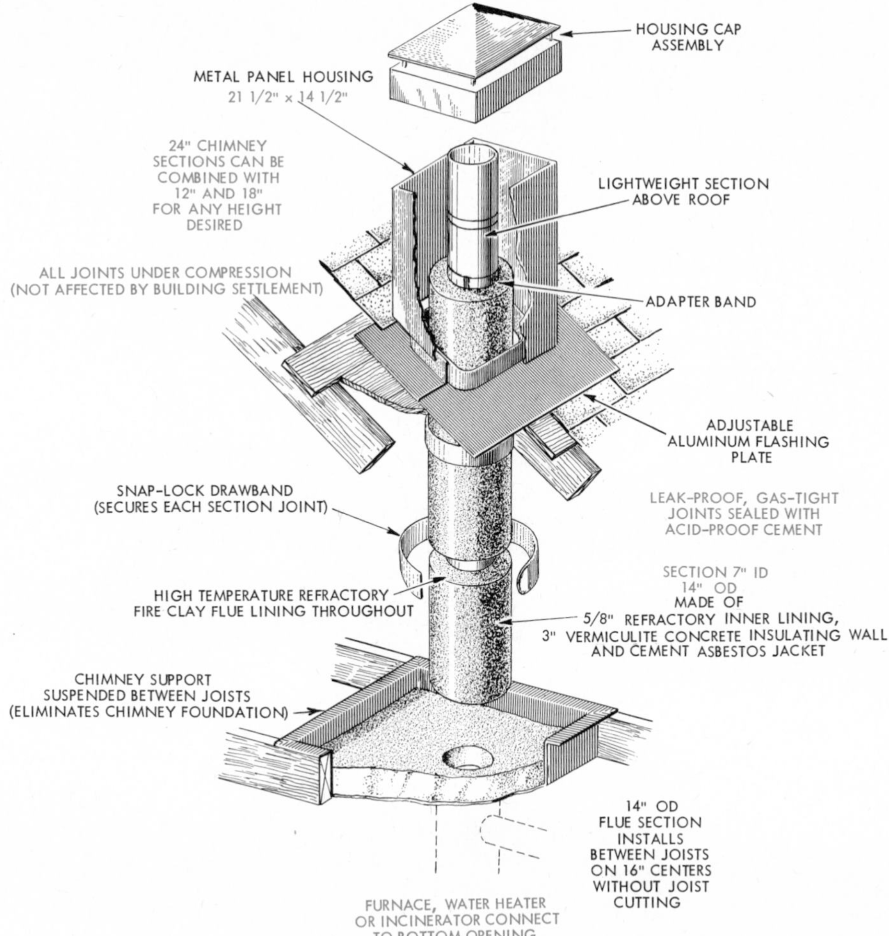

THE FLINTKOTE COMPANY, NEW YORK, NEW YORK.

Fig. 8-66. Metal chimneys (used where local building codes permit) eliminate the chimney foundation and allow greater freedom in floor planning.

For many who have small summer cottages where central heating would be a needless expense, a small fireplace can provide the necessary warmth for a chilly evening or morning.

Pre-Cast Chimneys

Pre-cast, light-weight chimneys are frequently used in areas where building codes permit. Their cost is low and they are easy to install. Brick walls and footings are not required with this type of chimney. Fig. 8-66 shows an exploded view of a factory-built chimney.

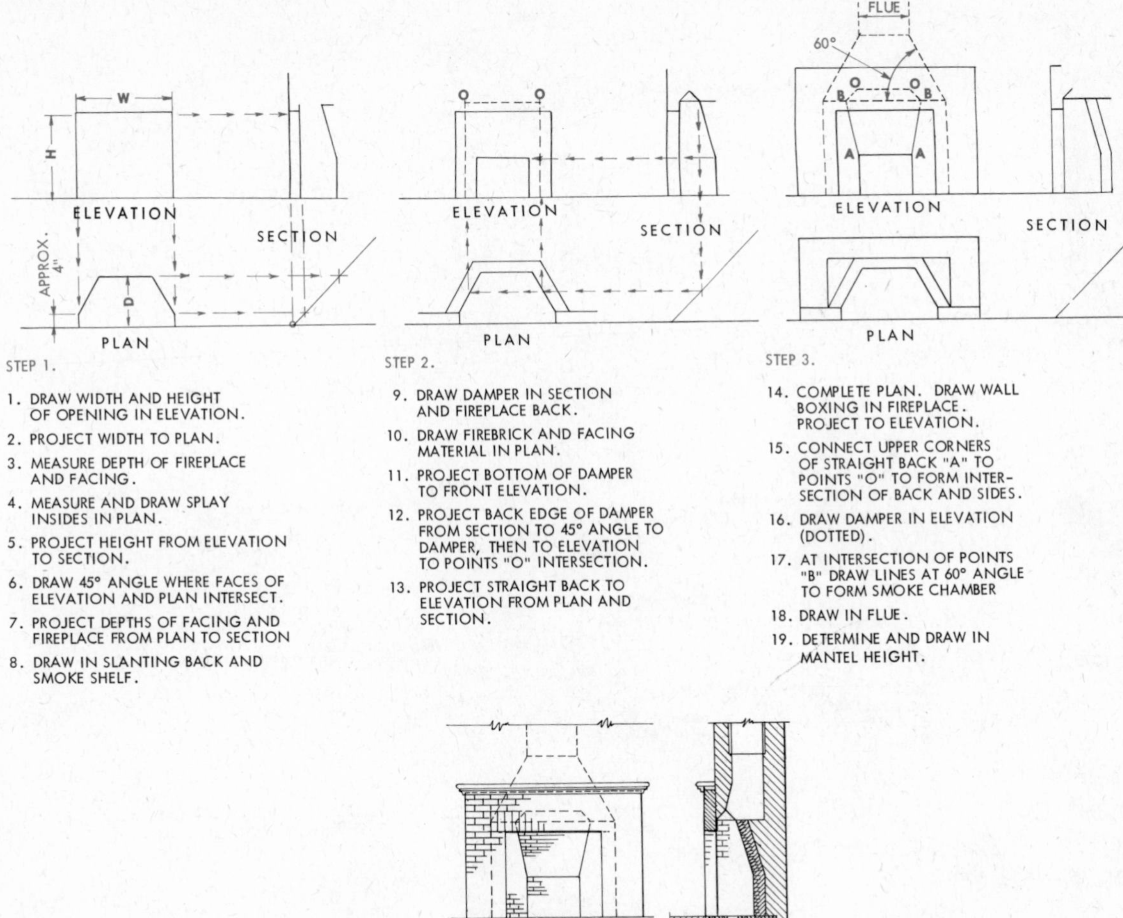

STEP 1.

1. DRAW WIDTH AND HEIGHT OF OPENING IN ELEVATION.
2. PROJECT WIDTH TO PLAN.
3. MEASURE DEPTH OF FIREPLACE AND FACING.
4. MEASURE AND DRAW SPLAY INSIDES IN PLAN.
5. PROJECT HEIGHT FROM ELEVATION TO SECTION.
6. DRAW 45° ANGLE WHERE FACES OF ELEVATION AND PLAN INTERSECT.
7. PROJECT DEPTHS OF FACING AND FIREPLACE FROM PLAN TO SECTION
8. DRAW IN SLANTING BACK AND SMOKE SHELF.

STEP 2.

9. DRAW DAMPER IN SECTION AND FIREPLACE BACK.
10. DRAW FIREBRICK AND FACING MATERIAL IN PLAN.
11. PROJECT BOTTOM OF DAMPER TO FRONT ELEVATION.
12. PROJECT BACK EDGE OF DAMPER FROM SECTION TO 45° ANGLE TO DAMPER, THEN TO ELEVATION TO POINTS "O" INTERSECTION.
13. PROJECT STRAIGHT BACK TO ELEVATION FROM PLAN AND SECTION.

STEP 3.

14. COMPLETE PLAN. DRAW WALL BOXING IN FIREPLACE. PROJECT TO ELEVATION.
15. CONNECT UPPER CORNERS OF STRAIGHT BACK "A" TO POINTS "O" TO FORM INTERSECTION OF BACK AND SIDES.
16. DRAW DAMPER IN ELEVATION (DOTTED).
17. AT INTERSECTION OF POINTS "B" DRAW LINES AT 60° ANGLE TO FORM SMOKE CHAMBER
18. DRAW IN FLUE.
19. DETERMINE AND DRAW IN MANTEL HEIGHT.

STEP 4.

20. DRAW IN BACK WALL IN SECTION, PROJECTING FROM PLAN.
21. DRAW IN HEARTH AND ASH DUMP IN SECTION.
22. PROJECT FLUE AND TOP OF SMOKE CHAMBER ACROSS TO SECTION FROM ELEVATION AND COMPLETE INSIDE OF SMOKE CHAMBER.
23. DRAW WALL ADJOINING FIREPLACE IN PLAN.

ELEVATION

SECTION

PLAN

STEP 5.

24. COMPLETE ELEVATION, SECTION AND PLAN. SHOW MATERIALS IN SECTION BY SYMBOLS. SHOW MATERIAL IN ELEVATION BY SYMBOLS.

Fig. 8-67. Follow this step-by-step drawing procedure in drawing fireplace details.

Fireplace Drawing Details

Fireplace details usually consist of three drawings. First, an *elevation* of the fireplace from the finished floor to the beginning of the flue tile. Second, a *plan view* in section where the cutting plane has been placed midway through the elevation. And third, a *vertical section* taken midway through the fireplace opening. (These three views were shown in Fig. 8-58 and 8-60.)

The *elevation view* shows the fireplace opening, general exterior design and materials, smoke chamber, and the lower portion of the flue (usually shown in hidden lines). The *plan view* shows the flue for the space heating facilities (if the same chimney is used), ash dump (if this is included), firebrick, and depth and angle (given in offset dimensions not degrees) of fire chamber sides and the hearth. The *vertical section* shows the placement of the ash dump, flue, damper, and the construction of the hearth. All these drawings give the dimensions necessary for the construction of the fireplace. The mason should be able to complete the job without any question.

The overall dimensions of the fireplace should be closely calculated. The brick size should be checked and ⅜″ should be allowed for each mortar joint. With this information, it is then possible to calculate the width and depth of the fireplace.

Step-by-Step Drawing Procedure: Fireplaces

Fig. 8-67 outlines the step-by-step procedure for detailing a fireplace. These general instructions may be used for a masonry fireplace, as well as for a metal built-in unit.

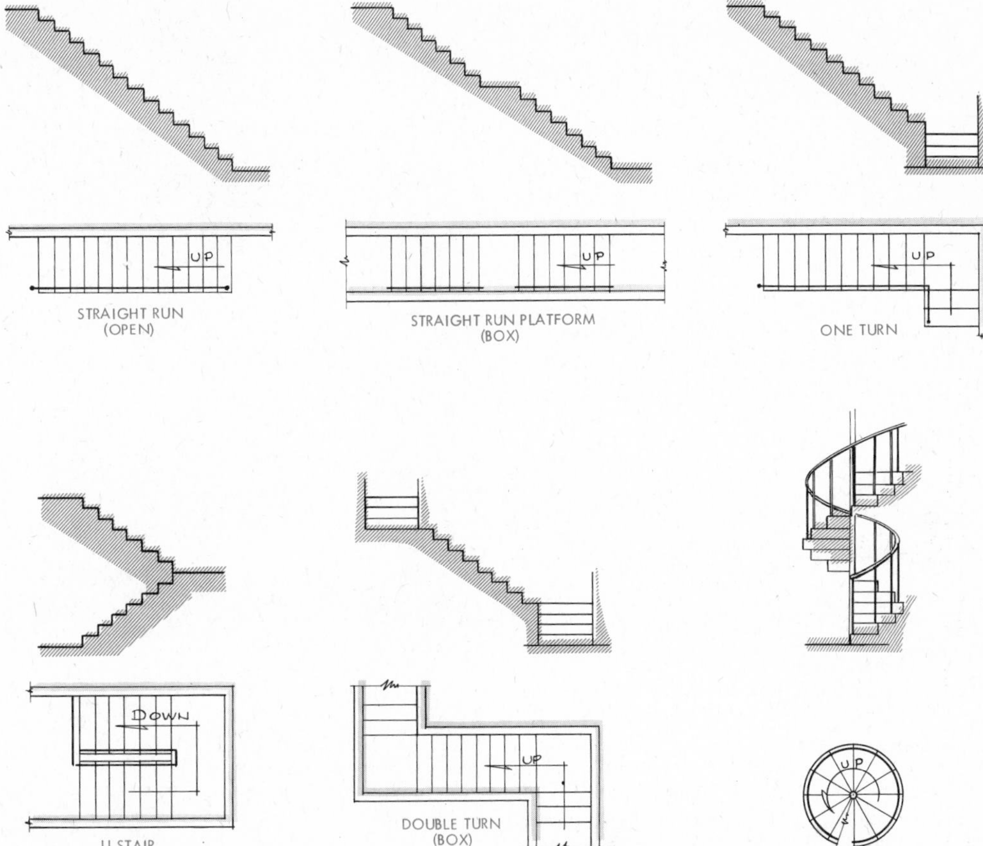

Fig. 8-68. Six basic types of stair flights are commonly used in residential housing.

Stairs

Stair construction is a specialized area within the home construction field. Many builders have found that stairs constructed by manufacturers or mills are more economical and just as efficient as those cut and built on the site. The designer should have knowledge of stair construction so he can provide the correct design and stair space. Care should be taken to assure that the stair construction is in keeping with the general house design.

A well-designed stairway should be based on three tenets: (1) the stair should be easy to ascend; (2) all stair treads and risers should be uniform; and (3) the stairs should have ample artificial and/or natural light.

Stair Types

Stairs are generally classified as "open" or "closed." A stair that has no wall on either side is an *open stair*. If the stair has a wall on one side, it is referred to as a *semi-housed stair;* if it is between two walls, it is then a *closed, housed,* or *box stair*.

It may be necessary to place a *platform* or *landing* in a *straight flight* of stairs; this is known as a *straight run* platform. Fig. 8-68 (top center). If the stair turns 90° with the landing, it is called *one turn* stair. Fig. 8-68 (top right). If a stair turns 180° at the landing, it is known as a U-stair. Fig. 8-68 (bottom left). A *double turn* stair turns 90° at each landing. Fig. 8-68 (bottom center). Circular or spiral stairs are also being used in some contemporary homes. Fig. 8-68 (bottom right) and Fig. 8-69.

Folding stairs are often used to reach attics and storage areas (such as the garage storage area). Fig. 8-70 illustrates the common design for a folding stair. These stairs are manufactured in various lengths suitable for residential ceiling heights. Tread widths are commonly 2′-0″, 2′-2″, or 2′-6″.

WOODBRIDGE ORNAMENTAL IRON CO., CHICAGO, ILLINOIS.

Fig. 8-69. The spiral stair is being used with increasing frequency.

Fig. 8-70. A folding stair may be used for reaching seldom-used spaces.

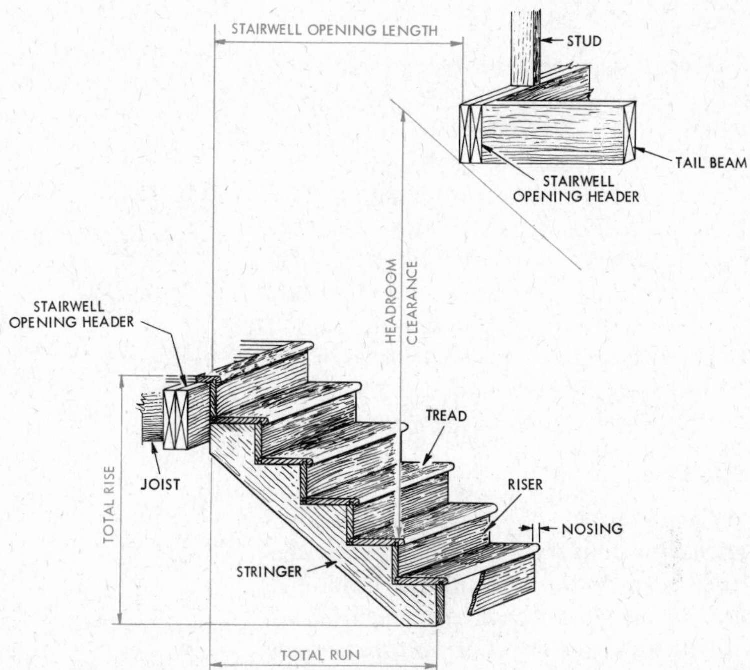

Fig. 8-71. Stair Details and Nomenclature. Stairs must be designed in accordance with the stairwell opening.

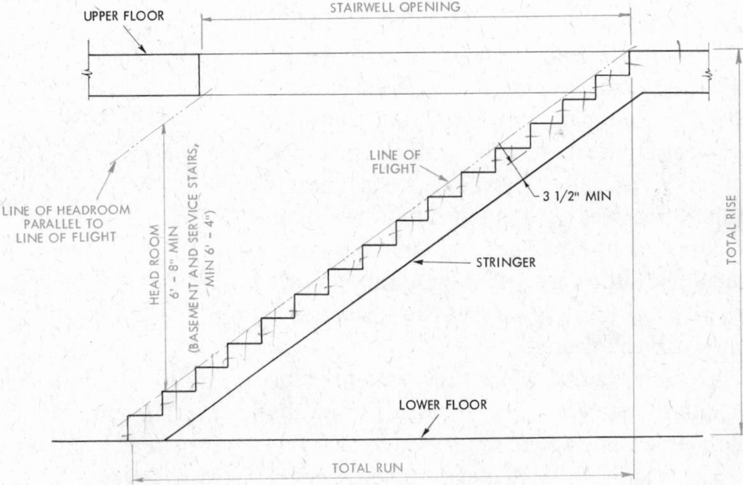

Fig. 8-72. Headroom is very important in stair design. The stairwell or the line of flight must be adjusted until the required headroom is obtained.

Basic Stair Parts

Stairs consist of three basic parts: *tread, riser,* and *stringer*. See Fig. 8-71. The *tread* is the horizontal member of the stair; the *riser* is the vertical member between any two treads or between a tread and the floor or landing. The portion of the tread extending beyond the face of the riser is called the nosing. *Stringers* carry the treads and risers through the stairwell opening.

The depth of the tread (exclusive of the nosing) is called the *run* and the height of the riser is referred to as the *rise*.

Staircase Layout

Headroom is the clearance (*measured vertically*) from the top of the tread at the front edge of the riser to the headroom line (*a line drawn from the underside of the stairwell opening header or trimmer and parallel to the line of flight.*) See Fig. 8-72 for headroom clearance and stairwell opening. Building codes specify a minimum headroom clearance of 6′-8″. Stairs between the first and second floors usually have a headroom clearance of 7′-0″. Tri-level homes require a stair headroom clearance of 7′-0″ for all stairs since each run of stairs receives approximately the same amount of traffic. The headroom for basement and attic stairs is a minimum of 6′-4″. In all cases local codes and FHA Standards should be consulted.

Opening length. The stair well opening length is important because it is during the floor framing stage of construction that this opening must be located and framed. Length of the stairwell opening, depending upon the amount of headroom clearance, is measured from header to header, or trimmer to trimmer.

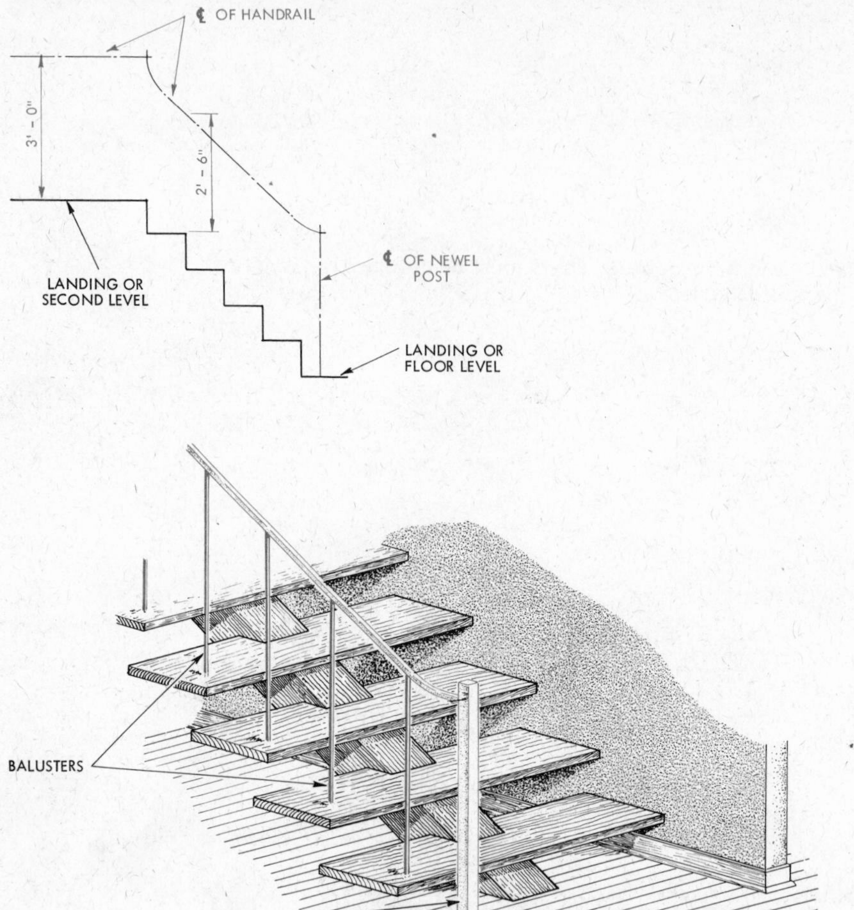

Fig. 8-73. This unusual stair adds a contemporary touch. Stair and rail parts are designated. Note the 2′-6″ height for the rail on the slope and the 3′-0″ height on the landing.

Railing. The *newel* (Fig. 8-73) is the main post, either at the top or the bottom of the stair, which receives the *handrail*. Small upright members called *balusters* are

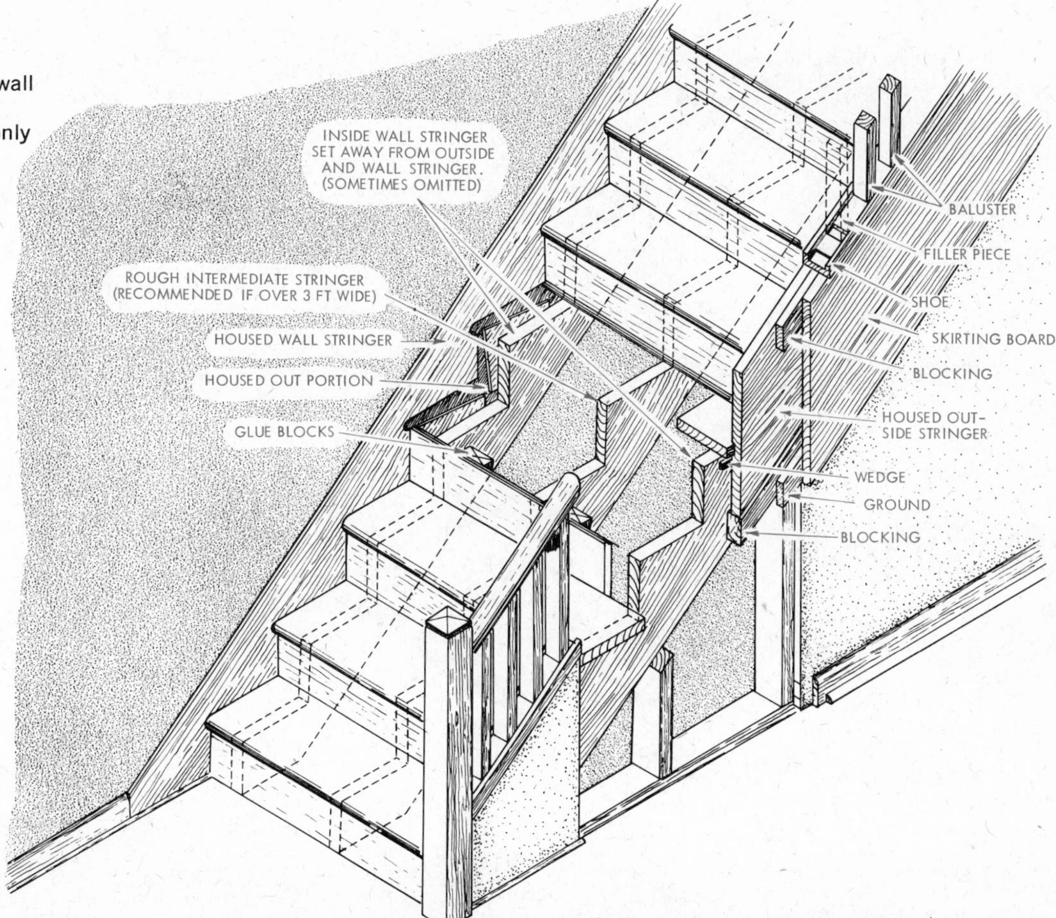

Fig. 8-74. The closed string stair uses housed wall and outside stringers to receive the tread and riser ends. The rough intermediate stringer is only used for wide stairways.

placed at the outer end of the stairs to support the handrail. The height of the handport the handrail. The height of the handrail is usually 2′-6″ from the top of the tread on a line with the face of the riser. On a landing, balcony, or main level the height of the handrail is increased to 2′-8″ or 3′-0″. The increase in height is necessary to afford the maximum protection at landings, balconies, and levels. To compensate for this increased height, the upper end of the handrail is curved upward at the top of the stairs. (This is called *ramping*.) The lower end of the handrail is finished similarly with an *easement* at the newel post. The easement prevents an abrupt change of direction. Fig. 8-73 illustrates the relationship of the newel, balusters, and railing.

Stringers. The treads and risers are supported by stringers (sometimes called carriages) which extend from floor to floor and are fastened to the double header by nails or clips. Two inside stringers are normally used for support. If the stair is wider

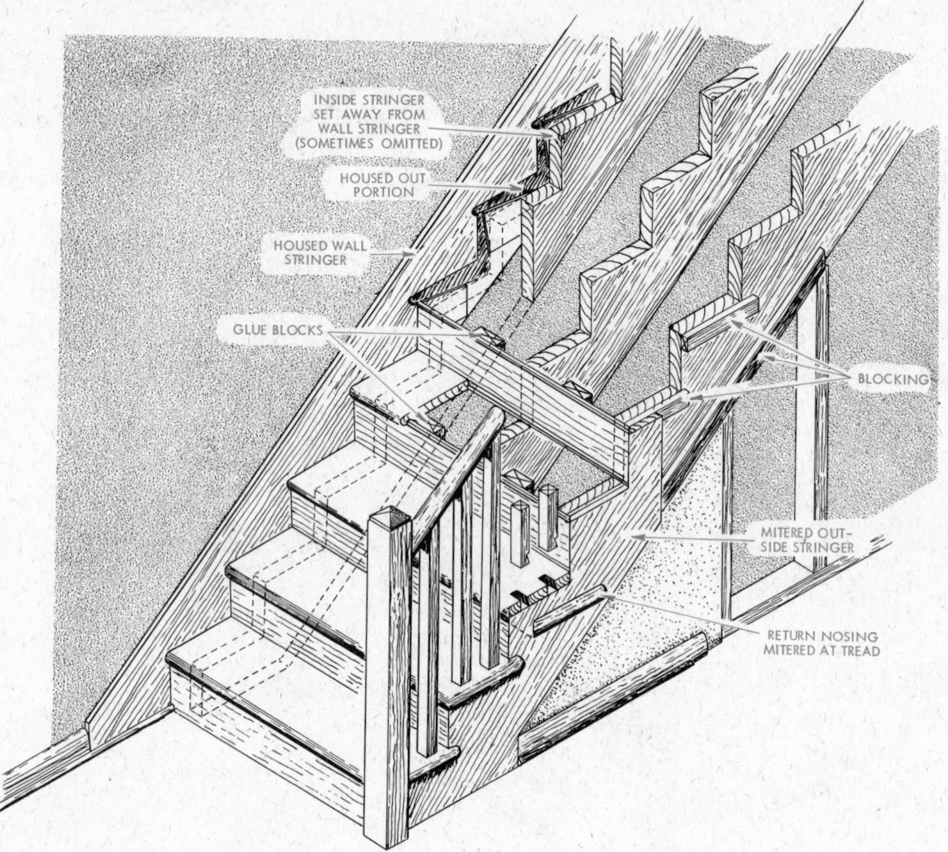

Fig. 8-75. The open string stair uses an outside stringer cut to the profile of the stair. The rough intermediate stringer is only used for wide stairways.

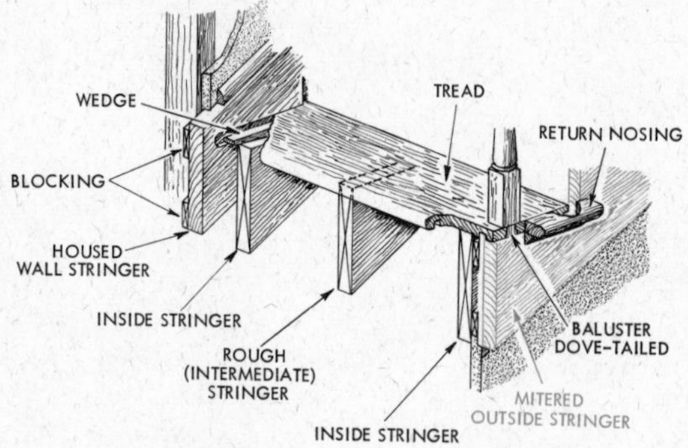

Fig. 8-75. Detail.

than 3′-0″ an intermediate stringer is used. A wall stringer and an outside stringer are used to receive the tread and riser ends. When wall and outside stringers are rabbeted (grooved, usually ½″ deep) to house the treads and risers, the stair is known as the *housed* or *closed string stair*. See Fig. 8-74. Note in Fig. 8-74 the use of wedges to insure a tight fit between the upper face of the tread and housed stringer. Note also the use of glue blocks.

In an *open string stair,* the outside stringer is cut to the profile of the stair and is *mitered* (cut and fit at an angle) against the end of the risers. Nosing is extended beyond the end of the tread by a separate solid molding. See Fig. 8-75.

Although the stair may have either closed

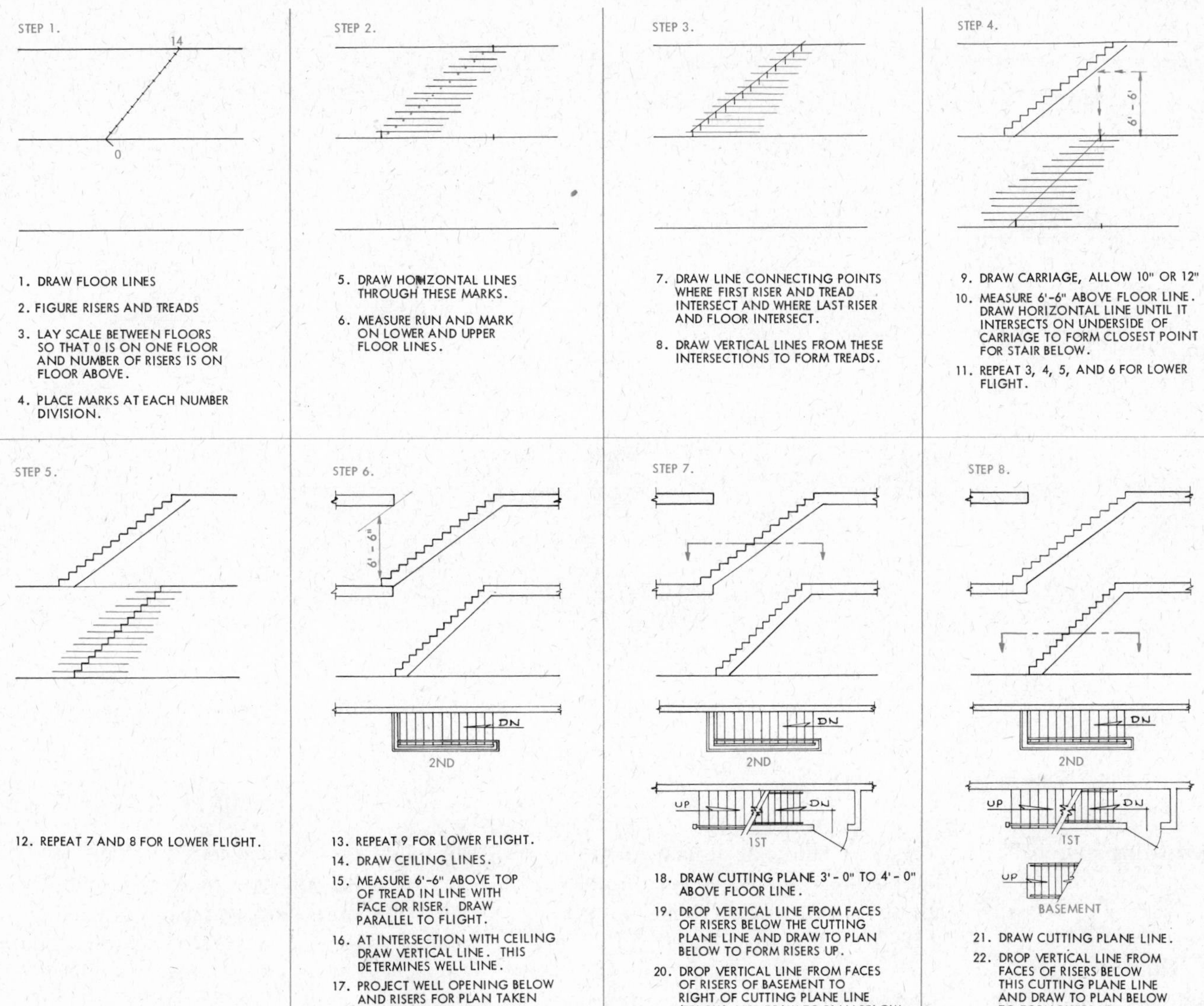

Fig. 8-76. Follow this step-by-step procedure in drawing the straight run stair.

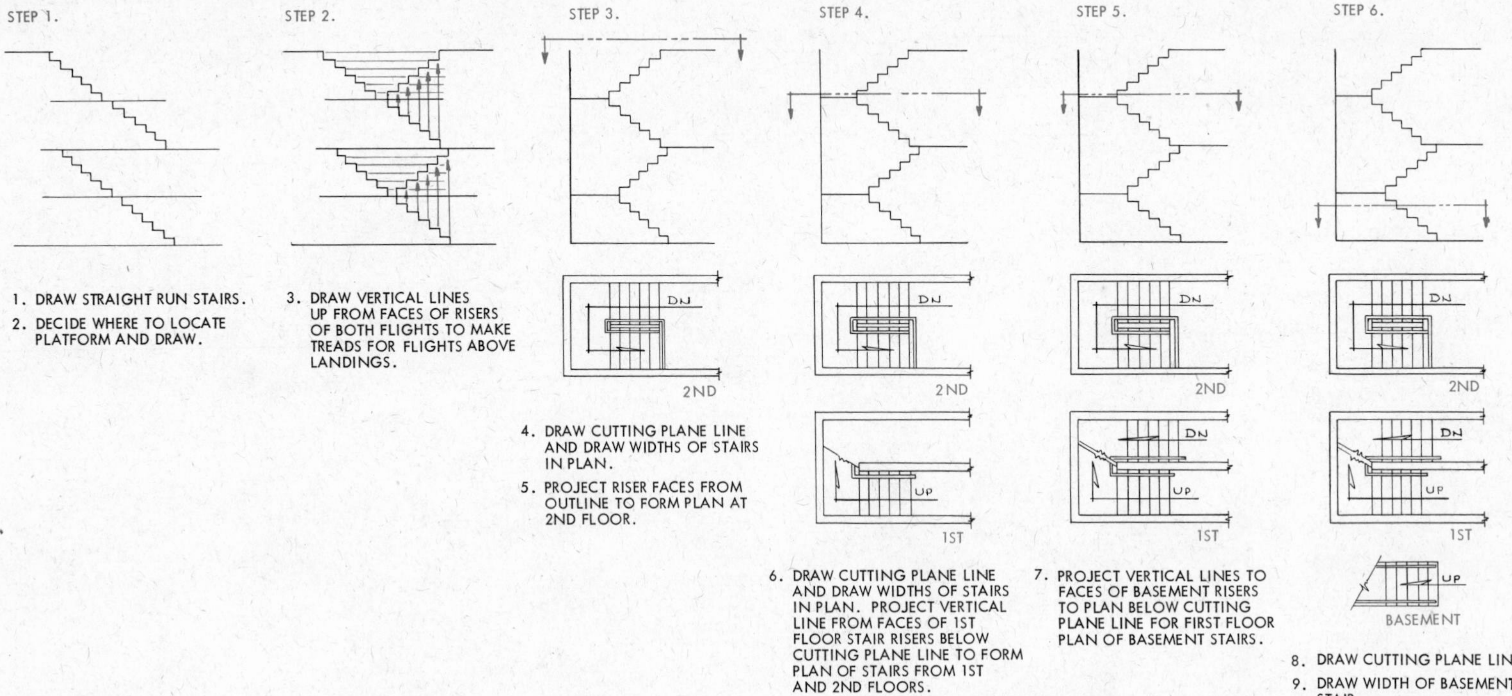

Fig. 8-77. Follow this step-by-step procedure in drawing the U-stair.

or open strings, the open string is probably the most common type.

Stair Design

Designing stairs is a matter of ascertaining a comfortable riser height and tread depth in relation to the space allotted for the stair. If a high riser is necessary, a shallower tread should be used. Conversely, if a low riser is used, a deeper tread is necessary. The total distance of two risers and one tread should be equal to the average stride of an adult while traveling the stair. *This is approximately 25″*. An uncomfortable step would result if a long tread and short riser were used. Some public buildings have long treads and short risers which are difficult to ascend or descend. Ideally a riser is 7″ to 7½″ high and the tread run is 10″ or 10½″. It is wise to follow these dimensions for stairs leading from the first to second floor and for *all* stairs in a split-level house if the required space is available. Basement or attic stairs which are usually not heavily travelled may have a slightly shorter tread and slightly higher rise. Stairs *may* be built at any angle from 20° to 50°. The *preferred* angle for safety and ease of travel is 30° to 35°.

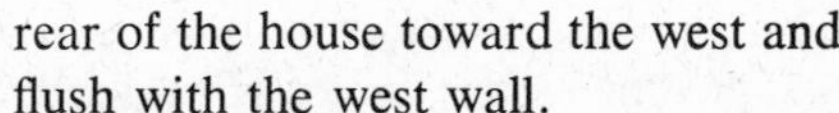

Manufacturers commonly supply stairs in widths of 3′-0″, 3′-6″, and 4′-0″; treads of 10″, 10½″, or 11½″; and risers of 7″, 7½″, or 8″.

To determine the number and dimension of risers and treads required for any stair run, the following procedure is helpful:

1. Determine the total rise of the stair (the distance from finished floor to finished floor) in inches. For purposes of illustration, this distance shall be assumed as 9′-6″ or 114″.
2. Determine approximately the number of risers (of average height) this stair will require. Assuming the average riser to be 7″, divide the total rise by the *trial* riser: 114″ ÷ 7″ = 16.285 or 16²⁄₇ risers. If, as in this illustration, the result is not a whole number, go to the *nearest* whole *number* (in this example *16 risers*).
3. Determine the exact height of each riser. Divide the total rise by the number of risers (from Step #2): 114″ ÷ 16 = 7⅛″ for each riser.
4. Determine the number of treads. The total number of treads in a stair run is one less than the number of risers. The floors are not counted as treads: 16 risers − 1 = 15 treads.
5. Determine the tread depth or run. Multiply the riser (Step #3) by 2 and subtract from 25″ (the stride of an adult's foot on a stair is approximately 25″, or 2 risers and 1 tread): 7⅛″ × 2 = 14¼″; 25″ −14¼″ = 10¾″ for each tread.
6. Determine the total run of the stair. Multiply the number of treads by the tread width: 15 × 10¾″ = 161¼″ or 13′-5¼″.

If the total run cannot be fitted into the *allotted* total run, increase the riser height (by eliminating one riser) and recalculate starting from Step #2. These six simple steps may be used to compute any type of stair—from the basement to first floor, first floor to second floor, between levels in a split level, etc.

Step-by-Step Drawing Procedure: Stairs

The step-by-step procedure for developing the stair detail is shown in Fig. 8-76. An additional illustration developing a U-type stair is depicted in Fig. 8-77.

Questions and Problems

1. Based on the pitch triangle give the amount of rise in inches of the following fractional pitches:

a. ¼	d. ⅐
b. ⁵⁄₁₂	e. ⅙
c. ⅓	f. ⅛

2. If a pitch triangle has a rise of 3½″ and a 12″ run, what is the fractional pitch?
3. A house has a floor plan with basic dimensions of 28′ × 48′, the long dimension faces the street which is on the north side of the house. A 22′ × 24′ garage is on the east side flush with the back of the house. A one-story projection of 4′-0″ × 16′-0″ is on the rear of the house toward the west and flush with the west wall.
   a. Draw a hip roof plan for a one-story building using this plan.
   b. Draw a gable roof plan for a two-story building.
   c. Draw a hip roof for a split-level house.
   d. Draw a gable roof with dormers for a one-and-a-half-story house.
4. In your own words, define the terms: *pitch, span,* and *run.*
5. Detail the following cornices using a scale of 1″ = 1′-0″, 1½″ = 1′-0″, or 3″ = 1′-0″. Call out all materials and sizes.
   A. An open cornice for a contemporary style home: The roof (built-up tar and gravel) has a rise of 1½″ in 12″ of run and overhangs the frame-backed brick veneer wall by 2′-6″. The interior finish is ½″ dry wall and the outside of the stud wall is covered with fabricated fiberboard. The ceiling joists are 2″ × 6″.
   B. A box cornice for a Cape Cod house: The roof overhangs the clapboard frame wall 3″, and has ⅓ pitch. The ceiling joist is a 2″ × 6″. The interior finish is plaster and the outside of the stud wall is covered with fabricated fiberboard. Three inch batts are used for insulation. Use a 6″ half-round hanging gutter.
   C. A box cornice for a 4″ rise in 12″.

run: A veneer wall with a concrete block backing of 16″ is used. Plaster is applied directly to the concrete block. A 2″ × 8″ plate is secured to the back-up units by a ¾″ × 16″ anchor bolt. Use a 2″ × 2″ lookout to carry the plancier level to the wall. Use a 5″ metal box gutter.

6. Select a standard size leader for a roof having the following specifications:
   a. Gable roof (⅛ pitch) on a rectangular plan, 36′ × 24′, having a leader at each corner.
   b. Hip roof (⅙ pitch all sides) on a rectangular plan, 50′ ×26′, having a leader at each corner.
7. Why is it necessary to place the gutter below the roof line?
8. What type of materials may be used for flashing:
   a. Around a chimney projecting through a roof?
   b. Around a window?
   c. At the base of a masonry veneer wall?
9. What is the general purpose of flashing?
10. What are the purposes of vents in a frame wall and weep holes in masonry veneer wall?
11. How may the decision to use trussed rafters rather than conventional framing affect:
    a. The room arrangement?
    b. The basic philosophy of planning?
12. What methods may be used for fabricating trussed rafters? What are the advantages and disadvantages of each method?
13. Compare the sizes of framing members necessary for a conventionally framed roof (include ceiling joist) with the sizes used for a trussed rafter. The roof has a ⅙ pitch and a clear span of 28′. Assume a partition is placed midway in the 28′ span.
14. Why is it necessary to have adequate ventilation in the attic?
15. What method(s) of venting the attic seem to be most advantageous?
16. Explain the causes for ice dams forming in the gutter. What are possible remedies?
17. Calculate the net free area for a roof having a ceiling area of:
    a. 975 sq. ft. with gable end louvers.
    b. 1,200 sq. ft. with continuous soffit vent.
    c. 1,000 sq. ft. with roof louvers.
    d. 1,175 sq. ft. with continuous ridge vent.
    e. 1,450 sq. ft. with continuous ridge and soffit vent.

    Specify from a manufacturer's brochure the necessary sizes of venting devices needed to satisfy the calculated requirements.
18. What methods are used to specify and indicate the sizes of windows on a set of drawings?
19. What type of window provides the *least* amount of draft when open?
20. What type of window may be opened during a thunder shower without the probability of having rain enter?
21. Using a scale of 1½″ = 1′-0″ draw a:
    a. Section on the vertical ℄ of a window.
    b. One-half exterior elevation and one-half interior elevation of a window.
    c. One-half plan on the exterior elevation of a double-hung 2 light 24/20 window with double strength glass.

    Indicate all materials and notes.
22. Why would it be advisable to use a louvered door on a closet?
23. A designer must select doors for a closet having an opening of 7′-0″. The room is occupied by two sisters; both frequently dress at the same time. What type of doors (kind, style, and action) would be best in this situation?
24. Select an opening size for a conventional, single-opening fireplace and sketch three different elevations using different materials.
25. Why should the chimney be carried above the highest point of the roof?
26. What purpose does the smoke shelf and damper serve in a well functioning fireplace?
27. What relation exists between the size of the fireplace opening and the flue?
28. Why are the sides of a single-opening fireplace angled?
29. Select a fireplace (single, projecting, double-opening, etc.), use the recommended proportional dimensions, and

make several sketched preliminary studies of the exterior treatment. Have the instructor criticize the studies. Change as per his suggestions. Make a set of detail drawings, complete with dimensions, at a scale of 1½″ = 1′-0″. Show an elevation from the finished floor to flue tile or appropriate point above. Take a vertical section through the fire chamber. Extend the vertical section up to flue tile and down to the ash pit and footing.

30. Calculate the height and number of risers and the depth and number of treads for a stair that will extend between the first and second floor (8′-8″). What is the length of the stairwell opening if the headroom is 6′-8″?
31. Make a sectional drawing of the stair calculated in problem 30 above. Show the floor framing tie-ins, headers, etc. Completely dimension and call out all materials and sizes. Scale: 1″= 1′-0″.
32. If space is limited for a stair run what type of stair could be designed to use a minimal amount of space?

RILCO LAMINATED PRODUCTS.

The loads of a structure must be carefully calculated to determine the support sizes needed. Here, fabricated wood trusses were used in constructing an Illinois airplane factory.

Support Members and Floor Plans 9

As mentioned earlier, a floor plan is a two dimensional drawing (length & width) which represents a specific floor or level of a building. The floor is represented, with its roof or ceiling removed, as it would appear when viewed from above. Fig. 9-1 illustrates this concept. The name given to a specific plan refers to the particular floor or level of the building, e.g., first floor, second floor, ground level, upper level, etc. Detailed floor plans are drawn to a small scale using various standardized symbols and conventions. Prior to actually drawing the detailed floor plan, however, it is necessary to compute the structural members which support a particular floor. Structural members (joists, girders, columns, etc.) are directly related to the function and size of the rooms which they will support.

This chapter discusses the computing and design of support members and the planning and drafting of floor plans.

Fig. 9-1 Each plan view represents a horizontal section through the structure.

Computing Support Members

Support members are those structural parts which carry the load of any structure. The size and layout of the structural members are usually shown on floor plans. Before drawing the floor plans, however, the loads must be determined, and the structural members must be computed. When the load on a particular support member is known, the size, depending upon the material, may be calculated using standard tables. Tables are issued by the Federal Housing Administration and by various manufacturing and research companies, giving sizes, lengths, strengths, and loading capacities of building materials and products.

Most cities and communities have building codes which specify the minimum strength of structural members. For safety, the architect or designer must *never* fall short of the legal minimum.

Loads imposed upon structural members are classified as *live loads* and *dead loads*. *Live loads* are those static or moving weights, not part of the original structure, which the building is designed to support. Examples of such weights are the occupants, furniture, equipment, snow, wind, etc. *Dead loads* are those static or fixed weights of the *material* of the structure itself. Examples of dead loads are the weights of the lumber, dry wall, flooring, roofing, etc. Dead load weight may be calculated using the size and established weights of the various materials.

Structures are designed to support predetermined loads. The following sections cover the loads of various support members.

Roof Loads

Roofs must be designed to withstand the live loads imposed by snow and wind.

The additional load imposed on a roof by snow will vary. The variance is dependent upon two factors: (1) the pitch of the roof and (2) the geographic area. A roof with a steep slope will impose a smaller load since the snow will slide or be blown off. A roof with a slight slope will have a greater tendency to retain the snow, thereby imposing a greater load. Table 9-1 gives loads in pounds per square foot for various roof angles.

Wind loads work exactly opposite of snow loads. The greater the slope of the roof the greater the wind pressure. Loads vary from 15 to 35 lbs. per sq. ft. for roofs with slopes from 15 to 45 degrees. Wind loads are not considered for flat or nearly flat roofs.

Building codes usually specify what loads are to be used. Normally, the snow and wind loads are usually taken as 30 lbs. per sq. ft. for all locations. In extreme situations, 40 lbs. per sq. ft. is considered adequate.

Sonic Booms. As we advance further into the age of jet transportation *sonic booms* become an increasingly significant factor in building construction. A sonic boom is a strong pressure wave created by an aircraft travelling at or exceeding the speed of sound. The swift movement of the aircraft compresses the air resulting in a pressure or sound wave. The shape of the sound wave is conical with the apex of the cone near the aircraft and the base trailing on the ground. The impact of the wave will impose a live load anywhere within the elliptical base of the cone.

A sonic boom is measured in pounds per square foot above the normal atmospheric pressure. The higher the aircraft, the smaller the boom and the smaller the load. Loads imposed by sonic booms are not prolonged, such as snow loads, but, rather, cause a momentary shock or impact. A load as much as 5 lbs. per sq. ft. may be exerted (in addition to atmospheric pressure) by a plane exceeding the speed of sound at 20,000 ft. or below. Large plate glass windows may be damaged by 3 to 5 lbs. per sq. ft. Ordinary residential windows may also be damaged by planes flying at the speed of sound between 20,000 and 30,000 ft. In the future, residential construction should take these added loads into consideration.

TABLE 9-1
SNOW LOADS

AREA UNITED STATES	ROOF ANGLE	
	FLAT OR SLIGHT ANGLE 0°–25°	STEEP ANGLE 25°–45°
NORTHWEST NORTHEAST	45 lbs/Sq. Ft.	15 lbs/Sq. Ft.
CENTRAL WESTERN	35 lbs/Sq. Ft.	10 lbs/Sq. Ft.
SOUTH PACIFIC COAST	10 lbs/Sq. Ft.	0 lbs/Sq. Ft.

Rafters

Support for the roof sheathing and roofing materials is provided by rafters. Rafters must be sufficiently strong to support the protective covering (roof boards, plywood decking, and roofing material) without deflection.

The selection of the correct rafter size is based on the following step-by-step procedure:

Step 1. *Determine rafter pitch.* If no pitch angle has been computed, scale the amount of rise for each foot of run from the elevation showing the roof slope. The roof in Fig. 9-2 has a slope angle of 26°-30′. This slope is properly referred to as a ¼ *pitch* roof which has 6″ rise in 12″ run.

Step 2. *Determine the span of the rafter.* This may be obtained by scaling the elevation. The span is measured horizontally from outside of the stud face to a ℄ dropped from the ridge, as shown in Fig. 9-2.

Step 3. *Determine the rafter size.* If the pitch of the roof is greater than 5″ rise in 12″ run, use Table 9-2, "Maximum Clear Spans of Rafters". (If the pitch of the roof is less than 5″ rise in 12″ run, use Table 9-4 and calculate as if the rafter was a floor joist.) Choose the type of lumber to be used, read down the column to the value nearest the actual clear span of the rafter, then read left. The column headed "Lumber Size" will indicate the proper size of rafter; the column headed "Spacing Center to Center" will give the distance rafters are spaced (O.C.). For example, a redwood rafter used in a roof with a slope of 7″ rise in 12″ run and with a clear span of 9′-10″, would require a lumber size of 2″ x 6″ and a spacing of 20″ O.C. Read down the

TABLE 9-2

MAXIMUM CLEAR SPANS OF RAFTERS

For Wood and Asphalt Shingle Roofs

(Rafters for slate, tile, or asbestos-cement (rigid) shingle roofs shall be of sufficient size to carry the load)

Assumed Total Live and Dead Load—40 lbs. per sq. ft.

(Clear span shall mean the distance measured *horizontally* from plate to a point directly beneath the ridge. The actual rafter length will depend on the roof slope and must be determined accordingly)

For Roof with a Minimum Slope of 5 to 12

Lumber Size		Spacing Center to Center	Maximum Clear Span					
			Minimum Fiber Stress, 1,200 Pounds		Minimum Fiber Stress, 1,000 Pounds		Minimum Fiber Stress, less than 1,000 Pounds	
Nominal	Actual		Douglas Fir (Coast Region and Inland Empire), Southern Yellow Pine, Western Larch		West Coast Hemlock, Cypress, Redwood, Tamarack		All Other Softwoods	
		Inches	Ft.	In.	Ft.	In.	Ft.	In.
2 x 4......	1⅝ x 3⅝	24	6	6	6	1	5	1
		20	7	3	6	7	5	6
		16	8	1	7	4	6	2
		12	9	4	8	6	7	2
2 x 6......	1⅝ x 5⅝	24	10	3	9	4	7	8
		20	11	4	10	5	8	8
		16	12	6	11	5	9	6
		12	14	2	13	1	11	0
2 x 8......	1⅝ x 7½	24	13	8	12	6	10	0
		20	15	2	13	8	11	0
		16	16	7	15	3	12	1
		12	18	4	16	7	14	3

NOTE.—Rafters on roofs with slopes less than 5 to 12 shall be figured same as floor joists.

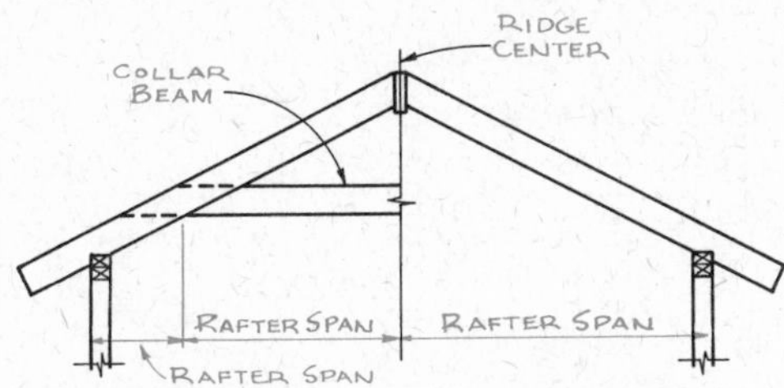

Fig. 9-2. The rafter span is the horizontal distance between the wall plate and ridge center, wall plate and collar beam, or collar beam and ridge center.

column under "Redwood" to the nearest maximum clear span (take the higher span — here 10′-5″) and then left to size and spacing.

Note: If a collar beam is used (See Fig. 9-2) a smaller size rafter is required since the longer of the two spans is used in selecting the correct rafter size. The collar beam prevents the rafters from spreading and serves to prevent deflection.

Roof Framing Plan

Sometimes it is desirable to draft a framing plan for the roof. Once the sizing of the members is determined, the details of the rafter run may be given, as illustrated in Plan A or B. Notes referring to the size of the roof framing members are usually called out with a leader. If the notes are extensive, as in Plan A for a flat roof, the information on sizing may be keyed in a series of notes on the drawing. On the other hand, if the notes relative to sizing and spacing are not as prevalent, they are called out with a leader as in Plan B for a gable roof. Many of the dimensions for the roof framing plans may be taken from the elevation and related details.

Trusses

The conventionally framed roof in contemporary residential construction is slowly being replaced in many instances by the trussed roof. Regardless of the style of roof, the principle of the truss may be employed. A detailed discussion of trusses is given in Chapter 8. The student may refer to this earlier chapter for detailed background information. Probably the most widely used truss in light frame house construction is the Fink truss (Fig. 9-3). This is not to say, however, that other truss designs are not also used. Table 9-3 gives sizing for the Fink truss (spaced 2′ O.C.) dependent upon the slope and span. (The dimensions and letters in Table 9-3 refer to Fig. 9-3.)

To determine the correct sizes of chords and webs for a Fink truss using Table 9-3

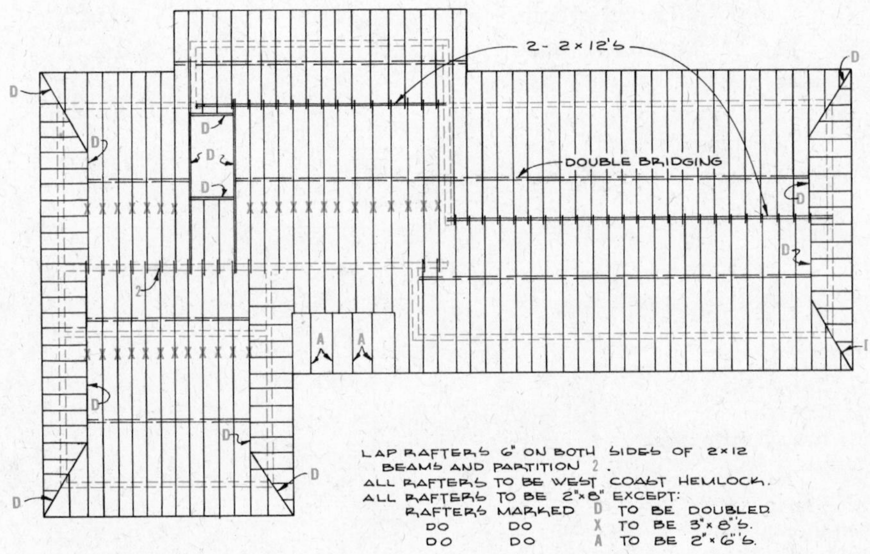

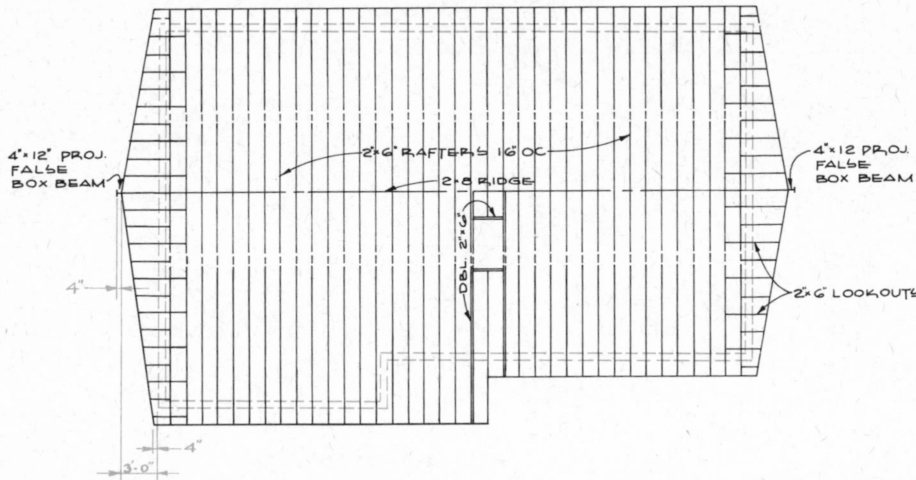

ROOF PLAN B

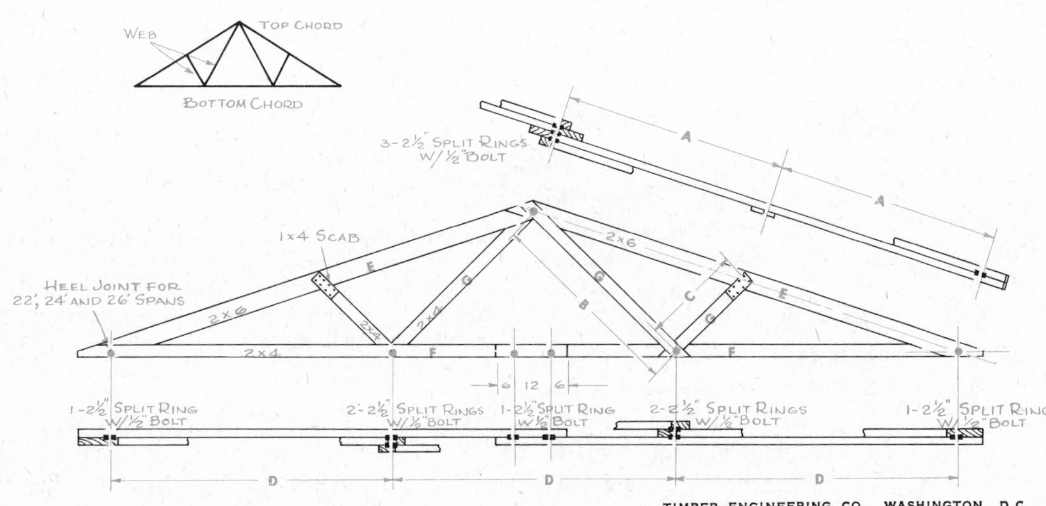

Fig. 9-3. The Fink truss is probably the most common design used in residential construction.

follow the steps outlined below.

Step 1. *Select the desired slope and length of span.* Assume a truss having a 4/12 rise and run with a 28′-0″ span is desired. Reading from left to right in the table, the top chord section (A) has a length of 7′-4⁹⁄₁₆″. The longer of the two webs (B) has a length of 6′-6¹³⁄₁₆″. The short web (C) is 3′-3¼″ long. One-third of the bottom chord (D) is 9′-4″ in length.

Step 2. *Determine the size dimension of the lumber.* Refer to the lumber heading of the table and obtain the size dimensions for the component members. For this example continue reading across the row for a 4/12 rise and run, 28′-0″ span. The top chord will be a 2″ x 8″, the bottom chord will be a 2″ x 6″, and the webs will be 2″ x 4″. The lumber lengths needed are also given.

Joists

The structural members which support the floor at each house level, including the attic, are called joists. These horizontal heavy members are laid edgewise and parallel with each other to form the floor support. Designing and selecting these joists depends entirely upon the loads which they are expected to support and their material strength.

The following step-by-step procedure illustrates the fundamental design criteria for

FINK TRUSS SIZING WITH DRYWALL CEILING

PITCH	LENGTH OF SPAN	DIMENSIONS A	DIMENSIONS B	DIMENSIONS C	DIMENSIONS D	LUMBER SIZE (TWO LENGTHS NEEDED) 2×8	2×6	2×4
4 / 12	20	5'-3 1/4"	4'-8 3/16"	2'-3 13/16"	6'-8"		E (12'-0")	F (12'-0") G (8'-0")
	22	5'-9 9/16"	5'-1 7/8"	2'-6 3/4"	7'-4"		E (14'-0")	F (14'-0") G (10'-0")
	24	6'-3 7/8"	5'-7 1/2"	2'-9 9/16"	8'-0"		E (14'-0")	F (14'-0") G (10'-0")
	26	6'-10 3/16"	6'-1 3/16"	3'-0 7/16"	8'-8"		E (16'-0")	F (16'-0") G (10'-0")
	28	7'-4 9/16"	6'-6 13/16"	3'-3 1/4"	9'-4"	E (16'-0")	F * (16'-0")	F (16'-0") G (12'-0")
	30	7'-10 7/8"	7'-0 1/2"	3'-6 1/16"	10'-0"	E (18'-0")	F * (18'-0")	F (18'-0") G (12'-0")
	32	8'-5 3/16"	7'-6 3/16"	3'-8 7/8"	10'-8"	E (18'-0")	F * (18'-0")	F (18'-0") G (12'-0")
5 / 12	20	5'-5"	5'-3 5/8"	2'-7 5/8"	6'-8"		E (12'-0")	F (12'-0") G (10'-0")
	22	5'-11 1/2"	5'-10 1/16"	2'-10 13/16"	7'-4"		E (14'-0")	F (14'-0") G (10'-0")
	24	6'-6"	6'-4 7/16"	3'-2"	8'-0"		E (14'-0")	F (14'-0") G (12'-0")
	26	7'-0 1/2"	6'-10 7/8"	3'-5 1/4"	8'-8"		E (16'-0")	F (16'-0") G (12'-0")
	28	7'-7"	7'-5 1/4"	3'-8 7/16"	9'-4"		E,F * (16'-0")	F (16'-0") G (12'-0")
	30	8'-1 1/2"	7'-11 11/16"	3'-11 5/8"	10'-0"		E,F * (18'-0")	F (18'-0") G (14'-0")
	32	8'-8"	8'-6 1/16"	4'-2 13/16"	10'-8"		E (20'-0") F * (18'-0")	F (18'-0") G (14'-0")
6 / 12	20	5'-7 1/16"	5'-11 11/16"	2'-11 5/8"	6'-8"		E (12'-0")	F (12'-0") G (10'-0")
	22	6'-1 13/16"	6'-6 7/8"	3'-3 1/4"	7'-4"		E (14'-0")	F (14'-0") G (12'-0")
	24	6'-8 1/2"	7'-2 1/8"	3'-6 7/8"	8'-0"		E (16'-0")	F (14'-0") G (12'-0")
	26	7'-3 3/16"	7'-9 5/16"	3'-10 7/16"	8'-8"		E (16'-0")	F (16'-0") G (12'-0")
	28	7'-9 15/16"	8'-4 9/16"	4'-2 1/16"	9'-4"		E (18'-0") F * (16'-0")	F (16'-0") G (14'-0")
	30	8'-4 5/8"	8'-11 3/4"	4'-5 11/16"	10'-0"		E,F * (18'-0")	F (18'-0") G (16'-0")
	32	8'-11 5/16"	9'-6 13/16"	4'-9 1/4"	10'-8"		E (20'-0") F * (18'-0")	F (18'-0") G (16'-0")
7 / 12	20	5'-9 7/16"	6'-8 3/16"	3'-3 7/8"	6'-8"		E (14'-0")	F,G (12'-0")
	22	6'-4 7/16"	7'-4 1/4"	3'-7 15/16"	7'-4"		E (14'-0")	F (14'-0") G (12'-0")
	24	6'-11 5/8"	8'-0 5/16"	3'-11 15/16"	8'-0"		E (16'-0")	F,G (14'-0")
	26	7'-6 5/16"	8'-8 3/8"	4'-4"	8'-8"		E (16'-0")	F (16'-0") G (14'-0")
	28	8'-1 1/4"	9'-4 7/16"	4'-8"	9'-4"		E (18'-0") F * (16'-0")	F,G (16'-0")
	30	8'-8 3/16"	10'-0 1/2"	5'-0 1/16"	10'-0"		E (20'-0") F * (18'-0")	F (18'-0") G (16'-0")
	32	9'-3 1/8"	10'-8 9/16"	5'-4 1/16"	10'-8"		E (20'-0") F * (18'-0")	F,G (18'-0")

* BOTTOM CHORD SIZES FOR PLASTER CEILING

LIVE LOAD, 35 LBS PER SQUARE FT; DEAD CEILING LOAD, 10 LBS PER SQUARE FT; SPACED 2'-0" OC

selecting the proper joists for a particular application.

Step 1. *Determine use and expected joist load.* If a selected set of joists is to be used to support a floor level, the load per square foot on one joist must first be determined. In most areas, building codes provide limitations and recommendations for joist loading. For example, if the joists are selected for supporting a floor area used for living, the recommended loading allowance would be 40 lbs. per sq. ft. for live loads and 10 lbs. per sq. ft. for dead loads. If the joists are to be used to support an attic floor which is not expected to carry any live loads (i.e., an attic floor having no storage space), the loading allowance would be only 10 lbs. per sq. ft. (dead load). If future storage or living space is desired, the attic will require 50 lbs. per sq. ft. (total allowance for live and dead loads).

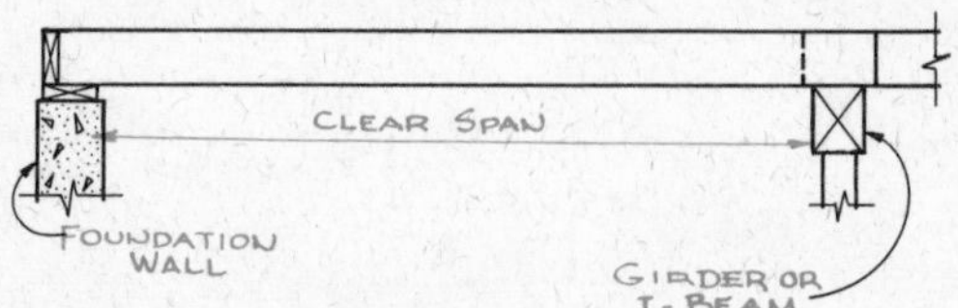

Fig. 9-4. The clear span length is measured from the **inside** of supports.

Step 2. *Determine the joist span.* Measure the length of joist span from support to support (See Fig. 9-4) and find the *maximum* span for each floor (the bearing sur-

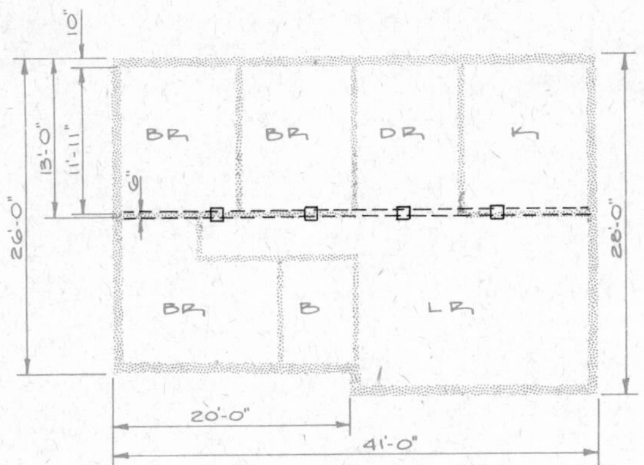

WOOD GIRDER ====
WOOD POST □

Fig. 9-5. This floor plan for a single-story, ranch-type home shows the placement of the girder and posts. The roof is framed in a conventional manner thereby requiring a bearing partition. The roof has a 1/4 pitch. No provision has been made for attic storage. The basement ceiling is finished with acoustical tile.

face, 3″ to 6″ at each end, is not counted). The maximum span is used so the joist sizes will be equal.

Fig. 9-5 shows a medium sized ranch type home, with a maximum load of 50 lbs. The girder is located in a central position below the wall separating the bedroom from the hall, and the dining room and kitchen from the living room (see figure). The clear span of the joists in the rear half of the house is 11′-11″; in the front half, 13′-11″. The joist span used in further calculations will be 13′-11″, since this is the greater of the two spans.

Step 3. *Determine the joist size.*

A. *Floor joists.* Table 9-4 gives

TABLE 9-4

MAXIMUM SPANS FOR FLOOR JOISTS

Assumed Live Load, 40 Pounds per Square Foot; Dead Load, 10 Pounds per Square Foot

LUMBER SIZE		Spacing Center to Center	MAXIMUM CLEAR SPAN					
			Minimum Fiber Stress, 1,200 Pounds		Minimum Fiber Stress, 1,000 Pounds		Minimum Fiber Stress, less than 1,000 Pounds	
Nominal	Actual		Douglas Fir (Coast Region and Inland Empire), Southern Yellow Pine, Western Larch		West Coast Hemlock, Cypress, Redwood, Tamarack		All Other Softwoods	
		Inches	Ft.	In.	Ft.	In.	Ft.	In.
2 x 6	1⅝ x 5⅝	16	9	1	8	6	7	9
		12	10	0	9	4	8	7
2 x 8	1⅝ x 7½	16	12	1	11	4	10	4
		12	13	3	12	5	11	4
3 x 8	2⅝ x 7½	16	14	0	13	2	12	1
		12	15	4	14	4	13	2
2 x 10	1⅝ x 9½	16	15	3	14	4	13	1
		12	16	8	15	8	14	4
3 x 10	2⅝ x 9½	16	17	8	16	9	15	2
		12	19	3	18	1	16	6
2 x 12	1⅝ x 11½	16	18	5	17	3	15	10
		12	20	1	18	10	17	3

the maximum spans for floor joists. Assume the normal load imposed on the floor joists is 50 lbs. (average for a one story house). Choose the type of lumber to be used, and read down the column to the desired clear span length. Read across this row to the column headed "Lumber Sizes". This figure represents the correct size of floor joist for the imposed load. Assume, for example, the type of lumber selected for the floor joists is yellow pine. Considering the type of lumber and span (See Step #2, 13′-11″), the nearest clear length is 14′-0″, therefore the resultant joist size is 3″ x 8″, with 16″ O.C.

B. *Ceiling Joists.* Table 9-5 gives the maximum spans for ceiling joists. Since many houses have low pitched roofs, the attic is virtually non-existent. A dead load of 10 lbs. per square foot may be assumed to be adequate. (If the attic floor is used for *light storage,* however, a live load of 20 lbs. per sq. ft. is necessary. If there is a possibility of converting to finished rooms, a live load of 40 lbs. per sq. ft. is recommended. See Table 9-4.) Normally the same type of lumber is used for both the floor and ceiling joists. Select the type of lumber, read down the column to the desired span, then across the row to the "Lumber Size." The resultant figure represents the correct size ceiling joist. With a 13′-11″ clear span, the size would be 2″ x 6″ for yellow pine, with 20″ O.C.

TABLE 9-5

MAXIMUM SPANS FOR CEILING JOISTS

Live Load, None; Dead Load, 10 Pounds per Square Foot

Lumber Size		Spacing Center to Center	Maximum Clear Span					
			Minimum Fiber Stress, 1,200 Pounds		Minimum Fiber Stress, 1,000 Pounds		Minimum Fiber Stress, less than 1,000 Pounds	
Nominal	Actual		Douglas Fir (Coast Region and Inland Empire), Southern Yellow Pine, Western Larch		West Coast Hemlock, Cypress, Redwood, Tamarack		All Other Softwoods	
		Inches	Ft.	In.	Ft.	In.	Ft.	In.
2 x 4	1⅝ x 3⅝	20	9	6	9	2	8	2
		16	10	0	9	8	8	7
		12	11	0	10	6	9	4
2 x 6	1⅝ x 5⅝	20	14	6	13	10	12	5
		16	15	4	14	8	13	3
		12	16	7	15	10	14	2
2 x 8	1⅝ x 7½	20	19	0	18	2	16	2
		16	20	2	19	3	17	2
		12	21	8	20	0	18	6

NOTE.—Where the attic space above ceiling joists is unfinished but is usable for storage space, or if the space is suitable for finishing into future habitable rooms, the spans for the ceiling joists shall be figured the same as for floor joists.

Bearing Walls

Bearing walls or partitions carry loads imposed by floor and/or ceiling joists above. Each stud in the wall acts as a small post or column. Since the stud is a 2″ x 4″, and the unsupported length must be reduced to prevent lateral flexure, it must be bridged near the center with horizontal solid bridging. See Chapter 7, Fig. 7-31.

Girders

In residential construction, the girder is a structural member that supports either a wall or joists. The inner ends of the joists usually rest on the girder. The outer ends of the joists rest on the foundation wall (or are supported by masonry, a sill, ribbon, or girt). Since most homes are wider than 14′ or 15′ it is desirable to plan the girder near the center of the structure to prevent flexure and to prevent the necessity of using extra heavy floor joists to cover a long span. The girder replaces an interior wall in the basement (which would be used to support the joists) and provides an open area. Girders may be steel I-beam, solid wood, or built-up or laminated from individual pieces of lumber.

The following explains the procedure used in selecting the proper girder size.

Step 1. *Determine the best location for the girder.* Locate the girder in a central position and under a partition if possible. The joist span should not exceed 15′-0″. If the joist span is greater the size of joist will be appreciably increased. The girder in Fig. 9-5 has been placed off center to coincide with the partition.

Step 2. *Compute the girder half width.* A girder will support one-half of the joist span on each side of the girder. See Figs. 9-6 and 9-7. To find half width, add the joist spans on each side of the girder and divide by 2. In the example in Fig. 9-5, the half width in the kitchen, living and dining areas is 12′-11″ (13′-11″ + 11′-11″ = 25′-10″; 25′-10″ ÷ 2 = 12′-11″) and the half width in the bed room area is 11′-11″ (11′-11″ + 11′-11″ = 23′-10″; 23′-10″ ÷ 2 = 11′-11″.)

Step 3. *Locate posts or columns.* As the distance between posts or columns is increased, the imposed load concentrated on each column becomes greater. It is advisable to space wood posts approximately 8′ apart and steel pipe or I-beam columns approximately 10′ apart. Referring to Fig. 9-5, it can be seen that the length of the house is 41′-0″. For purposes of illustration, wood posts have been selected to support the girder. Since the wood posts are spaced approximately 8′ apart, divide the

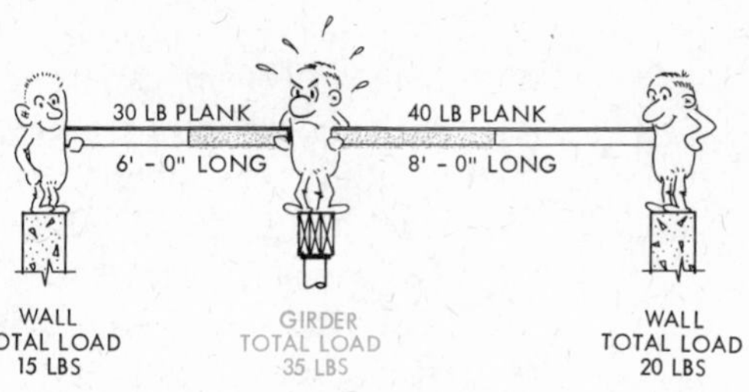

Fig. 9-6. The girder supports one half of the load on either side (girder half width).

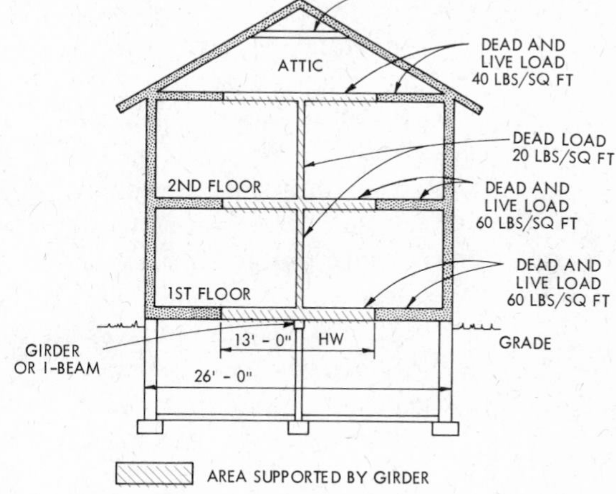

Fig. 9-7. This cross section shows the areas supported by the girders and outside walls.

length by the spacing (41′ ÷ 8′ = 5⅛). It is impossible to have 5⅛ equal post spaces; therefore, drop the fraction (⅛) and divide the girder length by the whole number (41 ÷ 5 = 8.2′ or 8′-2⅜″). *Four* posts are required, spaced 8′-2⅜″ O.C. (See Fig. 9-5.)

Step 4. *Determine the total load per squart foot.* From Table 9-6 select the proper total load per square foot. If, for example, the house shown in Fig. 9-5 is single story with provisions for attic storage, and has a bearing partition and a finished basement with acoustical tile ceiling, the total load per square foot is 90 lbs.

Step 5. *Calculate the lineal foot load.* To find the lineal foot load, multiply the girder half width (Step #2) by the square foot load (Step #4). From the example (Fig. 9-5), the girder half width load was found to be 12′-11″ and the total load was 90 lbs. per sq. ft. (For convenience use the decimal value 12.92′ rather than 12′-11″.) The lineal foot load is 1,163 lbs. (12.92 x 90 = 1,162.8 or 1,163 lbs.).

Step 6. *Calculate the total load on the girder.* Multiply the lineal foot load (Step #5) by the span or spacing of the posts or columns (Step #3). The lineal foot load was found to be 1,163 lbs. and the wood posts were spaced 8′-2⅜″ (8.2′) O.C. The total load on the girder is 9,537 lbs. (1,163 × 8.2 = 9,536.6 lbs. or 9,537 lbs.).

Step 7. *Determine the girder size.*

A. *Wood.* Refer to Table 9-7 and locate the span of the girder (Step #3), read down this column to the total load (Step #6) and across this row to the size of the girder required to carry this load.

The span of the girder was 8′-2⅜″. (Use column headed 8′-0″ since the span is less than 8′-6″.) The total load was calculated at 9,537 lbs. A 8″ × 8″ solid wood girder will amply carry the imposed load. If, however, the girder were to be laminated from four 2″ × 8″ dressed members, the load (9.24) must be multiplied by .867 (see footnote in table) since built-up or laminated girders carry a

TABLE 9-6

LOADS PER SQUARE FOOT OF FLOOR AREA USED IN CALCULATING GIRDER SIZE

BUILDING HEIGHT	COMPONENTS	TOTAL LOAD PER SQ FT
1 STORY*	Attic storage, bearing partition, plaster on basement ceiling.	100 lbs
	Attic storage, bearing partition, no plaster on basement ceiling.	90 lbs
	No attic storage, bearing partition, plaster on basement ceiling.	80 lbs
	No attic storage, bearing partition, no plaster on basement ceiling.	70 lbs
	No bearing partition, plaster on basement ceiling.	50 lbs
	No bearing partition, no plaster on basement ceiling.	40 lbs
1 1/2 or 2 STORY*	Attic storage, bearing partition supporting 2nd floor, plaster on basement ceiling.	150 lbs
	Attic storage, bearing partition supporting 2nd floor, no plaster on basement ceiling.	140 lbs
	No attic storage, bearing partition supporting 2nd floor, plaster on basement ceiling.	130 lbs
	No attic storage, bearing partition supporting 2nd floor, no plaster on basement ceiling.	120 lbs
2 1/2 or 3 STORY*	Attic storage, bearing partitions supporting 3rd floor, plaster on basement ceiling.	210 lbs
	Attic storage, bearing partitions supporting 3rd floor, no plaster on basement ceiling.	200 lbs
	No attic storage, bearing partitions supporting 3rd floor, no plaster on basement ceiling.	180 lbs

*If roof is framed so part of its weight is borne by bearing partitions; with composition shingled roof (light), add 20 lbs; with light slate or asbestos (medium), add 30 lbs; or with heavy slate or tile, add 40 lbs to the appropriate total load per square foot.

TABLE 9-7

SAFE LOAD FOR SOLID WOOD GIRDERS*

*Loads given in 1,000 Lbs

No. 1 common Douglas Fir and Southern Yellow Pine

NOMINAL SIZE	ACTUAL SIZE	LENGTH OF SPAN OF WOOD GIRDER									
		4'-0" 5'-0" 6'-0"	7'-0"	8'-0"	9'-0"	10'-0"	11'-0"	12'-0"	13'-0"	14'-0"	15'-0"
6 × 8	5½ × 7½	7.26	7.26	6.78	6.0	5.38	4.87	4.44	4.08	3.76	3.49
8 × 8	7½ × 7½	9.88	9.88	9.24	8.19	7.34	6.64	6.06	5.56	5.13	4.76
6 × 10	5½ × 9½	9.16	9.16	9.16	9.16	8.68	7.86	7.17	6.59	6.10	5.66
8 × 10	7½ × 9½	12.5	12.5	12.5	12.5	11.83	10.72	9.79	9.0	8.31	7.72
10 × 10	9½ × 9½	15.8	15.8	15.8	15.8	14.99	13.58	12.4	11.39	10.53	9.78
8 × 12	7½ × 11½	15.05	15.05	15.05	15.05	15.05	15.05	14.4	13.25	12.26	11.39
10 × 12	9½ × 11½	19.08	19.08	19.08	19.08	19.08	19.08	18.24	16.79	15.52	14.43
12 × 12	11½ × 11½	23.13	23.13	23.13	23.13	23.13	23.13	22.09	20.32	18.79	17.47
8 × 14	7½ × 13½	17.63	17.63	17.63	17.63	17.63	17.63	17.63	17.63	16.96	15.78
10 × 14	9½ × 13½	22.33	22.33	22.33	22.33	22.33	22.33	22.33	22.33	21.48	19.98
12 × 14	11½ × 13½	27.04	27.04	27.04	27.04	27.04	27.04	27.04	27.04	26.01	24.19
14 × 14	13½ × 13½	31.76	31.76	31.76	31.76	31.76	31.76	31.76	31.76	30.51	28.39

NOTE (1). Built up girders of dressed lumber will carry somewhat smaller loads than solid girders. It is, therefore, necessary to multiply the above loads for solid girders by the following:

0.887 when a 6" girder is made up of three 2" pieces
0.867 when a 8" girder is made up of four 2" pieces
0.856 when a 10" girder is made up of five 2" pieces

NOTE (2). If the load on a span is between two load figures, go to the nearest load.

smaller load than do solid girders. Multiplying 9.24 (safe load for a solid 8″ × 8″ with a span of 8″ O.C.) by .867 (correction factor for 8″ built-up girder) gives 8.01. This is too low. Therefore, it is then necessary to go to the next largest wood girder in load carrying capacity which is an 8″ × 10″. The corrected load capacity of a laminated 8″ × 10″ is 10,830 (12.5 × .867 = 10.83). This is ample to carry the imposed load.

B. *Steel.* Refer to Table 9-8 and locate the span of the steel I-beam (Step #3, use the same 8′-0″ span) read down the column to the total load (Step #6), and then read left across the row to the column headed, "Depth of I-beam." This value (6″ depth, 12.5 lbs. per ft.) represents the size I-beam which will safely carry the imposed load. (Depth refers to the thickness: distance between the two flanges measured from the outside of the flange.) There are three 6″ I-beams, each with a different load per foot. They are designed to carry heavier loads when they weigh more.

Posts or Columns

A bearing post or column is used to support the girder and may be of wood, steel, iron pipe, or lally column (iron pipe filled with concrete.) Fig. 9-8 illustrates the various posts or columns which may be used. The foundation supports a portion of the load carried by the girder. Between the opposite foundation walls, however, posts or columns must carry the load.

The following step-by-step procedure illustrates the method used for calculating the correct size for posts or columns.

Step 1. *Determine the total post or column load.* A post or column will carry the *girder load* to the mid-point of the span on both sides of the girder, see Fig. 9-9. The sum of the total load on the post or column is equal to one-half the load on one side of the post or column plus one-half the load on the other side of the column. (The same result may be obtained if the total loads on both sides of the column were added and divided by 2.) The total load on the girder (see Step #6 from the preceding section) was found to

TABLE 9-8
SAFE LOAD FOR STEEL I-BEAMS*

*Loads given in 1,000 Lbs

Fiber stress - 18,000 Lbs

DEPTH OF I BEAM	WEIGHT PER FOOT	LENGTH OF SPAN OF I BEAM										
		6'-0"	7'-0"	8'-0"	9'-0"	10'-0"	11'-0"	12'-0"	13'-0"	14'-0"	15'-0"	16'-0"
4"	8.5	6.3	5.4	4.7	4.2	3.8	—	—	—	—	—	—
4"	10.5	7.1	6.1	5.3	4.7	4.3	—	—	—	—	—	—
5"	10.0	9.7	8.3	7.3	6.5	5.8	5.3	—	—	—	—	—
5"	12.25	10.8	9.3	8.1	7.2	6.5	5.9	—	—	—	—	—
5"	14.75	12.0	10.3	9.0	8.0	7.2	6.5	—	—	—	—	—
6"	12.5	14.5	12.5	10.9	9.7	8.7	7.9	7.3	6.7	6.2	—	—
6"	14.75	15.9	13.6	11.9	10.6	9.5	8.7	7.9	7.3	6.8	—	—
6"	17.25	17.3	14.9	13.0	11.6	10.4	9.5	8.7	8.0	7.4	—	—
7"	15.0	20.7	17.7	15.5	13.8	12.4	11.3	10.3	9.5	8.9	8.3	7.7
7"	17.5	22.2	19.1	16.7	14.8	13.3	12.1	11.1	10.3	9.5	8.9	8.3
7"	20.0	24.0	20.5	18.0	16.0	14.4	13.1	12.0	11.1	10.3	9.6	9.0
8"	18.4	28.5	24.4	21.3	19.0	17.1	15.5	14.2	13.1	12.2	11.4	10.7
8"	20.5	30.1	25.8	22.6	20.1	18.1	16.4	15.1	13.9	12.9	12.0	11.3
8"	25.5	34.1	29.2	25.5	22.7	20.4	18.6	17.0	15.7	14.6	13.6	12.8
9"	21.8	37.7	32.3	28.3	25.2	22.6	20.6	18.9	17.4	16.2	15.1	14.2
9"	25.0	40.6	34.8	30.5	27.1	24.4	22.2	20.3	18.7	17.4	16.2	15.2
9"	30.0	45.1	38.6	33.8	30.0	27.0	24.6	22.5	20.8	19.3	18.6	16.9
9"	35.0	49.5	42.4	37.1	33.6	29.7	27.0	24.7	22.8	21.2	19.8	18.6
10"	30.0	53.4	45.8	40.1	35.6	32.0	29.1	26.7	24.6	22.9	21.0	20.0
10"	35.0	58.3	50.0	43.7	38.9	35.0	31.8	29.2	26.9	25.0	23.3	21.9
10"	40.0	63.2	59.2	47.4	42.1	37.9	34.5	31.6	29.2	27.1	25.3	23.7

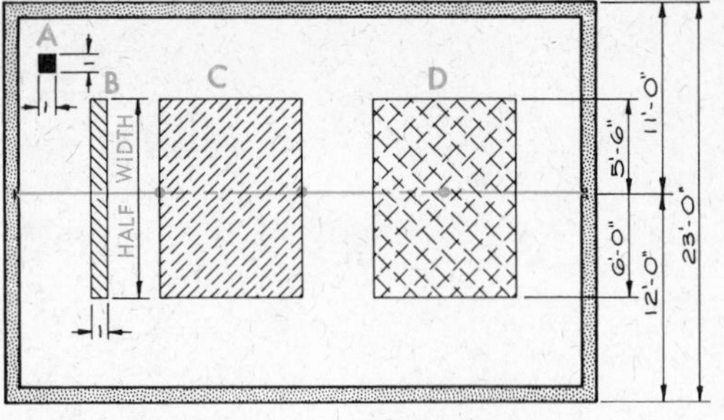

Fig. 9-9. This plan illustrates the lineal foot load, girder load, and post load.

be 9,537 lbs. 9,537 + 9,537 = 19,074 lbs.; 19,074 ÷ 2 = 9,537 lbs. The post load, though covering a different area, is the same as the girder load.

Step 2. *Determine the post or column height.* Decide on the amount of clear space you want under the

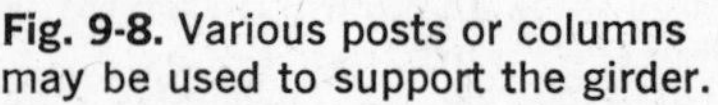

Fig. 9-8. Various posts or columns may be used to support the girder.

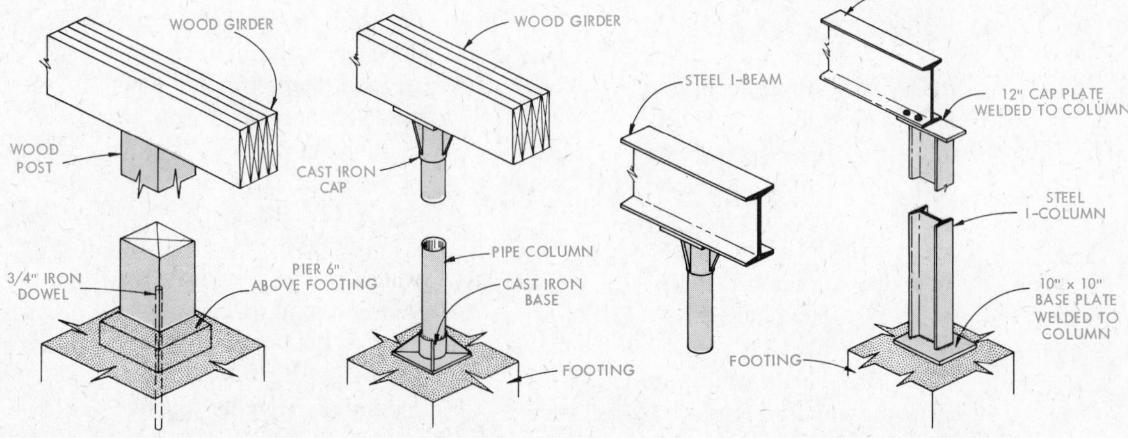

girder. Make allowance for a 4″ concrete floor. See Figs. 9-7 and 9-8.

If wood posts are used, *subtract* 6″ (allowance for the 4″ basement floor plus a 2″ rise above). If steel columns (pipe or I-beam) are used, no allowance is necessary because these rest directly on the footing. See Fig. 9-8.

Using Fig. 9-5 as an example, assume that the distance from the under side of a girder to the top of the concrete footing is 7′-2″. Again, assume that a wood post is used to support an 8″ × 8″ solid wood girder. In this case 6″ must be subtracted for the pier above the footing: 7′-2″ — 6″ = 6′-8″ post height. If steel columns are used, the height would be 7′-2″.

Step 3. *Determine the size of the post or column.*

A. *Wood.* Refer to Table 9-9, "Safety Loads for Wood Posts." Locate the column headed by the height nearest the measurement calculated in Step #2 above, then down the column to the total load calculated in Step #1 and then across to the specified wood post size. In the example being used (Fig. 9-5), the height of the post

TABLE 9-9

SAFE LOADS FOR WOOD COLUMNS OR POSTS*

*Loads given in 1,000 Lbs — No. 1 common Douglas Fir and Southern Yellow Pine

NOMINAL SIZE	ACTUAL SIZE	HEIGHT OF COLUMN OR POST					
		5′-0″	6′-0″	7′-0″	8′-0″	9′-0″	10′-0″
4 × 4	3⅝ × 3⅝	12.4	11.6	10.4	8.3	6.5	——
4 × 6	3⅝ × 5⅝	19.2	17.9	15.5	12.9	10.1	——
6 × 6	5½ × 5½	30.0	29.5	29.0	28.1	26.8	24.6
6 × 8	5½ × 7½	41.0	40.2	39.6	38.3	36.6	33.0
8 × 8	7½ × 7½	56.2	56.2	55.6	53.0	54.3	53.4

NOTE: If the load on a column is between two total figures, go to the nearest load.

TABLE 9-10

SAFE LOADS FOR STEEL PIPE COLUMNS*

*Loads given in 1,000 lbs

NOM SIZE (Inside Dia)	ACTUAL DIA (Outside)	HEIGHT OF PIPE COLUMN					
		5′-0″	6′-0″	7′-0″	8′-0″	9′-0″	10′-0″
2	2⅜	12.2	10.6	9.0	7.4	6.6	5.8
2½	2⅞	21.6	19.4	17.3	15.1	12.9	11.4
3	3½	29.0	28.6	26.3	24.0	21.7	19.4
3½	4	34.8	34.8	34.1	31.7	29.3	26.9
4	4½	41.2	41.2	41.2	40.1	37.6	35.1
4½	5	48.0	48.0	48.0	48.0	46.4	43.8
5	5 9/16	55.9	55.9	55.9	55.9	55.9	54.2

Note. If the load on a column is between two load figures, go to the nearest load.

TABLE 9-11

SAFE LOADS FOR I-BEAM COLUMNS*

*Loads given in 1,000 lbs — American Standard Sections

DEPTH	WEIGHT PER FT	HEIGHT OF I-BEAM COLUMN					
		5′-0″	6′-0″	7′-0″	8′-0″	9′-0″	10′-0″
3	5.7	17.2	14.6	12.3	10.5	——	——
4	7.7	25.3	21.8	18.7	16.1	13.9	——
5	10.0	35.1	30.7	26.8	23.4	20.4	17.9
6	12.5	46.9	41.8	37.0	32.7	28.9	25.5
7	15.3	60.0	54.1	48.5	43.3	38.6	34.5
8	18.4	74.9	68.3	61.8	55.7	50.1	45.0

Note. If the load on a column is between two load figures, go to the nearest load.

was 6′-8″. The column headed 7′-0″ would be correct since 6′-8″ is closer in height to 7′-0″ than 6′-0″. The total load was calculated to be 9,537 lbs. This load is under 10,400 lbs. It can be assumed that a 4″ × 4″ post is adequate to carry the imposed load on girder.

B. *Steel Pipe*. Use Table 9-10, "Safe Loads for Steel Pipe Columns." Locate the column headed with the nearest size to that found in Step #2 (7′-2″). Read down this column to the nearest load as found in Step #1 (9,537) and then across to the corresponding pipe diameter (2″).

C. *I-beam*. Refer to Table 9-11, "Safe Loads for I-beam Columns." Locate the proper column under "Height of I-beam Column" to correspond with height established in Step #2 (7′-2″). Then read down to the load ascertained in Step #1 (9,537) and across to the left to obtain the depth (3″) and weight per foot (5.7 lbs.) of the I-beam necessary to support girder.

Post and Column Footings

The footings which support the posts or columns must be sufficiently strong to carry the concentrated imposed load. If the footing is not capable of supporting the load, settlement will eventually occur.

The following steps illustrate the procedure used in determining the correct post or column footing.

Step 1. *Determine the total load on the footing*. The total load imposed on the footing is the same as the total load on the post or column as found in the preceding section, "Posts and Columns," Step #1.

TABLE 9-12

BEARING POWER OF SOILS IN TONS PER SQUARE FOOT*

MATERIAL	BEARING TONS PER SQUARE FOOT †
Crystalline bed rock — granite, gneiss, trap rock	100
Foliated rock — bedded limestone, schist, slate	40
Sedimentary rock — hard shale, siltstone, sandstone, soft limestone	15
Hard pan, gravel, sand, highly compacted	10
Gravel, sand and gravel mixture, compact	6
Gravel, loose, coarse sand, compact	4
Firm stiff clay	4
Coarse sand, loose; sand and gravel mixture, loose; fine sand compact; coarse sand, wet, confined	3
Sand clay mixed	3
Fine sand, loose; fine sand, wet, confined	2
Medium stiff clay	2 to 2.5
Soft clay	1 to 1.5

*If local building code specifies bearing capacity of soil, use those figures.

† Short ton = 2,000 lbs.

Step 2. *Determine the bearing power of the soil*. By visual inspection, determine the type of soil at the building site. Refer then to Table 9-12, "Bearing Power of Soils," to find the tons per square foot that particular type of soil will support. In some instances the local building code may specify the bearing capacity of the soil. Follow local codes if they are available. Assuming, for example, the soil at a site is medium stiff clay, it would support a load of 2 tons per square foot.

Step 3. *Determine the area of the footing*. Divide the total load on the footing (Step #1) by the bearing power of the soil (Step #2). In the assumed case: 9,537 ÷ 4,000 = 2.384 sq. ft. or 2.4 sq. ft. In other words it requires 2.4 sq. ft. of footing to support 9,537 lbs.

Step 4. *Determine the size of the footing*. Extract the square root of the area of the footing in Step 3 to obtain the length of the side of the footing:

$\sqrt{2.4} = 1.55'$ or 1′-6½″.

Step 5. *Determine the depth of the footing*. Adequate footing depth is equal to one-half the width of the footing, Step #4, plus 2″ or 3″. (Rarely less than 1′-0″.)

1′-6½″ ÷ 2 = 9¼″; 9¼″ + 3″ = 1′-0¼″. This is rounded off to 1′-0″.
Size of the concrete footing then is 1′-6½″ × 1′-6½″ × 1′-0″.

Wall Footings and Foundations

Footings and the foundation wall must be sufficiently strong to withstand the weight of the building. Regardless of how carefully a house may be framed or built, an inadequately designed footing and foundation wall may result in uneven settlement, cracked plaster or dry wall, ill-fitting windows and doors, and other difficulties.

Footings and foundation walls for residential construction are usually specified by local building codes. Building codes may specify the footing width to be twice the width of the foundation wall and its depth equal to the width of the footing projection. Some local building codes require the depth to be equal to the wall thickness *plus* 3″. Figs. 7-2 and 7-3 in Chapter 7 illustrate methods for calculating residential wall footing proportions.

Foundation wall thickness, just as with footing proportions, are usually specified in the local building code. Table 7-2, "Concrete Foundation Thicknesses," in Chapter 7 gives the accepted wall thicknesses for various types of residences.

Sketch Planning

To produce the final floor plan on the first or second attempt is a rarity. Experienced builders and designers still haven't designed the ideal, moderately priced home. Each builder and designer always has ways in which the next house can be improved.

After the development of several preliminary plans (see Chapter 4 for detail), the layout may be expanded further by sketching the plan on ⅛″ co-ordinate paper (each square then represents 1′-0″). The small scale forces the designer to consider only the main functions of the house. With this type of study one may determine, before drawing the quarter scale plan, if the floor plan is feasible. It is advisable to make several sketch plan studies on co-ordinate paper prior to any final decision. It may be helpful to draw the preliminary lines very lightly, then, as corrections are made and the final shapes are decided, the lines can be darkened.

Variations of an original plan may be quickly constructed by placing a piece of vellum or tracing paper over the original sketch and *tracing off* portions that remain unchanged. New areas may then be added.

For convenience, draw the thickness of an inside partition ½ square; an outside wall, ½ square; and an outside solid masonry wall, 1 square. The step-by-step procedure for making a sketch plan is shown in Fig. 9-10.

Modular Planning

The need for a co-ordinated system of modular dimensioning becomes more significant when one observes the amount of cutting, piecing, and splicing during house construction. The total amount of time, money, and materials involved in a single construction is sizeable. The building industry has made considerable progress in attempting to eliminate this loss by designing products based upon a predetermined module.

Modular planning, in essence, is keyed so that the dimensions of the structure are co-ordinated with standard sized building materials. This greatly reduces the need for alterations on the building site. The use of the modular method results in greater economy and efficiency in home construction.

The module is an established standard unit of measurement. The most commonly used and accepted unit is 4″. Studs are spaced 16″ (4 modules) apart; plywood is marketed in standard size sheets, 4′ × 8′ (12 × 24 modules).

Materials such as brick, tile, glass block, concrete block, wood and metal windows, cabinets, plywood, etc., are some of the items available in modular sizes. Not all manufacturers, however, produce building products based on the 4″ module.

The co-ordinated system of modular planning employs building materials fitted to a grid based on the 4″ module.

Modular drafting or planning is based on five fundamental principles.

1. *Design modules* must be in *multiples of 4″*.

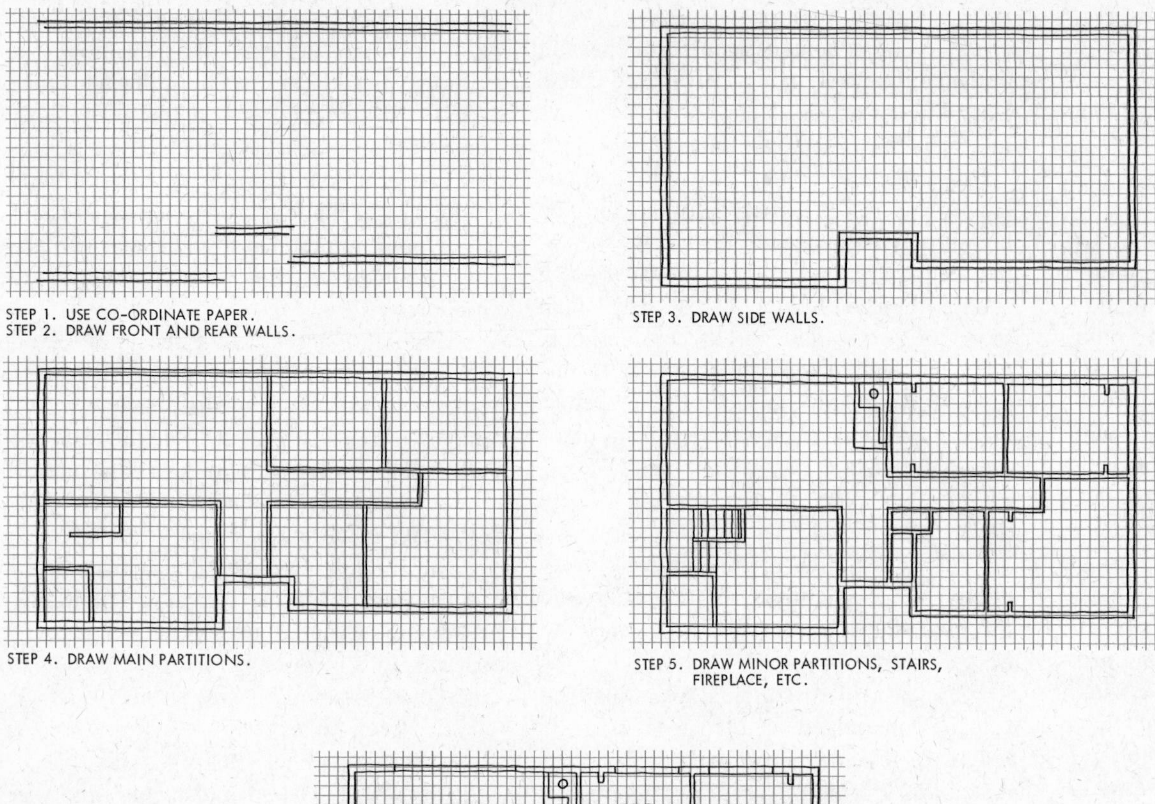

STEP 1. USE CO-ORDINATE PAPER.
STEP 2. DRAW FRONT AND REAR WALLS.

STEP 3. DRAW SIDE WALLS.

STEP 4. DRAW MAIN PARTITIONS.

STEP 5. DRAW MINOR PARTITIONS, STAIRS, FIREPLACE, ETC.

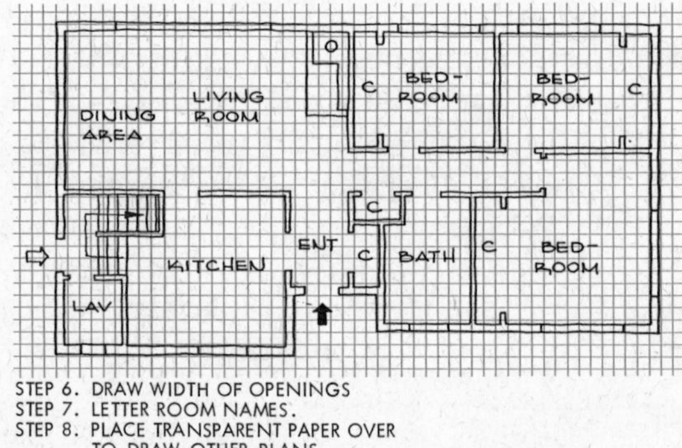

STEP 6. DRAW WIDTH OF OPENINGS
STEP 7. LETTER ROOM NAMES.
STEP 8. PLACE TRANSPARENT PAPER OVER TO DRAW OTHER PLANS.

Fig. 9-10. **Follow this step-by-step procedure in making a sketch plan.**

2. All *details begin with the grid lines.* Any dimensions to surfaces of the detail, centerlines, etc., must be dimensioned to the grid line, not to other points on the building. A modular detail requires fewer small fractional dimensions than a detail dimensioned in the regular method. See Fig. 9-11.
3. *Grid* dimensions are given in plans, sections, and elevations. On the small scale drawings (¾″ = 1′-0″, ½″ = 1′-0″, or ¼″ = 1′-0″) the 4″ grid lines usually do not appear—but they exist nevertheless. Often these lines are multiples of 4″: that is, 16″, 24″, or 48″. Small scale drawings should show nominal (rough size before finish) surfaces: nominal walls and partitions, nominal finished floor, etc. Usually the lines which indicate such surfaces will coincide with the grid lines.

   When working with modular planning, the walls and partitions should be laid out using one side of the rough members for dimensioning. A *single arrow* method is shown in Fig. 9-12 to illustrate the point.
4. Floor levels are located on the grid lines. In wood frame construction, the top of the sub-floor or top of the finished concrete slab (with finish floor on the slab) coincides with the grid line. (The top of the slab floor is located ⅛″ below the grid line—the ⅛″ allows for tiling.)
5. As mentioned, dimensions *to* a grid

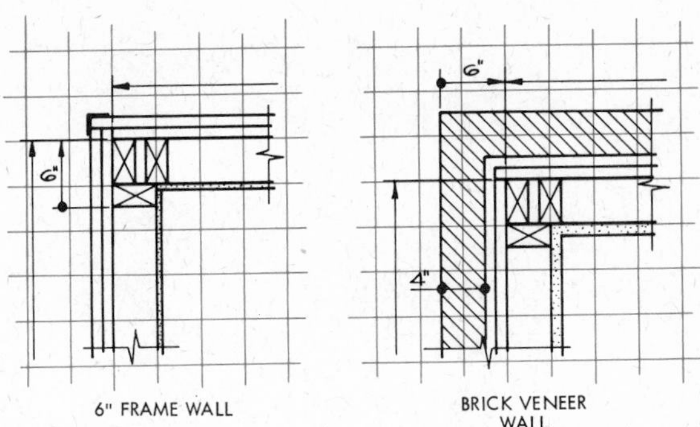

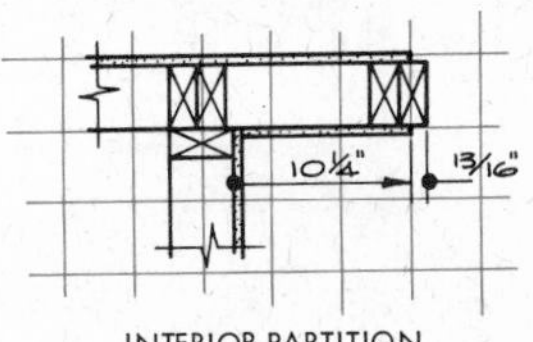

Fig. 9-11. In the modular system of planning all measurements are based on a 4″ multiple.

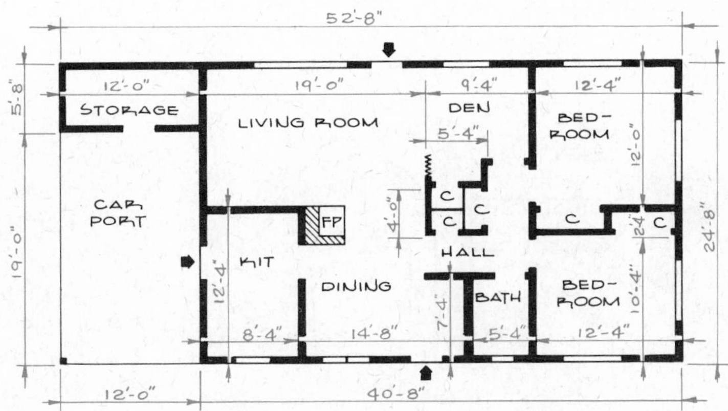

Fig. 9-12. Even though the grid does not appear, all dimensions on this small scale drawing are grid dimensions. Note the **single arrow** used for dimensioning.

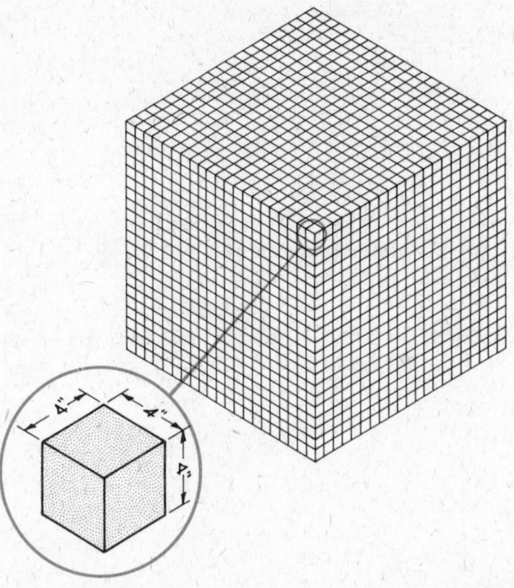

Fig. 9-14. The height, length, and width of a building may be laid out in modular grids.

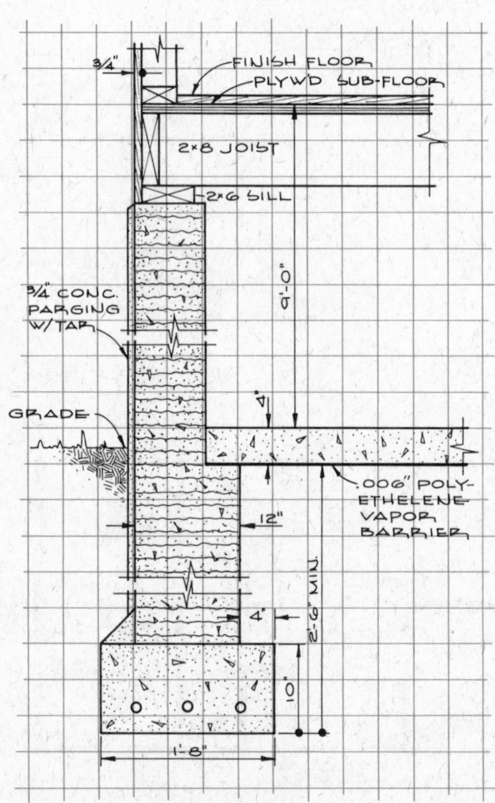

Fig. 9-13. Dimensions taken to a grid line are indicated by an arrow, those off the grid are indicated by a dot. Note the application of these principles in this foundation section.

line (module size) are indicated by an *arrow*. Dimensions which terminate *off* the grid line (non-module size) are signified with a *dot*. Fig. 9-13 illustrates this usage.

Modular measure makes possible an orderly and systematic dimensioning of the entire house. Vertical and horizontal reference planes, mutually perpendicular, grid the entire volume (length, depth, and height) of the building. See Fig. 9-14.

Uniform Components. Another modular system called the *Unicom Method of House Construction* is also used. The Unicom method uses multiples of 16″ and 24″. Component house panels are made using these dimensions.

Floor Plans

The floor plan, regardless whether the first floor, second floor, or basement, must clearly and accurately describe the size and shape of the house at each level. The following details should be shown on the floor plan: wall thickness and materials; placement of partitions and walls; location and sizes of doors and windows; location, size and detail of stairs and fireplace; location of built-in cabinets, range, oven, dish washer, etc.; location of plumbing fixtures; and the *approximate location* of electrical outlets, fixtures, and switches. In addition, notes are used to give any further information relating

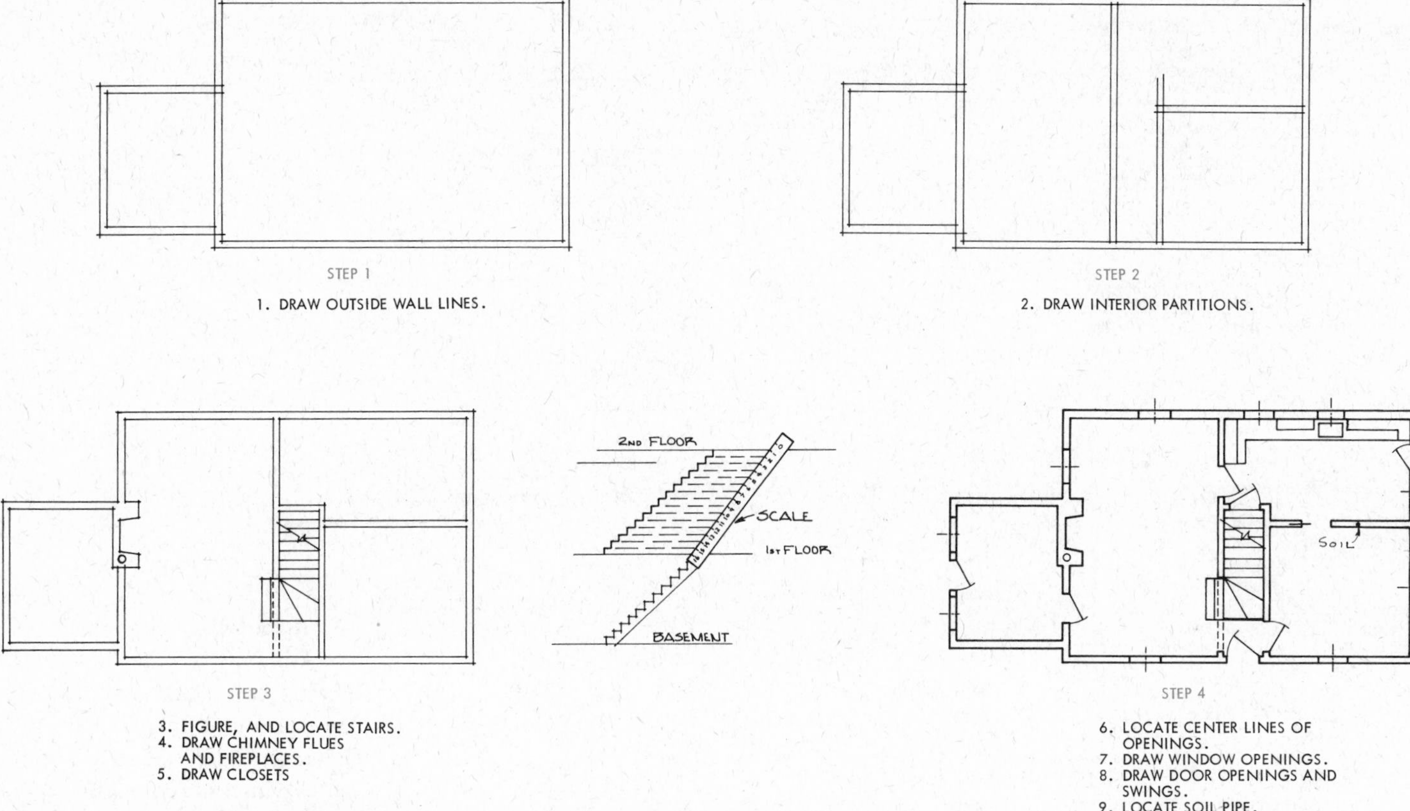

Fig. 9-15. Follow this step-by-step procedure in drawing the first floor plan.

to joist size and direction, girder size and location, floor materials, etc.

Floor plans are usually drawn at a scale of ¼″ = 1′-0″. For larger buildings, however, a scale of ⅛″ = 1′-0″ is used.

Step-by-Step Planning Procedure: First Floor or Level

The following steps enumerate the correct procedure in drawing the first floor plan. Fig. 9-15 illustrates the step-by-step procedure which is covered in detail below.

Step 1. Draw the outside wall lines to scale (based on the preliminary sketch) using the correct wall widths. See Table 9-13 for thicknesses of common types of walls.

Step 2. Locate and draw the main interior partitions, dividing the area into the main rooms.

Step 3. Locate and draw chimney flues and fireplace: allow 4″ around flues.

Design and locate stairs: first to second floor and first floor to basement.

Draw, on a separate sheet, a side

TABLE 9-13

ACTUAL AND NOMINAL THICKNESSES OF COMMON TYPES OF WALLS

Location	TYPE OF WALL	COMPONENT MEMBERS	ACTUAL DIMENSION	NOMINAL DIMENSION
EXTERIOR	FRAME	Siding, sheathing, studs, interior finish (lath and plaster or dry wall material)	5-3/4" or 6"	7"
	CONCRETE BLOCK, STONE, BRICK, TILE OR COMBINATION	Masonry units, furring, plaster	9-1/2" or 13-3/4"	10" or 14"
	BRICK AND STONE VENEER	Masonry units, air space, sheathing studs, interior finish (lath and plaster or dry wall material)	9-3/4" or 10"	11"
	ROLOK AND ROLOK BACK	Masonry units (8" or 12"), furring, plaster	9-1/8" or 13-1/8"	10" or 14"
	SCR BRICK	Masonry unit, furring, interior finish (lath and plaster or dry wall material)	7-5/8"* or 7-7/8"†	8"
INTERIOR	REGULAR PARTITIONS	Studs, interior finish (lath and plaster or dry wall material)	4-5/8"* or 5-1/8"†	5"* or 6"†
	NON-LOAD BEARING (Between closets)	Studs, interior finish (lath and plaster or dry wall material)	3-5/8"* or 4-1/8"†	4"* or 5"†
	STACK	Stud, stack, interior finish (lath and plaster or dry wall material)	6-5/8"† or 7-1/8"†	7"* or 8"†
BASEMENT	FOUNDATION	The foundation for a frame structure will be 8" or larger. This, however, will vary depending on the local building code requirements for different types of walls (above and below grade), depth of wall and location of the building.	8", 10" or 12"	8", 10", or 12"
	PARTITION	Studs, interior finish (lath and plaster or dry wall material.)	3-5/8"* or 4-1/8"†	4"* or 5"†

*Thickness based on dry wall.
† Thickness based on lath and plaster.

TABLE 9-14

COMMON DOOR OPENINGS

USE	SIZE									
	16'-0"	15'-0"	9'-0"	8'-0"	3'-0"	2'-8"	2'-6"	2'-4"	2'-2"	2'-0"
Main Entry way					X	X*	X			
Service					X	X				
Closet †					X	X	X	X	X	X
Bath and Lavatory								X		X
Bedroom and Other						X	X			
Garage 1-car			X	X						
Garage 2-car	X	X								

*May be used in pairs.

† Closet door widths vary depending upon type of door used: sliding, bi-fold, accordion, etc. Openings for closets may be larger than 3'-0".

view of the stairs showing headroom. Transfer plan to proper location on drawing.
Locate and draw closets.
Locate and draw the plumbing fixtures.

Step 4. Locate center lines of all openings.
Draw all windows, doors (indicating swings), and archways. See Table 9-14 for door openings.
Locate and draw soil pipe and necessary vents.
Locate and draw electrical fixtures, outlets and switches.
Locate and draw in girder.
Note direction of second floor ceiling joists with an arrow. (Give size and distance O.C.)
Dimension plan: See Fig. 9-16.
Letter names of rooms and room sizes below name of room.

Step-by-Step Planning Procedure: Second Floor or Level

The second floor plan is drawn next. See Fig. 9-17. Place a piece of vellum over the first floor plan and follow the step-by-step procedure given below.

Step 1. Trace outside wall lines.

Step 2. Trace stairs and draw stair well opening.

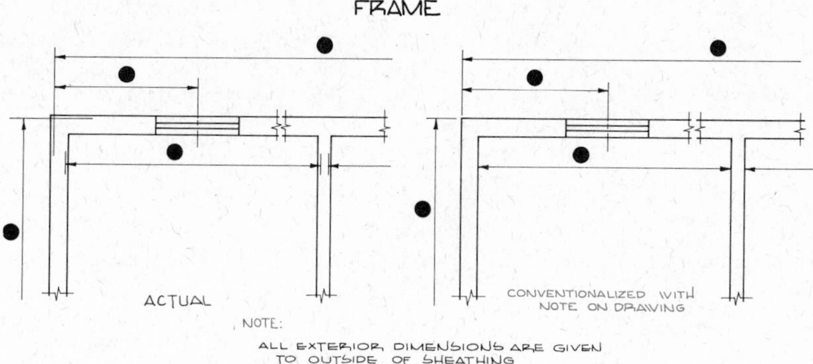

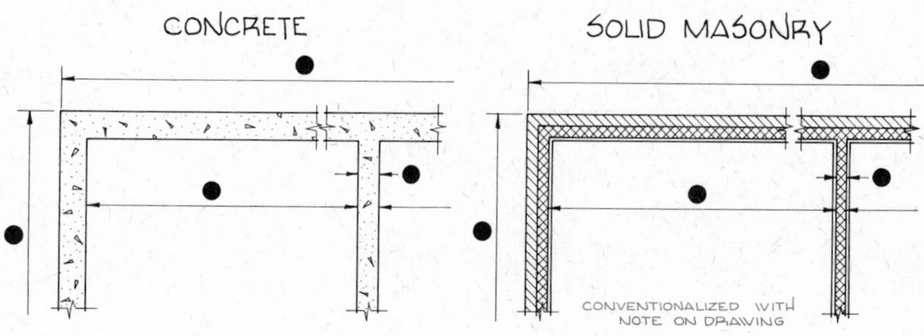

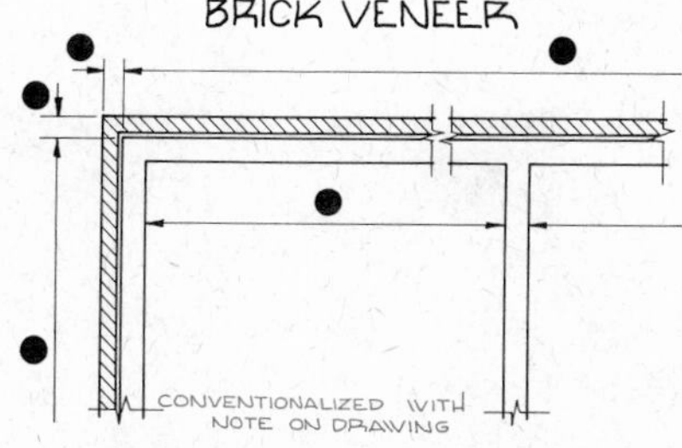

Fig. 9-16. Dimensioning practices vary with different wall types.

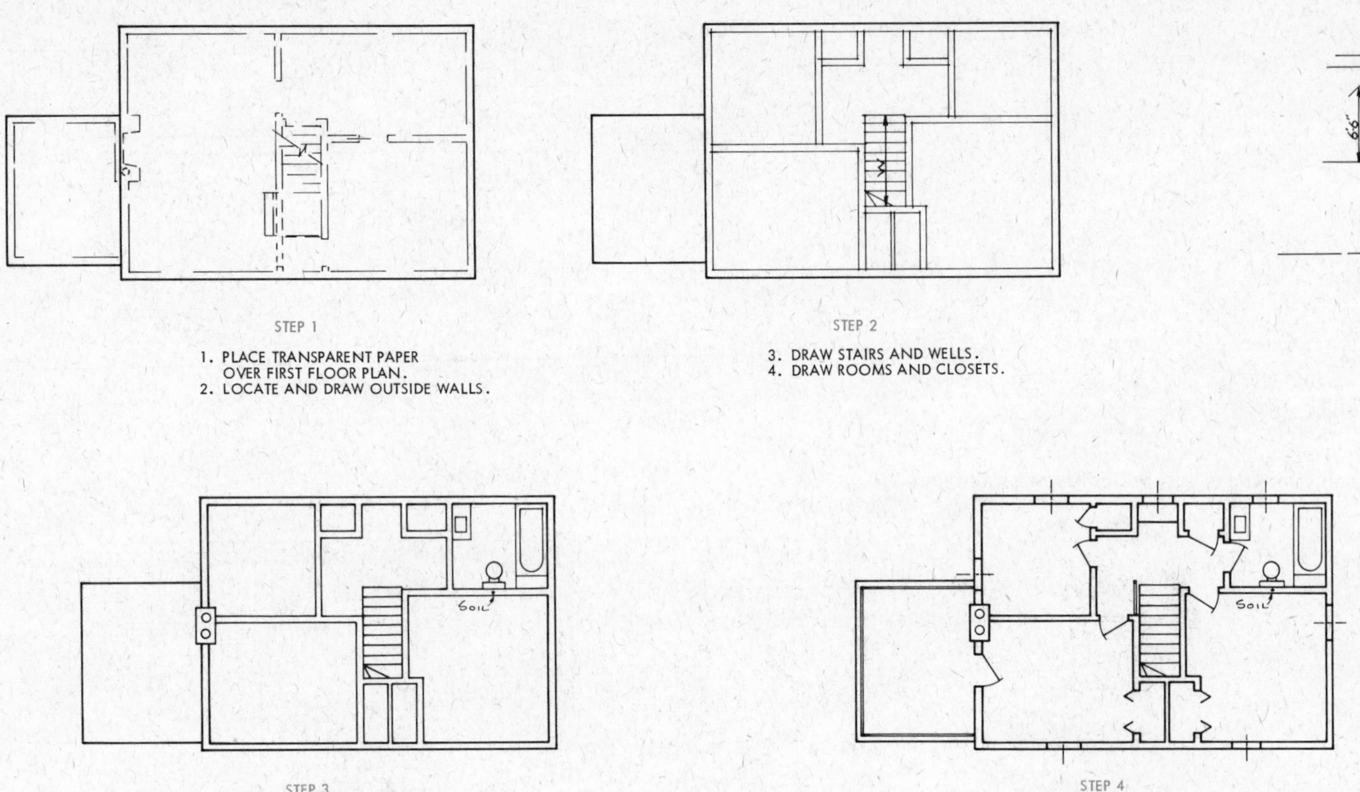

Fig. 9-17. Follow this step-by-step procedure for drawing the second-floor plan.

Trace chimney. (Note: The chimney changes shape between the first and second floors as the furnace flue and the fireplace flue are placed close to one another.)

Locate interior partition and the closets.

Step 3. Trace soil pipe and vents.
Locate and draw the bathroom fixtures.

Step 4. Locate and draw ℄ for windows and doors.
Draw doors (indicating swings).
Locate and draw electrical fixtures, outlets, and switches.

Note direction of attic joists with an arrow. (Give size and distance O.C.)

Draw roofs in plan if needed.

Dimension plan: See Fig. 9-16 for dimensioning practices.

Letter names of rooms and room sizes below name of room.

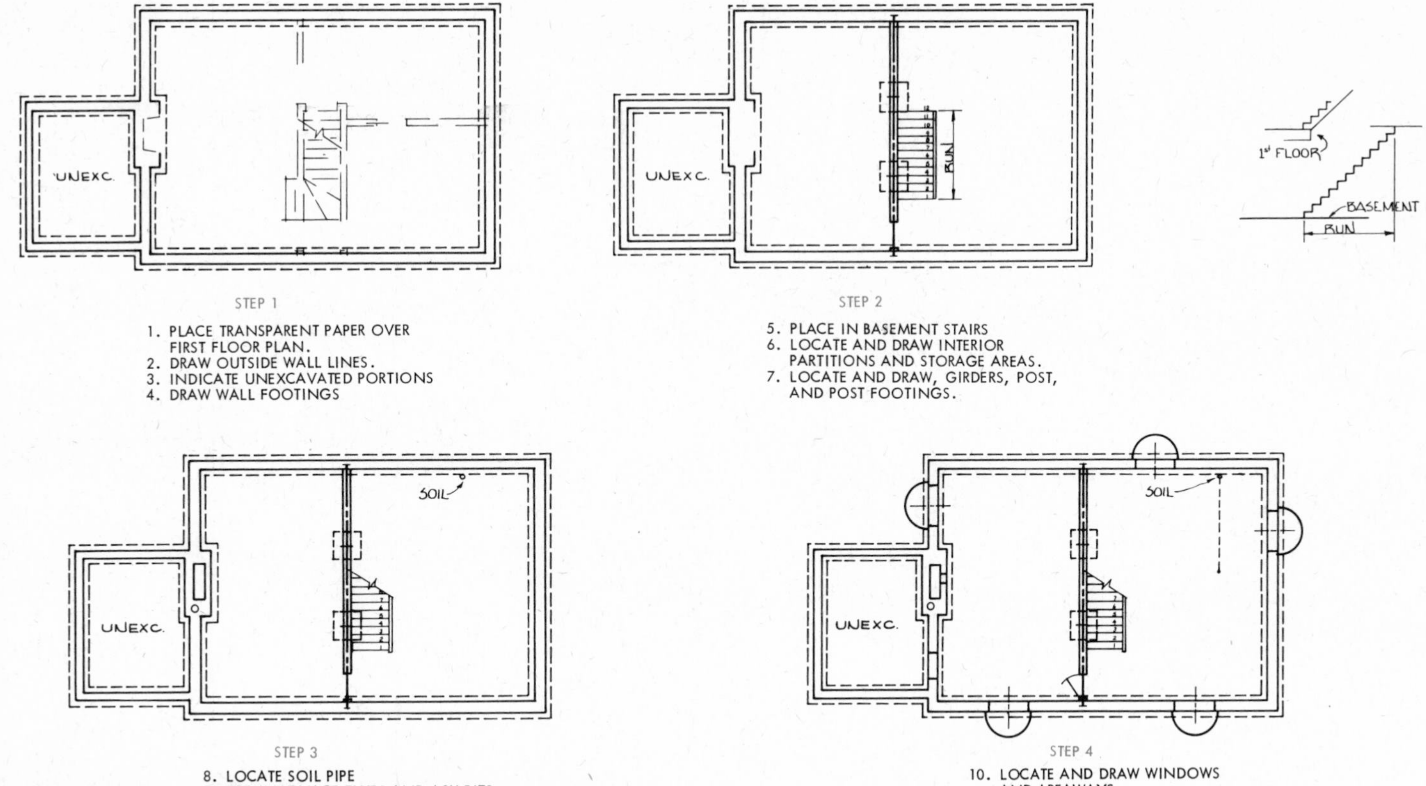

Fig. 9-18. Follow this step-by-step procedure for drawing the basement plan.

Step-by-Step Planning Procedure: Basement

The basement or foundation plan is drawn third. See Fig. 9-18. Place a piece of vellum over the first floor plan and follow the step-by-step procedure given below.

Step 1. Locate and draw outside wall lines. If the building is masonry or masonry veneer, the wall will be flush. If the building is frame, the foundation will be placed inside the line traced from the first floor plan enough to compensate for the siding thickness. If slab construction is used, locate and draw wall footings for bearing walls (if conventional roof framing is used).
Indicate any unexcavated areas and crawl spaces.
Draw wall footings.

Step 2. Trace basement stairs and draw stair well opening.
Locate and draw interior partitions and closets. Following the computations, locate and draw girders, posts or columns, and footing.

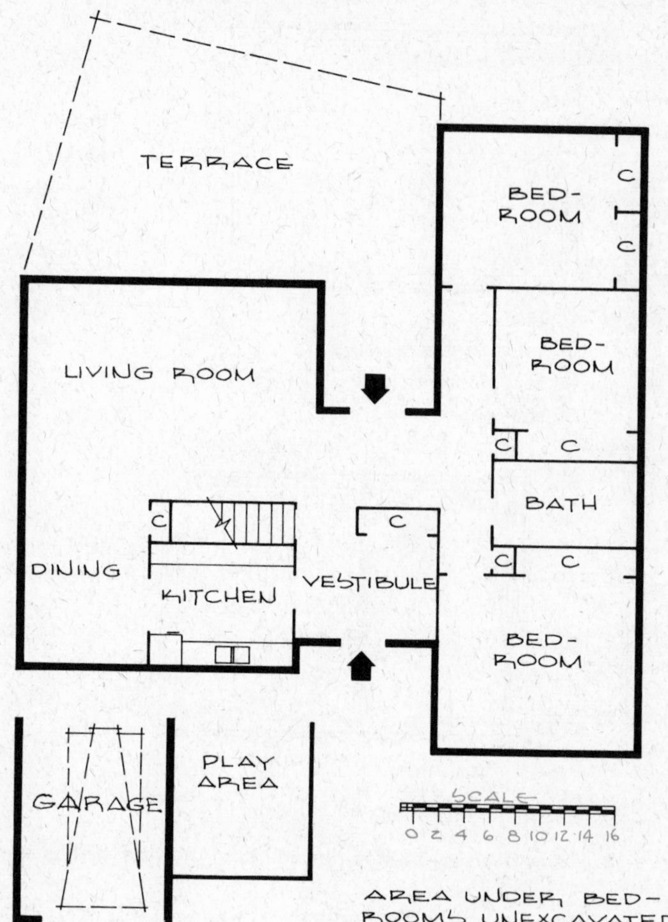

Fig. 9-19. Floor Plan and Perspective of a Contemporary House. (Approximately 1700 sq. ft.)

Step 3. Trace soil pipe.
Trace chimney.
Locate and draw fireplace, flue, ashpit, space heater, water heater, furnace or boiler, etc.

Step 4. Locate and draw ℄ for windows and doors.
Draw doors (indicating swings).
Draw windows and areaways.
Locate and draw the plumbing fixtures.
Locate and draw symbols for electrical fixtures, switches, and outlets.
Note size and location of girder, posts or columns, and footings.
Dimension plan: See Fig. 9-16.
Letter names of rooms and room sizes below name of room if applicable.

Check List

After completing the floor plans, each

plan should be thoroughly checked. The points listed below will aid in the checking procedure.

1. *Closet sizes.* Are the closets sufficient in number; do they have good location, adequate depth, etc.?
2. *Door locations and sizes.* Are doors located so as to receive the maximum use? Does door swing conflict with other doors, walls, etc.? Can furniture be arranged without sacrificing too much floor space? Is 4″ allowed for each door jamb? Do the doors swing in the proper direction? Are the pockets for sliding doors free from framing obstructions?
3. *Room sizes.* Are room sizes similar to the room cutouts and the sketch plan? Will standard size rugs fit the rooms? Do the room sizes fit the joist spans (maximum 16 feet)?
4. *Girder location.* Is the girder located mid-way between the foundation walls or beneath a partition?
5. *Chimney size and location.* Is the flue the correct size for the fireplace opening? Is there proper clearance around the chimney to prevent fire?
6. *Clearances.* Is there adequate space for good traffic circulation? Be sure to check clearances for furniture, bathroom fixtures, doors, etc.

Questions and Problems

1. Sketch 4 floor plans for each of the 4 corners of an intersection of two streets running north to south and east to west. Two of these floor plans should be basementless, each having 3 bedrooms, 1½ baths, family room, living room, dining room or ell, kitchen, utility room, and 1½ or 2 car garage. The other two houses should contain 3 bedrooms, living room, dining area in kitchen, family room, 1½ baths, basement, breezeway or patio, and 1½ or 2 car garage. The lot sizes are 100′ × 300′ Develop floor plans for one of these houses.
2. Fig. 9-19 shows the floor plan and a pictorial rendering of a contemporary home. From the information given on the plan, following the procedures used for computing the structural members, answer these questions:
   a. At what location should the girder be placed? What type of girder will be used?
   b. What is the longest joist span over the basement? Considering the joist must carry a 50 lb. load. what size joists must be specified if they are placed 16″ O.C.?
   c. What is the half width length?
   d. What is the total load per square foot?
   e. What is the lineal foot load?
   f. Depending upon the type of posts or columns selected, how many and how far apart will they be spaced?
   g. What will be the total load imposed on the girder?
   h. Depending on the type of girder selected, what will be its size?
   i. If the height from the basement floor to the under side of the girder is 7′-2″, what would be the height of a wood post? a steel I-beam?
   j. What size wood post and I-beam would be necessary to support the girder?
   k. If the house was built on hard clay, what size post or column footing would be necessary?

The outside of a home reflects the interior planning. Any one floor plan, however, may result in several different exterior designs.

Exterior House Design 10

In planning, the exterior appearance of a house is a major factor. The exterior design will emanate from and be dependent upon many previous decisions: choice of site, number of floors, style, available capital, future expansion, etc. The greatest determining influence on the exterior design, however, is exerted by the floor plan. This is particularly true in the pure forms of traditional and period styles. To design a preconceived exterior for some floor plans would be exceedingly difficult, if not impossible. A square plan, for example, does not lend itself to a ranch exterior, nor does a Cape Cod plan fit with a ranch elevation. However, a number of different exteriors **may usually** be developed for any one floor plan design.

Styles of residential architecture change just as women's fashions change. Architecturally (and this is particularly evident since the 1880's), home builders in any one area have tended to popularize particular types of architecture to the exclusion of others. Popularity of specific styles have become so great that in some areas styles are mixed. For example: the southern colonial ranch house, the Cape Cod rancher, or the salt-box split level. This is not to say, however, that "mixtures" of this nature are bad.

Each of these styles may be identified by certain characteristics that "ear mark" them from other styles.

Period Architectural Styles

The architecture of the early colonists has survived for three centuries. The first dwellings were cabins made from the ready supply of timber. As the colonists were able to build better homes, the cabin developed into one-and-a-half- and-two-story dwellings. Eventually, regional differences began to evolve, not only in style but in building materials as well. Homes in the New England area were predominantly wood, those in Delaware and Pennsylvania were stone, while those farther south used bricks made from local clay.

Until the mid-1700's the architect was practically non-existant in the colonies. Many of the early colonial houses were designed by the "master of the house," with

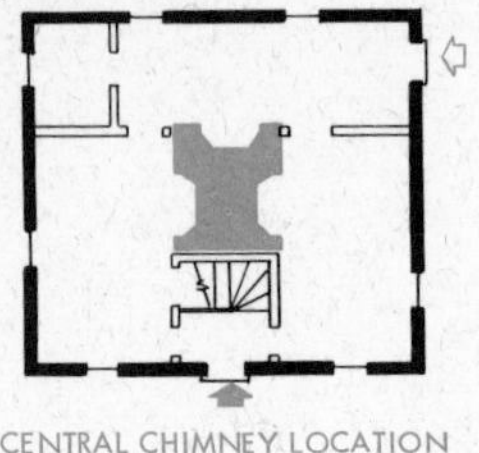

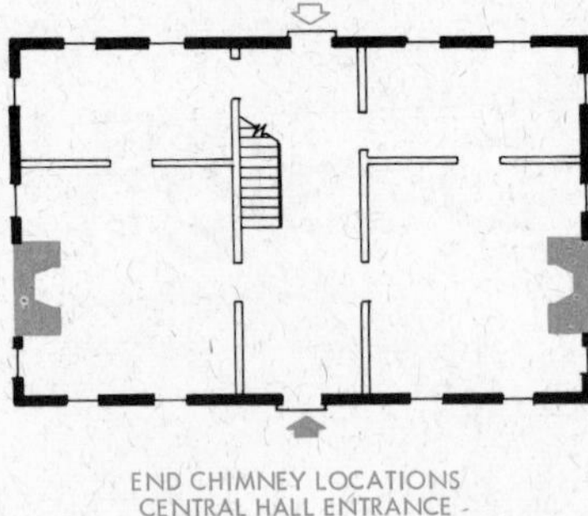

Fig. 10-1. Two basic plans were used in building colonial homes.

or without assistance from the master craftsman who would construct it later. The chief architectural references of the time were English books and periodicals. These publications showed perspectives, elevations, and details of English and European homes.

Basically, these colonial homes had a rectangular or square plan and were compact with the rooms grouped around a central stair hall or chimney. Fig. 10-1 illustrates two basic plans of many houses built during and following the colonial period. The plan built around the central chimney (Fig. 10-1, top) was common for a one-, one-and-a-half-, two-, or two-and-a-half-story house, one or two rooms deep. Fig. 10-1 (bottom) represents a plan built around the central hall. This type of plan was common to the Dutch style of architecture and was adapted to other styles as well.

Eventually these buildings were enriched, particularly along the eastern seaboard, by ships' carpenters who added delicate moldings, cornices, and ornate entrances. Many of these designs are still copied. Ships' carpenters were the first to introduce in the United States the double-hung sash, glass (oiled paper or parchment was previously used), *shakes* (hand split shingles) for exterior walls and roofing, and weather boards with rounded edges to combat the high winds. Large, efficient, and beautiful fireplaces were the focal points during the cold New England winters. The chimneys were masterpieces of design. The roof styles of these homes (whether gambrel, gable, shed, or hip) are still much in evidence on houses today.

One reason colonial designs have survived is because they can be adapted to changing situations. These houses are found as one-, one-and-a-half-, two-, or two-and-a-half-story dwellings and for that reason can be made to fit almost any size lot. Due to their extreme simplicity, the floor plan was easily expandable. For example, many of the one-and-a-half-, two-, and two-and-a-half-story buildings were expanded into saltbox style houses. This was accomplished by simply extending the rear of the house and continuing the rear half of the gable roof downward in the same plane. The profile or silhouette of this roof has the appearance of an inverted check mark.

Many designs were expanded, for example, into L, U, and T shapes. Because of the rugged, yet elegant, appearance of the colonial, Americans have continued making facsimiles—only improving the interiors with modern conveniences.

Structural Characteristics

The various styles of residential construction are the result of many conditions and influences. Some of the factors which may influence construction are availability of materials, climatic conditions, predominant religious beliefs, customs, living conditions, nationality, or ethnic origins.

Study houses and become familiar with good design. The ability to identify good and poor design requires experience in comparing various styles of buildings. Such publications as *Interiors, Architectural Record, House and Home, American Builder, Better Homes and Gardens,* and numerous other books dealing primarily with architecture, may serve as a basis for style values.

Characteristics of Various Styles

Figs. 10-2 through 10-26 give a brief pictorial resume of the more popular styles of architecture in the United States. All photographs are of the original, historical structures. Each photograph was selected as representative of that particular type of architecture in an "unadulterated" state.

Fig. 10-2. This photograph shows an excellent example of a two-and-a-half story salt-box colonial home. This is the Major John Bradford house, located in Kingston, Massachusetts and built in 1674.

HISTORIC AMERICAN BUILDING SURVEY, LIBRARY OF CONGRESS, WASHINGTON, D.C. PHOTO BY ARTHUR C. HASKELL.

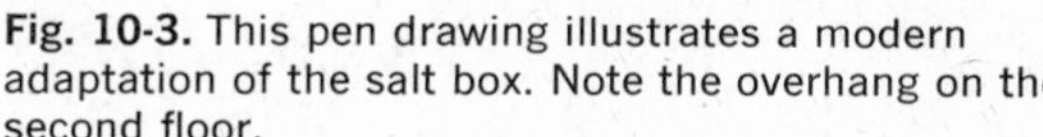

Fig. 10-3. This pen drawing illustrates a modern adaptation of the salt box. Note the overhang on the second floor.

Adjacent to each photo are perspective sketches which show modern applications of each style.

Salt-box Colonial—(Figs. 10-2 and 10-3.)

- Roof — Long slope on one side of the gable; no overhang. Dormers on the long sloping side. May have gambrel fronted roof.
  Long slope toward the direction of winter winds.
- Walls — Siding or shakes—little ornamentations. Double-hung windows and doors, symmetrical in appearance; shutters.
- Height — 1½ or 2 stories.
- Chimney — Large, centrally located in plan.
- Plan — Compact, rectangular.

Early American Colonial—(Figs. 10-4 and 10-5.)

- Roof — Steep gable, wood shingles.
- Walls — Siding, stained; small double-hung or casement windows, symmetrical; second floor overhangs; drops used.
- Height — 2½ stories.
- Chimney — Large centrally located in plan.
- Plan — Compact, rectangular.

New England Colonial—(Figs. 10-6 and 10-7.)

- Roof — Gable medium pitch, no overhang. Gambrel, no overhang on gable or eaves.
- Walls — Siding, shingles, brick.

HISTORIC AMERICAN BUILDING SURVEY, LIBRARY OF CONGRESS, WASHINGTON, D.C. PHOTO BY THOMAS T. WATERMAN.

Fig. 10-4. The early American Colonial is usually typified in part by the distinctive second floor overhang. Note the use of hand-carved drops or pendills at the corners and the use of brackets between stories. This is the Parson Capen house in Topsfield, Massachusetts; it was built in 1683.

Fig. 10-5. This drawing illustrates an adaptation of an early American Colonial L-shaped plan using a steep gambrel roof.

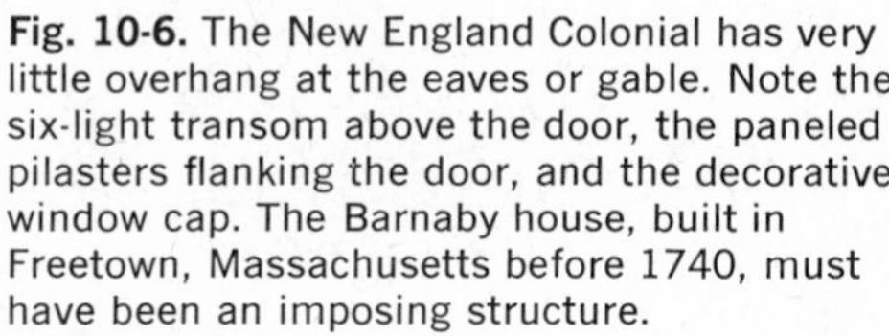
Fig. 10-6. The New England Colonial has very little overhang at the eaves or gable. Note the six-light transom above the door, the paneled pilasters flanking the door, and the decorative window cap. The Barnaby house, built in Freetown, Massachusetts before 1740, must have been an imposing structure.

HISTORIC AMERICAN BUILDING SURVEY, LIBRARY OF CONGRESS, WASHINGTON, D.C. PHOTO BY ARTHUR C. HASKELL.

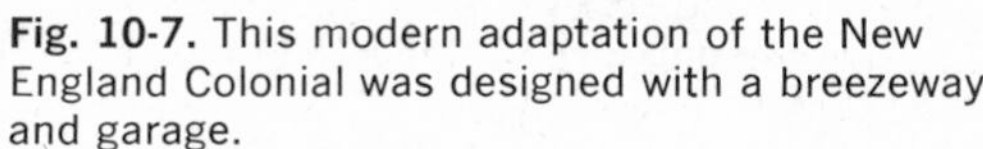
Fig. 10-7. This modern adaptation of the New England Colonial was designed with a breezeway and garage.

HISTORIC AMERICAN BUILDING SURVEY, LIBRARY OF CONGRESS, WASHINGTON, D.C. PHOTO BY ARTHUR C. HASKELL.

Fig. 10-8. The Cape Cod style is probably the simplest and smallest of all colonials. The Jonathan Kendrick house in South Orleans, Massachusetts was built in 1792 and is still occupied today.

Fig. 10-9. The Cape Cod colonial may be enhanced by adding shutters and side lights on either side of the door and yet still retain an authentic colonial appearance.

Fig. 10-10. The Southern Colonial is earmarked by large elaborate entrances using turned or paneled posts. The Dr. R. H. Richardson house, built in 1835 at Athens, Alabama, is still used as a residence.

HISTORIC AMERICAN BUILDING SURVEY, LIBRARY OF CONGRESS, WASHINGTON, D.C. PHOTO BY ALEX BUSH.

Double-hung windows and doors placed symmetrically; shutters.
Only entrance ornamented.

Height — 1, 1½, 2, and 2½ stories.
Chimney — Large centrally located in plan.
Plan — Square or rectangular, additions can be made.

Cape Cod Colonial—(Figs. 10-8 and 10-9.)

Roof — Medium pitch gable.
Small overhang on cornice.
Walls — Siding, painted.
Double-hung windows—symmetrically placed.
Height — 1½ stories.
Chimney — Large, centrally located in plan.
Plan — Compact, rectangular—wings may be added.

Southern Colonial—(Figs. 10-10 and 10-11.)

Fig. 10-11. This modern example of the Southern Colonial uses an off-center entrance yet still maintains the dignity of the style.

HISTORIC AMERICAN BUILDING SURVEY, LIBRARY OF CONGRESS, WASHINGTON, D.C. PHOTO BY R. MERRITT LACEY.

Fig. 10-12. The true Dutch Colonial is designed with a steep **gable** roof flared over the eaves. Though neglected, the Gerrit Haring house in Old Tappan, New Jersey is one of the few remaining true Dutch Colonials. This house was built between 1751-1762.

Roof — Hip, gable, or flat. Slate or metal.

Walls — Brick, stucco. Large double-hung windows and doors (symmetrical). Ornamentation of wood. Elaborate entrance, using turned or paneled posts.

Height — 2 stories.

Chimney — At each end projecting from or flush with gable end or short sides.

Plan — Limited flexibility (not advisable for small lot).

Dutch Colonial[1]—(Figs. 10-12, 10-13, and 10-14.)

Roof — Steep gable, gambrel, flush gable and eaves, or flush gable and flared eaves.

Walls — Brick, stone, wide siding, long shingles or combination. Double-hung windows and doors symmetrically placed.

Height — 1½ to 2½ stories.

Chimney — Flush or projected on gable ends.

Plan — Rectangular, may have additions.

1. The true Dutch Colonial was typified by a steep gable roof. On some houses the coping on the gable walls extended several inches above the roof and the chimneys were flush with these walls. The Dutch builders were probably acquainted with the gambrel roof through the English and Flemish colonists. The gambrel roof was adopted during the 18th Century. A combination of the wide gambrel with the flared overhang was apparently developed by the Flemish but credited to the Dutch. The gambrel type roof, however, is synonymous with "Dutch Colonial."

HISTORIC AMERICAN BUILDING SURVEY, LIBRARY OF CONGRESS. WASHINGTON, D.C.

Fig. 10-13. The "Dutch Colonial" may also be designed with a New York or Flemish type **gambrel** roof. Note the Dutch door with the "bull's eye" lights in the upper half. This is the David Desmarest house located in New Milford, New Jersey, built about 1681.

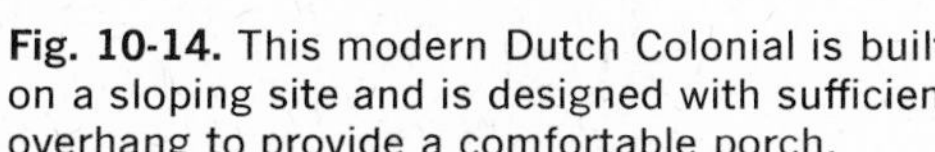

Fig. 10-14. This modern Dutch Colonial is built on a sloping site and is designed with sufficient overhang to provide a comfortable porch.

Fig. 10-15. This early U-shaped ranch house, date unknown, was the residence of General Beale. (Tejon Ranch, Kent County, California.)

Fig. 10-16. Many ranch-style houses are planned around a patio, court, or breezeway.

HISTORIC AMERICAN BUILDING SURVEY, LIBRARY OF CONGRESS, WASHINGTON, D.C. PHOTO BY HENRY F. WITNEY.

Fig. 10-17. La Casa del Rancho Aquaja de la Centinela, Inglewood, California, was built in 1822 and originally had a flat roof. The central portion of the building is original adobe. A later addition was made at the left using board and batten.

Ranch House—(Figs. 10-15 to 10-22.)

Roof	— Gable—slightly pitched, flat or shed. Wide overhangs, roof lower over garage and breezeway.
Walls	— Wood or masonry or combinations of materials. Large windows. Entrance without ornamentation.
Height	— 1 story.
Chimney	— Large, centrally located or projecting.
Plan	— Low, rambling for urban area. Open planning. Built-in furniture.

Fig. 10-18. In many "ranches" a porch-like projection is added by extending the roof beyond the normal overhang.

HISTORIC AMERICAN BUILDING SURVEY, LIBRARY OF CONGRESS, WASHINGTON, D.C. PHOTO BY LOUIS A. KONE.

Fig. 10-19. One of the original dwellings on the Sherwood Ranch, Monterey County, California, employs a continuous wide overhand roof to afford protection from the sun and weather. This was built in 1824.

Fig. 10-20. Frequently the contemporary ranch-type house has a rectangular floor plan and a wide overhang.

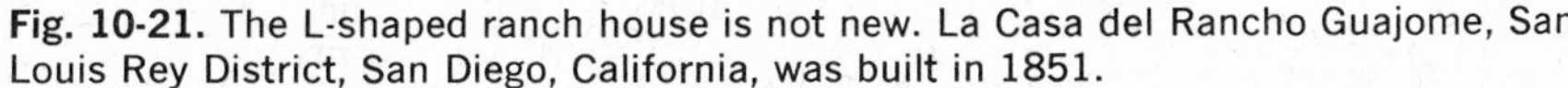

Fig. 10-21. The L-shaped ranch house is not new. La Casa del Rancho Guajome, San Louis Rey District, San Diego, California, was built in 1851.

HISTORIC AMERICAN BUILDING SURVEY, LIBRARY OF CONGRESS, WASHINGTON, D.C. PHOTO BY HENRY F. WITNEY.

Fig. 10-22. The ranch-type house may assume many plan shapes and may be designed to fit problem lots. The casual appearance of its design gives a feeling of openness.

Fig. 10-23. A split level designed for a sloping site uses mid-levels to the best advantage.

UNIVERSITY OF CHICAGO.

Fig. 10-24. The Robie House designed by Frank Lloyd Wright, though built in 1909, has the appearance of contemporary styling.

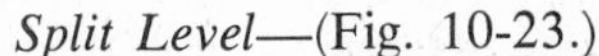

PHOTO BY ALLAN STAMBERG.

Fig. 10-25. This contemporary-style house shows Oriental influence. Note the use of horizontal and vertical lines to create a pleasing effect.

Split Level—(Fig. 10-23.)

Roof — Flat, shed, or low or medium pitched gable.
Irregular roof lines.

Walls — Masonry, wood, or combination.
Windows may be large, and/or regular types.

Height — Part 1 story, part 2 story.

Plan — Compact, economical, space-saving.
Fits problem lots, sloping sites.

Contemporary—(Figs. 10-24, 10-25, and 10-26.)

Roof — Flat or low pitched, gable and shed.

Fig. 10-26. The contemporary house fits the needs of the owner. It combines new methods of construction, new materials, and aesthetic principles into a functional whole.

Wide overhangs, low horizontal look.
Cantilevered roofs.
Walls — Masonry and wood, natural finish on both exterior and interior walls.
Large glass areas.
Height — Usually 1 story, may be 2.
Plan — Open or flexible plan, few interior walls.

Modern Adaptations

Period architectural styles that have survived are usually modern adaptations or borrowings in part or whole from the original designs.

The colonial-style homes that have been and are popular in New England are also prevalent, for example, in Kansas and Colorado, as well. Similarly, the rambling California ranch with its indoor-outdoor living is everywhere; the split level and contemporary are also located throughout the United States.

Cape Cod Colonial

The Cape Cod (Figs. 10-8 and 10-9) is the type of colonial that was originally native to the Cape Cod district of Massachusetts. Originally the plan was almost square, built close to the ground, and was one- or one-and-a-half-stories in height. This traditional style has regained its popularity over the country since 1930. Different window patterns are evident in the present day Cape Cods due to changes made in the basic arrangements of rooms. The modern plan is considerably narrower than its original models. This compact style is still one- or one-and-a-half-stories; the upper floor is often used for expansion.

Ranch Style

The ranch house (Figs. 10-15 to 10-22) is the result of a modern development over a long period of time. The ranch style was originated by Mexican and Spanish settlers in what is now Southern California. These dwellings were rambling, one-story houses with flat or low-pitched roofs. The rooms were planned around a patio or court. This type of home was extremely prevalent in the 1800's in Southern California and along the northern Pacific coast. Gradually the ranch house moved eastward into the prairie country.

The ranch home has undergone modifications, as have many of the other styles popular in the United States. The rancher as it is known today, is more compact and has smaller and fewer rooms than its western ancestor. The modern ranch-style home built in suburbia owes some of its salient features (such as open planning, floor to ceiling windows, corner windows, and built-in furniture) to Frank Lloyd Wright's early homes. Built-in furniture, coordinated and unified with the interior design gives the impressive decor.

Split Level

The split level (Fig. 10-23) evolved by placing a home on the side of a hill. Houses have long been placed on hilly terrain, but not until 1850, however, did the designer-craftsman elevate one portion midway between two others. Placing the split level on a flat site loses some of its effectiveness and exterior aesthetic value. Many of the split levels built in the 1950's and early 1960's have plans that are ranch type in nature. The change of levels provides a saving in costs because of grouped plumbing, increased living space, greater privacy, and a new freedom in exterior design.

Contemporary

Any home that is built today is really called *contemporary*. In the architectural sense, however, contemporary has a specific connotation. Contemporary (Figs. 10-24, 10-25, and 10-26) is an imaginative and exciting style that has been developed during the 20th Century by architects. Again, Frank Lloyd Wright has appreciably influenced this style through some of his homes built as early as 1912.

The contemporary house is not a particular style, but a philosophical aspect of architectural design. This is reflected in the planning of space to conform to the needs of the modern family. The contemporary house strives to make maximum use of living space; areas are kept flexible, and a feeling of space and openness is achieved.

The feeling of additional space is not only given by removing partitions (yet still providing the sense of a separate area), but also by allowing the underside of the roof to serve as the ceiling. In the urban

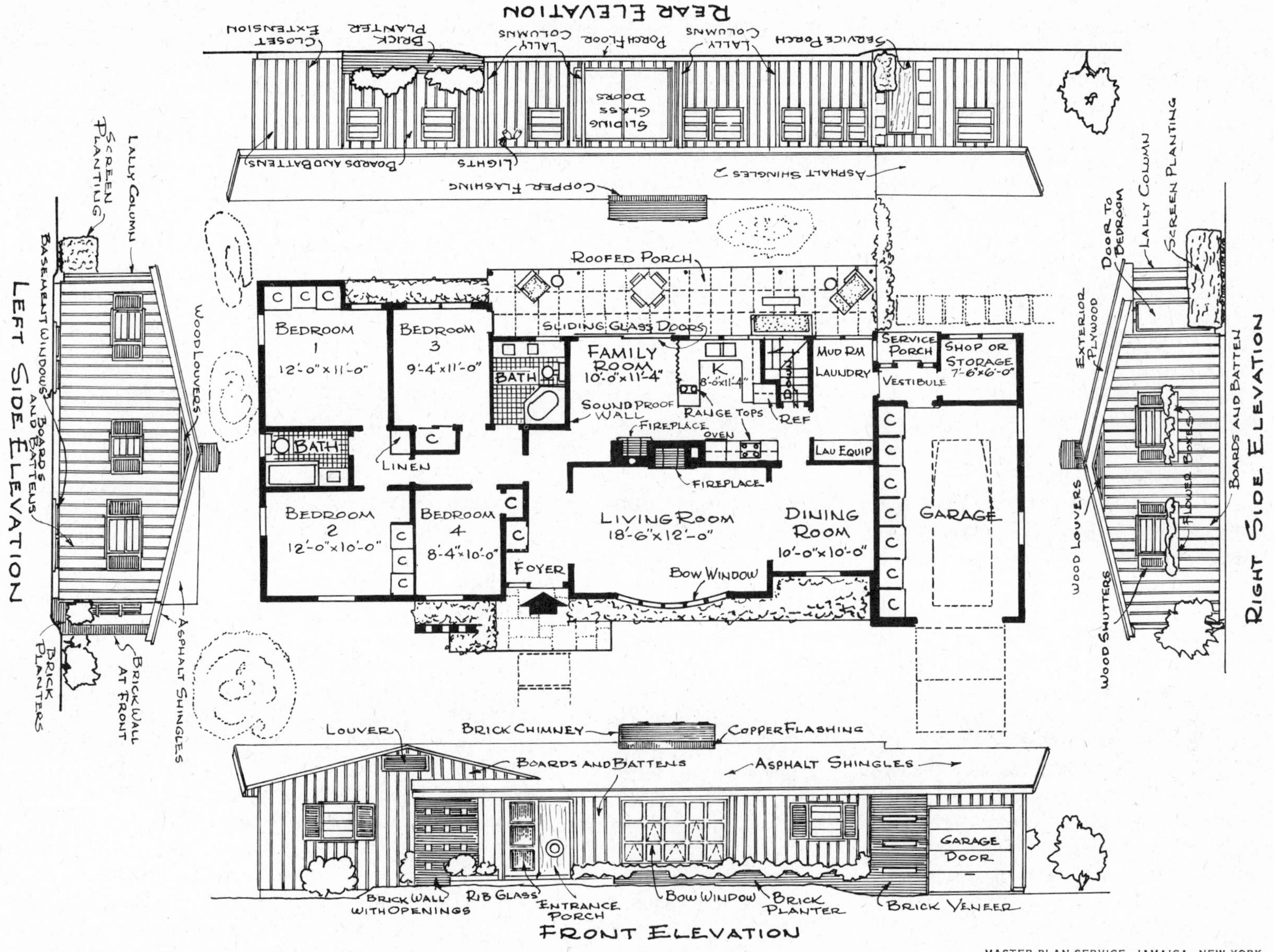

Fig. 10-27. Each elevation is drawn as if viewed from a point infinitely distant from each side.

setting, the contemporary house is oriented towards rear-area living. Contemporary style incorporates the outdoors by using walls of glass, sliding doors, patios, and sun porches.

The contemporary home is characterized by flat or low-pitched roofs, wide overhangs, and cantilevered (projecting) roofs. Many contemporary homes are built on a slab. Attics are usually omitted. *Radiant heating* (see Chapter 12) has eliminated the necessity of using wall space for radiators and heat vents. Heating pipes are placed in the floor or ceiling. Larger expanses of glass, both in height and width, may be used. Large roof overhangs shield the window areas in the summer but are planned to allow entrance of the winter sun. Stone, brick, or concrete block masonry are allowed to remain in their natural state on both the interior and exterior. This allows the house to blend in with the surrounding areas. Wood is frequently left unstained and unpainted to enable the beauty of the material to blend with nature.

Elevation Drawings

Drawings that indicate and show the exterior surfaces of the structure in their true proportions are called elevations. The elevations are designated *front, rear, left,* and *right side*. They are drawn as they would appear if viewed from a point directly in front of each side.[2] See Fig. 10-27. The basic purposes in drawing elevations are to graphically represent the extèrior treatments and to give (1) the builder the height dimensions of windows and doors; (2) distances from finished grade to finished floor, floor to ceiling, and floor to floor; and (3) the ridge and chimney heights. In addition, by means of notes, the elevations indicate the type of exterior wall covering, roof material, and type of window and door openings. Elevations not only serve to give information, but also enable the designer to visually check, in part, the aesthetic appeal. Floor plans show the placement and width of openings, but the elevations give the opportunity to "see" how a particular type of window, door, entrance, siding, stone, etc., will appear. Perspective sketches (such as Fig. 10-26, for example) are used to give a more easily visualized, realistic, and picturelike representation. This makes an attractive illustration which may serve both as a visual aid and as an advertising medium.

2. The elevations may sometimes be referred to as the North, South, East and West elevation if the house is to be placed facing one of these principal directions.

Wall Section

Preparatory to drawing the elevations, a wall section (carried from the footing through the cornice) must be drawn in the same scale as the floor plan and proposed elevations. The wall section should show the footing, foundation, sill floor joists (or slab if applicable), floor (sub- and finish), exterior wall, ceiling joints, cornice, and roof rafters or truss in approximately the correct pitch. Fig. 10-28 is an example of a wall section. It is necessary to have this section so the correct heights may be determined for the elevations.

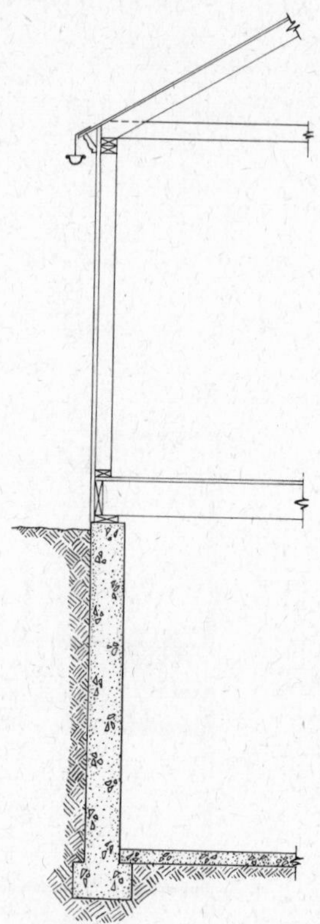

Fig. 10-28. The correct heights for an elevation are projected from the wall section.

In drawing the wall section the student may want to refer to the earlier step-by-step figures for the various parts. See Fig. 7-22 (footing section), Fig. 7-50 (sill section), Figs. 7-72 and 7-73 (wall-joist sections), and Fig. 8-15 (wall-roof section).

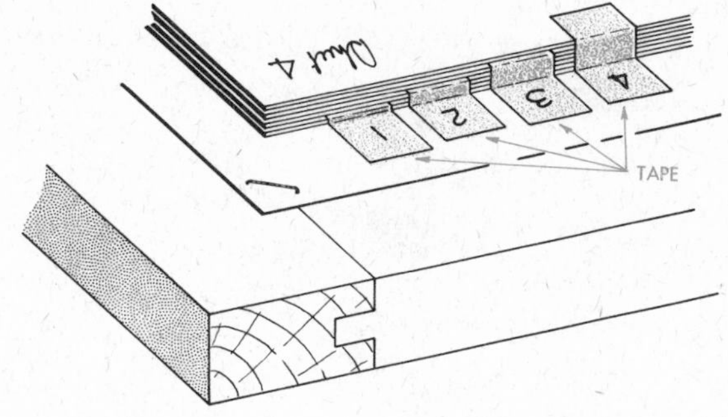

Fig. 10-29. Fasten four vellum sheets (B or C size) so they may be flipped over.

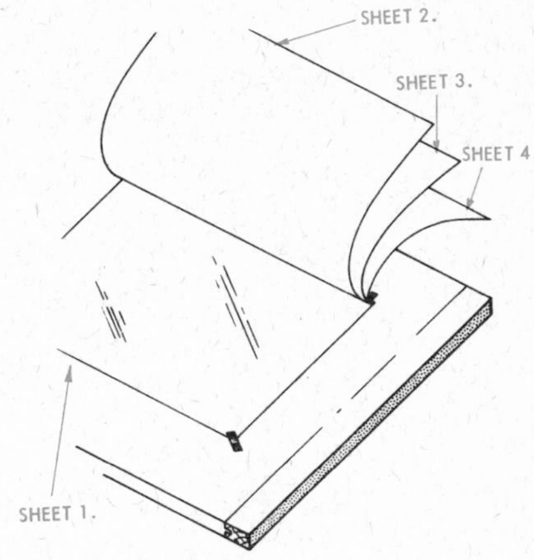

Step-by-Step Drawing Procedure: Elevations

There are a host of different methods used in drawing elevations. However, the method explained in the following step-by-step procedure has proved to be most expedient and systematic. Fasten four standard size sheets of vellum (size B or C) together at the top so they are free to be flipped over. See Fig. 10-29.

Elevations. See Fig. 10-30.

Step 1. Draw the wall section and fasten to the left of the sheets. See Fig. 10-30, Step 1.

Step 2. Flip the top three sheets (numbers, 4, 3, and 2) over. With light lines project the footing, basement floor, grade, and the joists (floor and ceiling) onto sheet No. 1. Flip over sheet No. 2 and trace these same features. Trace these same lines on sheets No. 3 and No. 4. See Fig. 10-30, Step 2.

Step 3. Transfer measurements with a *measurement strip* or *tick strip*[3] from the floor plan to the elevation. Indicate with a *tick mark* the exterior wall corners, window and door ℄'s, any wall offsets, and porch or stoop projections. These measurements are obtained by viewing the plan in the *same direction* as the elevation being drawn. See Fig. 10-30, Step 3.

Step 4. Transfer these locations to sheet No. 1 (side elevation). Draw vertical lines representing the outside wall corners and ℄'s representing window and door openings. See Fig. 10-30, Step 4.

Step 5. Project roof and outside wall intersections (point X) from wall section to the outside corners on the elevation. If the ridge is needed on this elevation, draw its ℄. See Fig. 10-30, Step 5.

Step 6. Draw roof slope B-A through point X. Draw other side of slope CA. If the slope doesn't appear satisfactory, erase original slope and revise. Check clearances, rafters, etc., of new slope. Revise wall section. See Fig. 10-30, Step 6.

Step 7. Tick off chimney location and size from the plan view and transfer to elevation. Draw in any unexcavated areas. See Fig. 10-30, Step 7.

3. The measurement strip or tick strip is used to transfer a series of measurements from one portion of a drawing to another. This is extremely useful when many distances must be duplicated and where a high degree of accuracy is not paramount. The tick strip used in this application is approximately 1″ × 15″. (See Fig. 10-30.)

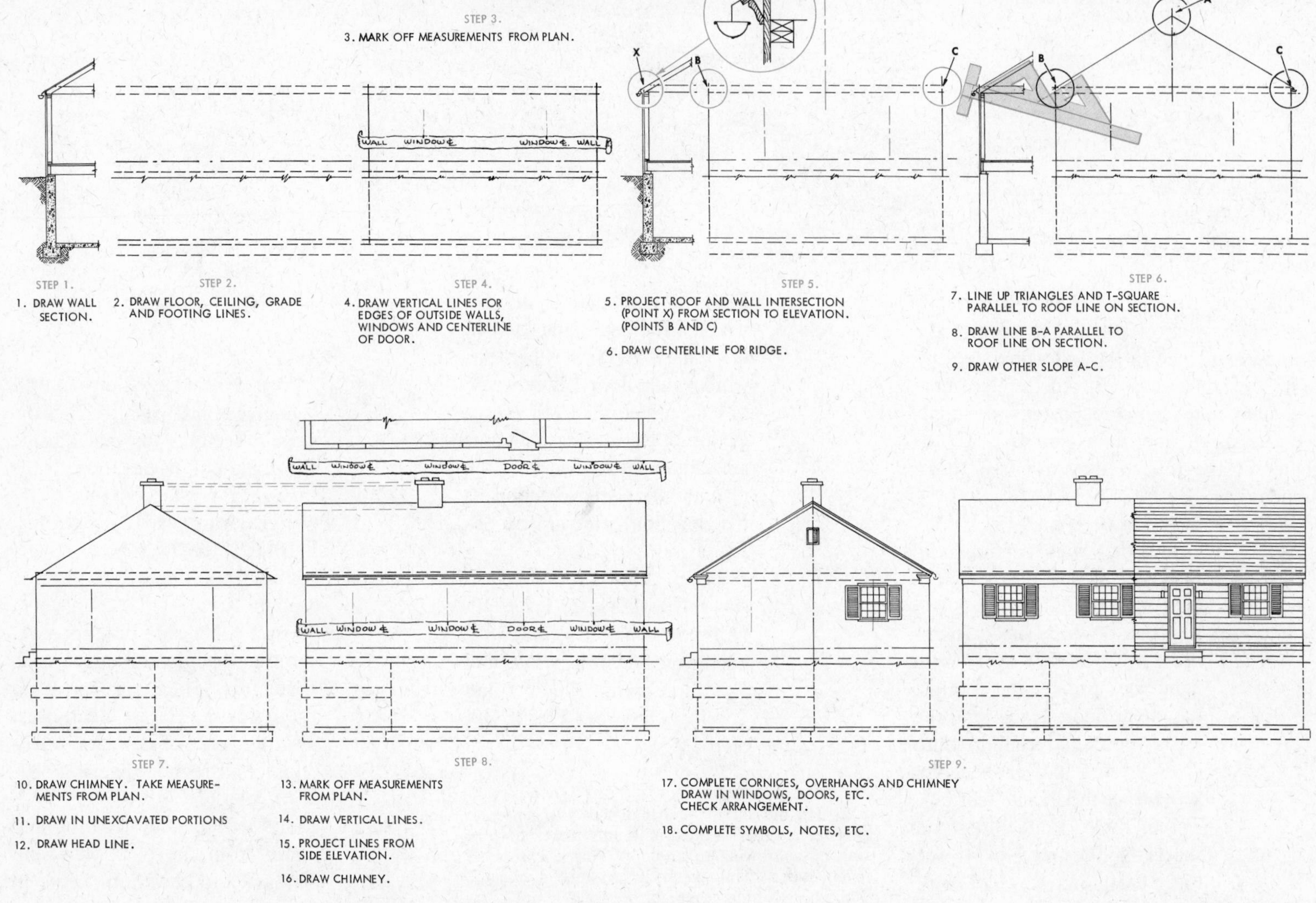

Fig. 10-30. Follow this step-by-step procedure in drawing elevations.

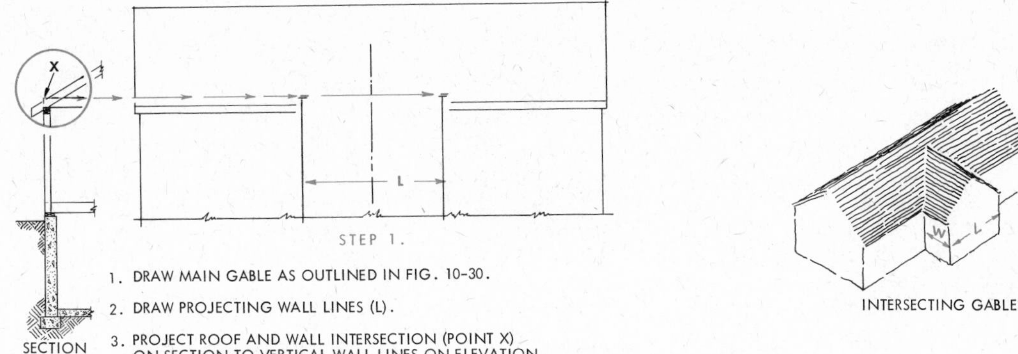

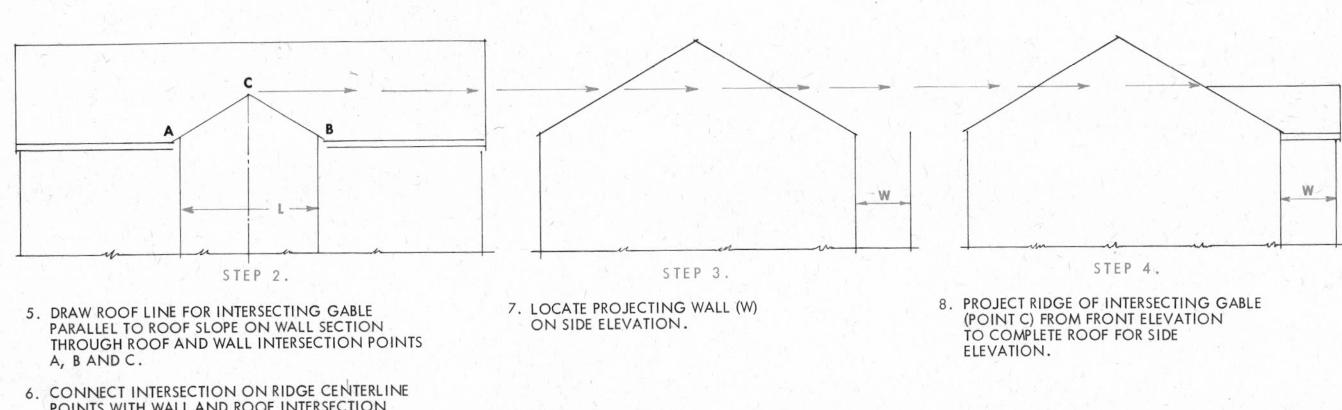

Fig. 10-31. Follow this step-by-step procedure in drawing an elevation with intersecting gables.

Step 8. Drop sheet No. 2 over and tick measurements for front elevation from plan.
Draw vertical lines for exterior wall corners and for window and door locations.
Tick off chimney location and size from plan and transfer to elevation.
Trace window and door head heights.
Trace chimney height and intersection with roof (if shown in front elevation) from side elevation.
Trace ridge. See Fig. 10-30, Step 8.

Step 9. Complete cornice overhang,

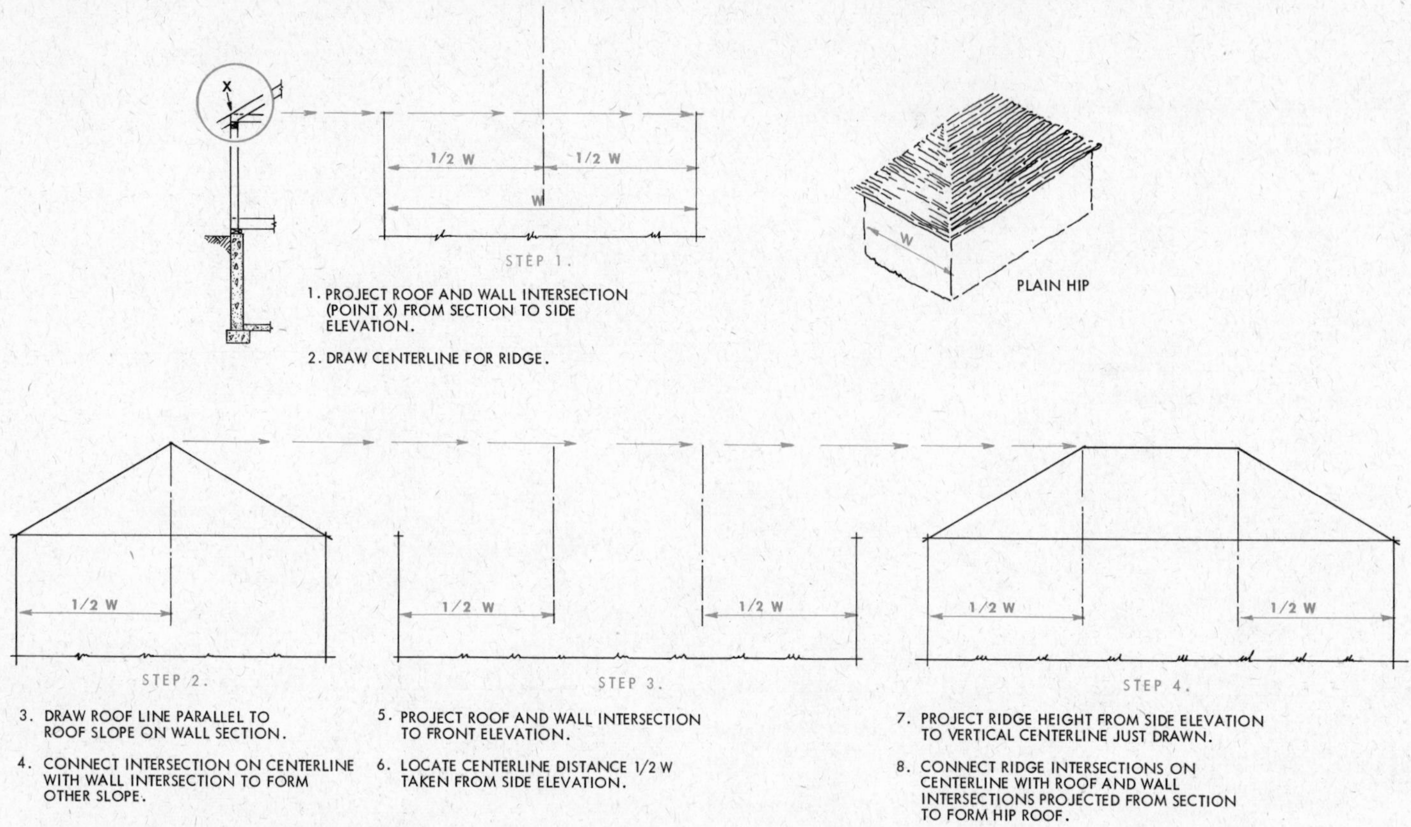

Fig. 10-32. Follow this step-by-step procedure in drawing an elevation with a plain hip roof.

gutters, etc., on side elevation (sheet No. 1).

Trace line of cornice, gutter, etc., on front elevation (sheet No. 2).

Draw in windows,[4] doors, etc.

Draw in exterior wall covering, roofing and other ornamentation.

Dimension finish grade to finish floor; finish floor to finish ceiling, ridge height, etc.

Note building materials (exterior wall covering, roofing material, chimney material, pitch triangle, ornamentation, finish grade, etc). See Fig. 10-30, Step 9.

---

4. Drawing windows may be simplified by using underlays available from window manufacturers, or by drawing the windows, at the same scale as elevations, on a piece of 8½″ × 11″ detail paper. Draw the casing and sill for each *different* type of window (see Chapter 8). *Note the catalog number, size,* and other pertinent data below each window.

Step 10. Draw the other elevations on Sheets No. 3 and No. 4 in the same manner as has been outlined in the previous 9 steps. Note: Do not trace the two remaining elevations directly from those elevations just drawn. All features will be reversed on opposite elevations, i.e., a porch attached to the front will appear on the left side of the right elevation, and on the right of the left elevation.

After the elevations have been completed, transfer the window openings by ticking off the proper size and ℄'s to the plan. Draw in the proper symbols for the particular openings on the plan.

Step-by-Step Drawing Procedure: Roofs

Occasionally problems are encountered in drawing the roof—particularly in deciding exactly where to begin. The procedure for drawing the plain gable roof has been pointed out in Fig. 10-30. To eliminate any questions which may occur, step-by-step procedures are given for drawing three other types of roof.

Intersecting Gables. See Fig. 10-31.

Step 1. Draw the main gable as outlined in Fig. 10-31. Locate and draw the projecting wall lines (L). Project or transfer roof and wall intersection (X) from wall section to vertical wall lines on the elevation.
Locate and draw the ℄ for ridge. See Fig. 10-31, Step 1.

Step 2. Draw roof line for intersecting gable parallel to roof slope on the wall section through roof and wall intersecting points A, B, and C. (The roof slope of the projection is usually the same as that of the main roof.)
Connect intersection of ridge ℄, C, with wall and roof intersection points A and B, to form slope. See Fig. 10-31, Step 2.

Step 3. Locate and draw projecting wall, W, on side elevation. See Fig. 10-31, Step 3.

Step 4. Project or transfer ridge height of intersecting gable (point C) from front elevation to side elevation to complete roof.
Complete cornice overhang, gutter, etc. See Fig. 10-31, Step 4.

Plain Hip. See Fig. 10-32.

Step 1. Project or transfer height of roof and wall intersection (X) from wall section to side elevation.
Draw ℄ for ridge. See Fig. 10-32, Step 1.

Step 2. Draw roof line extended to ridge ℄ parallel to roof slope on wall section.

Step 3. Project or transfer height of roof and wall intersection to front elevation.
Locate ℄ distance, ½ W, transferred from side elevation. See Fig. 10-32, Step 3.
Connect intersection of ridge ℄ with wall intersection to form other slope. See Fig. 10-32, Step 2.

Step 4. Project or transfer ridge height from side elevation to vertical ℄ for hip.
Connect ridge intersections on ℄ with roof and wall intersections projected from wall section to form hip.
Complete cornice overhang, gutter, etc.
See Fig. 10-32, Step 4.

Intersecting Hips. See Fig. 10-33.

Step 1. Draw elevation of main hip roof as described in the preceding section. See Fig. 10-32.
Locate and draw wall projections W_1, and W_2 on side elevations.
Locate and draw wall lines L_1, and L_2 on front elevation.
Locate and draw ℄ of L_1, and L_2. Extend these ℄'s so they intersect the main hip at points A and B. See Fig. 10-33, Step 1.

Step 2. Connect intersections of ℄ at points A and B on front elevation to respective roof and wall intersection of projecting walls.
Project or transfer ridge heights (points A and B) to side elevations.
Locate ½ L_1 and ½ L_2 (taken

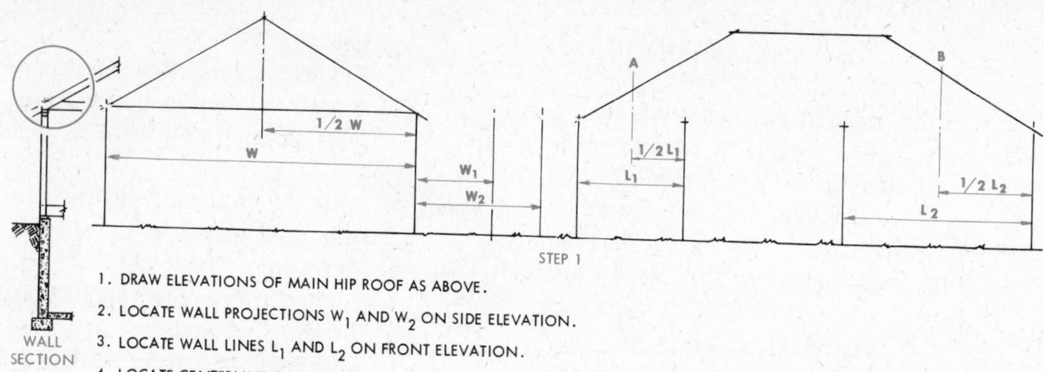

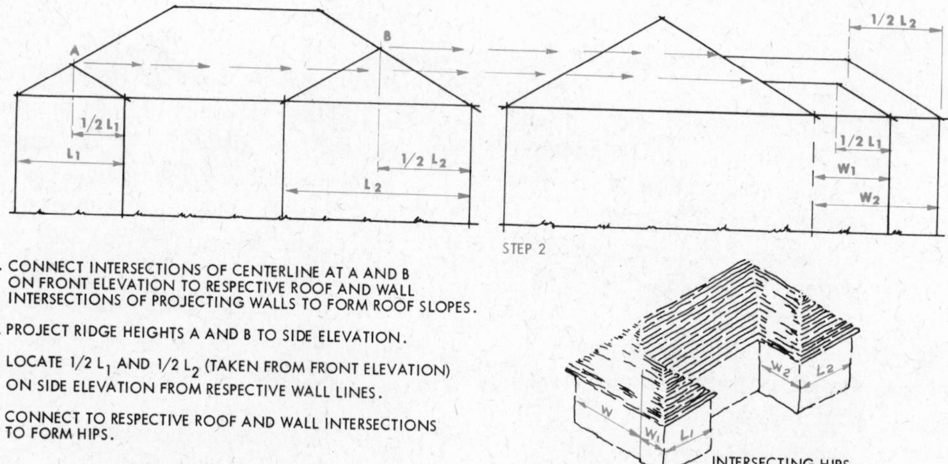

Fig. 10-33. Follow this step-by-step procedure in drawing an elevation with an intersecting hip roof.

from front elevation) on side elevation from respective wall lines. Connect to respective roof and wall intersection to form hips. See Fig. 10-33, Step 2.

Questions and Problems

1. Select an architectural, building trades, or home-making magazine from your classroom library, school library, or home.
   Examine the photographs or drawings of houses and identify the styles.
2. Draw an exterior wall section of western frame construction with a concrete block foundation wall. Call out all materials with notes. Insulate outside walls and attic ceiling with either 4″ fill, or foil type insulation. Use 2″ × 4″s for studs, plates, soles, and girts; 2″ × 8″ joists for 1st and 2nd floors and header joists; 2″ × 6″s for attic floor joists and rafters; 2″ × 6″ sills; ¾″ × 16″ W.I. bolts, 6′-0″ O.C.; ¾″ fabricated fibre board; ½″ exterior grade plywood for roof sheathing; ¾″ interior plywood for sub-flooring; and

Fig. 10-34. Use these plans to draw elevations.

A ONE STORY

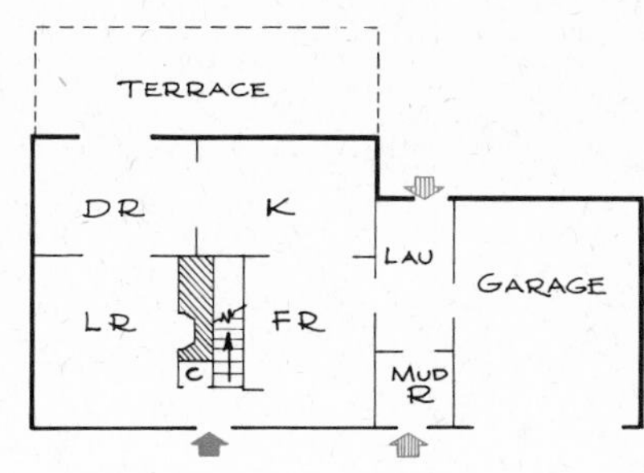

B TWO STORY

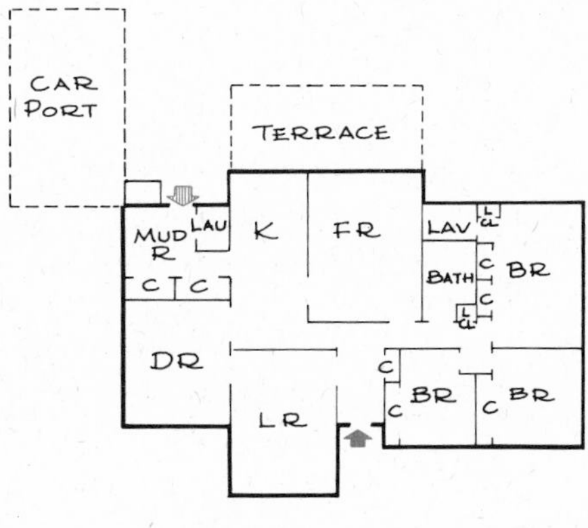

C ONE STORY

1″ × 2″ cross bridging between joists. Scale 1½″ = 1′-0″.

3. Draw an exterior wall section of balloon frame construction with a 10″ poured concrete foundation wall. Indicate all materials and notes. Insulate outside walls and attic ceiling with either 4″ fill, batt, or foil type insulation. Use 2″ × 4″ studs, plates, soles, and girts; 2″ × 8″ joists for 1st and 2nd floors and header joists; 2″ × 6″ joists for attic floor and rafters; 2″ × 6″ sills; 1″ × 6″ ledger or ribbon; 1″ × 4″ fire stop; ¾″ × 16″ W.I. bolts, 6′-0″ O.C.; ¾″ fabricated fibreboard; ½″ exterior grade plywood for roof sheathing; ¾″ interior plywood for sub-flooring; and metal cross bridging or 2″ × 8″ solid bridging between joists. Scale 1½″ = 1′-0″.
4. Draw or sketch three different style elevations using the plans shown in Fig. 10-34. (Select the type of styles shown in this chapter. It may be desirable to slightly alter the plans shown in Fig. 10-34.)
5. Is it possible that an elevation(s) may be completed before the plan? If so, state the circumstances where this may or may not be true.
6. Is a perspective sketch more important or valuable than a sketched elevation? Where may a perspective sketch be a significant aid?
7. Select 4 different *plans* and elevations from the home or real estate page of the daily newspaper, and sketch a elevation *different* than the one pictured. Do not change the floor plan.

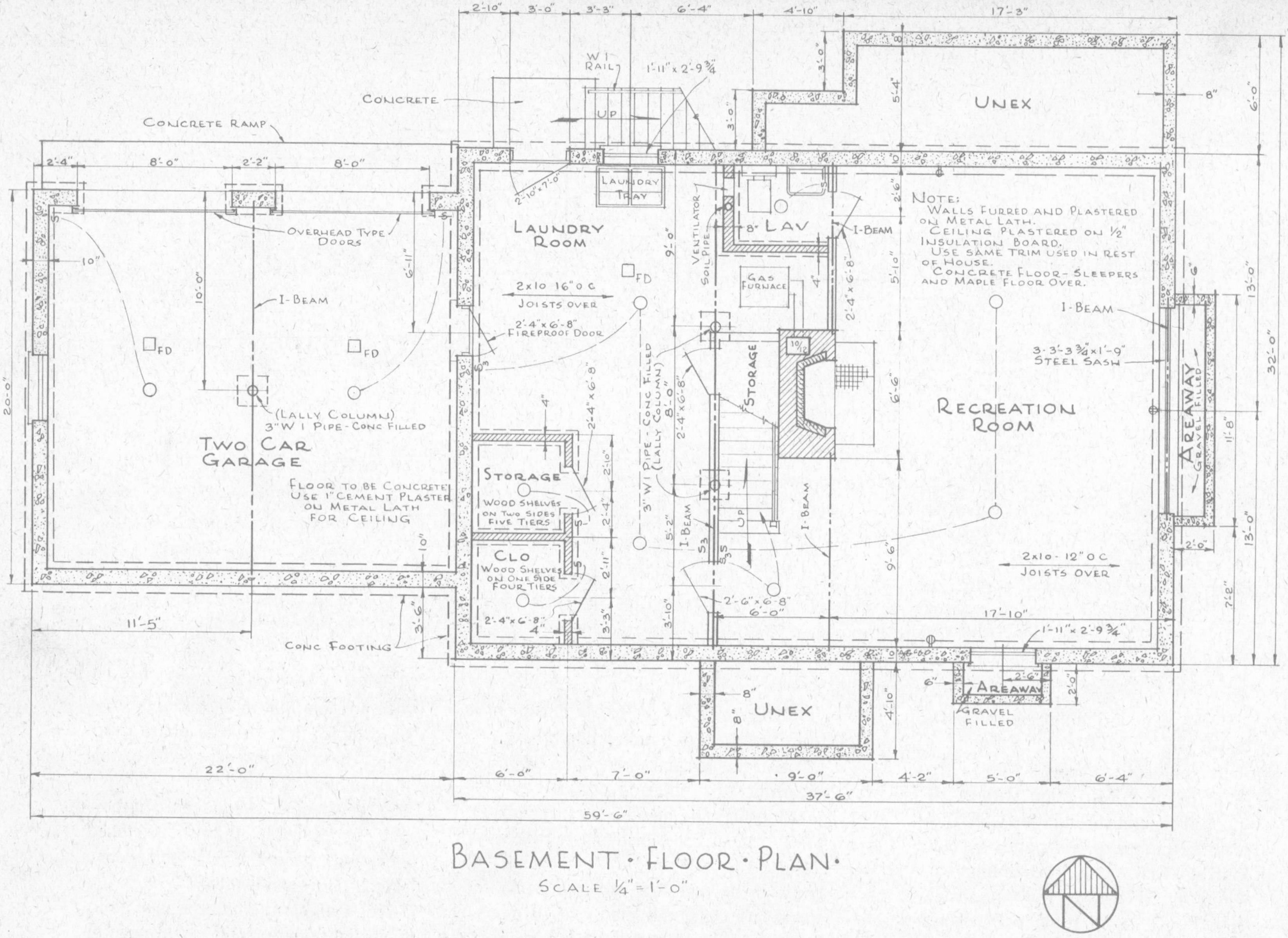

Concrete

Concrete Ramp

W I Rail

1'-11" x 2'-9 3/4"

Up

Unex

Laundry Tray

Laundry Room

2x10 16" O C Joists Over

2'-4" x 6'-8" Fireproof Door

Ventilator

Soil Pipe

Lav

I-Beam

Gas Furnace

Note:
Walls furred and plastered on metal lath.
Ceiling plastered on 1/2" insulation board.
Use same trim used in rest of house.
Concrete floor - sleepers and maple floor over.

Overhead Type Doors

I-Beam

(Lally Column) 3" W I Pipe - Conc Filled

Two Car Garage

Floor to be concrete. Use 1" cement plaster on metal lath for ceiling

Storage

Wood shelves on two sides five tiers

Clo

Wood shelves on one side four tiers

3" W I Pipe - Conc Filled (Lally Column)

Storage

Recreation Room

3-3'-3 3/4" x 1'-9" Steel Sash

Areaway

Gravel Filled

2x10 - 12" O C Joists Over

Conc Footing

Unex

Areaway

Gravel Filled

Basement · Floor · Plan ·

Scale 1/4" = 1'-0"

Symbols are used to show the locations of electrical fixtures and outlets. A broken, curved line runs from the switch to the outlets it controls.

Residential Lighting and Wiring 11

With increasing affluence the home owner's demand for labor-saving devices is rising. Many items that were once considered luxuries are now accepted as household necessities.

The number of appliances in common use has multiplied at an almost fantastic rate. For example, in the early 1900's the electric fan and flat iron were the only electric appliances available. This number slowly increased so that in 1930, 19 appliances were in common use in the average American household. By 1940 the number had increased to 36. Ten years later in 1950, 43 appliances were in common use. In 1960 well over 60 appliances were found in many average homes. To meet the demands of the "applianced" family, wiring must be up-to-date. It has been estimated that 4 out of 5 residences in existence today are inadequately wired. In many homes this has resulted in an octupus-like maze of appliances and lamps growing from an extension cord. Frequently this results in blown fuses or tripped circuit breakers. Extensive overloading may result in **fires.**

Many new homes now being constructed are inadequately wired because provisions for future electrical needs have been completely neglected. It is estimated that the electrical needs of the home will increase approximately 10 per cent every year. The circuit design and wiring layout must meet this increase of wattage requirements.

Electrical Needs

Since electricity plays an important role in our lives, all of its contributing features must be considered. As electrical power distribution is being planned in the house, an assessment must be made of the various types of portable and fixed electrical equipment that will be operated in each room. Attention must also be directed to the number of convenience outlets, switches, and lighting fixtures needed for each room.

Convenience outlets (receptacles which appliances plug into) are provided for the many different appliances used in the home: refrigerators, clocks, lamps, toasters, razors, fans, etc., etc. Convenience outlets are 115 to 120 volts. These outlets may have either single or double receptacles (duplex). Each area should be analyzed to determine the intended appliance use. Allowance must also

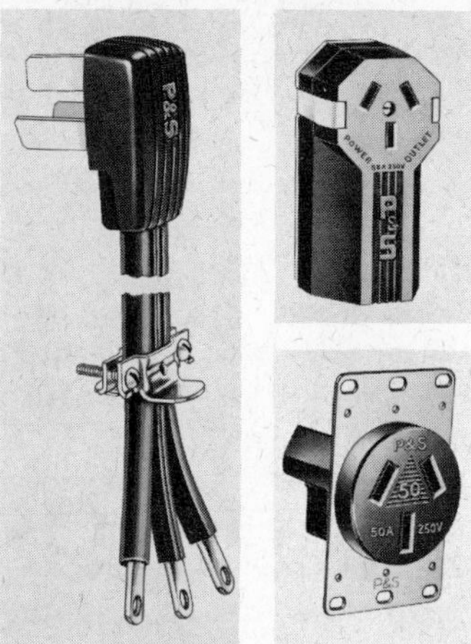

Fig. 11-1. Polarized receptacles and plugs are used for high voltage appliances.

TABLE 11-1

FIXTURE LIGHTING REQUIREMENTS

ROOM SIZE	CEILING FIXTURES		CORNICE, COVER, OR VALANCE LIGHTING
	MIN SIZE OF SHIELD	MIN WATTAGE	(LENGTH OF LIGHT SOURCE IN CORNICE, COVER OR VALANCE)
VERY SMALL (UP TO 125 SQ FT)	12" - 15"	ONE 100 W OR THREE 40 W	6 FEET
AVERAGE (125-225 SQ FT)	15" -17"	ONE 150 W OR FIVE 40 W	8-12 FEET*
LARGE (OVER 225 SQ FT)			16-20 FEET*

From: American Home Lighting Institute, FIXTURE LIGHTING GUIDE.

*Preferred in major living areas, such as living room, recreation room, etc. Recesses fixtures are acceptable for general lighting only when one 9"-12" box (100-150 w) is provided for each 40—50 sq ft of floor area. A combination of fixtures and wall lighting is desirable for added flexibility of lighting, especially in recreation or family room.

be made for future growth in use and number. A minimum of three outlets should be provided for each living area or room.

Special-purpose outlets, such as the polarized receptacle (and plug) shown in Fig. 11-1, are used for high voltage appliances or low voltage equipment which requires grounding. Polarized outlets are 230 to 240 volts. These outlets are designed so that two contacts carry the current and the third is grounded. This eliminates the possibility of serious electric shock. Appliances and equipment commonly found in the home which require special-purpose outlets are as follows: air conditioner, range, washer, dryer, water heater, power tools, water pump, sump pump, and freezer.

A check list should be made listing the appliances and equipment to be used for each room in the house. From this list the number and type of outlets may be computed. In addition, jacks must be provided for such things as the TV antenna, telephone, thermostat, door chimes, and intercom system.

Switches are required to operate lights, appliances and equipment, and convenience and special outlets. A list should be made for each room of the number of lights, etc., needed. This will give a rough estimate of the number of switches needed. Traffic paths must also be taken into consideration—convenience is an important factor.

If an outlet is controlled from only *one* switch, it is referred to as a single-pole switch (S). A three-way switch (S_3) is used to control an outlet from *two* locations, as in the case of a light on the stairwell. It may be switched on or off from either the bottom or top of the stair. A four-way switch (S_4) is used to control the current from *three* different locations. This last type of switching is not extensively used.

Lighting. The following general requirements are recommended by the American Home Lighting Institute:

1. All incandescent bulbs (ordinary bulbs) and fluorescent tubes shall be shielded in a manner which will minimize glare (except in closet and storage areas). Flashed opal and ceramic enameled glass and diffusing plastic materials are satisfactory for shielding incandescent bulbs. Materials having less diffusion (frosted or configurated glass) are satisfactory for shielding fluorescent tubes.

Low wattage (25w or less) lamps should be used in chandelier type fixtures that are equipped with clear or frosted glass shades for decorative effect. This type of fixture should be supplemented with indirect lighting.

2. A minimum of one fixture shall be controlled by a wall switch at the entrance of each

room. Where ceiling fixtures are not installed, a minimum of one wall bracket, valance, cove, or cornice lighting unit must be wall switched at the room entrance.

3. Where traffic pattern into a room is from two directions and more than ten feet apart, two-way control on general lighting is desirable.

The size of the room or area to be lighted determines the lighting requirement. In Table 11-1, two alternate lighting methods are given for each room size.

Residential Wiring Recommendations

As with other phases of home construction, residential wiring must follow standards. The National Electrical Code establishes minimum safety standards. The recommendations given below are designed to supplement the National Electrical Code (NEC).

The design standards given in the following paragraphs are from the *American Standard Requirements for Residential Wiring*. (Wiring symbols are illustrated in Chapter 6.)

Exterior Entrances — (Fig. 11-2)

A. *Lighting Provisions*. One or more lighting outlets, as architecture dictates, wall-switch controlled, at front and service entrances. Where a single wall outlet is desired, location on the latch side of the door is preferable.

It is recommended that lighting outlets, wall-switch controlled, be installed at the other entrances.

The principal lighting requirements at entrances are the illumination of steps leading to the entrance and of faces of people at the door. Outlets in addition to those at the door are often desirable for post lights to illuminate terraced or broken flights of steps or long approach walks. These outlets should be wall-switch controlled inside the house entrance.

B. *Convenience Outlets*. It is recommended that this (Fig. 11-2) outlet be controlled by a wall switch inside the entrance for convenient operation of outdoor decorative lighting. Additional outlets along the exterior of the house are recommended to serve decorative garden treatments and for the use of appliances or electric garden tools, such as lawn mowers and hedge trimmers. Such outlets should also be wall-switch controlled.

Living Room — (Fig. 11-3 and 11-4)

A. *Lighting Provisions*. Some means of general illumination is essential. This lighting may be provided by ceiling or wall fixtures, by lighting in coves, valances, or cornices, or by porta-

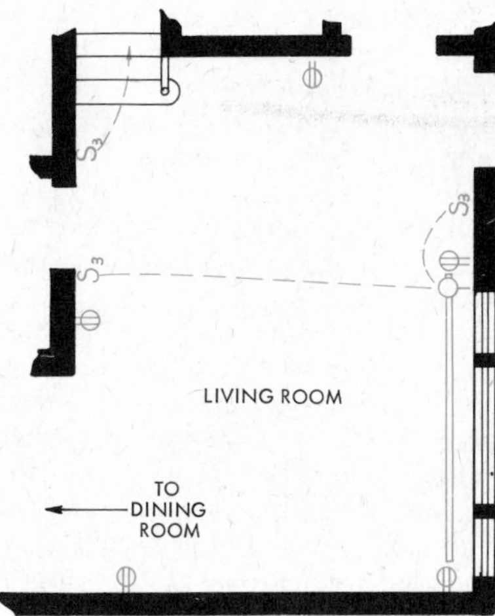

AMERICAN STANDARD REQUIREMENTS FOR RESIDENTIAL WIRING.

Fig. 11-3. Outlets should be placed so that no usable wall space is more than 6′ from an outlet. Note the fluorescent light above the window.

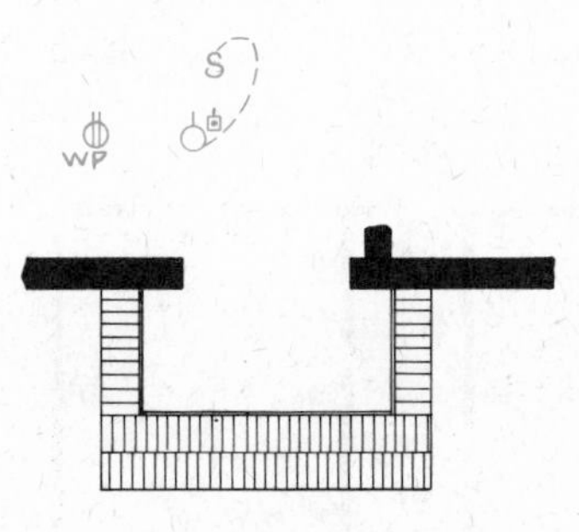

AMERICAN STANDARD REQUIREMENTS FOR RESIDENTIAL WIRING.

Fig. 11-2. One or more lighting sources are required for the entrance. The broken line represents the connection between switch and lighting outlet. Note also the weatherproof outlet.

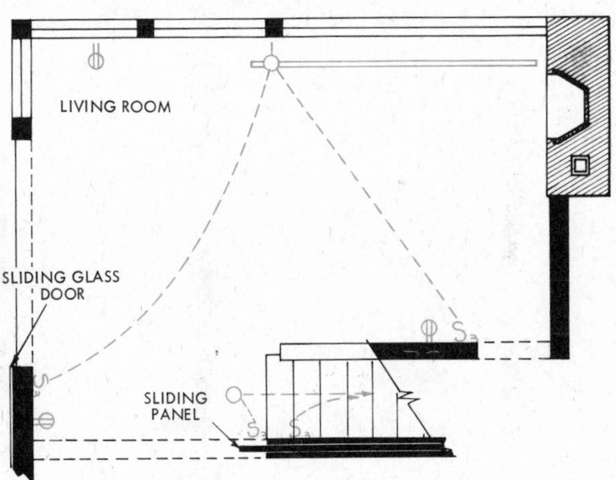

AMERICAN STANDARD REQUIREMENTS FOR RESIDENTIAL WIRING.

Fig. 11-4. Outlets are located for convenience.

ble lamps. Provide lighting outlets, wall-switch controlled, in locations appropriate to the lighting method selected.

These provisions also apply to sun rooms, enclosed porches, television rooms, libraries, dens, and similar areas.

The installation of outlets for decorative-lighting accent is recommended, such as picture illumination and bookcase lighting.

B. *Convenience Outlets.* Convenience outlets shall be placed so that no point along the floor line in any usable wall space is more than six feet from an outlet in that space. Where the installation of windows extending to the floor prevents meeting this requirement by the use of ordinary convenience outlets, equivalent facilities shall be installed using other appropriate means.

If, in lieu of fixed lighting, general illumination is provided from portable lamps, two convenience outlets or one plug position in two or more split-receptacle (double receptacle—one switch controlled, one independent) convenience outlets shall be wall-switch controlled.

In the case of switch-controlled convenience outlets, it is recommended that split-receptacle outlets be used in order not to limit the location of radios, television sets, clocks, etc.

It is recommended that one convenience outlet be installed flush in mantel shelf, if construction permits.

It is recommended that, in addition, a single convenience outlet be installed in combination with the wall switch at one or more of the switch locations for the use of the vacuum cleaner or other portable appliances. Outlets for the use of clocks, radios, decorative lighting, etc., in bookcases and other suitable locations are recommended.

C. *Special Purpose Outlets.* It is recommended that one outlet for a room air conditioner be installed wherever a central air-conditioning system is not planned.

Dining Areas — (Fig. 11-5)

A. *Lighting Provisions.* Each dining room, or dining area combined with another room, or breakfast nook, shall have at least one lighting outlet, wall-switch controlled.

Such outlets are normally located over the probable location of the dining or breakfast table to provide direct illumination of the area.

B. *Convenience Outlets.* Convenience outlets placed so that no point along the floor line in any usable wall space is more than six feet

TO LIVING ROOM

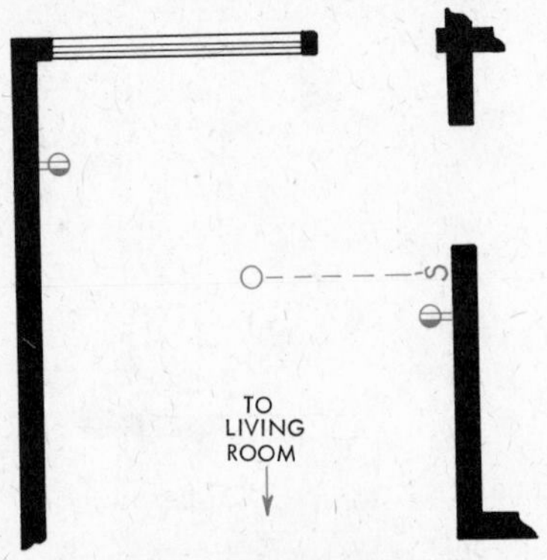

AMERICAN STANDARD REQUIREMENTS FOR RESIDENTIAL WIRING.

Fig. 11-5. The dining room should provide split-wired convenience outlets.

Fig. 11-6. Bedroom outlets should be positioned to accommodate various furniture arrangements. Note the closet lighting.

from an outlet in that space. When dining or breakfast table is to be placed against a wall, one of these outlets shall be placed at the table location, just above table height.

Where open counter space is to be built in, an outlet shall be provided above counter height for the use of portable appliances.

Convenience outlets in dining areas should be of the split-receptacle type for connection to appliance circuits.

Bedrooms — (Fig. 11-6)

A. *Lighting Provisions.* Good general illumination is particularly essential in the bedroom. This shall be provided from a ceiling fixture or from lighting in valances, coves, or cornices. Provide outlets, wall-switch controlled, in locations appropriate to the method selected.

Light fixtures over full-length mirrors, or a light source at the ceiling located in the bedroom and directly in front of the clothes closets, may serve as general illumination.

Master-switch control in the master bedroom, as well as at other strategic points in the home, is suggested for selected interior and exterior lights.

B. *Convenience Outlets.* Outlets shall be placed so that there is a convenience outlet on each side and within six feet of the center line of each probable individual bed location. Additional outlets shall be placed so that no point along the floor line in any other usable wall space is more than six feet from an outlet in that space.

It is recommended that convenience outlets be placed only three to four feet from the center line of the probable bed locations. The popularity of bedside radios and clocks, bed lamps, and electric bed cover, makes increased plug-in positions at bed locations essential. Triplex or quadruplex convenience outlets are therefore recommended at these locations.

It is recommended that, at one of the switch locations, a receptacle outlet be provided for the use of a vacuum cleaner, floor polisher, or other portable appliances.

C. *Special Purpose Outlets.* The installation of one heavy-duty, special-purpose outlet in each bedroom for the connection of room air conditioners is recommended. Such outlets may also be used for operating portable space heaters during cool weather in climates where a small amount of local heat is sufficient.

NOTE: The illustrations in Fig. 11-6 show the application of these standards to both double- and twin-bed arrangements and also their application where more than one probable bed location is available within the room.

Bathrooms and Lavatories — (Fig. 11-7)

A. *Lighting Provisions.* Illumination of both sides of the face when at the mirror is essential. There are several methods that may be employed to achieve good lighting at this location and in the rest of the room. Lighting outlets shall be installed to provide for the method selected, bearing in mind that a single concentrated light source, either on the ceiling or the side wall, is not acceptable. All lighting outlets should be wall-switch controlled.

A ceiling outlet located in line with the front edge of the basin will provide improved lighting at the mirror, general room lighting, and safety lighting for combination shower and tub.

When more than one mirror location is planned, equal consideration should be given to the lighting in each case.

It is recommended that a switch-controlled night light be installed.

Where an enclosed shower stall is planned, an outlet for a vapor-proof luminaire should be installed, controlled by a wall switch outside the stall.

B. *Convenience Outlets.* One outlet near the mirror, three to five feet above the floor.

It is recommended that an outlet be installed at each separate mirror or vanity space, and also at any space that might accommodate an electric towel dryer, electric razor, etc.

A receptacle which is a part of a bathroom lighting fixture should not be considered as satisfying this requirements unless it is rated at 15 amperes and wired with at least 15-ampere rated wires.

C. *Special Purpose Outlets.* It is recom-

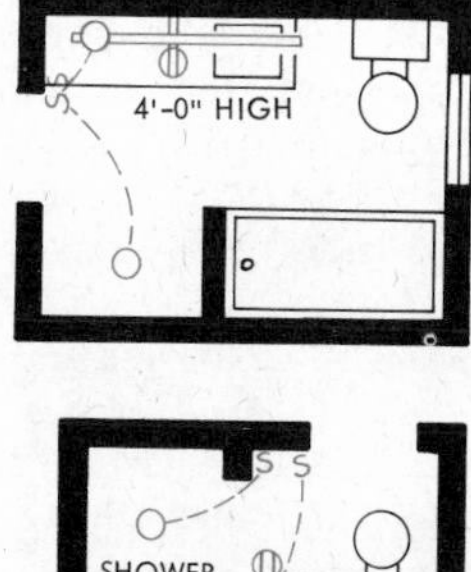

AMERICAN STANDARD REQUIREMENTS FOR RESIDENTIAL WIRING.

Fig. 11-7. Several light sources are needed for sufficient bathroom illumination.

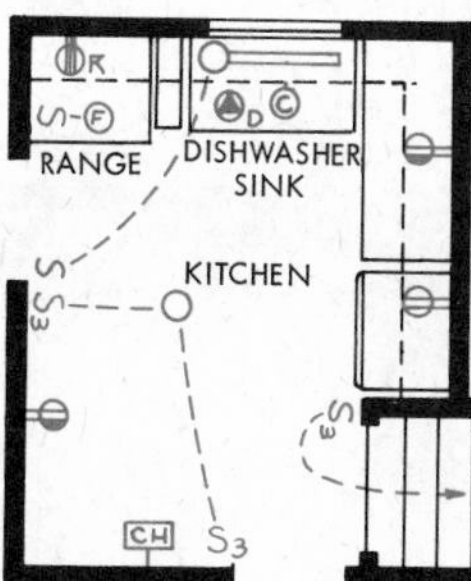

AMERICAN STANDARD REQUIREMENTS FOR RESIDENTIAL WIRING.

Fig. 11-8. Lighting design in the kitchen should provide for sufficient illumination of the work area.

mended that each bathroom be equipped with an outlet for a built-in type space heater.

Also recommended is an outlet for a built-in ventilating fan, wall-switch controlled.

Kitchen — (Fig. 11-8 and 11-9)

A. *Lighting Provisions.* Provide outlets for general illumination and for lighting at the sink. These lighting outlets shall be wall-switch controlled. Lighting design should provide for illumination of the work areas, sink, range, counters, and tables.

Undercabinet lighting fixtures within easy reach may have local-switch control. Consideration should also be given to outlets to provide inside lighting of cabinets.

B. *Convenience Outlets.* One outlet for the refrigerator. One outlet for each four linear feet of work-surface frontage, with at least one outlet to serve each work surface. Work-surface outlets to be located approximately 44 inches above floor line.

If a planning desk is to be installed, one outlet shall be located to serve this area.

Table space to have one outlet, preferably just above table level.

An outlet is recommended at any wall space that may be used for ironing or for an electric roaster.

Convenience outlets in the kitchen, other than that for the refrigerator, should be of the split-receptacle type (one 115v and one 230v) for connection to appliance circuits.

C. *Special Purpose Outlets.* One outlet each for a range and ventilating fan.

An outlet or outlets for a dishwasher or food waste disposer, if necessary plumbing facilities are installed.

Provision shall be made for the use of an electric clock.

The clock should be located so as to be easily visible from all parts of the kitchen. Recessed receptacle with clock hanger is recommended.

It is recommended that an outlet be provided for a food freezer either in the kitchen or in some other convenient location.

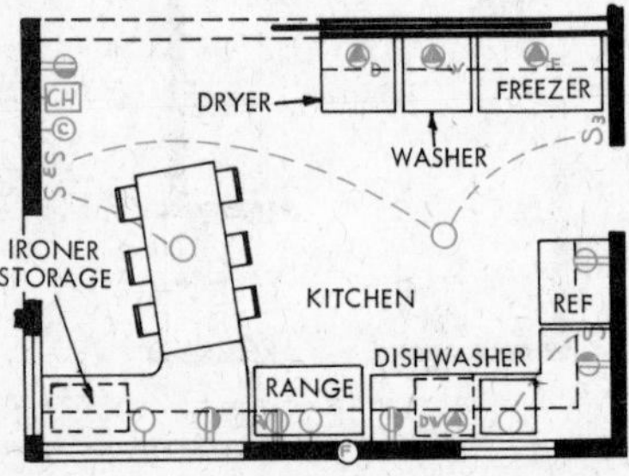

AMERICAN STANDARD REQUIREMENTS FOR RESIDENTIAL WIRING.

Fig. 11-9. Kitchen outlets should be provided near each part of the work area.

Laundry and Laundry Areas — (Fig. 11-10)

A. *Lighting Provisions.* For complete laundries, lighting outlets shall be installed to provide proper illumination of work areas, such as laundry tubs, sorting table, washing, ironing, and drying centers. At least one lighting outlet in the room shall be wall-switch controlled.

For laundry trays in unfinished basement, one ceiling outlet, centered over the trays.

It is recommended that all laundry lighting be wall-switch controlled.

B. *Convenience Outlet.* At least one convenience outlet. In some instances, one of the special-purpose outlets, properly located, may satisfy this requirement. The convenience outlet is intended for such purposes as laundry hot plate, sewing machine, etc.

Convenience outlets in laundry area should be of the split-receptacle type for connection to appliance circuits.

C. *Special Purpose Outlets.* One outlet for each of the following pieces of equipment:

Automatic Washer
Hand Iron or Ironer
Clothes Dryer

The installation of outlets for ventilating fan and clock are highly desirable. If an electric water heater is to be installed, the requirements may be obtained from the local utility.

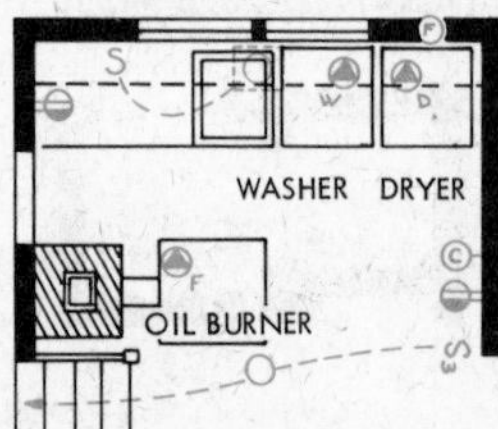

AMERICAN STANDARD REQUIREMENTS FOR RESIDENTIAL WIRING.

Fig. 11-10. The laundry area should have illumination over the work area.

Closets

Lighting Provisions. One outlet for each closet. Where shelving or other conditions make the installation of lights within a closet ineffective, lighting outlets should be so located in the adjoining space to provide light within the closet.

The installation of wall switches near the closet door, or door-type switches, is recommended.

Halls

A. *Lighting Provisions.* Lighting outlets, wall-switch controlled, shall be installed for proper illumination of the entire area. Particular attention should be paid to irregularly shaped areas.

These provisions apply to passage halls, reception halls, vestibules, entries, foyers, and similar areas.

It is recommended that a switch-controlled night light be installed in any hall giving access to bedrooms.

B. *Convenience Outlets.* One outlet for each 15 linear feet of hallway, measured along center line. Each hall over 25 square feet in floor area shall have at least one outlet.

In reception halls and foyers, convenience outlets shall be placed so that no point along the floor line in any usable wall space is more than ten feet from an outlet in that space.

It is recommended that at one of the switch outlets a convenience receptacle be provided for connection of vacuum cleaner, floor polisher, etc.

Stairways

A. *Lighting Provisions.* Wall or ceiling outlets shall be installed to provide adequate illumination of each stair flight. Outlets shall have multiple-switch control at the head and foot of the stairway, so arranged that full illumination may be turned on from either floor, but that lights in halls furnishing access to bedrooms may be extinguished without interfering with ground-floor usage.

These provisions are intended to apply to any stairway at both ends of which are finished rooms.

Whenever possible, switches should be grouped together and never located so close to steps that a fall might result from a misstep while reaching for a switch.

B. *Convenience Outlets.* At intermediate landings of a large area, an outlet is recommended for decorative lamps, night light, vacuum cleaner, etc.

Recreation Room — (Fig. 11-11)

A. *Lighting Provisions.* Some means of general illumination is essential. This lighting may be provided by ceiling or wall fixtures, or by lighting in coves, valances, or cornices. Provide lighting outlets, wall-switch controlled, in locations appropriate to the lighting method selected.

Selection of lighting method for use in the recreation room should take into account the

AMERICAN STANDARD REQUIREMENTS FOR RESIDENTIAL WIRING.

Fig. 11-11. Lighting in the recreation room should take into account the major activities for which the room is planned.

type of major activities for which the room is planned.

B. *Convenience Outlets.* Convenience outlets shall be placed so that no point along the floor line in any usable wall space is more than six feet from an outlet in that space.

It is recommended that one convenience outlet be installed flush in the mantel shelf, where construction permits. Outlets for the use of

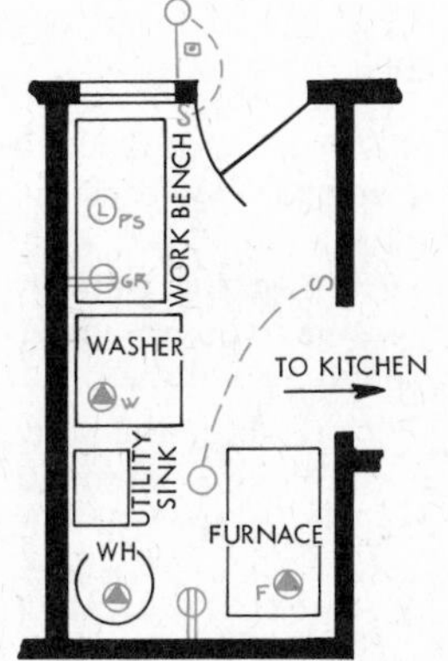

AMERICAN STANDARD REQUIREMENTS FOR RESIDENTIAL WIRING.

Fig. 11-12. Utility room lighting should illuminate the furnace area and work bench.

clock, radio, television, ventilating fan, motion picture projector, and the like, should be located in relation to their intended use.

Utility Room or Space — (Fig. 11-12)

A. *Lighting Provisions.* Lighting outlets placed to illuminate furnace area, and work bench, if planned. At least one lighting outlet to be wall-switch controlled.

B. *Convenience Outlets.* One convenience outlet, preferably near the furnace location or near any planned work-bench location.

C. *Special Purpose Outlet.* One outlet for electrical equipment used in connection with furnace operation.

Basement — (Fig. 11-13)

A. *Lighting Provisions.* Lighting outlets shall be placed to illuminate designated work areas or equipment locations, such as at furnace, pump, work bench, etc. Additional outlets shall be installed near the foot of the stairway, in each enclosed space, and in open spaces so that each 150 square feet of open space is adequately served by a light in that area.

In unfinished basements the light at the foot of the stairs shall be wall-switch controlled near the head of the stairs. Other lights may be pull-chain controlled.

In basements with finished rooms, with garage space, or with other direct access to outdoors, the stairway lighting provisions apply.

It is recommended that for basements which will be infrequently visited a pilot light be installed in conjunction with the switch at the head of the stairs.

B. *Convenience Outlets.* At least two convenience outlets shall be provided. If a work bench is planned, one outlet shall be placed at this location.

Basement convenience outlets are useful near furnace, at play area, for basement laundries, dark rooms, hobby areas, and for

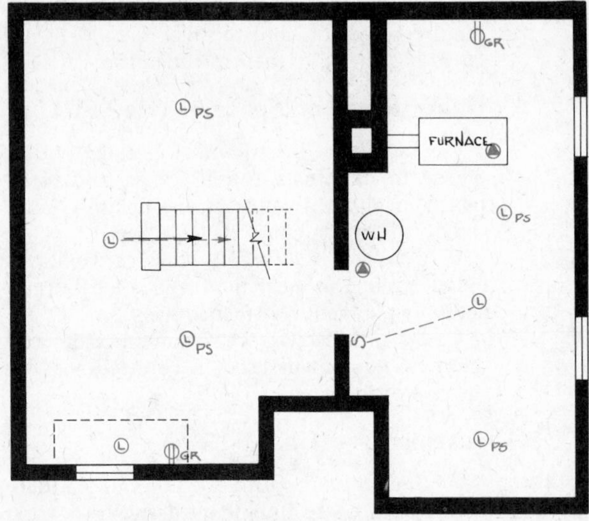

AMERICAN STANDARD REQUIREMENTS FOR RESIDENTIAL WIRING.

Fig. 11-13. Basement lighting should illuminate designated work areas and equipment locations.

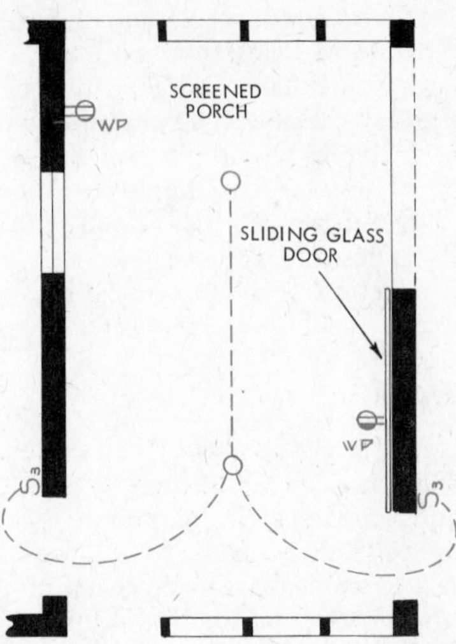

AMERICAN STANDARD REQUIREMENTS FOR RESIDENTIAL WIRING.

Fig. 11-14. Large or irregularly shaped porch areas may need two or more lighting outlets.

appliances, such as dehumidifier, portable space heater, etc.

C. *Special Purpose Outlet.* One outlet for electrical equipment used in connection with furnace operation.

An outlet for a food freezer is recommended.

Accessible Attic

A. *Lighting Provisions.* One outlet for general illumination, wall-switch controlled from foot of stairs. When no permanent stairs are installed, this lighting outlet may be pull-chain controlled, if located over the access door. Where an unfinished attic is planned for later development into rooms, the attic-lighting outlet shall be switch controlled at top and bottom of stairs.

One outlet for each enclosed space.

These provisions apply to unfinished attics. For attics with finished rooms or spaces, see appropriate room classifications for requirements.

The installation of a pilot light in conjunction with the switch controlling the attic light is recommended.

B. *Convenience Outlets.* One outlet for general use. If open stairway leads to future attic rooms, provide a junction box with direct connection to the distribution panel (panelboard) for future extension to convenience outlets and lights when rooms are finished.

A convenience outlet in the attic is desirable for providing additional illumination in dark corners and also for the use of a vacuum cleaner and its accessories in cleaning.

C. *Special Purpose Outlet.* The installation of an outlet, multiple-switch controlled from desirable points throughout the house, is recommended in connection with the use of a summer cooling fan.

Porches — (See Fig. 11-14)

A. *Lighting Provisions.* Each porch, breezeway, or other similar roofed area of more than 75 square feet in floor area shall have a lighting outlet, wall-switch controlled. Large or irregularly shaped areas may require two or more lighting outlets.

Multiple-switch control shall be installed at entrances when the porch is used as a passage between the house and garage.

B. *Convenience Outlets.* One convenience outlet, weatherproof if exposed to moisture, for each 15 feet of wall bordering porch or breezeway.

It is recommended that all such outlets be controlled by a wall switch inside the door.

The split-receptacle convenience outlet shown in the illustration (Fig. 11-14) is intended to be connected to a 3-wire appliance branch circuit. This area is considered an outdoor dining area.

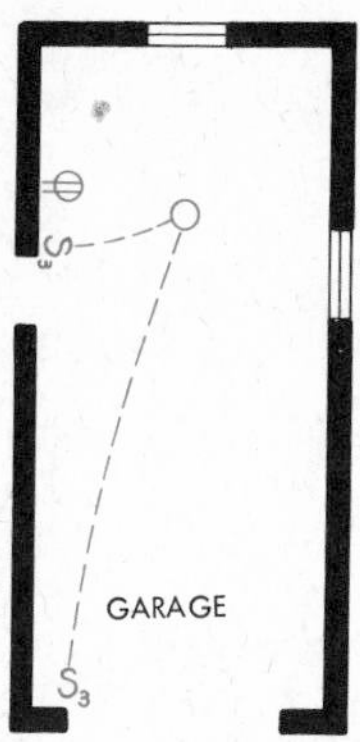

Fig. 11-15. At least one ceiling light, with a switch control at each entrance, is recommended for the garage.

Terraces and Patios

A. *Lighting Provisions.* The installation of an outlet on the building wall or on a post centrally located in the area is recommended for the purpose of providing fixed general illumination. Such outlets should be wall-switch controlled just inside the house door opening onto the area.

B. *Convenience Outlets.* One weatherproof outlet located at least 18 inches above grade line for each 15 linear feet of house wall bordering terrace or patio.

It is recommended that these outlets be wall-switch controlled from inside the house.

Garage or Carport — (See Fig. 11-15)

A. *Lighting Provisions.* At least one ceiling outlet, wall-switch controlled, for one-or two-car storage area.

If garage has no covered access from house, provide one exterior outlet, multiple-switch controlled from garage and residence.

If garage is to be used for purposes additional to car storage, such as to include work bench, closets, laundry, attached porch, etc., rules appropriate to these uses should be employed.

An exterior outlet, wall-switch controlled, is recommended for all garages. Additional interior outlets are often desirable even if no specific additional use is planned for the garage. For long driveways, additional illumination, such as by post lighting, is recommended. These lights should be wall-switch controlled from the house.

B. *Convenience Outlets.* At least one outlet for one- or two-car storage area.

C. *Special Purpose Outlets.* If food freezer, work bench, or automatic door opener is planned for installation in the garage, outlets appropriate to these uses should be provided.

Exterior Grounds

A. *Lighting Provisions.* Lighting outlets for floodlights are often desirable for illumination of surrounding grounds. These outlets may be located on the exterior of the house or garage, or on posts or poles appropriately placed. All outlets should be switch controlled from within the house. Multiple- and master-switch control from strategic points is also desirable.

The recommendations given above provide the planner with a guide for designing home wiring plans. However, the wiring design must stay within the specification limits of the state or local building codes and the National Electrical Code. In some cases, the wiring plans must also meet requirements given by the local utility companies.

Because of the increasing need for electric power, minimum wiring requirements today may be inadequate tomorrow. When planning the electrical distribution, it is advisable to check and make sure that the wiring plan allows additional outlets to accommodate future electrical needs. The initial cost of planning and installing extra outlets is negligible when compared to the cost of addition later.

Power Control Centers

Power from the local distributor is delivered into the house through lead-in cables called a *service drop.* A *watt-hour meter,* connected between the lead-in cables and the main power switch or *service disconnect,* measures the amount of power used by the house circuits. The amount of electricity used is measured in kilowatt-hours: 1000 watts (w) equal one kilowatt (kw); one kilowatt used for an hour equals one kilowatt-hour (kwh). A main control center or *panelboard,* which contains the *fuse box* or *circuit breaker,* connects to the service disconnect and delivers current to the various outlets. Fig. 11-16 graphically describes the path of the current from the pole to service head, etc. Some communities or areas within a community have underground services that enter the house below grade. The meter is then placed indoors. This arrangement eliminates the unsightly overhead wires strung from pole to house.

There is a marked trend in contemporary residential construction to modify the direct connection from the panelboard to the circuit outlets. This relatively new method employs a main control or panelboard to which several *branch control centers* are connected. Fig. 11-17 shows the current path in this system. The number of branch or power

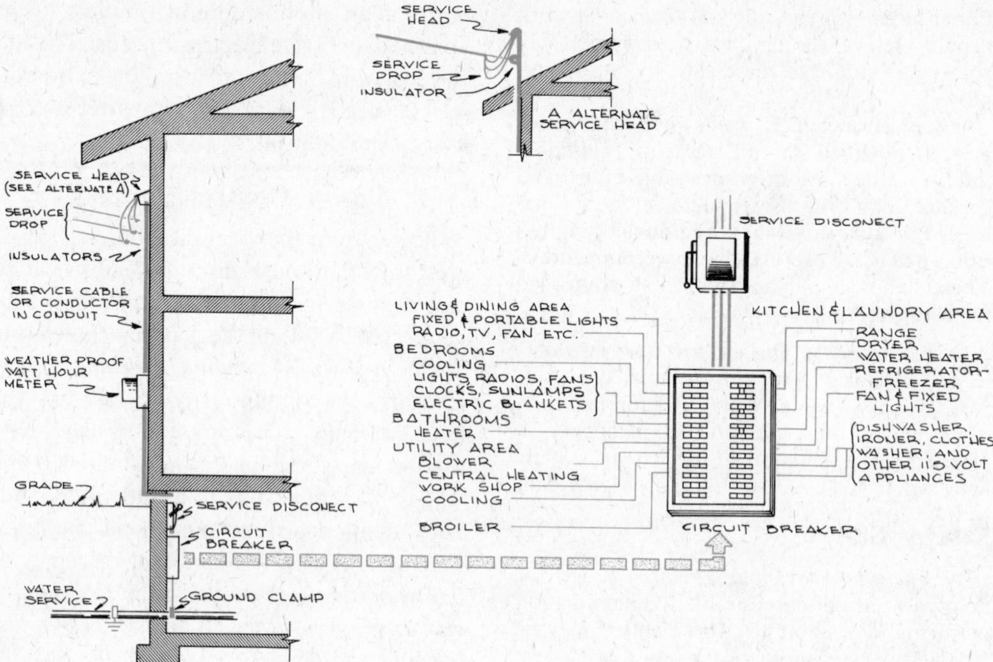

Fig. 11-16. This figure gives a section through a house showing a schematic diagram of a typical electrical distribution system. Note the 230 V circuit breakers for range, dryer, and water heater.

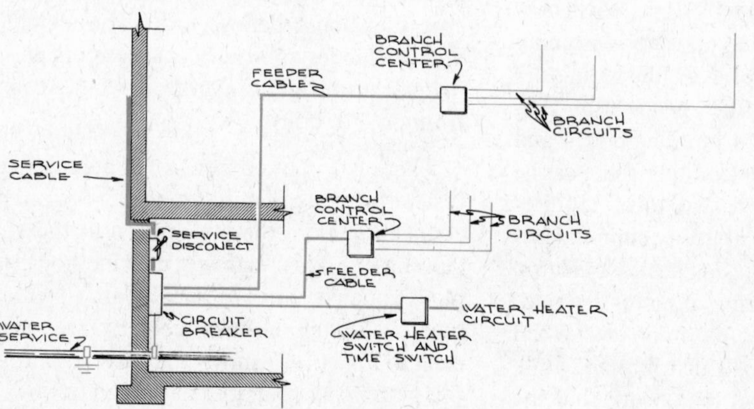

Fig. 11-17. There is a trend in residential construction to use branch control centers.

centers is dependent upon the number and type of circuits required. These centers are located throughout the house as close to the point of usage as possible. For the average single family dwelling it is recommended that (1) the *main control center* be limited to twelve positions: that is, there may be, for example, six single pole and three double pole circuit breakers; and that (2) the *branch control center* be restricted to eight positions (eight single poles or four double poles). The number of branch control centers is dependent upon the needs of the home. The branch control centers may be conveniently located in the kitchen, utility room, front hall, or closet. By placing the branch control centers close to the loads, the possibility of a voltage drop is greatly reduced.

Home Wiring Design

Current in the house is measured in amperes (amps). Power is measured in watts. These are calculated for two voltages: 115V and 230V. Voltage may be thought of as pressure on the line. When a light bulb, for example, reads 120V/100W, this means that connected into a current source with around 120 volts of pressure (the source varies 110V-120V) the lamp will use 100 watts of power. Wattage is used to measure the electricity used by appliances. If only the amperage is known, the wattage may be found using this formula:

$$\text{Watts} = \text{Volts} \times \text{Amps}$$

For example, if an electric iron was rated at 10 amps (at 115V) the wattage would be 1150W. If the wattage is known, the amps may be found using this formula:

$$\text{Amps} = \frac{\text{Watts}}{\text{Volts}}$$

For example, a 120V/110W bulb would use 0.83 amps. Amps are used in calculating the wiring size.

Loads

The load placed on the wiring system should not, of course, exceed the capacity of the wiring system. When an electrical load becomes too great for the wiring system, the efficiency of an electrical device drops. At one time or another we have experienced a momentary decrease in the size of a television picture, or a dimming of an incandescent bulb over a desk when an electrical motor was turned on or when an iron was used. A 5 per cent voltage drop due to inadequate wiring produces a 10 per cent loss of heat in an appliance or a 17 per cent loss in illumination from an incandescent lamp. Obviously, by overloading any circuit, the maximum efficiency is not received from each appliance or light. This loss of efficiency not only causes inconvenience but also creates a possible fire hazard.

The diameter of the wire in *any* wiring system determines the amount of current which may be carried. If the appliances or equipment in a circuit require more current than the wire is designed to carry, the wire heats up. This is referred to as "overloading." The circuit should be designed for pre-determined wattage use.

Branch Circuits

The wattage of the appliances, electrical equipment, or lights in a circuit determines the circuit size. If, for example, a lighting circuit is designed for 1500 watts, and a TV set (700W), a vacuum cleaner (500W), and five 120W bulbs were in operation, an overload would result. (The wattage use for each appliance is given by the manufacturer.) In every case the wattage being used may be determined by *adding* together the wattages of the appliances, lights, etc., which are in use. In planning the branch-circuit wiring size the projected use (with allowance for growth) is the determining factor. No. 14 wire is considered safe in a lighting circuit; however, a No. 12 wire is recommended. Special-purpose circuits usually require heavier wire. (Note: As the wire number becomes lower, the diameter becomes larger.)

Table 11-2 gives wiring sizes based on the amperage of the circuit.

Fuses or circuit breakers are calculated in amps. They should not be larger than the current capacity of the circuit they are designed to protect. Fuse or circuit breaker capacities may be calculated from Table

TABLE 11-2

WIRING SIZES (115V OR 230V)

WIRE SIZE	CONDUIT WIRING
No 14	15 Amp
No 12	20 Amp
No 10	30 Amp
No 6	50 Amp

TABLE 11-3

INDIVIDUAL EQUIPMENT CIRCUITS	
ITEM	CAPACITY
RANGE (UP TO 21-KW RATING)	50A-3W-115/230V*
COMBINATION WASHER-DRYER OR	40A-3W-115/230V*
AUTOMATIC WASHER	20A-2W-115V
ELECTRIC CLOTHS DRYER	30A-3W-115/230V*
FUEL-FIRED HEATING EQUIPMENT (IF INSTALLED)	15A or 20A-2W-115V
DISHWASHER AND WASTE DISPOSER (IF NECESSARY PLUMBING IS INSTALLED)	20A-3W-115/230V*
WATER HEATER (IF INSTALLED)	CONSULT LOCAL UTILITY
ATTIC FAN	20A-2W-115V (SWITCHED)
ROOM AIR CONDITIONERS OR CENTRAL AIR-CONDITIONING UNIT	20A-2W-230V OR 20A-3W-115/230V* 40A-2W-230V
FOOD FREEZER	20A-2W-115 or 230V
WATER PUMP (WHERE USED)	20A-2W-115 or 230V
BATHROOM HEATER	20A-2W-115 or 230V
WORK SHOP OR BENCH	20A-3W-115/230V*

From: American Standard Requirements for Residential Wiring.

*A 115/230V circuit is a three wire (3w) circuit that terminates in an outlet with a split-wired receptacles: one 115v receptacale and one 230v receptacale.

11-2. No. 12 wiring in conduit, for example, would require a fuse or circuit breaker rated at 20 amps.

Convenience Circuits. It is recommended that two or more 20 amp (115V) circuits should be provided for the small appliance load in cooking and eating areas. This provides for 2300 watts on each circuit (20 amp × 115V).

Special-Purpose Circuits. Three wire circuits (230V), are provided for large appliances and equipment. It is recommended that heavy wattage appliances, such as the range (around 12,000W), should have an individual branch circuit. Table 11-3 gives the capacities for commonly used household appliances and equipment.

Lighting Circuits. NEC standards state that one lighting circuit should be provided for each 500 sq. ft. of house area (measured from outside walls). A 20 amp circuit is recommended. If a 15 amp circuit is used, it is recommended that no more than 375 sq. ft. be served. Lighting may also be figured as a minimum of 3 watts per sq. ft. However, these are *minimum* requirements—good design may require more lighting. The lights in any one room, for example, should be on more than one circuit. This prevents a total blackout if the fuse blows.

Feeders

Feeder cables run from the main control center or panelboard to the branch control center. (See Fig. 11-17 for a feeder run.) In some instances the feeder cable must be of sufficient size to carry 100 per cent of the branch center load if all of the equipment is in operation at the same time. Usually the rule of thumb is to use 75 per cent of the branch load to calculate the wire size. For example, an electric range may be rated between 8,000 and 14,000 W, but it is seldom that all four surface units, broiler, and oven would draw current at the same time. Similarly, this would be true with the other appliances connected to a branch circuit. The National Electrical Code gives standards for calculating load requirements. Feeder lines to the branch centers should not have wires any smaller than No. 10.

Service Conductors

To supply full house power, the service conductor (see Fig. 11-16) must be of ample size to assume the electrical needs of the house. As with feeder cable, service conductor sizing assumes that not all the circuits are in use at any one time. A 3-wire service entrance with a 100 amp service switch is recommended by the Adequate Wiring Bureau. In many areas, the minimum service entrance requirement on new construction is 100 amps. The 150 amp service would be necessary if, in addition to the usual equipment, the house used a range, water heater, high speed dryer, and central air conditioning. If the house were heated electrically, in addition to the above mentioned items, a 200 amp service would be required.

Wiring Circuit Protection

In any house wiring circuit the cables or wires must be protected by some insulated covering. Essentially, there are four types of cable used in contemporary residential construction—each has its own particular use and special covering.

Rigid and Thin-wall Conduit. This type of indoor wiring is the most expensive, but it is also the safest. It provides the best protection against mechanical damage; at the same time it grounds the entire electrical system. It also provides fire protection since all wires are encased in tubing. Some building codes (for safety) require that conduit be used to protect all wires leading from the bottom of the first floor joists to the convenience outlets along the basement wall. Conduit is generally used only in new construction—since installation in old buildings is expensive and difficult. Some communities require all wiring to be conduit.

Rigid and thin-wall types of conduit may be used in wet or dry areas. It may also be used in masonry and concrete.

Rigid conduit is made of steel which is coated with enamel or zinc. Thin-wall conduit or tubing is also of steel, but it is lighter and easily cut or bent with a forming tool. No threading is required on thin-wall conduit.

Armored Cable. This type of indoor wiring consists of two or more insulated wires

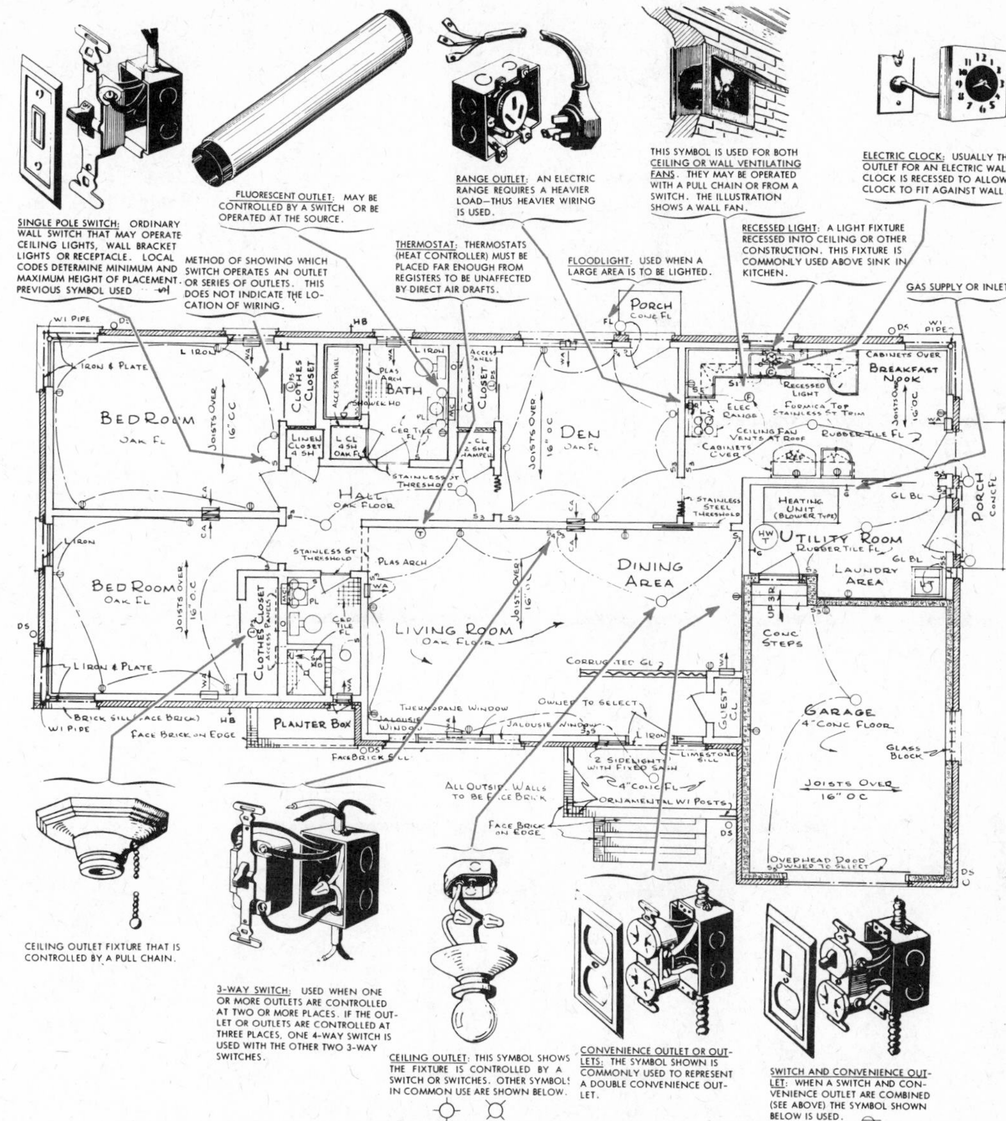

Fig. 11-18. This floor plan illustrates the symbols for switches, fixtures, and outlets.

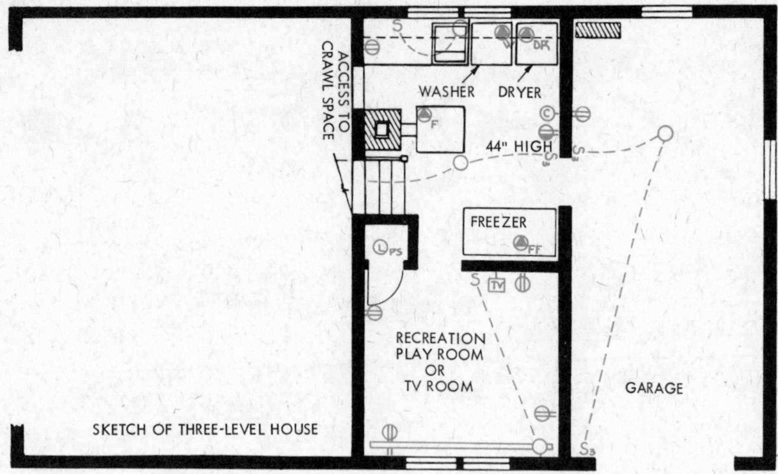

Fig. 11-19. This plan illustrates the basement wiring for a three-level house.

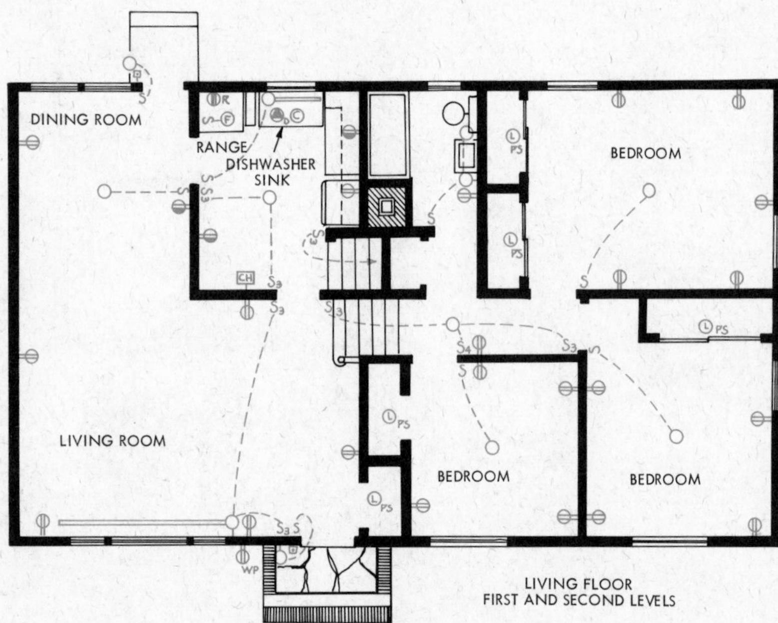

Fig. 11-20. This figure illustrates the wiring for the first and second levels of the same three-level home.

protected by a wound, galvanized steel strip cover. This metal winding forms a flexible tube. Frequently, armored cable is referred to as "B-X". Armored Cable is limited to indoor, dry locations. Because of its flexible covering, this type of cable can be used as an extension to a previously installed conduit system. Armored cable is considered acceptable by most building codes. It offers protection similar to rigid conduit.

Non-metalic Sheathed Cable. This is a flexible cable which may be used for surface or concealed wiring in damp locations. Because of its non-metalic sheathing, this type type of cable may not be used underground or in masonry work. The cable consists of two or more wires encased in a braided fabric jacket which resists fire, moisture, and acid vapors. An advantage of a sheathed cable is that it is easily "fished" through floors and walls. It can be readily attached to floor and wall surfaces.

Plastic Sheathed Cable. This type of cable is replacing the old lead sheathed cable. The wires are sheathed by a plastic material which is highly resistant to damage by fire, rodents, acid, weather, or mechanical injury. An advantage of this type of cable over the non-metalic sheathed type, is that it may be buried underground. A plastic sheathed cable is flexible enough to be pulled through walls and floors, thus permitting its use in existing construction.

Working Drawings

All electrical outlets, switches, and fixtures are shown on *all* plans that contain those electrical components. The path of the switch(s) to fixtures and/or convenience outlets is shown graphically by a curved broken line. An irregular curve is used to draw the line. *It is not drawn freehand!* (These lines do *not* show the actual path of the wiring.) Fig. 11-18 shows the wiring for a first floor plan. Observe the single-pole switch in the bedroom adjacent to the living room. All convenience outlets are controlled by this single switch. Contrast this with the switching arrangement for the convenience outlets in the living room.

The basement plan would depict, if these items were to be included in the house, the following: convenience outlets, special purpose outlet, drop cord equipped outlet, clock outlet, single-pole switches, three-way switches, inter-connecting telephone, television outlet, and a distribution panel. Fig. 11-19 illustrates the basement wiring of a split-level house. The wiring of the first and second levels of the same house is shown in Fig. 11-20.

The drawings are given to the electrical contractor to plan the type of wiring and to estimate the cost of services and materials. The contractor should receive the full set of plans so that he may determine the type of construction and the problems he may encounter relative to walls, floors, interior partitions, attic construction, crawl space, location of furnace and water heater, etc.

Questions and Problems

These questions and problems have been devised as a learning experience for you. Answer each carefully.

1. In your home, how many extension cords are used to supply current to small appliances?
2. How may an overloaded circuit be detected other than by a fuse failure?
3. How many electrical appliances has your family purchased in the past two years that have not been replacements for previously used appliances?
4. Study the lighting arrangement in your house. Is it adequate? How could the arrangement be improved? Draw a floor plan showing the existing (or improved) lighting.
5. Following the "Residential Wiring Recommendations" section in this chapter, plan the placement of fixtures, switches, outlets, etc., for the accepted floor plan designed in Chapter 4.
6. How many general purpose circuits will be necessary for your plan based on 15 amp rated circuits? 20 amp rated circuits?
7. What difference exists between a polarized outlet and a double convenience outlet? What purpose or advantage does the polarized outlet have?
8. Rearrange the bedroom furniture in problem 5. Sketch the new furniture arrangement. Will all of the convenience outlets be usable? What changes were necessary and why?
9. From how many locations may a 3-way switch be operated?

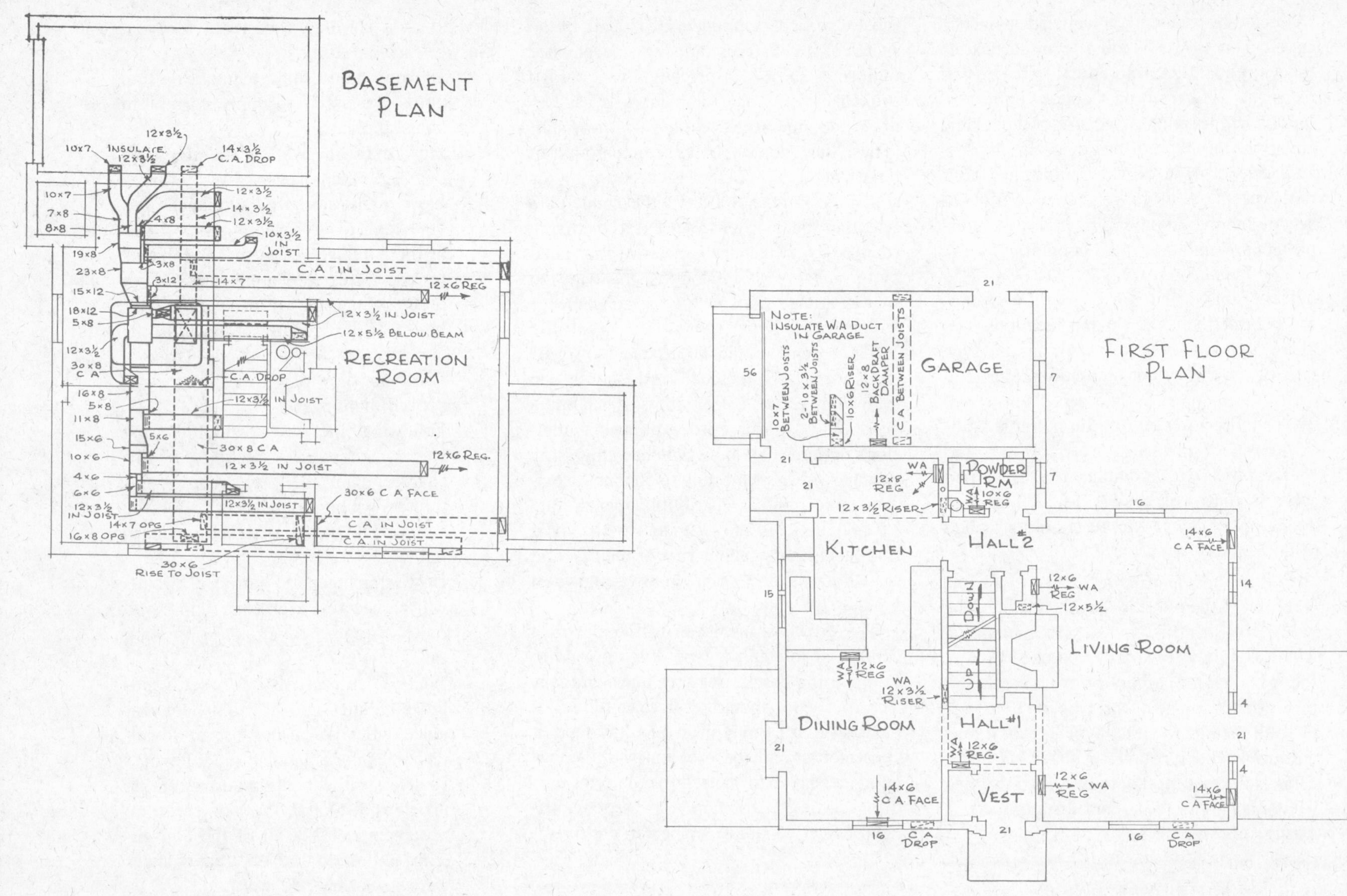

The ductwork and outlets of the heating system are sometimes shown on floor plans.

Residential Air Conditioning 12

As indicated in the preceding chapter, the architect usually does not plan in detail the electrical wiring for the house; similarly, he does not plan the whole air conditioning system. (**Air conditioning** as used here includes both the heating and cooling systems.) Specialized contractors normally do the actual detail planning. The architect or designer should, however, be able to locate the outlets and "size" the heating and cooling units. This is necessary since the contractors base their planning on the working drawings and specifications.

For utmost comfort air conditioning must perform four basic functions: (1) temperature control, (2) humidity control, (3) air circulation and ventilation control, and (4) air filtering. Fig. 12-1 illustrates the main functions of the residential air conditioning system.

Residential Heating Systems

Methods of home heating have changed since the late 1940's and early 1950's. Prior to this period the stoker or hand-fired coal furnace with a gravity hot-air system was the most common type of heating unit. Due to the price of coal and the consumer's desire for a cleaner burning fuel (plus the convenience of not having to shovel coal and remove ashes) the public has gradually moved to gas and oil. Before the mid 1950's new homes were frequently equipped with one- and two-pipe hot water and steam systems, as well as forced and gravity warm-air systems. Today, few steam, gravity hot water, or gravity warm-air systems are installed in new construction. Fig. 12-2 gives an analysis of heating systems, their outlets, and suitability.

Factors involved in selecting the type of heating facility are many. However, the basic choice is dependent upon: (1) the geographic location, relative to the availability of fuels; (2) the severity of the temperatures during the heating season; and (3) the cost and installation fee of the heating unit.

Heat Distribution

There are two basic methods by which heat may be distributed to the rooms: pipe and duct. Pipe requires the least amount of space to transmit the heat. Pipes are used to carry hot water or steam to a radiator, baseboard unit, or radiant panel located in the floor, ceiling, or wall. Ducts require more space than pipes. However, the ease

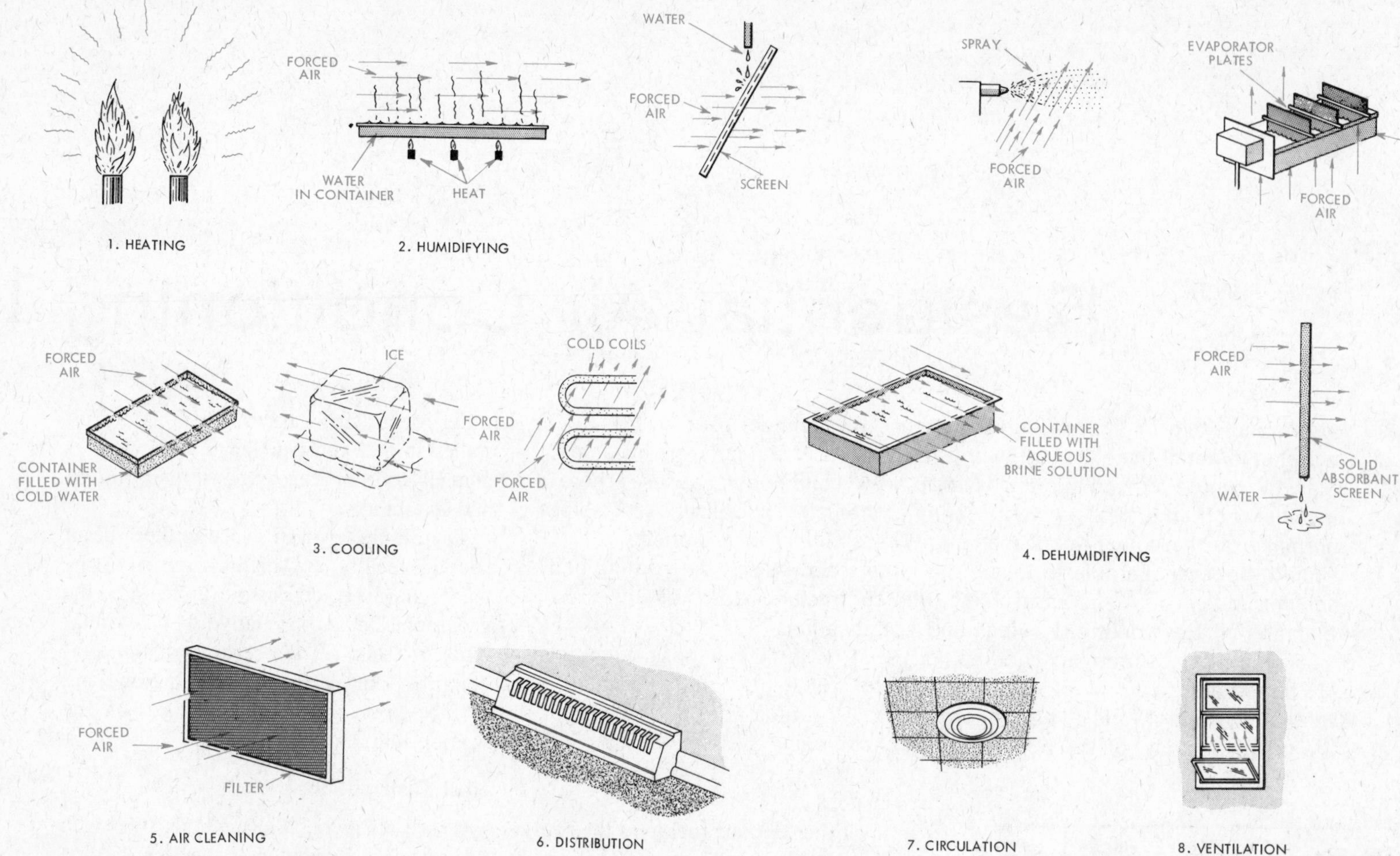

Fig. 12-1. Eight functions are performed with true year-round air conditioning.

with which ducts may be used for cooling and for humidification from one central location is a distinct advantage. (A pipe system may also be used for cooling if blower-equipped convector outlets are used.) Ducts are placed between floor or ceiling joists and between studs in walls.

Different methods are available to distribute heat: (1) baseboard, floor, and wall diffusers, used for warm air systems; (2) convectors, radiators, and baseboard (radiant and convector) type units, used for steam and hot water systems; and (3) radiant panel units, used for hot water and electrical systems. See Figs. 12-3 and 12-4.

TYPE OF HEAT		HEAT OUTLETS	
		TYPE	IDEALLY SUITED FOR
WARM AIR	FORCED	Resister Diffuser	Houses with or without basements
	GRAVITY	Register	Rarely used in new construction or basementless houses
HOT WATER	FORCED	Baseboard unit Hollow or Finned Radiator Convector Radiant Panel	Houses with or without basements
	GRAVITY	Baseboard unit Hollow or Finned Radiator Convector	Rarely used in new construction or basementless houses
STEAM	ONE PIPE	Radiator Convector	Not used in basement—less houses Rarely used in new construction
	TWO PIPE	Baseboard Hollow or Finned Radiator Convector	

Fig. 12-2. Analysis of Heating Systems: The heating system should be suited to the house.

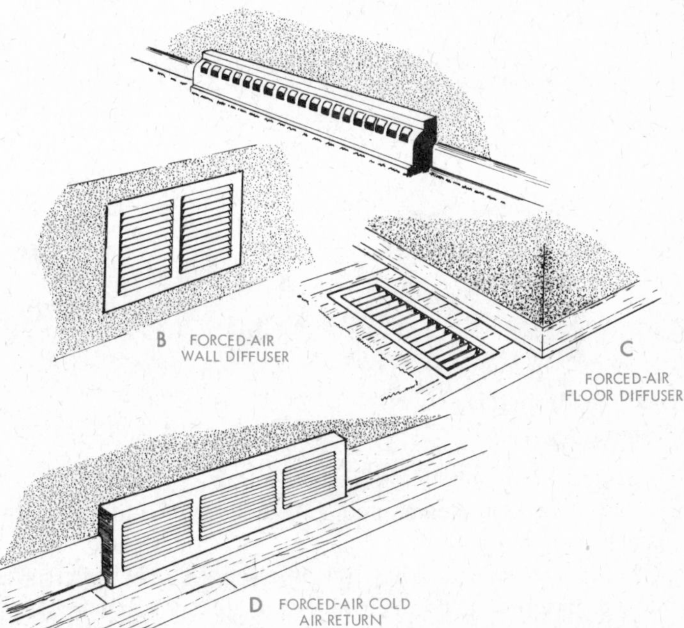

Fig. 12-3. Wall diffusers are used in the forced-air system.

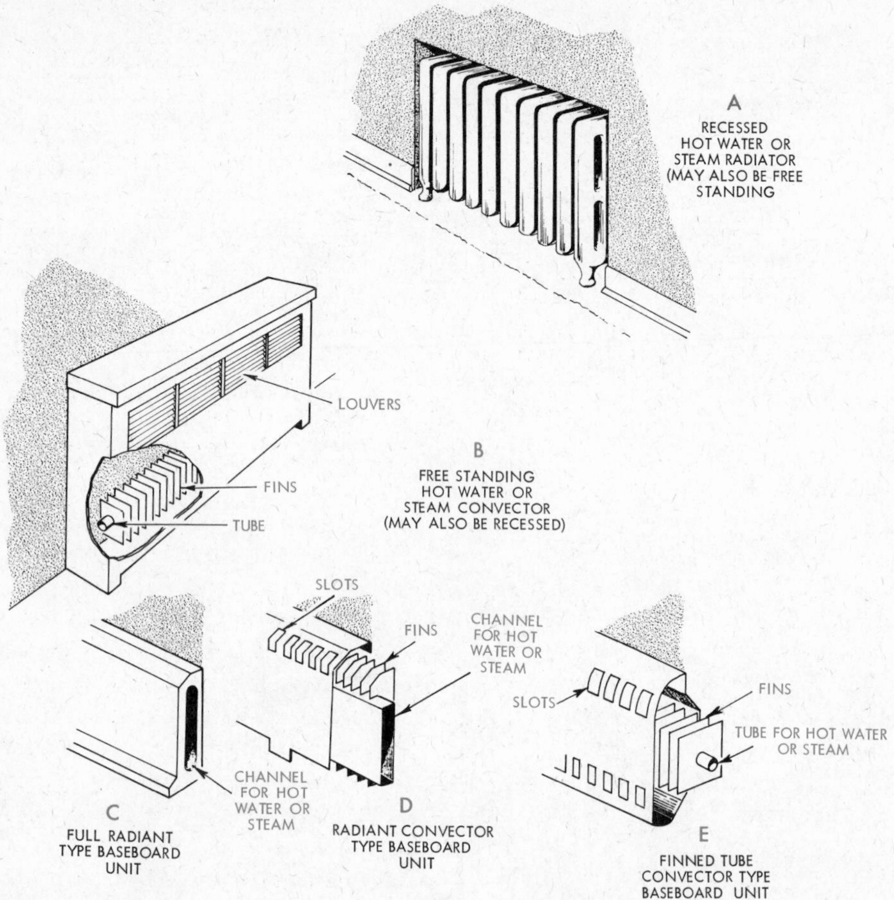

Fig. 12-4. These room heating devices are used for hot water or steam systems. **(Note:** Some convector units are equipped with fans.)

Heating Methods

Fundamentally, there are three methods of heating the home: (1) forced warm air, (2) hot water or steam, and (3) radiant panel.

Forced warm air is driven into the room through baseboard, floor, or side-wall diffusers or registers. The warm air rises (since it is lighter), then cools and settles. Circulation of air is aided by a blower, hence the name *forced air*. The blower returns the cool air to the furnace through a cold-air return located along the baseboard.

Hot Water or Steam. Room air, with hot water or steam heat, is warmed by hot water or steam passing through a radiator, convector, or baseboard unit. The radiator radiates a certain amount of heat, but the majority of heat is given off through convection. The convector, as its name implies, transmits heat by convection: that is, the air is heated by passing over the convector fins. Both methods of heating the room are efficient. Baseboard units may be used to heat the room in lieu of radiators or convectors.

Radiant Panel. The last method of heating the house is by means of radiant panels (pipes, ducts, or electric resistance wire) installed in the floor, wall, or ceiling. The room is warmed by heat rays reflecting off various surfaces in the room. True radiant heat does not employ any radiators or baseboard diffusers.

Thermostat

All types of heating equipment installed in new construction may be regulated by a thermostat which can be set for a desired temperature. If the temperature falls below this indicated point, the space heater will automatically turn on. Most thermostats are designed to maintain a constant temperature. Some are designed to permit a low temperature for a specified length of time, and at a certain time the temperature will be raised to the desired degree. Location of the thermostat is an important feature not to be overlooked. An ideal location is on an inside wall approximately 4′-6″ or 5′-0″ from the floor. For the utmost efficiency the thermostat should be placed away from (1) the warm afternoon sun; (2) heat from a warm-air outlet; (3) cold air from an exterior door; and, especially, (4) the direct or reflected heat rays from the fireplace. The thermostat is usually placed in or near the living room area where most social activity takes place.

Humidity

During the heating season it is desirable that moisture be used to condition the indoor air. Outside air during the cold season is normally much drier than inside air and when mixed they tend to lower the indoor relative humidity.

Storm windows, weatherstripping, and tighter house construction has decreased the amount of infiltrating outdoor air. Although moisture is added to the indoor air by cooking, bathing, dishwashing, and laundering, it is not sufficient to raise the humidity to a desirable, healthful level. New homes with effective vapor barriers need less humidifying than normally required to maintain the desired indoor relative humidity.

Generally a relative humidity of 50 per cent is considered ideal. This amount provides the best protection against airborne infections and has a soothing effect upon the nose and throat. In addition, sufficient humidity permits woodwork and other home furnishings to retain their moisture; it also retards rapid deterioration.

When the outdoor temperature drops below 40° the relative humidity should be lowered enough to prevent excessive condensation on windows and structural components.

Forced Warm-Air Heating

Heating systems in many new homes being built use forced warm air. This system is an advancement over the gravity warm-air system. The gravity system employs large round pipes that extend octopus-like from the furnace to wall registers and cold-air returns. The forced-air system has replaced the old outlets with smaller ducts and neat, functional wall-type or base-type grilles. The forced-air or blower system insures a more direct and even circulation than the old gravity-type furnace.

All warm-air heating systems are composed of four parts: (1) a *firebox* in which the fuel (gas or oil) is burned, (2) an *air chamber* in which the air is heated, (3) a *cold air box or chamber* in which the air is returned for circulation, and (4) the *ducts* in which the heated air is carried to various rooms of the house. Humidifiers, either evaporating plate or atomizer, are installed to add moisture (50 per cent relative humidity) to the air. This makes the air more comfortable to breathe. Air filters may be installed in the cold-air return of the furnace to remove dust and dirt particles prior to their entry into the heating chamber. The filter may be an easily cleaned permanent type, an inexpensive throw-away type, or an electrostatically charged type. Any of the three methods of filtering the air is satisfactory.

The forced warm-air system should provide approximately four to six air changes per hour for the average size five or six room house. The warm air leaves the air chamber at approximately 155° F and arrives at the room at approximately 140° F. Some of the heat is lost in the transmission from the furnace to the rooms.

Forced-air furnaces do not depend upon the different weights of hot and cold air to provide circulation within a room. The forced-air furnace, either gas or oil fired or heated by electric coils, is equipped with a blower that draws cool air into the air chamber and expels the heated air through the ducts to the outlets in the various rooms. Since the heated air is moving under force through the ducts, the furnace need not be placed in a central location of the house and may be above or below floor level. Outlet grilles or registers may be placed high on the walls or near the floor. Placement has been widely discussed among heating engineers and contractors. By placing the warm-air outlet high on the wall and deflecting the warm air stream downward at a 15° angle, a more uniform temperature between the floor and ceiling may be achieved. The outlet is usually placed so that its top edge is 6″ below the ceiling line. Outlets located in this position force the warm air over the heads of the persons in the room to produce an even temperature. Heat may also be distributed by baseboard registers. This is probably the most common method. The duct is connected directly to the baseboard unit. This "register" has a narrow opening along the top edge that emits a film of warm air along the wall. In addition, the baseboard becomes warm and heats the room as a small radiant panel.

Each area in the house must be supplied with a warm-air outlet and a cold-air return. The kitchen and bathroom, however, *do not usually* have a cold-air return. Cold-air returns are normally placed on a warm or inside wall at baseboard level to collect the downdrafts. Forced warm-air outlets are placed so that warm air is blown against or across outside walls and/or windows. Rooms larger than 10′ × 10′ will require two or more warm-air outlets. Ducts to supply the outlets may be run in the basement or attic space or along the ceiling of the room to be heated. The home designed with a basement or with a crawl space will usually have the ductwork between the floor joists. Basementless homes may have the supply ducts placed in the ceiling or imbedded in the floor.

Warm-Air Perimeter-Loop System

Perimeter-loop heating, used almost exclusively in basementless slab houses, has a duct system which encircles the slab. Fig. 12-5 shows the general principle of the perimeter-loop system with four feeder ducts supplying the perimeter duct. The ducting may be sheet metal, concrete pipe, vitrified tile, or other precast materials. Because the perimeter-loop system is used essentially in slab homes, a downdraft furnace is necessary. (Be sure to note the differentiation in furnaces when selecting from a catalog.) Warm air is forced through the ducts and is discharged into the room through floor or baseboard diffusers. The air is returned to the furnace via air intakes either on an inside wall or in a hallway ceiling close to the furnace.

This type of system is economical to install and needs little floor space. Because the perimeter duct is imbedded in the floor and is connected to the furnace by feeder ducts, cold floors are eliminated. A humidifier and filter may be installed to eliminate dryness and dirt.

Forced Warm-Air Extended-Plenum System

Air warmed by the heating unit may also

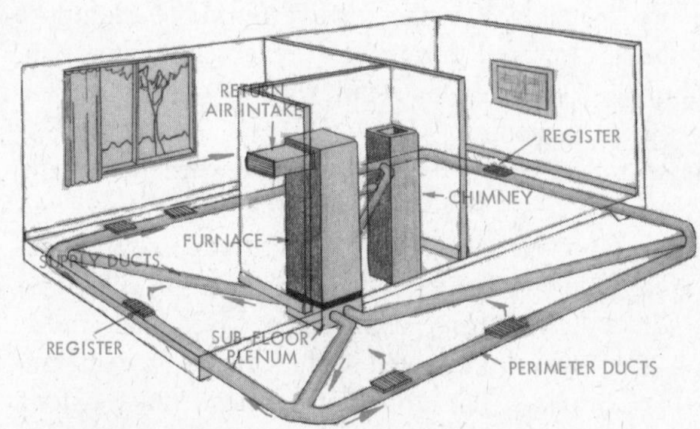

Fig. 12-5. Warm-Air Perimeter-Loop System.

be distributed by a blower through the *plenum* and ducts to the baseboard diffusers. (A plenum system functions by placing the air under a higher *pressure.)* The blower draws the room air back to the furnace through the cold-air return and return ducts to be filtered, reheated, and humidified. After it has been heated, the air is then distributed again. Fig. 12-6 illustrates a portion of an extended-plenum installation. Note the baseboard diffuser is placed below a window and the return air intake is located along an inside wall.

In comparison to hot water and steam heating systems, the extended-plenum system has the advantage of being more economical to install. This system is well adapted to houses with and without basements because the blower maintains air circulation.

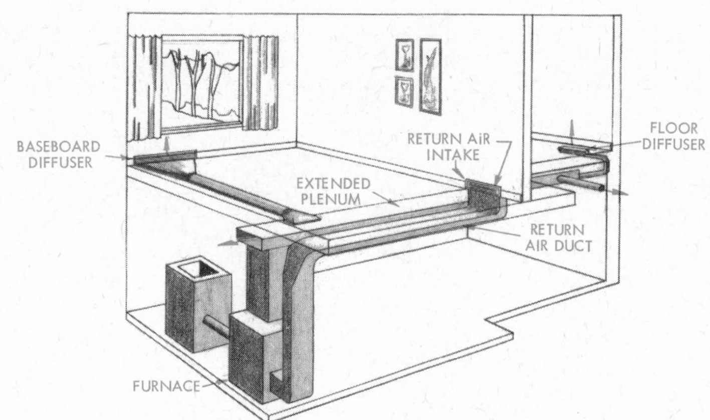

Fig. 12-6. Forced Warm-Air Extended-Plenum System.

One-Pipe Hot Water System

The one-pipe, forced hot water system, shown in Fig. 12-7, is probably the most widely used of all *hydronic* (heating or cooling with water) systems in residential construction. Heat for this system is generated by an automatically controlled gas or oil burner that heats the water in the boiler. With the one-pipe system the boiler may be located in the basement or in the utility room of a basementless house. A single *main* pipe usually follows the perimeter of the building, and *branches* or *risers* connect to the radiators, convectors, or baseboard units. Special flow fittings are placed at the return of each radiator or convector so that

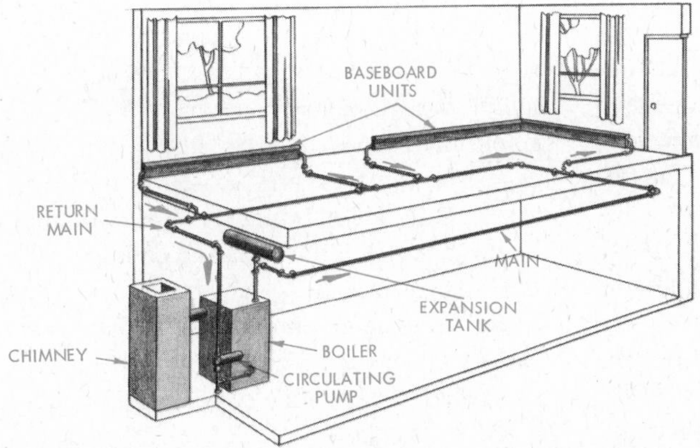

Fig. 12-7. Forced Hot Water System.

a single pipe may be used for supply and return of the water. The flow fittings separate the cooled water from the hot water leading to the next unit. As the *main* leaves the boiler, a flow valve is placed at the first elbow. This valve opens under the flowing water pressure when the circulating pump is operating and closes when the pump is not operating. If this flow valve were not placed in the main, the water would continue to circulate, causing overheated radiators and convectors. An expansion tank permits the water to expand and contract with the changes in temperature, thereby keeping the boiler and radiator filled with water.

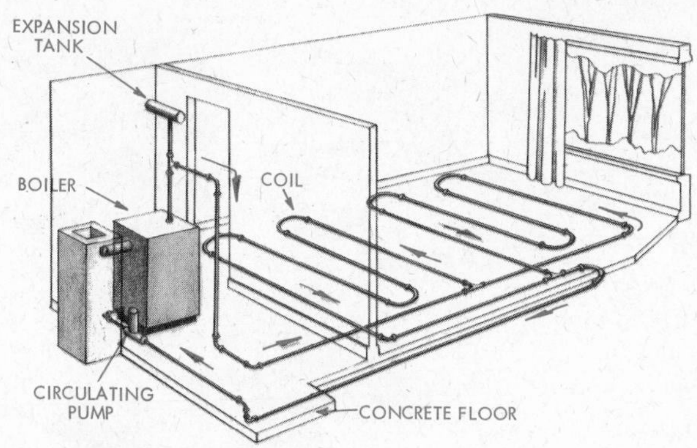

Fig. 12-8. Hot Water Panel System.

Radiant Heat Panels

One of the general laws of physics states that heat will radiate from a source of higher temperature to one of lower temperature. The same principle applies in heating individual rooms. When one is in a room and "feels" comfortable, his body is maintaining or losing a *normal* amount of heat. If the body loses a high degree of heat, one "feels" cold. For example, if the room temperature is 50° F and the body is at a normal 98.6° F, the body is losing more than the average amount of heat and "feels" cold. If the room has a temperature of 100° F one will experience a warm sensation since the body is receiving heat.

With air current heating (convection) the occupant is surrounded with circulating warm air; with radiant heating the occupant is surrounded with warm surfaces and objects. No air currents are set in motion with radiant heating since the heat rays go directly between the heated wall, ceiling, or floor to other surfaces. Almost all surfaces in the room act as reflectors, and an infinite number of reflecting, radiant rays travel in all directions. When all objects in the room have been brought to an adequate temperature, the room and its occupants will be comfortable. Comparatively little temperature difference exists between the floor and ceiling in a radiantly heated room. For example, if the heat source (hot water pipes or resistance wires) are located in the floor, a temperature difference of approximately 7° exists between the floor and ceiling.

Many basementless slab houses, as shown in Fig. 12-8, have some form of radiant floor panel heat. If the radiant panel is heated by hot water, a serpentine coil, as in Fig. 12-9 is used. The coil is placed on a prepared base, usually concrete, and another layer of concrete is poured over the coil. The hot water is then circulated through the pipe by a pump. The amount of heat is controlled by the temperature of the water circulated through the pipe coil. Some radiant panels are heated by electric resistance wire. These, too, may be located in floors, ceiling, or walls.

Since the weight and mass of a radiant panel located in a ceiling or wall is considerably less than that of a floor panel embedded in concrete, the room temperature can be changed more rapidly. Lower night temperatures can be obtained more satisfactorily if the panel is located in the ceiling.

Electric Heat

In some areas of the United States and in several European countries, rapid progress has been made in residential electric heating. Power companies that offer attrac-

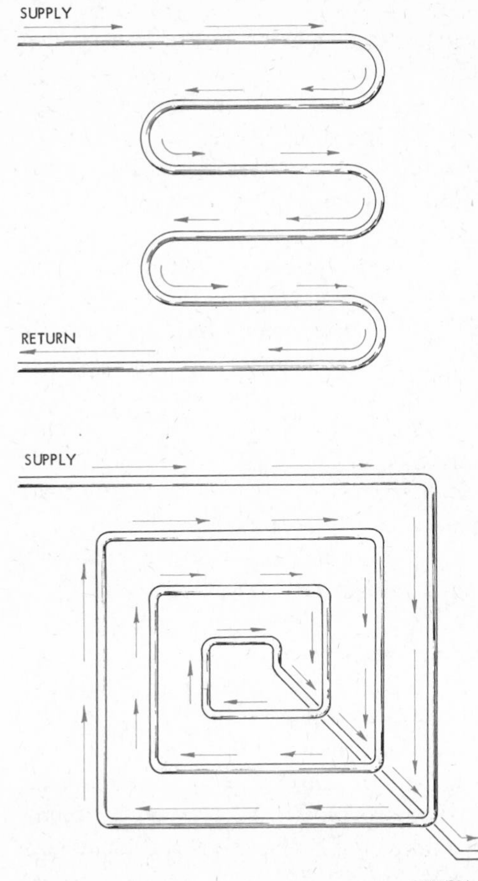

Fig. 12-9. Serpentine or square coils are used in radiant panel, floor, and ceiling heating.

tive kilowatt-hour rates to the consumer, as well as new and more effective types of insulative materials, have placed electric heat within the reach of many home owners. However, many misconceptions exist about the function of electricity in residential heating. This section will attempt to point out the various types of electric heating equipment and their basic principles.

Heating the home by electricity offers a number of decided advantages over the "conventional" methods previously discussed. Electric heating provides an even, draft-free warmth without periodic cooling or overheating. Temperatures in each room may be maintained at the desired level since individual thermostats or automatic controlling devices are installed with each unit. To economically heat the home by electricity, consideration must be given to proper insulation to reduce the heat loss. This added insulation not only serves as a sound deadener, both from the outside and from floor to floor, but also aids in reducing the inside temperature during the summer months.

With many electric heating devices, maintenance is cut or practically eliminated since the individual room control thermostat is usually the only moving part. To many, the silence of the electric heating system is a great asset. In new construction, often an electrical heating system can be installed for the same amount as the regular gas- or oil-fired systems. Since the chimney and space for fuel storage is eliminated, and in most electric heating systems duct work is nonexistent, lower building costs can be achieved. (This may be reflected in the size of a mortgage loan and may result in lower monthly payments.)

There are, however, disadvantages. In some areas, in comparison with other fuels, operating costs are higher. Some power companies, however, give very favorable rates to consumers having electric heat. Electric power failure is a disadvantage. However, any system using a blower will not function without electricity. More insulation is required to hold the heat than with conventional heating systems. Humidity control can be a problem with resistance type radiant heaters because these do not employ moving air. To counteract the absence of humidity, a humidistat-operated ventilating fan may be necessary.

Electrical Heating Methods

Various means are available for the builder to equip the home for electric heating. Principles of operation vary. The various electrical heating units and their operation are examined in the following paragraphs.

Baseboard Electric Heating Units. Baseboard units give a uniform degree of heat over a wide area. Some of these units emit heat by both radiation and convection and are designed to replace the standard base and shoe moldings. See Fig. 12-10. These

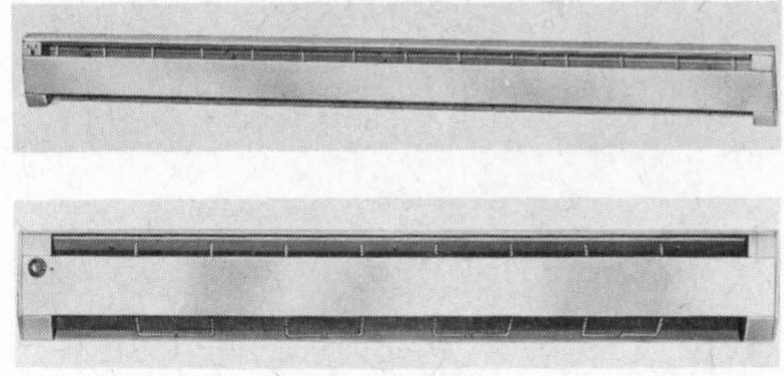

BERKO ELECTRIC MFG. CORP.; JAMAICA, NEW YORK.

Fig. 12-10. Electric baseboards heat by radiation and convection. Some convection baseboard units are equipped with an individual thermostat.

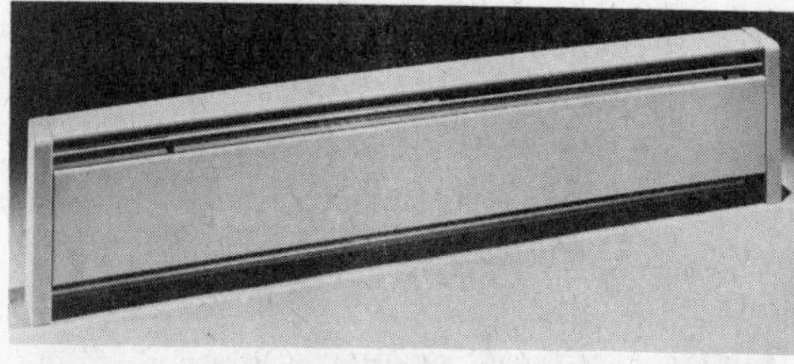

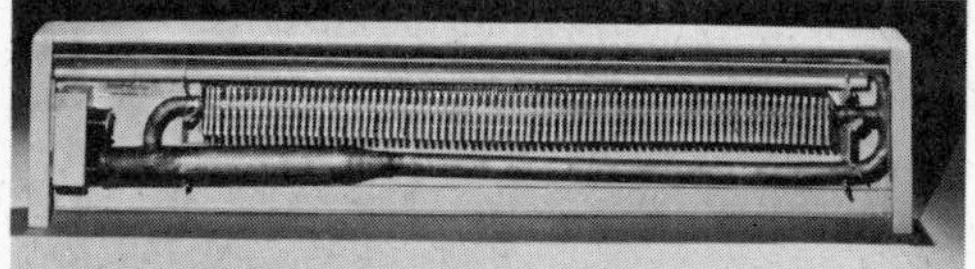

INTERNATIONAL OIL BURNER CO.; ST. LOUIS, MISSOURI.

Fig. 12-11. Hydronic baseboard heaters are a relatively new innovation in electric heating. Each unit is self contained.

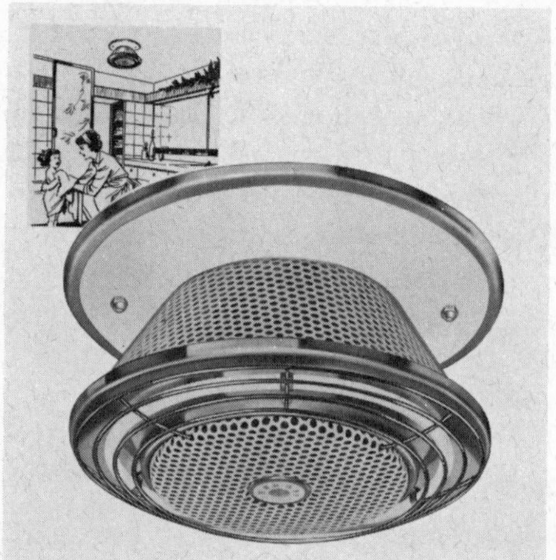

MARKEL ELECTRIC PRODUCTS, INC.; BUFFALO, NEW YORK.

Fig. 12-12. Electric ceiling heaters, such as this resistance type, are used in bathrooms to provide warmth after leaving the bath. Some units are equipped with a quiet fan.

SUN-HEAT INC., ELECTRIC HEAT DIVISION OF INSTO-GAS CORP.; DETROIT, MICHIGAN.

Fig. 12-13. Radiant glass panels are used in the ceiling or wall to provide spot heating. In some instances a series of panels are used to heat rooms.

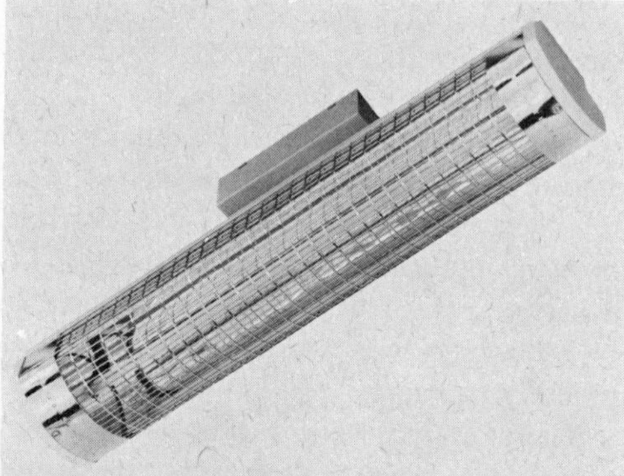

ELECTROMODE, DIVISION FRIDEN, INC.; ROCHESTER, NEW YORK.

Fig. 12-14. Quartz tube heaters provide infrared rays for heating.

units have an opening at the bottom that allows the air to enter and pass over the resistance element. Another opening at the top allows the air to escape. Some baseboard units have attached thermostats (Fig. 12-10, bottom) but frequently they are controlled by a wall mounted device. A recent development in baseboard heating is the *hydronic* unit (Fig. 12-11). Each hydronic baseboard unit is filled with water and is heated by an immersion element, thus producing more evenly distributed heat since the water-filled tubes will not cool as rapidly as a resistance element.

Both the convector and hydronic units are used to heat entire residences. They are also used to heat individual rooms that have been added to an existing dwelling.

Ceiling and Wall Electric Heating Units. Electric ceiling units or electric wall units warm the occupants of a room with radiant heat rays. The most common type of ceiling or wall unit is the resistance heater that radiates heat through a protective metal grille or screen. Fig. 12-12 shows a ceiling-type resistance radiant heater. Radiant glass panels (Fig. 12-13) are similar to the resistance heater with the exception that the resistance element is covered or imbedded in glass. Since the glass becomes hot, the panel is covered with a grille. Some wall and ceiling heaters may be equipped with a thermostat and/or fan to promote heat circulation. Frequently, rather than installing a resistance heater, an infrared unit may be desired for the wall or ceiling (Fig. 12-14).

Wall and ceiling heaters are used in bath-

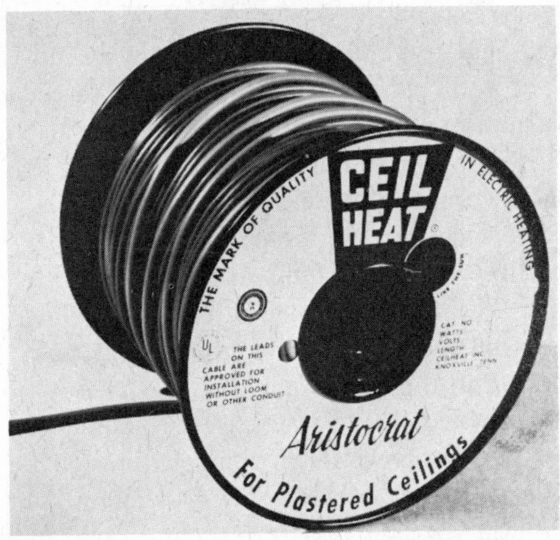

CEIL HEAT, INC.; KNOXVILLE, TENNESSEE.

Fig. 12-15. Various types of radiant cable are available for heating ceilings, walls, and exterior areas of the house.

rooms where additional heat is required for short periods of time. Occasionally these are placed in kitchens, recreation areas, family rooms, or enclosed porches. Series of radiant glass panels may be used to heat an entire house. Infrared units are used mostly in bathrooms.

Electric Cable Units. Electric wire used as a radiant cable converts electrical energy to heat energy. This works in the same way as the common resistance unit. Cable units (see Fig. 12-15) placed in plastered ceilings or walls are commonly covered with plastic or a non-flammable vinyl plastic material. The electric cable is installed before the dry wall, plaster ceiling, or wall surface is applied. The whole wall or ceiling then radiates heat to the room. This form of equipment is inexpensive, but it does not respond as well as other types of heating devices.

THERMADOR, DIVISION OF NORRIS-THERMADOR CORP.; LOS ANGELES, CALIFORNIA.

Fig. 12-16. The electric duct heater is inserted directly into the ductwork.

Cable may be used to heat one room or the entire home. It may also be placed in concrete floors, driveways, sidewalks, steps, downspouts, gutters, or roof edges to melt snow and ice. Cable is a temporary measure that may be used to eliminate ice dams that cause damage to gutters and shingles.

Duct and Floor Insert Heaters. Electric duct heaters (Fig. 12-16) are placed in forced-air ducts. The duct heater, in essence a resistance heater, is controlled by an integral or wall-located thermostat. The floor insert heater, shown in Fig. 12-17, is similar to the duct unit and it is placed in the floor. This unit is thermostatically controlled. These heaters are used to give additional heat or to provide complete heating requirements. The floor heater is ideally suited for installation below ceiling to floor windows and sliding glass patio doors.

Electric Furnaces. The exterior of many electric furnaces, as shown in Fig. 12-18, is well designed and pleasing in appearance. Electric furnaces heat *only* by convection. The resistance heating elements (Fig. 12-19) are arranged in a series and operate only as heat is needed. The motor driven blower propels the air over the heating elements, through the ducts, and into the rooms. Electric furnaces are not limited to forced-air heating; they may also be used with a boiler to supply hot water for radiators, convectors, and radiant panel heaters.

ELECTROMODE, DIVISION FRIDEN, INC.; ROCHESTER, NEW YORK.

Fig. 12-17. Floor insert heaters are particularly suited for installation below floor to ceiling windows or sliding glass doors.

Some electric furnaces for residential heating are small enough to be placed in a closet or suspended from the basement ceiling. These are always used to heat an entire house.

Electric Heat Pumps. One of the most recent developments in home heating has been the heat pump (Fig. 12-20). The nat-

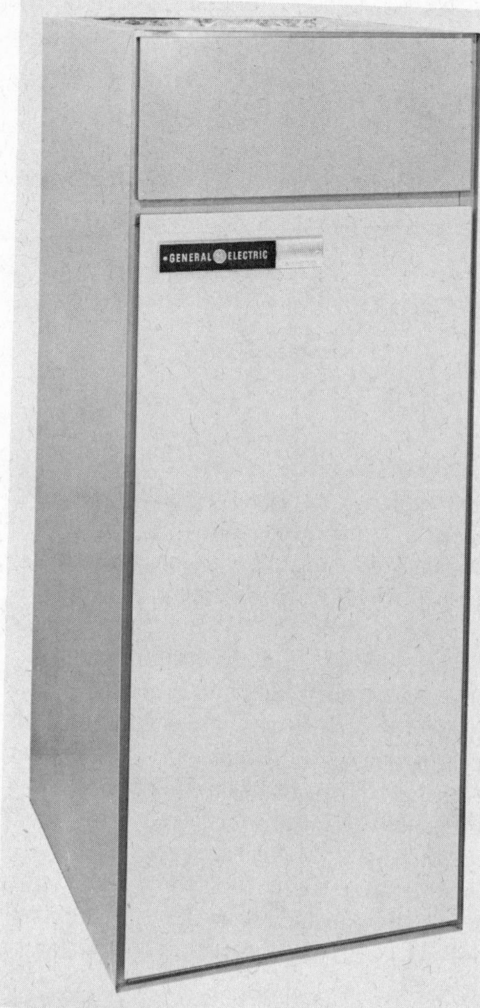

GENERAL ELECTRIC CO.; LOUISVILLE, KENTUCKY.

Fig. 12-18. The exterior of many furnaces are tastefully designed.

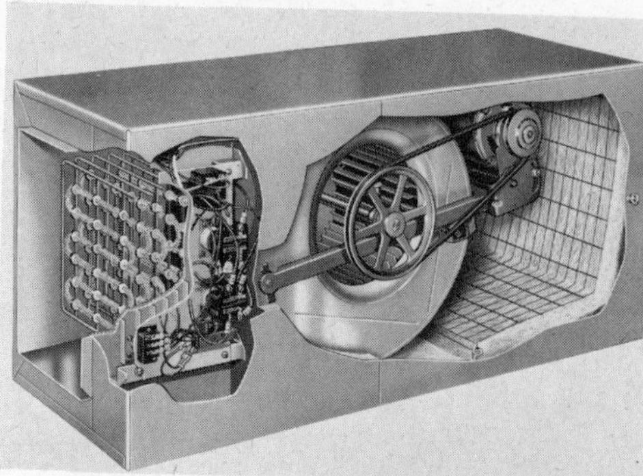

LENNOX INDUSTRIES, INC.; MARSHALLTOWN, IOWA.

Fig. 12-19. This view shows the interior of an electrical furnace. Note the resistance elements, blower, and filter. (Many electric furnaces are small enough to be concealed in a closet.)

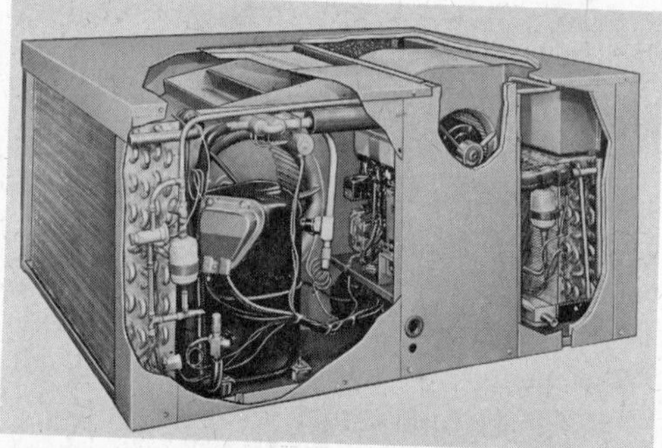

WORTHINGTON AIR CONDITIONING CO., CLIMATROL DIVISION; MILWAUKEE, WISCONSIN.

Fig. 12-20. Heat pumps may draw heat from air, earth, or water. This is an air-cooled heat pump. Ductwork is required.

ural heat from the outside air may be utilized with either a hot water or a forced warm-air system. Earth and water may also be used as a source of natural heat. The basic principle of the heat pump is similar to reverse refrigeration. In the summer months the heat pump acts as a cooling unit. The processes of heating and cooling are controlled by one or more thermostats located in the house.

For example, if water is the source of heat, the water will be pumped through a pipe coil buried below the frost line. As the water circulates through the coils of the heat pump, the heat is removed, thereby lowering the water temperature. The chilled water is then returned to the underground coil. The heat that has been removed is concentrated and distributed. When outside temperatures are low, 20° F or lower, heat pumps using the outside air or earth as a source of heat operate at a materially reduced level of efficiency. This requires a supplemental heat source. Some heat pump manufacturers employ an outdoor temperature control that disconnects the unit when the temperature drops below 20° F; the entire heating load is shunted to supplemental heaters. In areas where temperatures dip low, the size of the heat pump is determined by the summer cooling load. The additional heat that is required during the winter months is obtained from resistance heaters located in the duct work. (See Fig. 12-16.)

Installation costs of a heat pump are naturally higher than a resistance installation. However, the costs are comparable to separate heating and cooling systems. Reports indicate that operating costs of heat pumps are lower than the operating costs of resistance type units.

Insulation

The conveniences of electric heat can pay dividends *only if the house is properly insulated.* Proper insulation will mean greater comfort, heating efficiency, and economy. Common insulating materials used in electrically heated homes are: (1) loose fill (blown or poured) cellulose fiber, mineral wool, perlite, or expanded vermiculite; (2) blankets and batts of mineral wool or cellulose fiber; (3) roof deck panels, blocks, and slabs; (4) exterior fiber sheathing; (5) perimeter slabs, and block for concrete floor perimeters; (6) reflective insulation; and (7) interior panels, blocks, and tiles.

The insulation manufacturers' association has adopted a uniform method of rating the effectiveness of all types of insulation when installed according to instructions. The purpose of any insulative material is to *resist* heat flow; the "resistance" of a specific thickness and type of insulation is indicated by an "R" value. This number designates the amount of resistance the material has to heat passage. For example, a piece of insulative material of a given thickness may have a R value of 12 (this is written as R-12). The insulation just specified, having a value of R-12, would offer only ¾ as much resistance as one having a value of R-16. *The higher the R value, the higher the resistance.* The following quantities of insulation are recommended for electrically heated residences:

Ceilings:	8″ or equivalent to R-28
Side walls:	4″ or equivalent to R-13
Floors:	4″ or equivalent to R-14

Zoned Heat Control

Zone control of the heating system is becoming more important because of the changing habits of the home owner, as well as the contemporary methods of construction and architectural styles. One thermostat located in a central position cannot satisfy the heating requirements for an entire house. This is particularly true in large homes and in split-level or rambling ranch-type homes. For some dwellings several control devices may be necessary to provide the desired heat ranges throughout the house.

Prior to modern advances in home heating it was customary to wear heavy clothing indoors throughout the winter. This provided a definite control of the loss of body heat. Room to room temperatures could vary since the clothing afforded the necessary protection.

The architectural trends toward large windows, rambling and less compact buildings, and multi-level dwellings have complicated the problem of temperature control. Frequently, one section of the house may be sheltered, while another section may be exposed to a hard driving winter wind. One section may be exposed to the warm afternoon sun, while another may be shaded. Each section of the home has its own requirements according to its orientation and the desires of the family.

To accommodate these differences in heating requirements, the distribution of heat may be *zoned.* A zone is an area in which the temperature is controlled separately from another area of the building. A dwelling may be zoned by rooms, groups of rooms, or by levels. The size, orientation, protection surrounding the house, and the living habits of the family will determine the number of zones required.

Zoned heat is based on the premise that the piping, air ducts, or radiant panels are arranged so that heat to each area can be controlled with automatic valves, circulating pumps, or dampers. Hydronic systems probably offer more advantages than other systems because of their obvious adaptability to zone control. Overheating the entire house to increase the heat in one area is eliminated with multiple controls. The cost of zoning a house, of course, is greater because additional equipment is necessary. Over the years, however, the extra investment will be returned in added comfort and lower fuel costs.

Planning Points

The following set of items should be considered in planning the heating system and in planning the house. These criteria are by no means definitive, but they do provide a framework which may be used as a guide.

1. Modern space heaters are compactly and attractively designed and may function as furniture. Heating units

placed in the basement or recreation area may serve as a source of direct heat without detracting from the appearance of the room.

2. Second floor partitions should be placed directly over the first floor partitions so ducts may run directly between floors. Ducts that cut partition caps weaken the house frame. However, if this is necessary, the caps should be reinforced with steel plates. (Floor plans drawn on tracing paper are laid over each other to follow vertical duct runs.)
3. Floor joists should line up with wall studs if ducts are to be run horizontally.
4. Warm-air ducts should be located in interior partitions. If they are run in outside walls, they must be insulated to prevent heat loss.
5. For efficiency, duct runs should be as short as possible with a minimum number of turns and offsets.
6. If possible, registers and grilles should be located between studs and joists.
7. Forced warm-air outlets should be placed so warm air is blown against or across colder outside walls and/or windows.
8. Cold-air returns should be located low on a warm or inside wall to collect the downdrafts.
9. Radiators should be placed below windows or near cold walls. This allows cold air to be warmed before circulating in the room.
10. Baseboard heating units should be located around colder, outside walls. (They should blow upwards to counter downdrafts from windows.)
11. Radiant baseboard, floor insert heaters, or forced warm-air outlets may be used under picture windows.

Heat Loss and the Structure

Heat Loss

No material used in home construction is a perfect insulator. As heat passes through the building materials, either by radiation or conduction, a significant amount of heat will be lost due to the lack of insulative qualities of the materials. Heat within the structure is also "lost" due to the air which infiltrates through the cracks around and in the frames of windows and doors. The combination of these factors is called *heat loss* and is measured in Btu's (British thermal units).

The Btu is the amount of heat required to raise the temperature of one pound of water through one degree Fahrenheit. If we raise the temperature of one pound of water from 96° F to 97° F, for example, the amount of heat (regardless of its nature) used to increase the temperature one degree is equal to one Btu. Conversely, the amount of heat loss required to *reduce* the temperature of one pound of water one degree is also one Btu. All heat losses are expressed in terms of Btu's per hour or *Btuh.* This is the rate or amount of heat transferred or lost as expressed in British thermal units per hour.

Variations in construction, as well as the amount of insulation and ventilation, will control the amount of heat a structure may lose. *It is at this point in planning* that the architect or designer may utilize his knowledge of home heating to specify those materials which will be most advantageous in retarding the flow of heat from the house. As mentioned earlier, one of the basic principles of science is that heat is readily transferred to colder objects. In other words, it travels from a high temperature source to one of a lower source. Walls, floors, windows, and other structural elements in a dwelling act as transmission agents. Heat is transferred from the higher temperature source on the inside to the cooler temperature on the outside. This is called *heat loss.* (The reverse situation is called *heat gain.* Here the high temperature on the outside is transmitted to the cooler temperature on the inside. Heat gain is covered in the latter part of this chapter.)

Heat loss (or gain) will always occur as long as there is a temperature difference. To determine the amount of heat that is lost, each component material that forms the exterior wall, floor, or roof must be identified as to the amount of insulative value it has. This quality of retarding heat flow is called a *transmission coefficient,* and is referred to as the *U-factor.* In addition, the difference between the outside and inside temperature will affect the *rate* at which the heat is lost. Clarifying this further, *the amount of heat loss* for a given area is dependent upon: (1) the type of construction, (2) the amount

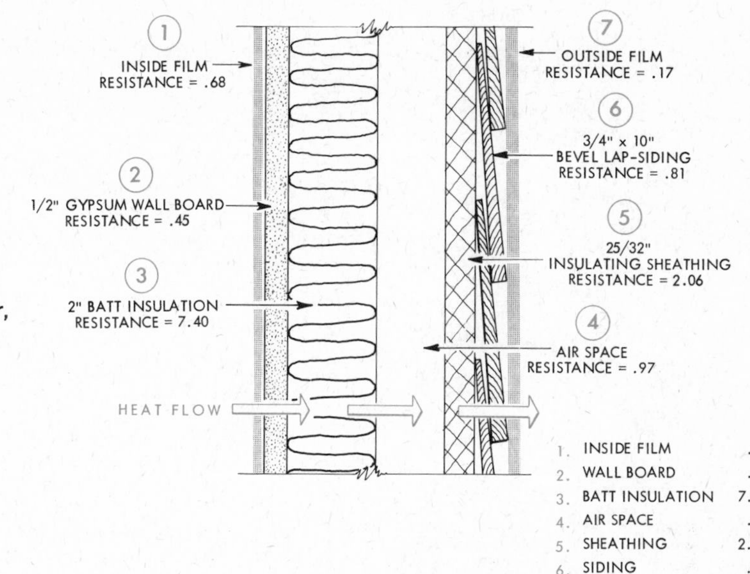

Fig. 12-21. Thermal resistance of a frame wall. To determine the U factor, all of the components must be added together (12.54) and the reciprocal calculated: 1 ÷ 12.54 = .0797. The **U factor** or **heat transmission factor** is .080. **Note:** This same wall **without insulation** would have a U factor of 0.195.

and type of insulation, (3) the temperature differential between the inside and outside, and (4) the amount of air infiltrating into the structure.

Calculating Heat Loss

To determine the amount of heat a structure will lose, it is necessary to calculate or locate in a prepared heat loss table the following:

1. Structural area
2. U values of
   a. type of exterior wall
   b. windows and doors in the wall
   c. ceiling
   d. floor
3. Temperature difference between inside and outside
4. Amount of air infiltrating into the room or structure

The formula for finding the heat loss is basically concerned, for the moment at least, with items 1, 2, and 3.

Heat loss = structural area × construction effectiveness × temperature difference.

Structural area refers to the area which is exposed to a different temperature than that in the room. This area may be the walls, ceiling, floor, or windows. The standard abbreviation for area is "A".

Construction effectiveness refers to the type of construction (that is, solid masonry, brick veneer, siding, stucco etc.) and the amount of insulation included in the wall. Every kind of wall has a specific ability to transfer heat. Each type of building material has been tested and assigned a *U-factor* (sometimes called a Btu Constant). The U-factor gives the number of Btu units transmitted per square foot per hour per degree difference of inside and outside temperatures. This is abbreviated "U". Fig. 12-21 shows an example of one type of frame wall and the *thermal resistance* of each component and the resulting *U-factor*. It is interesting to note that by removing the mineral insulation from this wall the U-factor will increase, indicating that the wall will permit

TABLE 12-1

U-FACTORS FOR COMMON TYPES OF RESIDENTIAL CONSTRUCTION AND BUILDING COMPONENTS

STRUCTURAL COMPONENT	NOT INSULATED U	INSULATED U
I. EXTERIOR WALLS		
Frame Superstructure		
a. Interior finish, insulation board sheathing (25/32") and wood siding or shingles.	.21	.10
b. Interior finish, insulation board sheathing (25/32") and cement asbestos siding or shingles.	.24	.10
c. Interior finish, insulation board sheathing (25/32") and 1" stucco.	.24	.10
d. Interior finish, insulation board sheathing (25/32") and insulating siding (1/2") or wood shingles over insulating backing board (5/16")	.18	.10
e. Interior finish, insulation board sheathing (25/32") and face brick veneer (4") or stone (4").	.22	.10
Solid Masonry		
a. Interior finish, and 8" face or common brick.	.31	.10
b. Interior finish, and 12" face or common brick.	.25	.10
c. Interior finish, gravel aggregate concrete block (4") and face brick (4") or stone (4").	.32	.10
d. Interior finish, gravel aggregate concrete block (8") and face brick (4") or stone (4").	.28	.10
e. Interior finish, cinder aggregate concrete block (4") and face brick (4") or stone (4").	.28	.10
f. Interior finish, cinder aggregate concrete block (8"), and face brick (4") or stone (4").	.24	.10
Masonry Cavity		
a. Interior finish, gravel aggregate concrete block (4") and face brick (4") or stone (4").	.25	.10
b. Interior finish, gravel aggregrate concrete block (4") and common brick (4").	.21	.10
c. Interior finish, and SCR brick (5 1/2").		
Glass Block (4" nominal thickness)		
a. 5 3/4" x 5 3/4" x 3 7/8"	.60	
b. 7 3/4" x 7 3/4" x 3 7/8"	.56	
c. 11 3/4" x 11 3/4" x 3 7/8"	.52	
d. 7 3/4" x 7 3/4" x 3 7/8" with glass fiber screen dividing the cavity	.48	
e. Corrugated structural glass	1.36	
2. INTERIOR PARTITIONS		
Frame Superstructure		
a. Interior finish (3/4" plaster) one side.	.67	.12
b. Interior finish (3/4" plaster) both sides.	.39	.11
c. Interior finish (3/8" dry wall) one side.	.60	.11
d. Interior finish (3/8" dry wall) both sides.	.34	.10
Masonry—Concrete block		
a. No interior finish, concrete aggregate block (4")	.49	
b. Interior finish (3/4" plaster) one side, concrete aggregate block (4")	.32	
c. Interior finish (3/4" plaster) both sides, concrete aggregate block (4")	.28	

TABLE 12-1 (Continued)

STRUCTURAL COMPONENT	NOT INSULATED U	INSULATED U
3. WINDOWS		
a. Single glazed	1.13	
b. Double glazed (welded insulating glass)	.61	
c. Wood storm sash—permanent	.47	
d. Metal storm sash—permanent	.59	
e. Wood storm sash—installed and removed annually	.75	
4. DOORS		
a. All doors are calculated the same as though they were windows		
5. CEILING		
a. Interior finished (3/8" dry wall), no floor above.	.65	.13
b. Interior finish (3/8" dry wall) sub-floor above.	.30	.11
6. FLOOR		
Unheated below		
a. Exposed joist, sub-floor, building paper and finish floor (25/32")	.28	.13
b. Dry wall (3/8"), sub-floor, building paper, and finish floor	.21	.09
c. Concrete floor (4")	.10	
7. ROOF		
Frame		
a. Ceiling part of roof—Asphalt shingles, building paper, and plywood sheathing (5/16"), no ceiling as such	.57	
b. Ceiling part of roof—Asphalt shingles, building paper, plywood sheathing (5/16") and dry wall ceiling (3/8")		
1) Unvented	.34	.12
2) Vented	.54	
c. Flat roof, built-up, roofing, concrete slab, and dry wall ceiling (3/8") or lath (3/8") and plaster (1/2")	.38	.19
8. SKYLIGHTS		
a. Single glass	1.40	
b. Double glass, 1/4" air space	.94	
9. BASEMENT WALL AND CRAWL SPACE		
Above Grade		
a. Poured concrete (6")	.75	
1) Rigid insulation (1")		.24
2) Rigid insulation (2")		.16
b. Poured concrete (8")	.67	
1) Rigid insulation (1")		.23
2) Rigid insulation (2")		.16
c. Concrete block (8")	.52	
1) Rigid insulation (1")		.21
2) Rigid insulation (2")		.15
d. Concrete block (10")	.50	
e. Concrete block (12")	.47	
1) Rigid insulation (1")		.20
2) Rigid insulation (2")		.14
Below Grade		
a. Poured Concrete (6", 8", or 10")	.06	
b. Concrete Block (8", 10", or 12")	.06	

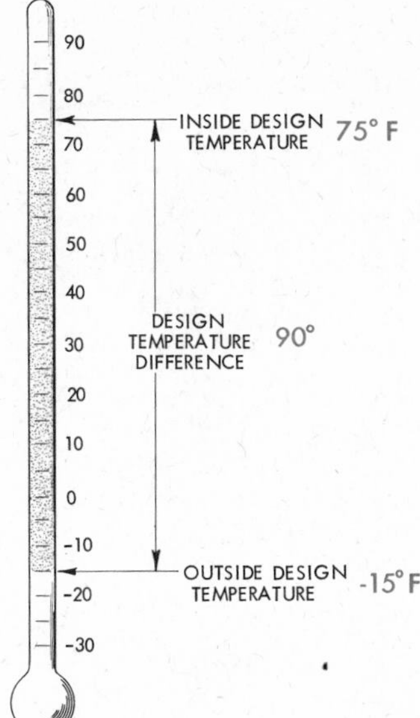

Fig. 12-22. The design temperature is based on the difference between the inside and outside design temperatures.

a greater heat loss. *The lower the U-factor the greater the insulative value of that structural member.* In other words, a smaller amount of Btu's are lost through the material per square foot. Table 12-1 gives the U values for some of the common types of residential construction.

Temperature differential is a necessary factor that must be considered in correctly determining the size of the heating system. As the name implies, it is the difference between the colder outside temperature and the warmer inside temperature (see Fig. 12-22). This difference is abbreviated "T". The question arises—"What temperature do I choose—the coldest winter temperature?" No. A *design temperature* is used to calculate the temperature differential. Design temperatures are *not* the coldest temperatures recorded for a specific locality. They are the coldest *likely* to occur during an average heating season. A list of design temperatures for many cities in the United States and Canada is given in Table 12-2. As an example, the lowest temperature recorded in Kalamazoo, Michigan over a 100 year period was −25° F. The reasonable *minimum* winter temperature in Kalamazoo, according to the Table 12-2, is recorded as −5° F. It would be senseless to design a heating facility in Kalamazoo to accommodate the −25° F temperature since this temperature was reached only for a short period of time and is not common during the heating season. The design temperature difference will vary with the location within the hemisphere. For a specific locality, however, it will be constant.

Values usually used for the inside design temperature are 70° or 75° F. In some instances the local building codes will specify which temperature is to be used in a multi-family type dwelling. Some heating codes specify that the heating system must be adequate to heat the structure to at least 70° F. However, the number of home owners who request an inside design temperature of 75° F is increasing. Many contractors building speculative homes are designing on the basis of a 75° F inside temperature.

With a 75° F inside temperature, and a −5° F outside temperature, for example, the temperature differential (T) would be 80° F.

Heat Loss Formula. By taking the heat loss formula and substituting the accepted symbols, we have:

Heat loss = A × U × T

The U-factors (given in Table 12-1) times the temperature differentials (refer to Table 12-2), times the square footage gives the total heat loss per hour. For instance, the winter outside design temperature in Cedar Rapids, Iowa is −15° F. The prospective builder may decide the inside temperature in the living area of the home will be 75° F. The design temperature difference (T) is 90° F. If the heat loss was to be calculated for 160 sq. ft. of brick veneer wall, with insulation, the heat loss formula would be:

Btuh = 160 × .10 × 90 = 1,440

Infiltration. As mentioned earlier, heat is lost not only through walls, but also through

TABLE 12-2 OUTSIDE DESIGN CONDITIONS FOR UNITED STATES AND CANADA

State & City	Winter DB	Summer DB	Daily Range	Latitude Deg.
ALABAMA				
Anniston	10	95	M	35
Birmingham	10	95	M	35
Gadsden	10	95	M	35
Mobile	20	90	L	30
Montgomery	20	95	M	30
Tuscaloosa	10	95	M	35
ALASKA				
Anchorage	–24	70	M	60
Barrow	–48	—	—	70
Bethel	–43	—	—	60
Cordova	–13	—	—	60
Fairbanks	–57	80	M	65
Juneau	–5	—	—	60
Ketchikan	4	—	—	55
Kodiak	4	—	—	55
Kotzebue	–46	—	—	65
Nome	–36	—	—	60
Seward	–4	—	—	60
Sitka	2	—	—	60
ARIZONA				
Bisbee	30	100	H	30
Flagstaff	–5	85	H	35
Globe	30	105	H	35
Nogales	30	105	H	30
Phoenix	35	105	H	35
Tucson	30	100	H	30
Winslow	–5	95	H	35
Yuma	40	110	H	35
ARKANSAS				
Bentonville	0	95	M	35
Fort Smith	5	95	M	35
Hot Springs	10	95	M	35
Little Rock	10	95	M	35
Pine Bluff	10	95	M	35
Texarkana	10	100	M	35
CALIFORNIA				
Bakersfield	30	105	H	35
El Centro	35	110	H	35
Eureka	30	90	M	40
Fresno	30	105	H	35
Long Beach	35	90	M	35
Los Angeles	40	90	M	35
Montague	15	95	M	40
Needles	25	115	H	35
Oakland	30	80	M	40
Pasadena	40	95	M	35
Red Bluff	15	100	H	40
Sacremento	30	95	H	40
San Bernardino	30	105	H	35
San Diego	45	80	L	35
San Francisco	35	80	M	40
San Jose	40	90	M	35
COLORADO				
Boulder	–15	95	M	40
Colorado Springs	–10	95	H	40
Denver	–10	95	H	40
Durango	–5	95	H	35
Fort Collins	–15	95	M	40
Grand Junction	–5	95	H	40
Leadville	–10	95	M	40
Pueblo	–15	95	H	40
CONNECTICUT				
Bridgeport	0	85	L	40
Hartford	0	90	M	40
New Haven	0	85	M	40
New London	5	85	L	40
Norwalk	0	85	L	40
Torrington	0	90	M	40
Waterbury	0	90	M	40
DELAWARE				
Dover	10	90	M	40
Milford	10	90	M	40
Wilmington	5	90	M	40
DIST. OF COLUMBIA				
Washington	10	90	M	40
FLORIDA				
Apalachicola	25	95	L	30
Fort Myers	40	95	M	25
Gainesville	30	95	M	30
Jacksonville	30	95	M	30
Key West	55	100	L	25
Miami	45	90	L	25
Orlando	35	90	M	30
Pensacola	25	95	L	30
Tallahassee	25	95	M	30
Tampa	35	95	M	30
GEORGIA				
Athens	10	95	M	35
Atlanta	10	95	M	35
Augusta	20	100	M	35
Brunswick	25	95	L	30
Columbus	20	100	M	35
Macon	20	95	M	35
Rome	10	95	M	35
Savannah	25	95	M	30
Way Cross	25	95	M	30
IDAHO				
Boise	–10	95	H	45
Idaho Falls	–15	90	H	45
Lewiston	–10	95	H	45
Pocatello	–15	90	H	45
Twin Falls	–15	95	H	40
ILLINOIS				
Aurora	–10	95	M	40
Bloomington	–10	95	M	40
Cairo	0	100	M	35
Champaign	–10	95	M	40
Chicago	–10	95	M	40
Danville	–10	95	M	40
Decatur	–10	95	M	40
Elgin	–15	95	M	40
Joliet	–10	95	M	40
Moline	–10	95	M	40
Peoria	–15	95	M	40
Rockford	–15	95	M	40
Rock Island	–10	95	M	40
Springfield	–10	95	M	40
Urbana	–10	95	M	40
INDIANA				
Elkhart	–10	95	M	40
Evansville	–5	95	M	40
Fort Wayne	–5	95	M	40
Indianapolis	–10	95	M	40
Lafayette	–10	95	M	40
South Bend	–10	95	M	40
IOWA				
Burlington	–10	95	M	40
Cedar Rapids	–15	95	M	40
Charles City	–20	95	M	45
Clinton	–15	95	M	40
Council Bluffs	–15	100	M	40
Davenport	–10	95	M	40
Des Moines	–15	95	M	40
Dubuque	–15	95	M	40
Fort Dodge	–15	95	M	40
Keokuk	–15	95	M	40
Marshalltown	–15	95	M	40
Sioux City	–15	95	M	40
Waterloo	–15	95	M	40
KANSAS				
Atchison	–10	100	M	40
Concordia	–10	95	M	40
Dodge City	–10	95	H	40
Iola	–5	100	M	40
Leavenworth	–10	100	M	40
Salina	–10	100	M	40
Topeka	–10	95	M	40
Wichita	–5	100	M	40
KENTUCKY				
Bowling Green	0	95	M	35
Frankfort	0	95	M	40
Hopkinsville	0	95	M	35
Lexington	0	95	M	40
Louisville	0	95	M	40
Owensboro	0	95	M	40
Shelbyville	0	95	M	40
LOUISIANA				
Alexandria	20	95	M	30
Baton Rouge	20	95	M	30
New Orleans	25	95	L	30
Shreveport	15	95	M	30
MAINE				
Augusta	–15	85	L	45
Bangor	–20	85	L	45
Bar Harbor	–10	85	L	45
Belfast	–10	85	L	45
Eastport	–10	85	L	45
Lewiston	–10	85	L	45
Millinocket	–15	85	M	45
Orono	–20	85	M	45
Portland	–10	85	M	45
Presque Isle	–20	85	L	45
Rumford	–15	85	L	45
MARYLAND				
Annapolis	10	90	M	40
Baltimore	10	90	M	40
Cambridge	10	90	L	40
Cumberland	0	90	M	40
Frederick	5	90	M	40
Frostburg	–5	90	M	40
Salisbury	10	90	M	40
MASSACHUSETTS				
Amherst	–5	90	M	40
Boston	0	85	M	40
Fall River	0	85	L	40
Fitchburg	–5	90	M	45
Framingham	–5	85	L	40
Lawrence	–5	85	M	40
Lowell	–5	85	M	45
Nantucket	0	85	L	40
New Bedford	0	85	L	40
Pittsfield	–10	90	M	40
Plymouth	0	85	L	40
Springfield	–5	90	M	40
Worcester	–5	90	M	40
MICHIGAN				
Alpena	–10	90	M	45
Ann Arbor	–5	90	M	40
Big Rapids	–5	90	M	45
Cadillac	–10	90	M	45
Calumet	–20	80	M	45
Detroit	–5	90	M	40
Escanaba	–20	85	M	45
Flint	–10	90	M	45
Grand Haven	–5	90	M	45
Grand Rapids	–5	90	M	45
Houghton	–20	80	M	45
Kalamazoo	–5	90	M	40
Lansing	–10	90	M	45
Ludington	–5	90	M	45
Marquette	–15	80	M	45
Muskegon	–5	90	M	45
Port Huron	–10	90	M	45
Saginaw	–10	90	M	45
Sault Ste. Marie	–20	80	M	45
MINNESOTA				
Alexandria	–25	85	M	45
Duluth	–25	80	M	45
Minneapolis	–25	90	M	45
Moorhead	–30	95	M	45
St. Cloud	–25	90	M	45
St. Paul	–25	90	M	45
MISSISSIPPI				
Biloxi	25	90	L	30
Columbus	10	95	M	35
Corinth	5	95	M	35
Hattiesburg	20	95	M	30
Jackson	15	95	M	30
Meridian	15	95	M	30
Natchez	15	95	L	30
Vicksburg	15	95	L	30
MISSOURI				
Columbia	–10	100	M	40
Hannibal	–10	95	M	40
Kansas City	–10	100	M	40
Kirksville	–10	95	M	40
St. Joseph	–10	100	M	40
St. Louis	–5	95	M	40
Springfield	–5	100	M	40

TABLE 12-2 (continued)

State & City	Winter DB	Summer DB	Daily Range	Latitude Deg.
MONTANA				
Anaconda	–30	85	H	45
Billings	–30	90	H	45
Butte	–30	85	H	45
Great Falls	–40	90	H	50
Havre	–40	95	H	50
Helena	–40	90	H	45
Kalispell	–30	90	H	50
Miles City	–35	95	H	45
Missoula	–30	90	H	45
NEBRASKA				
Grand Island	–15	95	H	40
Hastings	–15	95	M	40
Lincoln	–15	95	M	40
Norfolk	–15	95	M	40
North Platte	–15	100	H	40
Omaha	–15	100	M	40
Valentine	–20	95	M	45
York	–15	95	M	40
NEVADA				
Elko	–10	95	H	40
Las Vegas	10	110	H	35
Reno	5	95	H	40
Tonopah	5	90	M	40
Winnemucca	–10	95	H	40
NEW HAMPSHIRE				
Berlin	–15	85	H	45
Claremont	–15	85	M	45
Concord	–10	85	H	45
Franklin	–15	85	M	45
Hanover	–15	85	M	45
Keene	–10	85	M	45
Manchester	–10	85	M	45
Nashua	–10	85	L	45
Portsmouth	–5	85	L	45
NEW JERSEY				
Asbury Park	5	90	L	40
Atlantic City	10	90	L	40
Bayonne	0	90	L	40
Belvidere	0	90	M	40
Bloomfield	0	90	L	40
Bridgeton	5	90	L	40
Camden	5	90	L	40
East Orange	0	90	L	40
Elizabeth	0	90	L	40
Jersey City	0	90	L	40
Newark	0	90	M	40
New Brunswick	5	90	L	40
Paterson	0	90	L	40
Phillipsburg	0	90	M	40
Trenton	0	90	L	40
NEW MEXICO				
Albuquerque	10	95	M	35
El Morro	0	85	H	35
Raton	–5	95	H	35
Roswell	5	100	H	35
Santa Fe	5	90	M	35
Tucumcari	5	95	H	35
NEW YORK				
Albany	–10	90	M	45
Auburn	–10	90	M	45
Binghamton	–5	90	M	40
Buffalo	–5	85	M	45
Canton	–20	85	M	45
Cortland	–10	90	M	45
Elmira	–5	90	M	40
Glens Falls	–15	90	M	45
Ithaca	–5	90	M	40
Jamestown	–5	90	M	40
Lake Placid	–15	90	M	45
New York	5	90	M	40
Niagara Falls	–5	85	M	45
Ogdensburg	–20	85	M	45
Oneonta	–10	90	M	45
Oswego	–5	90	M	45
Port Jervis	0	90	L	40
Rochester	–5	90	M	45
Schenectady	–10	90	M	45
Syracuse	–10	90	M	45
Watertown	–15	85	M	45
NORTH CAROLINA				
Asheville	5	90	M	35
Charlotte	15	95	M	35
Greensboro	10	90	M	35
Hatteras	20	90	L	35
New Bern	20	95	L	35
Raleigh	15	95	M	35
Salisbury	10	90	M	35
Wilmington	20	90	M	35
Winston-Salem	10	90	M	35
NORTH DAKOTA				
Bismarck	–30	95	H	45
Devils Lake	–30	90	M	50
Dickinson	–30	95	H	45
Fargo	–30	95	H	45
Grand Forks	–30	90	M	50
Jamestown	–30	95	M	45
Minot	–35	90	M	50
Pembina	–35	90	M	50
Williston	–35	90	M	50
OHIO				
Akron	–5	90	M	40
Cincinnati	–5	95	M	40
Cleveland	–5	90	M	40
Columbus	–5	90	M	40
Dayton	–5	90	M	40
Lima	–5	90	M	40
Marion	–5	90	M	40
Sandusky	–5	90	M	40
Toledo	–5	90	M	40
Warren	–5	90	M	40
Youngstown	–5	90	M	40
OKLAHOMA				
Ardmore	5	100	M	35
Bartlesville	–5	100	M	35
Guthrie	0	100	M	35
Muskogee	0	95	M	35
Oklahoma City	0	100	M	35
Tulsa	0	100	M	35
Waynoka	–5	105	M	35
OREGON				
Arlington	5	95	M	45
Baker	–15	90	M	45
Eugene	15	90	H	45
Medford	20	95	H	40
Pendleton	–10	90	H	45
Portland	10	85	M	45
Roseburg	20	90	H	45
Salem	15	90	H	45
Wamic	0	90	H	45
PENNSYLVANIA				
Altoona	–5	90	M	40
Bethlehem	0	90	M	40
Coatesville	5	90	M	40
Erie	–5	85	M	40
Harrisburg	5	90	M	40
New Castle	–5	90	M	40
Oil City	–5	90	M	40
Philadelphia	5	90	M	40
Pittsburgh	–5	90	M	40
Reading	5	90	M	40
Scranton	0	90	M	40
Warren	–5	90	M	40
Williamsport	–5	90	M	40
York	5	90	M	40
RHODE ISLAND				
Block Island	5	85	L	40
Bristol	0	90	L	40
Kingston	0	85	L	40
Pawtucket	0	90	M	40
Providence	0	90	M	40
SOUTH CAROLINA				
Charleston	20	90	L	35
Columbia	20	95	M	35
Florence	20	95	M	35
Greenville	10	95	M	35
Spartanburg	10	95	M	35
SOUTH DAKOTA				
Aberdeen	–25	95	M	45
Huron	–20	100	H	45
Pierre	–20	95	M	45
Rapid City	–20	95	H	45
Sioux Falls	–20	95	H	45
Watertown	–25	95	M	45
TENNESSEE				
Chattanooga	10	95	M	35
Jackson	5	95	M	35
Johnson City	0	95	M	35
Knoxville	5	95	M	35
Memphis	5	95	M	35
Nashville	5	95	M	35
TEXAS				
Abilene	5	95	M	30
Amarillo	0	95	H	35
Austin	15	100	M	30
Brownsville	30	95	M	25
Corpus Christi	25	95	M	30
Dallas	10	100	M	35
Del Rio	20	100	H	30
El Paso	20	100	M	30
Fort Worth	10	100	M	35
Galveston	25	95	L	30
Houston	20	95	M	30
Palestine	10	100	M	30
Port Arthur	20	95	M	30
San Antonio	20	100	M	30
Waco	10	100	M	30
UTAH				
Logan	–10	95	H	40
Milford	–5	95	H	40
Ogden	–5	90	H	40
Salt Lake City	0	95	H	40
VERMONT				
Bennington	–10	90	M	45
Burlington	–15	90	M	45
Montpelier	–20	90	M	45
Newport	–20	85	M	45
Northfield	–20	90	M	45
Rutland	–15	90	M	45
VIRGINIA				
Cape Henry	15	90	L	35
Charlottesville	10	90	M	40
Danville	10	90	M	35
Lynchburg	10	90	M	35
Norfolk	15	90	L	35
Petersburg	10	90	M	35
Richmond	10	90	M	40
Roanoke	5	90	M	35
Wytheville	5	90	M	35
WASHINGTON				
Aberdeen	20	85	L	45
Bellingham	10	80	L	50
Everett	15	80	L	50
North Head	20	80	L	50
Olympia	15	80	H	45
Seattle	15	80	M	50
Spokane	–15	90	H	50
Tacoma	15	80	M	45
Tatoosh Island	20	80	L	50
Walla Walla	–10	90	H	45
Wenatchee	–10	90	M	50
Yakima	–5	90	H	45
WEST VIRGINIA				
Bluefield	0	95	M	35
Charleston	0	90	M	40
Elkins	–5	90	M	40
Fairmont	0	90	M	40
Huntington	0	90	M	40
Martinsburg	0	90	M	40
Parkersburg	0	90	M	40
Wheeling	–5	90	M	40
WISCONSIN				
Ashland	–25	80	M	45
Beloit	–15	95	M	45
Eau Claire	–20	90	M	45
Green Bay	–20	90	M	45
La Crosse	–20	95	M	45
Madison	–20	90	M	45
Milwaukee	–15	90	M	45
Oshkosh	–20	90	M	45
Sheboygan	–20	90	M	45
WYOMING				
Casper	–25	90	H	45
Cheyenne	–20	90	H	40
Lander	–30	90	H	45
Sheridan	–30	90	H	45
Yellowstone Park	–35	85	H	45

TABLE 12-2 (continued)

Province & City	Winter DB	Summer DB	Daily Range	Latitude Deg.
ALBERTA				
Banff	-30	—	H	50
Camrose	-35	—	H	55
Calgary	-30	90	H	50
Cardston	-30	—	H	50
Edmonton	-35	90	H	55
Grande Prairie	-40	—	H	55
Hanna	-35	—	H	50
Jasper	-30	—	H	55
Lethbridge	-30	—	H	50
Lloydminster	-40	—	H	55
McMurray	-40	—	H	55
Medicine Hat	-35	90	H	50
Red Deer	-35	—	H	50
Taber	-35	—	H	50
Wetaskiwin	-35	—	H	55
BRITISH COLUMBIA				
Chilliwack	5	—	M	50
Courtenay	10	—	M	50
Dawson Creek	-40	—	H	55
Estevan Point	15	—	M	55
Fort Nelson	-40	—	H	60
Hope	0	—	M	50
Kamloops	-20	—	H	50
Kimberly	-25	—	H	50
Lytton	-5	—	H	50
Nanaimo	10	—	M	50
Nelson	-10	—	H	50
Penticton	-5	—	H	50
Port Alberni	10	—	M	50
Prince George	-30	—	H	55
Prince Rupert	10	—	L	55
Princeton	-15	—	H	50
Revelstoke	-25	—	H	50
Trail	-10	—	H	50
Vancouver	10	80	L	50
Vernon	-15	—	H	50
Victoria	15	—	L	50
Westview	10	—	M	50
LABRADOR				
Goose Bay	-25	—	L	55
MANITOBA				
Boissevain	-35	—	H	50
Brandon	-30	—	H	50
Churchill	-40	—	L	60
Dauphin	-35	—	M	50
Flin Flon	-40	—	M	55
Minnedosa	-35	—	H	50
Neepawa	-35	—	H	50
La Prairie	-30	—	M	50
Swan River	-35	—	M	55
The Pas	-40	—	M	55
Winnipeg	-30	90	M	50
NEW BRUNSWICK				
Bathurst	-10	—	L	45
Campbellton	-10	—	L	45
Chatham	-10	—	M	45
Edmunston	-15	—	M	45
Fredericton	-5	90	L	45
Moncton	-10	—	M	45
Saint John	-5	80	L	45
Woodstock	-15	—	M	45
NEWFOUNDLAND				
Corner Brook	0	—	L	50
Gander	-5	—	L	50
Grand Falls	-5	—	M	50
St. John's	0	—	L	50
NORTHWEST TERRITORIES				
Aklavik	-45	—	L	70
Fort Norman	-40	—	M	65
Frobisher	-50	—	L	—
Resolute	-40	—	L	—
Yellowknife	-50	—	L	60
NOVA SCOTIA				
Bridgewater	0	—	L	45
Dartmouth	0	—	L	45
*Halifax C	5	80	L	45
*Halifax A	0	80	L	45
Kentville	0	—	L	45
New Glasgow	0	—	L	45
Spring Hill	-5	—	M	45
Sydney	0	85	L	45
Truro	0	—	L	45
Yarmouth	5	—	L	45
ONTARIO				
Bancroft	-20	—	M	45
Barrie	-5	—	M	45
Belleville	-10	—	M	45
Brampton	-5	—	M	45
Brantford	-5	—	M	45
Brockville	-15	—	M	45
Chatham	0	—	M	45
Cobourg	-10	—	M	45
Collingwood	0	—	M	45
Cornwall	-15	—	M	45
Ear Falls	-35	—	M	50
Fort Frances	-30	—	M	50
Fort William	-25	85	M	50
Galt	-5	—	M	45
Geraldton	-35	—	M	50
Goderich	0	—	M	45
Guelph	-5	—	M	45
Hamilton	0	—	M	45
Haileybury	-25	—	M	50
Hanover	-5	—	M	45
Huntsville	-15	—	M	45
Kapuskasing	-30	—	M	50
Kenora	-35	—	M	50
Kingston	-10	—	M	45
Kirkland Lake	-25	—	M	50
Kitchener	-5	—	M	45
Lindsay	-15	—	M	45
London	0	—	M	45
Moonsonee	-35	—	M	50
Newmarket	-5	—	M	45
Niagara Falls	0	—	M	45
North Bay	-20	85	M	45
Orillia	-10	—	M	45
Oshawa	-5	—	M	45
Ottawa	-15	90	M	45
Owen Sound	0	—	M	45
Parry Sound	-15	—	M	45
Pembroke	-20	—	M	45
Peterborough	-10	—	M	45
Port Arthur	-25	—	M	50
Port Colborne	0	—	M	45
Renfrew	-20	—	M	45
St. Catharines	0	—	M	45
St. Thomas	0	—	M	45
Sarnia	0	—	M	45
Sault Ste. Marie	-10	85	M	45
Simcoe	0	—	M	45
Sioux Lookout	-35	—	M	50
Smith Falls	-15	—	M	45
Stratford	-5	—	M	45
Sudbury	-20	—	M	45
ONTARIO				
Timmins	-25	—	M	50
*Toronto C	0	90	M	45
*Toronto A	-5	90	M	45
Trenton	-10	—	M	45
Walkerton	-5	—	M	45
Welland	0	—	M	45
Windsor	0	95	M	40
Woodstock	-5	—	M	45
PRINCE EDWARD ISLAND				
Charlottetown	-5	80	L	45
Summerside	-5	—	L	45
QUEBEC				
Amos	-25	—	—	—
Arvida	-20	—	M	45
Asbestos	-15	—	M	45
Chibougamau	-30	—	—	—
Chicoutimi	-20	—	M	45
Dorval	-10	—	M	45
Drummondville	-15	—	M	45
Fort Chimo	-40	—	M	60
Gaspe	-10	—	L	50
Granby	-15	—	M	45
Harrington Harbour	-15	—	—	—
Joliette	-15	—	M	45
Knob Lake	-40	—	—	55
Lac Megantic	-15	—	M	45
La Tuque	-25	—	M	45
Magog	-15	—	M	45
Mont Joli	-10	—	L	50
Mount Laurier	-20	—	M	45
*Montreal C	-10	90	M	45
*Montreal A	-10	90	M	45
Noranda	-25	—	—	—
Port Harrison	-40	—	L	60
Quebec	-15	85	M	45
Rimouski	-10	—	L	50
Riviere Du Loup	-10	—	L	45
Rouyn	-25	—	—	—
Ste. Agathe	-15	—	M	45
St. Hyacinthe	-15	—	M	45
St. Jerome	-15	—	M	45
St. Johns	-15	—	M	50
Seven Islands	-20	—	L	50
Shawinigan Falls	-15	—	M	45
Sherbrooke	-15	85	M	45
Sorel	-15	—	M	45
Thetford Minés	-15	—	M	45
Three Rivers	-15	—	M	45
Val D'Or	-25	—	—	—
Valley Field	-15	—	M	45
Victoriaville	-15	—	M	45
SASKATCHEWAN				
Biggar	-35	—	H	55
Estevau	-35	—	H	50
Humbot	-40	—	H	55
Moose Jaw	-35	—	H	50
Moosomin	-35	—	H	50
Nipawin	-40	—	H	55
North Battleford	-35	—	H	55
Prince Albert	-40	—	H	55
SASKATCHEWAN				
Regina	-35	90	H	50
Saskatoon	-40	90	H	55
Shaunavon	-35	—	H	50
Swift Current	-35	—	H	50
Uranium City	-45	—	—	—
Weyburn	-35	—	H	50
Yorkton	-35	—	H	50
YUKON TERRITORY				
Dawson	-55	—	H	65
Whitehorse	-45	—	M	60

*C—City

*A—Airport

From: National Warm Air Conditioning Association, Cleveland, Ohio; LOAD CALCULATIONS MANUAL J. SECOND EDITION

infiltration. Infiltration is caused by the air leaking through cracks around and in windows and doors, and through the walls and floor.

Heat loss calculators must also include the infiltration factor since every cubic foot of cooler outside air which leaks into the room will create a greater load on the heating system. Tight-fitting windows and doors, storm windows and doors, and weather stripping and calking around all door and window frames will appreciably reduce the amount of air leakage.

To compensate for heat lost by infiltration, simply multiply the volume of each room (V) by the *infiltration coefficient* (C), and then by the design temperature difference (T). Table 12-3 gives the infiltration co-efficients. (Doors are figured as if they were double-hung windows without weather stripping.) The formula is:

$$\text{Infiltration Btuh} = V \times C \times T$$

The product is then added to the total Btuh calculated for the heat lost for each room.

Heat Loss Record Sheet

As with any mathematical calculation, the best results are usually obtained when all operations within the problem are set down in a logical, orderly manner. Fig. 12-23 shows a heat loss calculation sheet based on a step-by-step arrival at the heat losses for all areas within a home. Each calculation area has a space provided for the width and depth of that particular room, the square footage or volume, the design temperature

TABLE 12-3

INFILTRATION HEAT LOSS COEFFICIENTS BASED ON PER CENT OF GLASS OF WALL AREA

TYPE OF WINDOW	PER CENT OF GLASS WALL AREA	COEFFICIENT
DOUBLE HUNG a. no weatherstripping	under 25% 25% to 50% 50% and over	.020 .025 .035
b. weatherstripping or storm sash	under 25% 25% to 50% 50% and over	.015 .020 .030
CASEMENT	under 25% 25% to 50% 50% and over	.030 .035 .045

HEAT LOSS CALCULATOR

CONTRACTOR ______
HOUSE LOCATION ______
CONSTRUCTION ______
INSULATION 3"

DESIGN TEMPERATURE 80°
OUTSIDE -5° INSIDE 75°

NO ___ LIVING ROOM	H	W	D	SQ FT VOL	DES TEMP	U	BTUH	NO ___	H	W	D	SQ FT VOL	DES TEMP	U	BTUH
1 GROSS WALL	8	42.5		340	80			1 GROSS WALL							
2 WINDOWS	4	9.7		38.7	80	.61	1888	2 WINDOWS							
3 NET WALL				301.3	80	.10	2410	3 NET WALL							
4 CEILING								4 CEILING							
5 FLOOR								5 FLOOR							
6 INFILTRATION	8	20.5	22	3608	80	.015	4330	6 INFILTRATION							
TOTAL BTUH →							8628	TOTAL BTUH →							

NO ___	H	W	D	SQ FT VOL	DES TEMP	U	BTUH	NO ___	H	W	D	SQ FT VOL	DES TEMP	U	BTUH
1 GROSS WALL								1 GROSS WALL							
2 WINDOWS								2 WINDOWS							
3 NET WALL								3 NET WALL							
4 CEILING								4 CEILING							
5 FLOOR								5 FLOOR							
6 INFILTRATION								6 INFILTRATION							
TOTAL BTUH →								TOTAL BTUH →							

NO ___	H	W	D	SQ FT VOL	DES TEMP	U	BTUH	NO ___	H	W	D	SQ FT VOL	DES TEMP	U	BTUH
1 GROSS WALL								1 GROSS WALL							
2 WINDOWS								2 WINDOWS							
3 NET WALL								3 NET WALL							
4 CEILING								4 CEILING							
5 FLOOR								5 FLOOR							
6 INFILTRATION								6 INFILTRATION							
TOTAL BTUH →								TOTAL BTUH →							

NO ___	H	W	D	SQ FT VOL	DES TEMP	U	BTUH	NO ___	H	W	D	SQ FT VOL	DES TEMP	U	BTUH
1 GROSS WALL								1 GROSS WALL							
2 WINDOWS								2 WINDOWS							
3 NET WALL								3 NET WALL							
4 CEILING								4 CEILING							
5 FLOOR								5 FLOOR							
6 INFILTRATION								6 INFILTRATION							
TOTAL BTUH →								TOTAL BTUH →							

PAGE ___ OF ___

Fig. 12-23. The heat loss calculation and record sheet is used to assure an orderly and exact presentation. Partial calculations for a two-story house are shown.

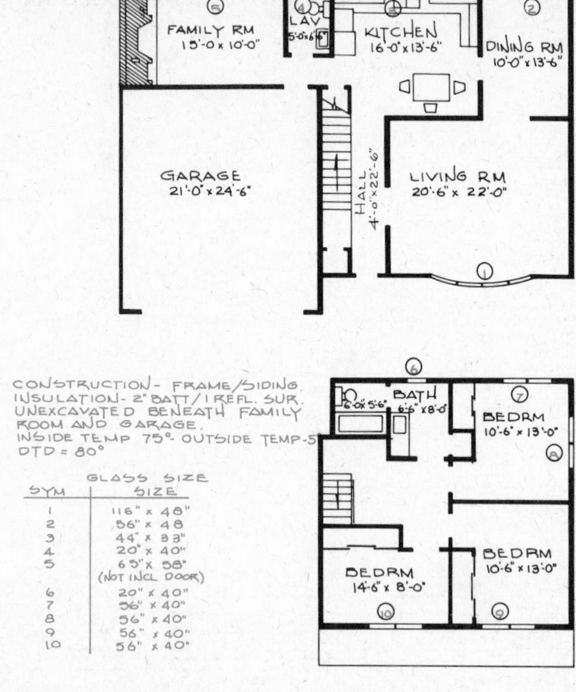

Fig. 12-24. This plan of a two-story house with basement is used in calculating heat loss. (See Heat Loss Calculator Sheet, Fig. 12-23.)

difference, the U-factor, and the Btuh. The advantage of the heat loss being calculated as shown in Fig. 12-23 is that all steps used in arriving at the total heat loss are logically figured and recorded, thereby allowing all computations to be easily checked. Questions such as "Where did this figure come from?" or "How did I arrive at this answer?" or "What does this number refer to?" will be eliminated.

Fig. 12-24 gives the plan of a two-story home with basement. The calculations necessary to determine the total heat loss for the living room are shown in Fig. 12-23. First the gross exposed wall area must be calculated (8′ × 42.5′ = 340 sq. ft.). Next, the heat loss must be computed for the windows (as shown in Fig. 12-24). A picture window (double-hung sections) is used in the living room. From the chart accompanying this figure, the glass size of this window is 116″ × 48″. This is recorded on the calculation sheet as 9.7′ × 4′ = 38.7 sq. feet. Employing the heat loss formula: 38.7 (A) × 80 (T) × .61 (U) = 1,888 Btuh. By subtracting the total square feet of windows from the gross wall square footage, we then arrive at the net wall, square footage. Calculating the total heat loss of the net wall, we would have 301.3 × 80 × .10 = 2,410.

Since the plan shown in Fig. 12-24 is a two story, there will be no appreciable heat loss because the second level is heated. The same is true of the floor as the basement would also be heated. Therefore, there would be no heat loss calculation in this case for the floor or ceiling. Infiltration is calculated for the living room by figuring the volume 8′ × 20.5′ × 22′ = 3,608 cu ft.), multiplying it by the design temperature difference (80), and then by the infiltration heat loss coefficient (.015); this gives 4,330 Btuh. The total heat loss (8,628 Btuh) is the total of lines, 2, 3, and 6 in Fig. 12-23.

Various formulas exist for computing heat loss and infiltration. Each method results in the approximate same answer. More exact methods are used by heating and ventilating engineers or heating contractors. For the architect's or designer's purpose, the approximate method will be sufficient.

Sizing

All home heating units are "sized". Sizing is based on the total heat loss calculated for a particular residence, *and* the total amount of Btu's the furnace can produce per hour. This later figure is stated as an AGA (American Gas Association) guaranteed figure. For instance, the Bryant-395 gas-fired, forced-air, upflow type (model 80-395) has an AGA output rating of 64,000 Btu's per hour. The size of the furnace must be based on the *total heat loss* calculated for the house.

Residential Cooling

Although the small air cooling unit was developed at the start of the 1930's, it did not gain significantly in popularity until the late 1940's and early 1950's. It's wide acceptance as a means of providing the home owner with relief from the summer heat has overshadowed the original reason for air cooling—to serve the production phase of industry.

Today, there is an increasing growth in the use of residental cooling units. Both individual room units and compact, centrally located cooling systems may be used. A central air cooling system may either have its own ducts or it may use the existing heating ducts or pipes. If a central air cooling system is used, it may be combined with the heating system into a single, central air conditioning unit. This combined unit gives year-round air conditioning.

Cooling Plant

The cooling plant should be able to reduce the residence to a comfortable temperature with little or no variation between floor and ceiling. Varying factors must be considered when determining the size of the cooling unit. Some of the more pertinent factors are *heat gain* through: (1) infiltration, (2) heat conducted by windows, walls, etc., (3) heat radiated by occupants, and (4) heat produced by household activities and appliances.

During the periods when residential cooling is required, the indoor temperature can more easily be maintained if the sun's rays are prevented from striking the walls, glass areas, and roof. Sun screens, roof overhangs, and plantings can protect a home from the direct rays of the sun. Insulating materials with a high R value and building materials with a low U-factor will reduce the heat conducted into a residence.

The cooling part of an air conditioning system usually removes moisture from the air. (The heating system, as mentioned earlier, adds moisture.) The ability of outdoor air to hold moisture increases as the temperature increases. Moist outdoor air infiltrating a residence will increase the indoor relative humidity. When the moist infiltrating air is added to the humidity produced by normal household activities, the moisture may rise to an uncomfortably high level.

In general the relative humidity should not exceed 60 per cent when the temperature is 76°. Most cooling equipment is designed to maintain a relative humidity within comfortable limits.

The cooling system should also provide some means of cleaning the air either by a simple mesh filter or by the highly effective electrostatic precipitate filters. The latter type of cleaner protects the health of the occupants by trapping air-borne dust and pollens.

Distribution

The distribution system should deliver its required share of cooling to each room. In a *forced-air system,* this is accomplished with the air ducts. Conditioned air is discharged into each room through diffusers. A return system is required to send the warmed air back through the cooling plant. In a *liquid-cooling system* chilled water is piped to blower-equipped convector units in each room. (Convector units are equipped with small blowers that circulate the room air over the chilled coils. In the winter these blower-equipped convector units may be used with steam or hot water heat.)

Constant air motion is desirable to maintain uniform temperature and humidity. Care must be exercised in the selection and installation of the cooling unit because the maximum allowable air velocity (in a zone between 4′ and 5′ above floor level) is approximately 50′ per minute. The distribution system may be considered satisfactory if the temperature varies 3° or less throughout the room.

Ventilation

Some degree of ventilation is essential in the air conditioned home because there are physical and chemical changes that occur to the air as a result of human occupancy. The air in the residence will become "stale" when there is a reduction in oxygen, an increase in carbon dioxide, or an unpleasant amount of cooking and household odors.

Fortunately, some degree of ventilation is obtained by infiltration through doors and windows. If infiltration does not provide enough ventilation, an exhaust fan in the kitchen and/or bath may be used. The forced-air cooling system may require a duct to bring in outside air.

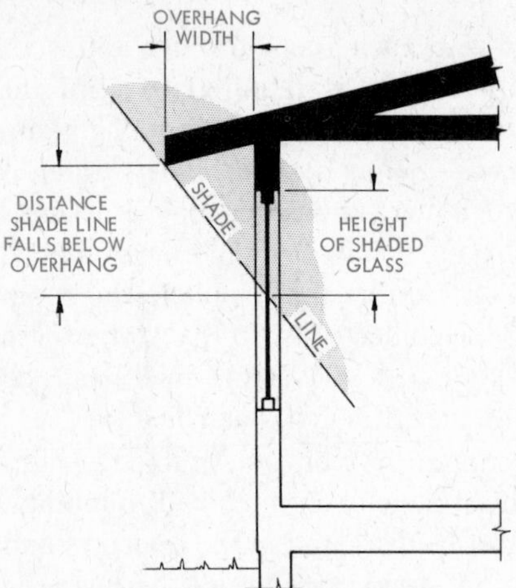

Fig. 12-25. The shade line is based on the latitude, width of overhang, and location of window.

Cooling Load Calculations

The size of the cooling system required to provide comfort in the home is based primarily on the summer outside design temperature. These temperatures are shown in Table 12-2. As in the case of the winter temperatures previously discussed, the summer temperatures are not the highest temperatures recorded. It will also be noted that Table 12-2 lists the daily temperature ranges for each city. The range refers to the average maximum and minimum temperature fluctuation occurring during the cooling season. For convenience these are expressed as H (high), M (medium), and L (low) ranges. (These ranges are used in later calculations.)

Generally, the most comfortable inside temperature is 75° F. If an inside design temperature lower than 75° F is specified by the home owner, the heat gain factors for a higher outside design temperature should be used.

Heat gain must be calculated for *all rooms and* areas that are to be cooled. When determining the amount of heat gain for a room, all surfaces that are exposed to the outside must be considered. Heat gain that is transmitted from floors over a basement, enclosed crawl space, or a concrete slab on the ground is so negligible that it is not calculated. Similarly, walls that are below grade are not calculated. However, the exposed portion of a basement wall, as in the case of a house designed with a walk-out basement, must be calculated.

During the summer months, sunlight through windows will constitute a large portion of the heat gain. The intensity of the sun's rays varies with the orientation of the various rooms.

The position of the sun, location of the structure relative to latitude, and the amount of overhang determine the heat gain through a window. The amount of overhang is perhaps the most significant of these factors. Glass that is protected by a permanent shading device, such as a roof overhang or awning, is considered as a northward facing window, even though the window does not face north. That portion of glass that is not screened from the sun's rays is referred to as *sunlit* glass. The line that divides the shaded from the unshaded portion is called the *shade line*. Fig. 12-25 shows the shade line caused by the sun. The sunlit area as well as shaded area must be calculated separately for each window.

As was indicated in the first portion of this chapter, heat is lost within the structure by infiltration. A similar situation also exists when cooling the structure—warm, exterior air will enter the house and an equivalent amount of cooled air will exit. To simplify infiltration calculations, the area of the exposed wall is employed to determine the amount of infiltration in each room.

The occupants of the house should not be overlooked since the human body produces heat. This adds to the heat gain within the structure. During the summer a room will be considerably "warmer" with eight occupants, for example, than with two. Of course, humidity is a contributing factor. For heat gain, 300 Btuh (British Thermal Units Per Hour) per person is considered average. If the number of occupants is not known, simply multiply the number of bedrooms by 2. This factor of 300 Btuh per person is calculated only once for the living area. (It is recommended that a *minimum* of 1,000 Btuh be used for the living area of the home.) A constant figure of 1,200 Btuh must also be added to the kitchen to compensate for the increased temperature created by cooking.

To obtain a correctly sized cooling unit for the residence, the *sensible heat gain* must be computed. The sensible heat gain is the total of all heat gains for each room plus the halls. The *final* heat gain used in "sizing" is arrived at by multiplying the sensible heat gain by the figure 1.3. This factor (1.3) is

HEAT GAIN CALCULATOR

CONTRACTOR ______
HOUSE LOCATION 914 Sixth Street, Eau Claire, Wisconsin
CONSTRUCTION Brick Veneer
INSULATION
WALLS 3" TYPE Batt
CEILINGS 4+" TYPE Blown
FLOORS ______ TYPE ______

LATITUDE: N 45°
TEMPERATURE RANGE: M
OUTSIDE DESIGN TEMPERATURE: 90°
INSIDE TEMPERATURE: 75°
OVERHANG: 1'-6" Uniform

	NO. Living Room SIZE 23'x17'			NO Bed Room SIZE 10'x11', 2'x5			NO Kitchen SIZE 18'x8', 3'x6'			NO SIZE			NO. SIZE		
	AREA LIN. FT	HTM	BTUH	AREA LIN. FT	HTM	BTUH	AREA LIN. FT.	HTM	BTUH	AREA LIN. FT	HTM	BTUH	AREA LIN. FT	HTM	BTUH
LINEAL FEET EXPOSED WALL	23+4+23			10			18+10								
CEILING HEIGHT	8			8			8								
GROSS EXPOSED WALL	400			80			224								
WINDOWS SHADE DIRECTION	(A) W 6	14	84	(B) W 3	14	42	(D) E 3	14	42						
WINDOWS SHADE DIRECTION	(C) E 3	14	42												
WINDOWS SHADE DIRECTION															
WINDOWS SUNLIT DIRECTION	(A) W 54	44	2376	(B) W 12	44	528	(D) E 18	44	792						
WINDOWS SUNLIT DIRECTION	(C) E 29	44	1276												
WINDOWS SUNLIT DIRECTION															
NET EXPOSED WALL	308	1.5	462	65	1.5	98	203	1.5	305						
WARM PARTITION	104	1.4	146				120	3.4	408						
CEILING	391	1.6	626	120	1.6	192	162	1.6	259						
FLOORS															
INFILTRATION	400	1.1	440	80	1.1	88	224	1.1	246						
PEOPLE @ 300 BTUH		6	1800												
APPLIANCES @ 1200 BTUH									1200						
SENSIBLE-HEAT GAIN			7252			948			3252						
× 1.3															
TOTAL HEAT GAIN (SHG × 1.3)			9428	TOTAL		1232	TOTAL		4228	TOTAL			TOTAL		

Fig. 12-26. The heat gain calculation sheet is used to figure the loads in sizing cooling units. Partial calculations for a single-story house are shown.

the performance expectancy used in sizing cooling equipment and will result in a total heat gain adequate for most regions. The product of the sensible heat gain multiplied by 1.3 will equal the required size of the unit.

Heat Gain Record Sheet

To facilitate calculating the total heat gain for a house, the best results are obtained when a logical method is used. Fig. 12-26 shows a heat gain calculation sheet that may be used for all rooms and areas in the home. Each portion of the record sheet has space for room dimensions, factors, sunlit glass windows, exposed walls, infiltration, etc.

The necessary calculations to arrive at the heat gain for a bedroom, kitchen, and living room are illustrated on Fig. 12-26 in color. These calculations refer to the partial plan of a single-story, ranch-type house with a basement shown in Fig. 12-27. This illustration is used in the sample calculations given below.

Preliminary to making any calculations, the upper portion of the heat gain calculation sheet should be completed; i.e., location, construction, latitude, outside temperature, temperature range, etc. Part of this information is obtained from Table 12-2. For purpose of example Eau Clair, Wisconsin is used. The calculations given below are for the living room shown in Fig. 12-27.

First, the lineal footage of exposed wall (in this case: 23′ + 4′ + 23′) and the ceiling height (8′) for the living room are recorded on the heat gain calculator sheet. From this the gross exposed wall is calculated.

Next the Btuh heat gain for the windows must be computed. When figuring the heat gain for windows, the direction and the area of sunlit and shaded glass must be taken into account. Window A is 12′-0″ long by 5′-0″ high and faces west. Table 12-4 lists the shaded glass areas based on window width per foot of overhang. Since Window A is 12′ long and the maximum length of the window shown in the table is 6′-0″, simply consider Window A to be two 6′-0″ windows. To obtain the shaded area, locate the window width and compass direction

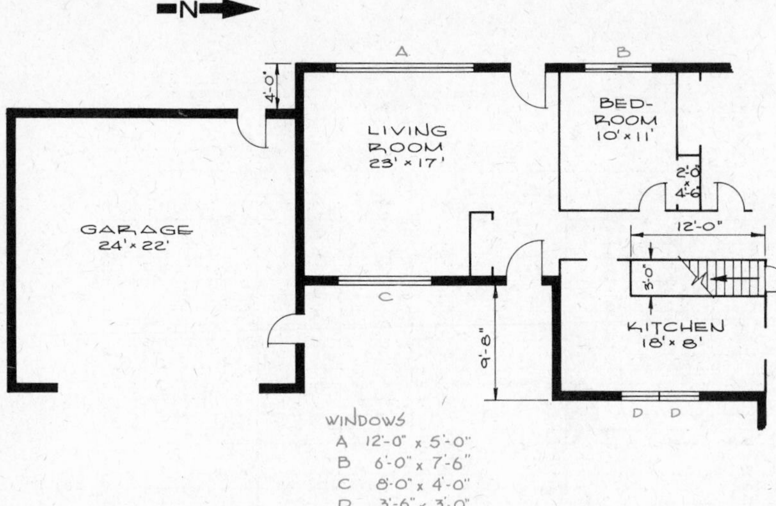

Fig. 12-27. Use this plan for calculating heat gain. (See Heat Gain Calculator Sheet, Fig. 12-26.) This is a portion of a single story, three bedroom ranch-type house with a basement, located in Eau Claire, Wisconsin. The roof overhangs the house a uniform 1'-8". All exterior walls are brick veneer with 3" batt insulation. The roof, over a naturally vented attic, is covered with black asphalt shingles. The ceiling of the house, excluding the garage, is insulated with 4"+ of blown insulation. The windows in the living room and bedrooms are welded insulating glass (double glazed), while the kitchen windows are equipped with storm and screens. The kitchen windows have venetian blinds and the living and bedroom windows are draped. All windows are set at a 6'-8" head height.

TABLE 12-4
SHADED GLASS AREAS

WINDOW WIDTH, FT	LESS THAN 2.0			2.0 TO 2.5			2.6 TO 3.0			3.1 TO 3.5			3.6 TO 4.0			4.1 TO 4.5			4.6 TO 5.0			5.1 TO 5.5			5.6 TO 6.0		
DIRECTION WINDOW FACES	E W	SE SW	S	E W	SE SW	S	E W	SE SW	S	E W	SE SW	S	E W	SE SW	S	E W	SE SW	S	E W	SE SW	S	E W	SE SW	S	E W	SE SW	S
LATITUDE, DEGREES	AREA OF SHADED GLASS PER FOOT OVERHANG, SQ FT																										
25	0	2	17	1	3	22	1	4	26	1	5	31	1	5	36	1	6	41	1	7	46	2	7	50	2	8	55
30	0	2	9	1	2	11	1	3	14	1	4	16	1	4	18	1	5	21	1	5	23	2	6	26	2	6	28
35	0	2	5	1	2	7	1	2	9	1	3	10	1	3	12	1	4	13	1	4	15	2	5	16	2	5	18
40	0	1	4	1	2	5	1	2	6	1	3	7	1	3	8	1	3	9	1	4	10	2	4	11	2	5	12
45	0	1	3	1	1	3	1	2	4	1	2	5	1	2	6	1	3	6	1	3	7	2	3	8	2	3	9
50	0	1	2	1	1	3	1	1	3	1	2	4	1	2	5	1	2	5	1	2	6	2	3	6	2	3	7
55	0	1	2	1	1	2	1	1	2	1	1	3	1	2	3	1	2	4	1	2	4	2	2	5	2	2	5

NOTE: If top of window is more than 1 ft below edge of overhang the wall area between top of window and overhang must be subtracted from shaded area obtained from Table 12-4. Shades areas are not calculated for NE, N, or NW windows. Use glass heat transfer multiplier indicated in Table 12-5 for entire glass area of window facing these directions.

[1]From: National Warm Air Heating & Air Conditioning Association, Cleveland, Ohio; LOAD CALCULATIONS: MANUAL J, SECOND EDITION.

(west) and read down vertically to the row indicating the closest latitude (45°). The square foot area of shaded glass per foot of overhang is 2 sq. ft. The roof overhangs the window 1′-6″ (or a factor of 1.5). Therefore, 2 sq. ft. × 1.5 = 3 sq. ft. Since there are two windows, 2 × 3 sq. ft. = 6 sq. ft. This is the amount of shaded glass area. Window C faces east and is 8′-0″ × 4′-0″. Since the window is more than 6′ it will have to be broken into two 4′ windows. Locate the width in the proper column (4.0′) under compass direction (east) and read downward to the 45° latitude row. The square foot area of shaded glass per foot overhang is 1 sq. ft. Multiply the shaded glass by the overhang factor. 1 sq. ft. × 1.5 = 1.5 sq. ft.; 1.5 sq. ft. × 2 = 3 sq. ft. These are recorded, indicating the direction and area, as: W-6 and E-3.

Any *shaded portion* of a window is considered as a *northward facing window,* regardless of its direction. Table 12-5 lists the glass *heat transfer multiplier* (HTM) for windows based on type of glazing and outside design temperature. Both living room windows are double glazed. The outside design temperature in Eau Claire, Wisconsin is 90°. (See Table 12-2.) Locate the proper section marked "Regular Double Glass" and the column labeled "90°". Both Windows A and C are draped. Read down that column to the correct HTM (14). Record the figure 14 in the HTM column of the calculator. To obtain the Btuh gain, multiply the shaded area by the HTM: 6 × 14 = 84 Btuh and 3 × 14 = 42 Btuh.

TABLE 12-5

GLASS HEAT TRANSFER MULTIPLIER (COOLING)

Cooling load due to transmitted and absorbed solar energy and air-to-air temperature difference

OUTSIDE DESIGN TEMP	REGULAR SINGLE GLASS					REGULAR DOUBLE GLASS					HEAT ABSORBING DOUBLE GLASS				
	90	95	100	105	110	90	95	100	105	110	90	95	100	105	110
DIRECTION WINDOW FACES	NO AWNINGS OR INSIDE SHADING														
NORTH (OR SHADED)	27	31	35	38	44	21	24	26	28	30	14	17	19	21	23
NE AND NW	60	64	68	71	77	48	51	53	55.	57	29	32	34	36	38
EAST AND WEST	85	89	93	96	102	70	73	75	77	79	44	47	49	51	53
SE AND SW	74	78	82	85	91	61	64	66	68	70	37	40	42	44	46
SOUTH	44	48	52	55	61	35	38	40	42	44	21	24	26	28	30
	DRAPERIES OR VENETIAN BLINDS														
NORTH (OR SHADED)	19	23	27	30	36	14	17	19	21	23	11	14	16	18	20
NE AND NW	36	40	44	47	53	29	32	34	36	38	22	25	27	29	31
EAST AND WEST	52	56	60	63	69	44	47	49	51	53	32	35	37	39	41
SE AND SW	44	48	52	55	61	37	40	42	44	46	26	29	31	33	35
SOUTH	27	31	35	38	44	22	25	27	29	31	17	20	22	24	26
	ROLLER SHADES HALF-DRAWN														
NORTH (OR SHADED)	22	26	30	33	39	17	20	22	24	26	12	15	17	19	21
NE AND NW	44	48	52	55	61	40	43	45	47	49	26	29	31	33	35
EAST AND WEST	65	69	73	76	82	56	59	61	63	65	37	40	42	44	46
SE AND SW	56	60	64	67	73	48	51	53	55	57	32	35	37	39	41
SOUTH	33	37	41	44	50	29	32	34	36	38	20	23	25	27	29
	AWNINGS														
NORTH (OR SHADED)	24	28	32	35	41	15	18	20	22	24	12	15	17	19	21
NE AND NW	25	29	33	36	42	16	19	21	23	25	13	16	18	20	22
EAST AND WEST	26	30	34	37	43	16	19	21	23	25	14	17	19	21	23
SE AND SW	25	29	33	36	42	16	19	21	23	25	13	16	18	20	22
SOUTH	24	28	32	35	41	15	18	20	22	24	13	16	18	20	22

NOTE: Factors in this table are based on data for 30 degrees and 40 degrees north latitude and are expressed in Btu per hr per sq ft.

From: National Warm Air Heating and Air Conditioning Association, Cleveland, Ohio; LOAD CALCULATIONS MANUAL J. SECOND EDITION

Now the Btuh gain for the sunlit glass must be calculated. To determine the area of sunlit glass for each window, subtract the shaded glass area from the window area. Window A has 60 sq. ft. of area and the shaded portion occupies 6 sq. ft.; therefore, 60 − 6 = 54 sq. ft. Window C has an area 32 sq. ft. with 3 sq. ft. being shaded. The sunlit portion is 29 sq. ft. These are recorded on the calculator with an indication of the compass direction, W-54 and E-29.

To obtain the Btuh heat gain for the windows, refer again to Table 12-5. Locate the type of glazing and outside design temperature "Regular Double Glass"—"90°". Read downward to the row marked "Draperies or

Venetian Blinds" and "East and West." The HTM is 44. Multiply the sunlit portion of each window by the HTM. Window A = 54 sq. ft. × 44 = 2,376 Btuh; and Window C = 29 sq. ft. × 44 = 1,276 Btuh.

The next heat gain component to be calculated is the *net amount* of exposed wall (the gross wall area minus window area.) The net exposed wall area = 308 sq. ft. (23′ + 4′ + 23′ = 50′; 50′ × 8′ = 400 sq. ft. gross wall; 400 sq. ft. −92 sq. ft. = 308 sq. ft. net wall). The net exposed wall area is multiplied by the HTM given in Table 12-6. This table lists the HTM per sq. ft. of various types of walls, partitions, ceilings, floors, and infiltration. Locate the daily temperature range and outside design temperature columns marked "Medium" and "90°" (obtained from Table 12-2) and read downward to the specified type of exterior wall construction—"Veneer on Frame—More than 2 in. insulation." The HTM for this type of construction in the medium temperature range for 90° is 1.5. Multiply the net exposed wall area by the HTM. 308 × 1.5 = 462 Btuh.

Any partitions that are not conditioned, such as the 13′ length of wall separating the living room from the garage, must be calculated. Locate the same column as above in Table 12-6 and read downward to the row labeled "Frame, finished both sides more than 1 in. insulation." Multiply this HTM by the area of the warm wall: 104 sq. ft. × 1.4 = 146 Btuh.

TABLE 12-6
HEAT TRANSFER MULTIPLIER (COOLING)

Daily Temperature Range	Low		Medium				High			
Outside Design Temperature, F	90	95	90	95	100	105	95	100	105	110
WINDOWS										
No. 1 through No. 5—Obtain factors from Table 12-5										
DOORS										
No. 6 Wood doors. (Consider glass area of doors as a window)	11.4	14.0	9.4	12.0	14.0	17.0	9.4	12.0	14.0	17.0
WALLS										
No. 7 Frame and Veneer-on-frame										
(a) No insulation	6.0	7.2	4.8	6.0	7.5	8.7	4.8	6.0	7.5	8.7
(b) Less than 1-in. insulation, or one reflective air space	4.3	5.1	3.5	4.5	5.4	6.3	3.5	4.5	5.4	6.3
(c) 1-in. to 2-in. insulation, or two reflective air spaces	2.9	3.6	2.4	3.1	3.7	4.4	2.4	3.1	3.7	4.4
(d) More than 2-in. insulation, or three reflective air spaces	1.8	2.2	1.5	1.9	2.3	2.7	1.5	1.9	2.3	2.7
No. 8 Masonry walls, 8-in. block or brick										
(a) Plastered or plain	7.2	9.7	5.4	7.9	10.4	12.5	5.4	7.9	10.4	12.5
(b) Furred, no insulation	4.6	6.0	3.4	4.9	6.3	7.9	3.4	4.9	6.3	7.9
(c) Furred, with less than 1-in. insulation, or one reflective air space	3.1	4.1	2.3	3.3	4.3	5.4	2.3	3.3	4.3	5.4
(d) Furred, with 1-in. to 2-in. insulation, or two reflective air spaces	2.1	2.8	1.6	2.3	3.0	3.7	1.6	2.3	3.0	3.7
(e) Furred, with more than 2-in. insulation or three reflective air spaces	1.4	1.8	1.0	1.5	1.9	2.4	1.0	1.5	1.9	2.4
No. 9 Partitions										
(a) Frame, finished one side only, no insulation	8.5	11.4	6.0	9.1	12.0	15.0	6.0	9.1	12.0	15.0
(b) Frame, finished both sides, no insulation	4.8	6.6	3.4	5.1	6.9	8.5	3.4	5.1	6.9	8.5
(c) Frame, finished both sides, more than 1-in. insulation, or two reflective air spaces	2.0	2.7	1.4	2.1	2.8	3.5	1.4	2.1	2.8	3.5
(d) Masonry, plastered one side, no insulation	2.6	4.4	1.2	3.0	4.7	6.6	1.2	3.0	4.7	6.6
CEILINGS AND ROOFS										
No. 10 Ceilings under naturally vented attic or vented flat roof										
(a) Uninsulation (attic must be vented for cooling) —dark	10.0	11.0	9.1	10.0	11.4	12.5	9.1	10.0	11.4	12.5
—light	8.2	9.1	7.2	8.2	9.4	10.4	7.2	8.2	9.4	10.4
(b) Less than 2-in. insulation, or one reflective air space —dark	4.3	4.8	3.9	4.4	4.9	5.4	3.9	4.4	4.9	5.4
—light	3.5	4.1	3.1	3.6	4.1	4.6	3.1	3.6	4.1	4.6
(c) 2-in. to 4-in. insulation, or two reflective air spaces —dark	2.6	2.9	2.3	2.6	2.9	3.2	2.3	2.6	2.9	3.2
—light	2.1	2.4	1.9	2.2	2.5	2.8	1.9	2.2	2.5	2.8

The area above the ceilings in this single story house is not air conditioned so this must also be computed when figuring total heat gain. Multiply the area of the ceiling (23′ × 17′) by the HTM found in Table 12-6: 391 sq. ft. × 1.6 = 626 Btuh.

If the floor of the room to be conditioned is over a basement, enclosed crawl space,

TABLE 12-6 (continued)

Daily Temperature Range		Low		Medium				High			
Outside Design Temperature, F		90	95	90	95	100	105	95	100	105	110
(d) More than 4-in. insulation, or three or more reflective air spaces	—dark	1.8	1.9	1.6	1.8	2.0	2.2	1.6	1.8	2.0	2.2
	—light	1.4	1.6	1.2	1.4	1.6	1.8	1.2	1.4	1.6	1.8
No. 11 Built-up roof, no ceiling											
(a) Uninsulated	—dark	17.0	19.0	16.0	18.0	20.0	22.0	16.0	18.0	20.0	22.0
	—light	14.2	16.4	12.5	14.0	16.0	18.0	12.5	14.0	16.0	18.0
(b) 2-in. roof insulation	—dark	8.5	9.7	7.9	8.7	9.7	11.0	7.9	8.7	9.7	11.0
	—light	6.9	7.9	6.3	7.2	8.2	9.1	6.3	7.2	8.2	9.1
(c) 3-in. roof insulation	—dark	6.0	6.6	5.4	6.3	6.9	7.5	5.4	6.3	6.9	7.5
	—light	4.9	5.6	4.3	5.1	5.6	6.3	4.3	5.1	5.6	6.3
No. 12 Ceilings under unconditioned rooms		2.7	3.6	1.9	2.9	3.8	4.8	1.9	2.9	3.8	4.8
FLOORS											
No. 13 Over unconditioned rooms		3.4	4.6	24	3.6	4.8	6.0	2.4	3.6	4.8	6.0
No. 14 through No. 18 Over basement, enclosed crawl space, concrete slab on ground, basement or crawl space floor		0	0	0	0	0	0	0	0	0	0
No. 19 Over open or vented space		4.8	6.6	3.4	5.1	6.9	8.5	3.4	5.1	6.9	8.5
INFILTRATION AND VENTILATION											
No. 20 Infiltration, Btuh per sq ft of gross exposed wall area		1.1	1.5	1.1	1.5	1.9	2.2	1.6	1.9	2.2	2.6
No. 21 Mechanical ventilation, Btuh per cfm		16.0	22.0	16.0	22.0	27.0	32.0	22.0	27.0	32.0	38.0

[1]From: National Warm-Air Heating & Air Conditioning Association, Cleveland, Ohio; LOAD CALCULATIONS: Manual J. Second Edition.

concrete slab on the ground, etc., there will be no heat gain. However, if the floor is over an unconditioned room or over an open or vented space, the heat gain must then be calculated and entered on the calculator.

Heat gain due to infiltration must be calculated next (use Table 12-6) by multiplying the gross exposed wall area by the infiltration HTM: 400 sq. ft. × 1.1 = 440 Btuh.

Also figured in the heat gain are the number of occupants. This home has 3 bedrooms. As stated previously, multiply the number of bedrooms by 2. Each person is calculated to emit 300 Btuh: 6 × 300 Btuh = 1,800 Btuh. This figure is listed only once on the calculator because the heat gain, 1,800 Btuh, is averaged over all the living areas.

The *sensible heat gain* is a summation of all heat gains: 84 + 42 + 2,376 + 1,276 + 462 + 626 + 440 + 1,800 = 7,252 Btuh.

To obtain the *total heat gain* for the room, the sensible heat gain is multiplied by a constant 1.3, as discussed previously: 7,252 × 1.3 = 9,428 Btuh. This is the number of British Thermal Units that must be removed per hour to achieve an inside temperature of 75°F under the stated conditions. (This heat gain applies to the living room shown in Fig. 12-27.)

When calculating the kitchen, a heat gain of 1,200 Btuh must be added for the appliances.

Each room, hall, and/or other area is calculated in the same manner as the living room. The total heat gain for the entire house would then be the *sum* of all heat gains and would be a guide for selecting the proper size cooling unit. Manufacturers give the Btuh removal rate of cooling units. Cooling units are also rated in tons. A ton is the amount of refrigeration that will be produced by a ton of ice melting over a twenty-four hour period (this has a heat absorption of 288,000 Btu's). A ton is equivalent to removing 12,000 Btuh.

As with heat loss calculation, different methods exist for computing the heat gain. The method just described will produce a very close estimate of the heat gain.

Working Drawings

The air conditioning system is sometimes included in the set of working drawings. The Federal Housing Administration's *Minimum Property Standards* (FHA No. 300) requires that the following be included in the working drawings:

Heating system, on separate drawing or as part of floor or basement plan showing:

a. Layout of system.
b. Location and size of ducts, piping, registers, radiators, etc.
c. Location of heating unit and room thermostat.
d. Total calculated heat loss of dwelling including heat loss through all vertical surfaces, ceiling, and floor. When a duct or piped distribution system is used, calculated heat loss of each heated space.

Cooling system, on separate drawings or as part of heating plan, floor or basement plan showing:

a. Layout of system.
b. Location and size of ducts, registers, compressors, coils, etc.
c. Heat gain calculations, including estimated heat gain for each space conditioned.
d. Model number and Btuh capacity of equipment or units in accordance with applicable ARI (Air Conditioning and Refrigeration Institute) or ASRE (American Society of Refrigerating Engineers) Standard.
e. Btuh capacity and total KW input at stated local design conditions.
f. If room or zone conditioners are used, provide location, size and installation details.

Questions and Problems

1. Based on the community in which you live, what system of heating would you choose for heating a:
   a. split-level house having 1,300 sq. ft?
   b. ranch house having 1,100 sq. ft.?
   c. two-story house having 1,100 sq. ft.?
2. Have your instructor assign a class member to contact the local electric company concerning the rate for an electrically heated home. Are these rates based on a specific amount of electricity consumed? Is this a favorable rate? Is the rate competitive with other types of fuel?
3. What advantages and disadvantages does a hydronic system have in comparison with a warm-air system?
4. What logical reason could be stated for placing a warm-air diffuser or register on a cold wall particularly below a window?
5. Would it be sound economy to install some form of electric heating in an enclosed porch that has been added on to an existing dwelling? What factors would be considered as important in arriving at a decision?
6. What is a coefficient of transmission? Does an insulating material that has a high U-factor indicate that it is better than one having a low factor?
7. Shortly after a new snowfall, can you identify, from the street, those dwellings that do not have insulation in attic floor? What signs tell you that the home does not have insulation? What causes this occurrence?
8. Using the house plan and related information shown in Fig. 12-24, which of the following furnaces with guaranteed Btuh ratings (at sea level) would most adequately heat the structure:
   a. 90,000 Btuh at the bonnet
   b. 100,000 Btuh at the bonnet
   c. 120,000 Btuh at the bonnet
   d. None of the above
9. Using the house plan shown in Fig. 12-24, sketch a warm-air heating system. Sketch a basement plan and show the arrangement. What would be the best way to provide for summer air conditioning?
10. List the basic functions of air conditioning.
11. When sizing a cooling unit, what gain factors must be considered when detailing the heat gain?
12. What is the ideal relative humidity level during the summer months?
13. What maximum temperature variation is considered satisfactory in an air conditioned room?
14. What reasons may be given for the necessity of requiring constant air motion in home cooling?
15. It is understood that ventilation is necessary in the air conditioned home. What factors contribute to stale air? How may each of these be remedied?
16. What building components (material, structural members, etc.) cause the greatest amount of heat gain?

17. What kinds of devices may be used to reduce the amount of heat gain on an exterior wall?
18. Calculate the heat gain for your bedroom at home.
19. Sketch the plan of your house or apartment. Using the tables provided in this chapter, calculate the total heat gain. Be sure to specify the type of construction, insulation, overhang, compass direction, window sizes, window protection, etc. Record your calculations in a manner similar to that illustrated by heat gain calculator or set down your results in a logical, understandable order.

ELJER PLUMBINGWARE DIVISION, THE MURRAY CORPORATION OF AMERICA; PITTSBURGH, PENNSYLVANIA.

Sound plumbing is necessary for the health of the occupants. Plumbing fixtures not only are functional but they may also be pleasing in appearance.

Residential Plumbing 13

The plumbing system is one of the least understood, yet most essential of our modern living conveniences. Perhaps this is true because most plumbing, like electric wiring, is hidden within the walls and floors. It is necessary, however, for the architect to have a competent understanding the general plumbing layout and to co-ordinate the plumbing with the over-all house plan. Detail planning is usually done by the plumbing contractor.

Plumbing System

The residential plumbing system is designed to carry water to the various outlets in the house and to remove waste water and materials to the sanitary sewer or septic tank. Also included under plumbing is the piping for gas.

Plumbing pipes are installed after the house has been "roughed in" (exterior shell with sheathing and interior partition walls, but with no plaster or dry wall). Pipes are placed in the walls, ceilings, and floors, and are carried to the points where the fixtures will be attached. The fixtures are added after the dry wall or plaster has been applied. Meters for water and gas must also be located and connected.

Today, much of the piping for supply and drainage is copper. Heretofore lead or steel pipe was used. Copper pipe has an advantage over steel pipe in that the junction between a run of pipe and a fitting (tee, elbow, ell, etc.) is soldered rather than threaded. Most plumbing jobs will allow copper piping one size smaller than steel for the same flow rate. Copper tubing is available in either flexible or rigid form. The drainage system carrying the waste water and material to the house drain may be copper, cast iron, or steel.

Almost all plumbing installations are governed by some type of building code. In a few areas, however, the installation of the plumbing is left to the judgment of the plumber with no specific code to guard the home owner. If a code exists, the designer should follow it in laying out the plumbing system.

Water Supply

Plumbing supply systems, regardless of size or capacity, all have the same basic features. A water supply pipe brings the water into the house from either a city water main (under pressure) or a private well. If a pri-

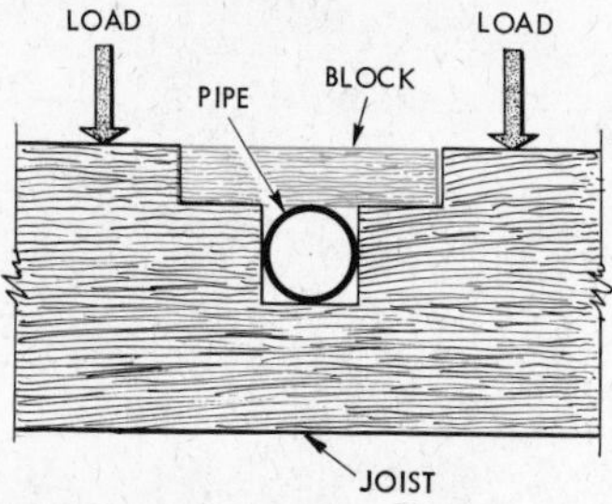

Fig. 13-1. A pipe that passes through a joist **must** be placed at the top and blocked to prevent appreciable weakening of that member.

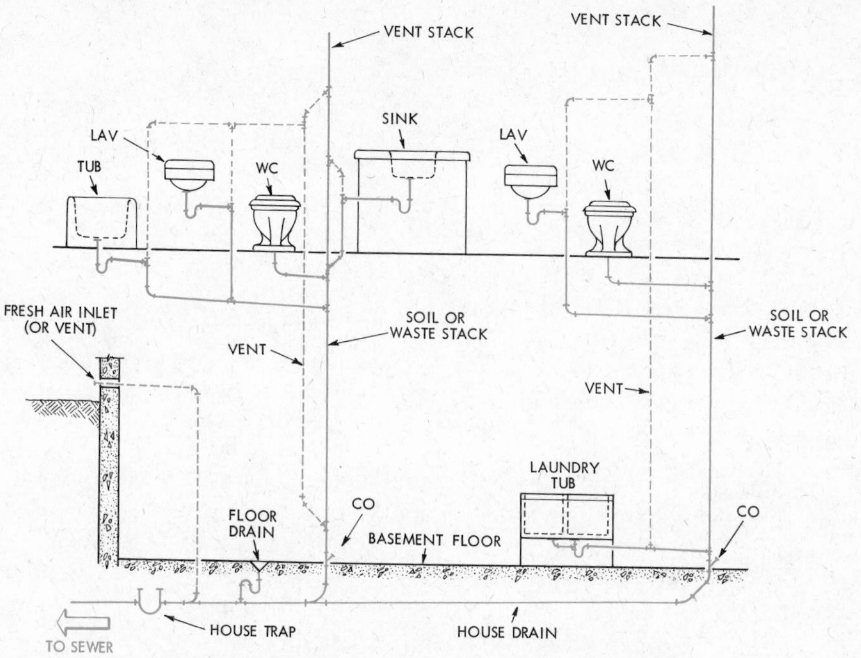

Fig. 13-2. This figure illustrates a typical sewage disposal and venting system for a residential dwelling.

vate well is used, pumping will be required. Smaller pipes distribute the cold water directly to the outlets at the tub, shower, lavatories, toilet flush boxes, heating plant, hose bibs, etc. A branch line feeds the hot water heater. A main pipe with branches leads from the heater to faucets located at the fixtures. Cold and hot water pipes that run vertically are called *risers*.

Fixtures Branches

Each plumbing fixture is connected to a soil or waste stack by the means of a fixture branch. (These branches are horizontal with a slope of 1/4″ per foot.) Branch runs must of necessity be kept as short as possible, especially if they are laid between joists with flooring above and ceiling material below.

In areas where temperatures drop below freezing, precautions must be taken to provide adequate insulation for pipes placed in outside walls. Some plumbing fixtures, notably cast iron and vitrified clay, are often heavy and the floor joists supporting these loads must be reinforced by doubling, or by placing the joists closer together. The only area where this is usually applicable is under the bathroom. In some instances it may be necessary to run a pipe *through* a joist; provisions should be made to strengthen this opening by means of a block, see Fig. 13-1. Of necessity this cut must be placed near the top of the joist to retain the maximum load bearing quality of the joist.

Water and Waste Removal

Water that has been used for washing or as a vehicle for disposing of waste matter must have an escape to the sanitary sewer or septic tank. To serve this end a companion pipe system, carefully isolated from supply pipes, is required to guard the health of the occupants. This is probably the most important and most complicated feature in the plumbing system.

Between the fixtures and the soil and waste stacks, a water seal is necessary. Normally a P-trap is used. Fig. 13-2 illustrates a typical sewage disposal system for a residential dwelling. Note the trap.

Soil and Waste Stacks receive the waste water and materials from the various plumbing fixtures, such as lavatories, sinks, washers, dishwashers, water closets, etc. These stacks connect to the house drain. From an economic standpoint, plumbing should be grouped to require as few stacks as possible, both on a single floor and on a multilevel dwelling. The whole layout of the building must be taken into consideration in laying out the soil and waste stacks. To achieve the shortest and most practical route it is advisable to consult with the plumbing contractor. Due to the size of the soil and waste stacks (minimum 3″, usually 4″ in residential housing), partitions (with 2″ x 6″ studs) are commonly located after the pipe run has been planned. Cast-iron piping is usually used in residential construction. The soil and waste stacks are extended through the highest part of the roof for ventilation.

House Drain. The vertical soil and waste stacks empty into the house drain. The house drain is usually located immediately beneath the basement floor provided the city sanitary sewer is below this elevation. If the city sewer is higher in elevation, then the house drain is fastened along the inside of the foundation wall or hung from the ceiling. The house drain should, if possible, have a pitch of ¼″ per foot. A 4″ inside diameter for cast iron pipe and a 6″ inside diameter for vitrified clay pipe is usually adequate for a small residential dwelling. However, local plumbing codes should be consulted to determine the exact sizing.

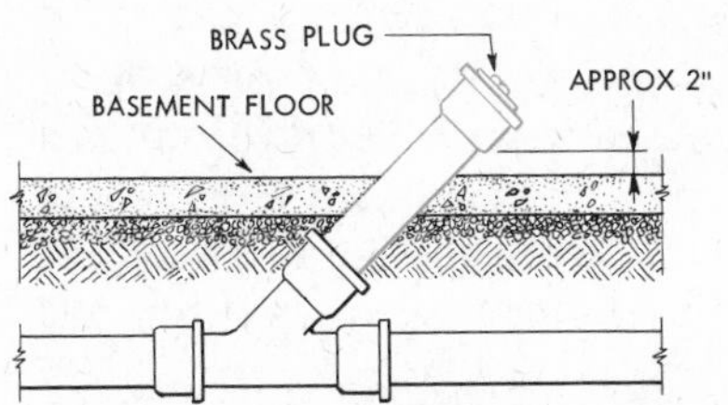

Fig. 13-3. The cleanout is located at the end of the last vertical stack and at each change in direction of the house drain.

Drain tile (usually 3″) may also be laid around the inside and outside of the footing. Sometimes the seepage from this is carried by the house drain. However, the local building code must be consulted since this practice is not permitted in all cities.

Cleanouts (CO) should be provided at the end of the last vertical stack and at each change in direction of the house drain. Fig. 13-3 illustrates a cleanout.

House Trap. The purpose of the house trap is to prevent sanitary sewer gases from entering into the plumbing. The trap is located immediately on the inside of the foundation wall and has the same diameter as the house drain. Usually a U-shaped trap is used. To facilitate cleaning, cleanouts are provided at one or both of the "horns" or "outlets" placed at the top of the U. Local plumbing codes should be checked to see if there is any restriction on the use of a house trap.

House Sewer. The house sewer connects the house trap and drain at the foundation wall to the main sanitary sewer located in the street or to the septic tank. This is usually the first part of the plumbing system to be installed.

Either cast-iron or vitrified clay pipe may be used in the house sewer. The choice may depend upon local or state plumbing codes. Cast-iron pipe should have at least a 4″ inside diameter. Vitrified clay pipe should have at least a 6″ inside diameter. Cast-iron is recommended if there are any trees in the vicinity or if the soil is unstable. Tree roots might enter between the vitrified clay pipe joints and clog the system. If vitrified clay pipe is used in unstable soil, some support must be provided.

The slope of the house sewer depends upon the difference between the depth of the house drain outlet and the depth of the street sewer. The difference is distributed over the total length of the house sewer run. Usually the slope of the house sewer is at least ¼″ per foot.

If the basement is below the level of street sewer a sump pit with a pump must be employed to pump the waste water up to the house sewer. The sump pit is a covered, cylindrical recess in the basement floor into which the waste water from the basement plumbing fixtures is drained. When the water reaches a particular level the sump pump automatically draws up the water to the level of the house sewer. Fig. 13-4 illustrates the use of a sump pump.

Storm Drain. Outside drain pipes (leaders) should *not* be connected to the house drain or sewer. Water run-off in some cities may be connected into a storm drain sys-

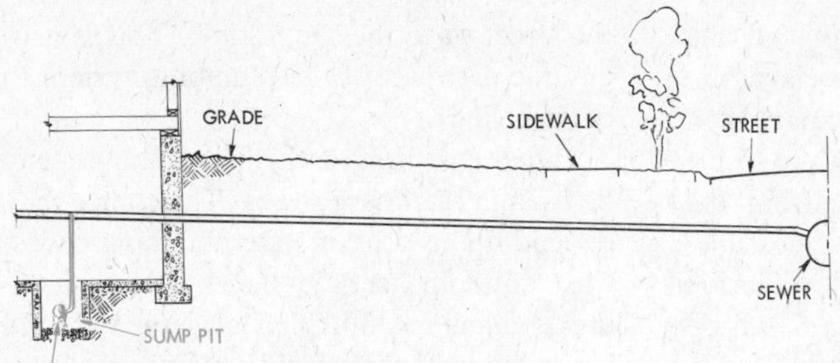

Fig. 13-4. A sump pump may be used to raise the waste water up to the house sewer.

tem. If there is no storm drain, a natural drainage basin or dry well may be used. The water from the footing drain tile is sometimes carried into the storm drain. In all cases, consult the local plumbing or building code.

Venting

Venting is needed to equalize the pressure within a drainage system. Equalization of pressure prevents trap loss, back pressure, and retardation of flow. Venting also serves to remove gas and unpleasant odors from the system. Fig. 13-2 illustrates a venting system.

Vent Stacks. The vent stack is a continuation of the soil and waste stack *above* the highest branch intersection with the waste stack. Its sole purpose is to permit air to enter and circulate in the soil and waste lines. The vent stack should extend at least 8″ above the roof. This dimension may vary depending upon the local code. The *main vent* begins at the base of the soil and waste stack, its purpose is to relieve any back pressure in the system. It joins the vent stack at least 3′ above the highest installed fixture branch. The diameter of the vent stack is usually one-half the diameter of the soil and waste stack.

Branch Vents. Each fixture branch must be vented by a branch vent. This serves in a capacity similar to the large vent stack. Waste matter flowing through the fixture branches must not be allowed to clog the branch vents. This may be prevented by attaching the vent as shown in Figs. 13-2 and 13-5. The inside diameter of the branch vent should not be less than 1¼″.

Fresh Air Inlet. Since the house trap acts as a seal preventing the back-up of sewer gases from the street, it also prevents the outlet of air or gases. A fresh air inlet or pipe is placed adjacent to the house trap to serve as an escape and avoid the compression of gases. This inlet also allows air to enter the system if necessary. The inside diameter of the fresh air inlet should not be less than 2″. A 4″ pipe is recommended.

Sewage Disposal

In most cities sewer service is provided.

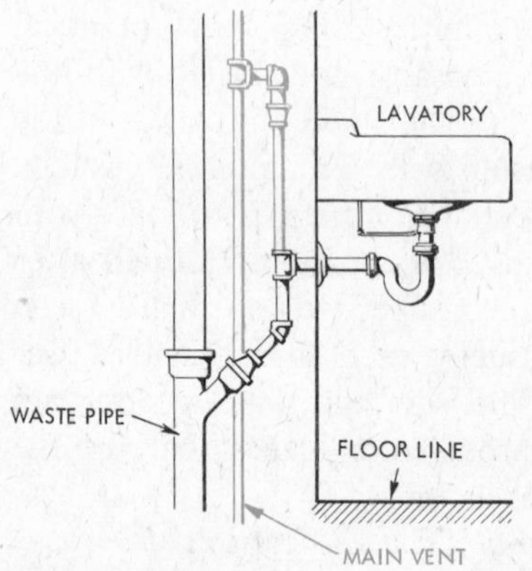

Fig. 13-5. Fixture venting is necessary to prevent the loss of the water seal.

Frequently, however, in newly developed areas the city sewer lines have not kept up with the unusual growth. In city locations and in country and suburban areas where sewers are not available, house sewerage is disposed by means of a cesspool or septic tank.

Leaching Cesspool. The leaching cesspool is essentially a cylindrical hole in the ground lined around the outer surface with

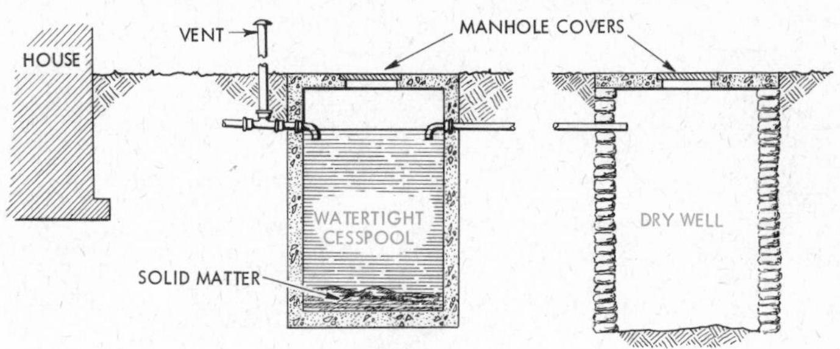

Fig. 13-6. The watertight cesspool has a distinct advantage over the leaching type in that the solid matter is not allowed to pass into the surrounding earth.

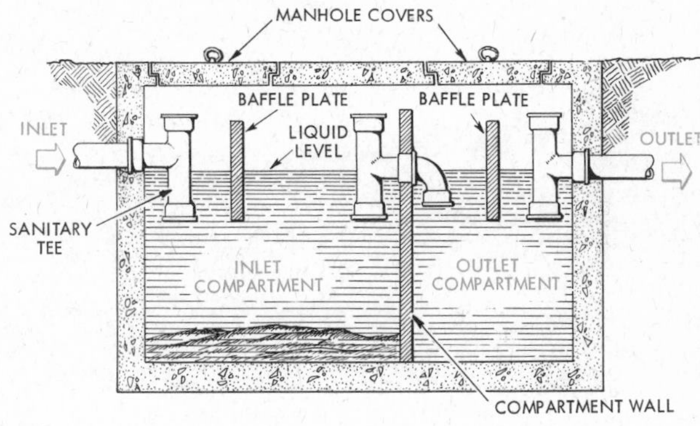

Fig. 13.7. Double Compartment Septic Tank. This system prevents pollution.

bricks, stones, or cement blocks with unfilled joints. The diameter of the cesspool is between 6′-0″ to 8′-0″; it is approximately 10′-0″ deep. The top of the cesspool should be close to the surface of the grade. Sewage is drained into the cesspool and is allowed to gradually seep into the surrounding soil. The solid matter is retained. If the cesspool is located too far below the grade or in hard earth, the drainage is inhibited. One of the problems with this method of sewage disposal is that the immediate area surrounding the cesspool may become contaminated, thereby poluting wells in the area. The leaching cesspool should only be used in loose or sandy soil. It should *not* be used in coarse gravel or fissured rock as contamination may extend for great distances.

Watertight Cesspool. This particular type of cesspool has a distinct advantage over the leaching cesspool in that the waste material is retained in the watertight compartment. Often a watertight cesspool is connected with a dry well. See Fig. 13-6. The watertight cell may be poured concrete, or brick or block parged on the interior with waterproof cement. A metal prefabricated tank may also be used. Sewage drains into the waterproof cell and fills until the liquid reaches the overflow pipe. The overflow liquid then runs into the dry well. The material that accumulates in the watertight unit need not be cleaned so frequently. (Caution must be exercised in cleaning a watertight cesspool as there will be little free oxygen, also the gases formed may be both explosive and poisonous.)

Rain run-off from roofs should not be

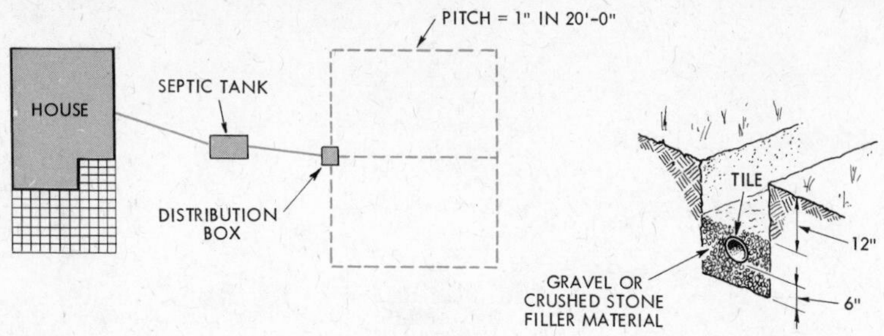

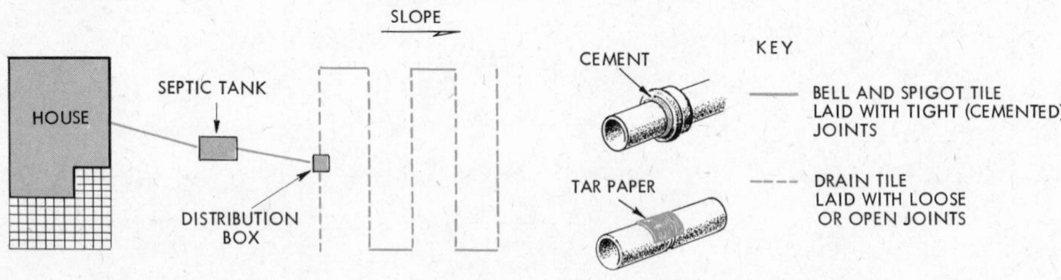

Fig. 13.8. This figure illustrates septic tank disposal systems for sites having level and sloping topography.

TABLE 13-1

MINIMUM SEPTIC TANK CAPACITIES

NUMBER OF BEDROOMS	LIQUID CAPACITY BELOW OUTLET
2 OR LESS	750 GAL.
3	900 GAL.
4	1000 GAL.
EACH ADDITIONAL BEDROOM, ADD	250 GAL.

permitted to flow into the cesspool since this may cause excessive overflow. All cesspools must be vented with a 4″ pipe to prevent the build-up of gas pressure. The watertight cesspool (by itself) can be placed as close as 30 ft. to a well or water-tight cistern.

Septic Tank. The septic tank serves four basic functions: (1) it holds the sewage, (2) effects decomposition of waste matter, (3) retains any solids that have not been dissolved, and (4) permits the liquid overflow to drain into a distribution (purification) field. Disintegration in the septic tank itself takes place by the action of anaerobic bacteria on the waste. This chemical action takes place only in the absence of oxygen. After this initial purification, the liquid flows into the distribution system for further purification. In the purification field, chemical action takes place as the liquid overflow comes in contact with the air contained in the upper layers of soil. The oxygen and aerobic bacteria work together

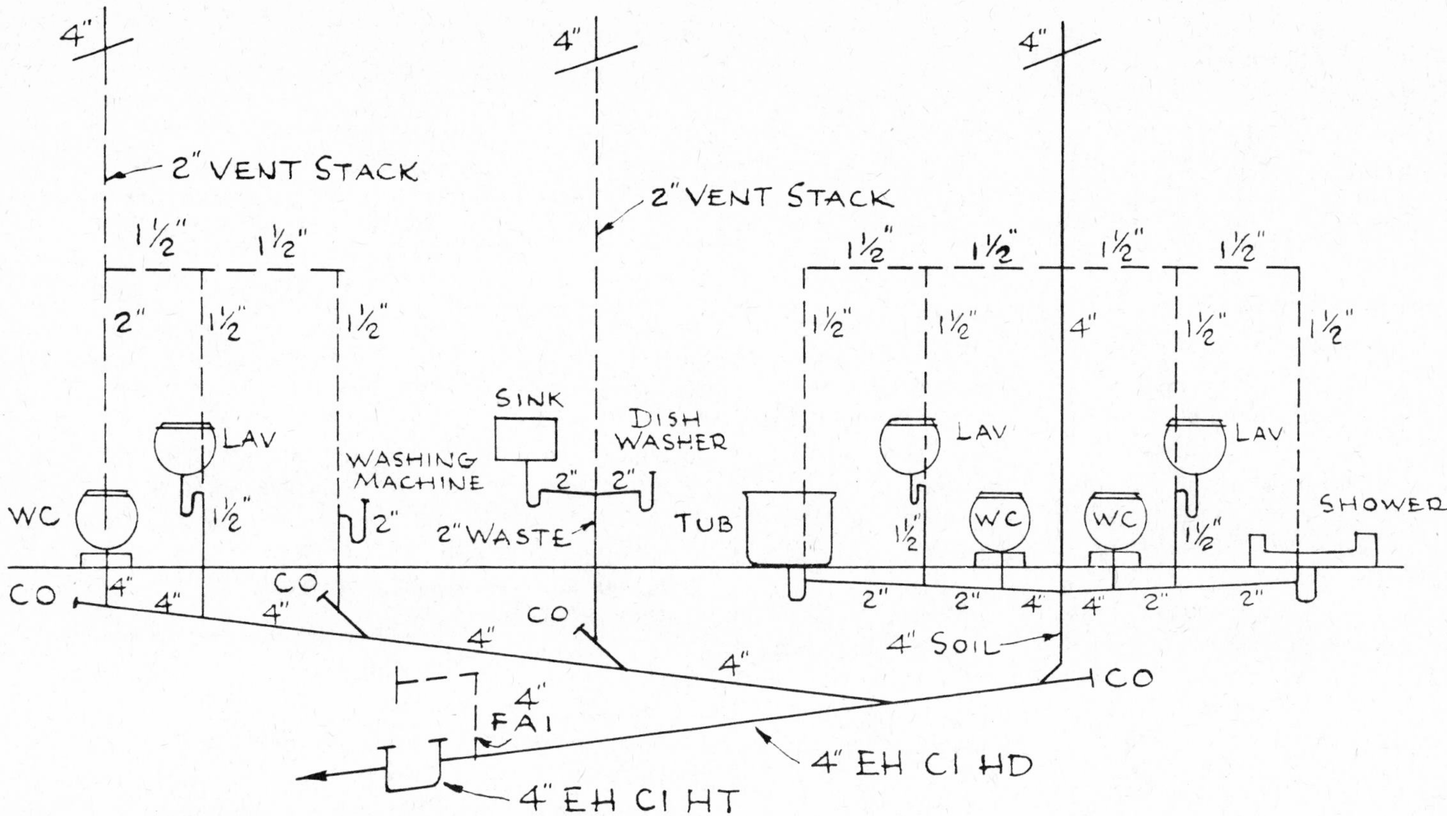

Fig. 13-9. A plumbing diagram is sometimes included in the working drawings.

to transform waste material into harmless chemical compounds.

The advantage of the septic tank over the cesspool is that it does not permit polluted waste to enter the soil. The septic tank holds the sewage (see Fig. 13-7) for a sufficient time to allow the solid waste material to become diluted. Any solids that do not completely dissolve are retained as sludge. The overflow liquid then drains into a distribution system, located 12″ below grade. This consists of 4″ field tile laid with loose joints. To prevent each joint from becoming clogged with dirt, a strip of tar paper is placed over each joint. Each joint allows the liquid to be drained into the soil and filtered. The purification and leaching field should consist of 150′ to 200′ of tile for adequate dispersion. On flat land the tile has a slope of 1″ per 20′. Fig. 13-8 shows typical distribution fields associated with a septic tank.

The capacity of the septic tank is usually based on the number of bedrooms in the dwelling. Minimum capacities for septic tanks are given in Table 13-1. The capacities shown in this table are sufficient to accommodate fixtures and appliances including automatic washers, garbage disposers, and dishwashers. These tanks are normally prefabricated. They may be either concrete or metal.

Planning Points

In laying out a plumbing system, the practical considerations listed below should be taken into account. The designer should *always* follow the local plumbing code. What is standard in one section of the country may be restricted or forbidden in another section.

1. Water supply piping should be as direct as possible (with few offsets) to avoid friction which may cause "hammering" and retard the flow.
2. Hot and cold water pipes should be at least ½ ft. apart to prevent heat transfer. If they are closer than ½ ft., insulation is necessary.
3. Usually, as a rough rule, one set of *stacks* (one soil and one vent) is required for each set of *risers* (hot and cold water pipes).
4. Use 2″ x 6″ studs in the partitions which house the soil pipe.
5. The hot water heater should be as close as possible to the area of main usage (usually the kitchen). Keep hot water pipe runs as short as possible to avoid excessive heat loss.
6. A cleanout (CO) should be located at each change in direction of the drainage system.
7. Underground piping should be below the frost line to avoid freezing. If the piping is above the frost line, insulation may be necessary.

Plumbing and Working Drawings

The location of *all* plumbing fixtures is shown on *all* floor plans that contain those fixtures. The *basement plan* would show (if these items were to be included in the house) the water heater, exterior hose bibs, stationary tubs, bibs for automatic washer, lavatory, water closet, sump pump, and floor drains. The *first floor plan* would show the kitchen sink, dishwasher, water closet(s), lavatories, tub, shower, and frost-proof hose bibs. The *garage area,* if attached, would show a bib for automatic washer, and the floor drain. The *second floor* would show the lavatories, water closet, tub, and shower. Location of fixtures is usually all that is necessary since the plumbing contractor knows the local plumbing code and can install the piping and fixtures correctly.

In some instances the plan will show the runs of hot, cold and soft water pipes and, if used, the gas lines. These will be shown by coded single or broken lines representing each pipe run. Pipe sizes should be called out. Occasionally a section is taken through a specific portion of the house to show a particular plumbing installation (for example, pipes, valves, or elevation of fixtures). This, however, is not a common practice. A plumbing diagram, such as that shown in Fig. 13-9, is sometimes included in the working drawings.

If a septic tank or cesspool is the means of sewage disposal, a single line representation of the disposal system is included in the working drawings. The lot line, house, septic tank, drainage field, or cesspool are shown in outline only. The only dimensions that are necessary are the location dimension of the septic tank or cesspool, the outline dimensions of the drainage field, and the capacity of the septic tank. The septic tank or cesspool is also sometimes shown on the plot plan. If a lawn sprinkler system is installed, this may also be shown on the plot plan.

Questions and Problems

1. What are the disadvantages of selecting a rocky site in regard to problems of non-public sewage disposal?
2. Why must the sewer and house drain be pitched? What pitches must be maintained for each of these lines?
3. Is it necessary to prepare a piping diagram for the water supply or sewage disposal system for the average single family dwelling?
4. What purpose does the water seal serve in the house trap and in the traps below plumbing fixtures?
5. How many advantages could you specify for selecting a septic tank for a lot that is not served by municipal

sewage disposal in comparison with a leaching type cesspool?

6. Why must tar paper, or other suitable material be placed over the loose joints of field tile in the leaching system?
7. Why is the house trap the same diameter as the house drain?
8. Why should sanitary or water pipes not be placed on an outside wall?
9. Could a soil or waste stack be placed in a "horizontal" position?
10. Why should the designer be aware of the probable placement of vent stacks?
11. Draw a plot plan showing the septic system for a two-story, three bedroom home with two baths and a basement. Draw a basement plan showing the drainage system.
12. Draw a plumbing diagram for the two-story home laid out in the problem above (Problem 11).

WESTERN PENNSYLVANIA CONSERVANCY.
PHOTO BY JERRY DAVIS.

Frank Lloyd Wright's "Falling Water" home for Edgar Kaufman, Bear Run, Pennsylvania, illustrates the basic principles of perspective by its receding lines.

Perspective 14

Perspective drawings serve many purposes for the architectural designer. They may be used: (1) to illustrate alternate design principles, (2) to illustrate the proposed structure for a client, and (3) as a basic foundation in sketching. Within the broad field of graphics the area of perspective drawing offers perhaps the most varied means for arriving at the desired end. Through the years many books have been authored on the science of perspective. Each author has developed a slightly different innovation which has led to a host of methods. This examination attempts to present a practical application of perspective as it is useful to the drafting student. (Texts which give a more exhaustive study of the theory and physiological principles of perspective are listed in Appendix D at the end of the book.)

In this chapter, the three types of perspective drawing are discussed: parallel or one-point, angular or two-point, and oblique or three-point. Common drawing methods for parallel and angular perspective are discussed in detail with step-by-step drawing guides. The latter portion of this chapter is devoted to rendering, that is, "dressing the perspective."

Perspective

The study and observation of the phenomena of perspective dates back far into history. The *science* of perspective (and it is a science) as we know and understand it today, goes back 250 years. Some of the laws of perspective were realized even a century earlier. Prior to this time, man groped, most often in an unrealistic manner, to achieve a natural appearance in his drawings. Evidence of this is shown in the two dimensional art forms that remain from the Greco-Roman period. Man's earliest attempts to communicate graphically are represented by the engravings found on bones and by the drawings and paintings found on cave walls of the Late or Upper Paleolithic period (35,000 to 15,000 years ago). These "Ice Age" paintings are the earliest known examples of perspective realism. At this time, of course, no systematic knowledge existed of the laws of perspective.

The desire to draw a three dimensional shape in its approximate true representation is as old as man himself.

Perspective drawings give the most natural appearance of any type of graphic description. If a photograph and a perspective drawing is made (from the same position and angle) of the same object and com-

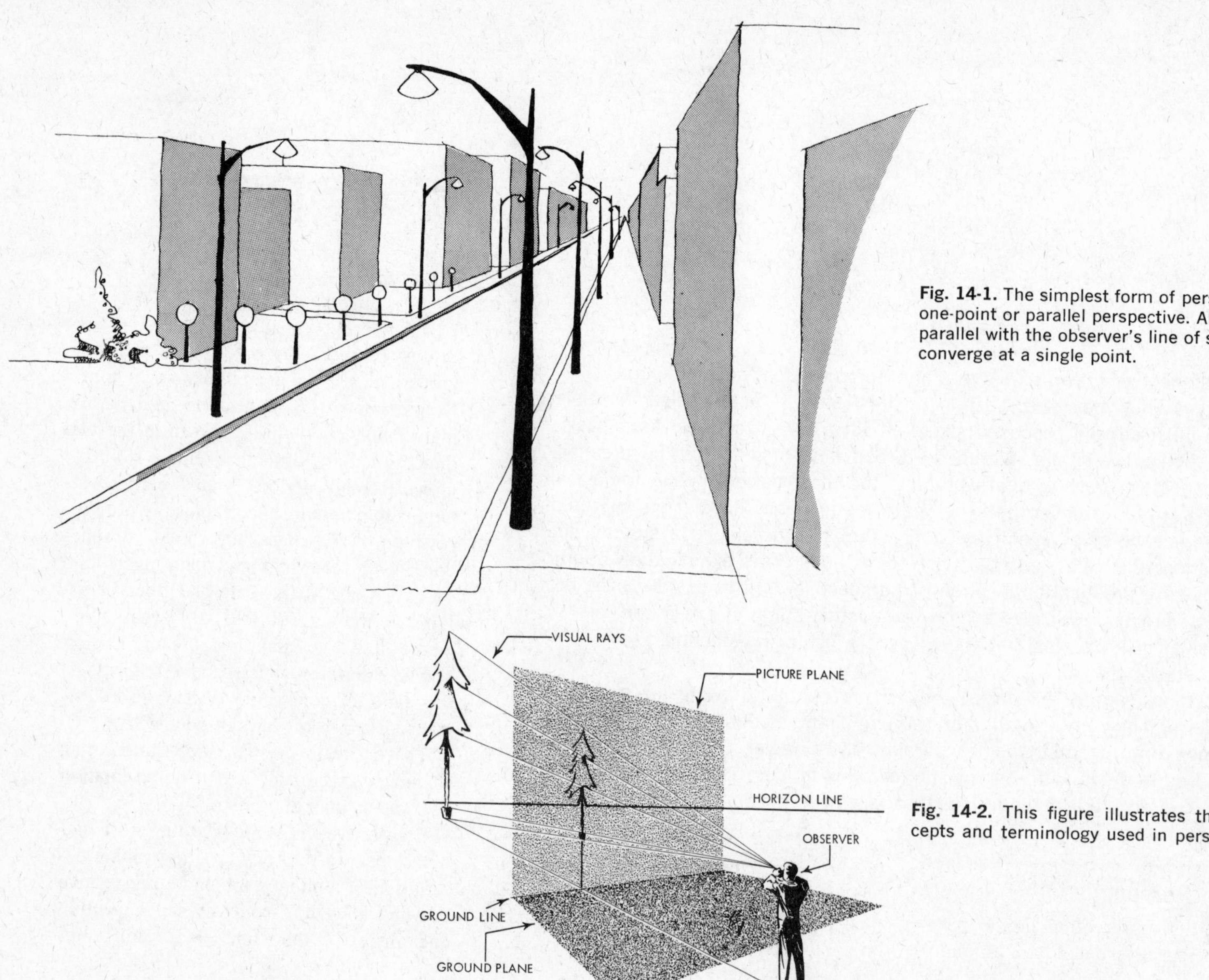

Fig. 14-1. The simplest form of perspective is the one-point or parallel perspective. All lines parallel with the observer's line of sight converge at a single point.

Fig. 14-2. This figure illustrates the basic concepts and terminology used in perspective.

pared, the photo and drawing will be essentially the same. A correctly constructed perspective drawing will represent a true "picture" of the object.

If you stand on the sidewalk (as in Fig. 14-1) and look into the distance, the street lamps, sidewalk, street, and curb converge at a single point. This example illustrates the basic theory of perspective: all parallel lines which extend away from the observer will converge at a common distant point. This simple type of perspective drawing is called a one-point or *parallel perspective*. Before we can go any further, however, some terminology universal to all forms of perspective must be understood.

In perspective drawing, the observer assumes he is viewing all objects through a transparent *picture plane* (an imaginary plane) upon which the object is projected. (See Fig. 14-2 for an illustration of this concept and others given below.) The point from which the observer sights is called the *station point* and the plane on which he stands (and on which the object rests) is the *ground plane*. The intersection of the picture plane and the ground plane is called the *ground line*. The lines which extend from the viewer's eye to the object are the *visual rays* or *lines of sight*. Each perspective drawing contains a *horizon line:* this is a real or an imaginary line in the distance at *the eye level of the viewer*. The *vanishing points* are the points on the horizon line where the lines of the object meet. A perspective drawing gives a view as seen from only *one* station point (eye view).

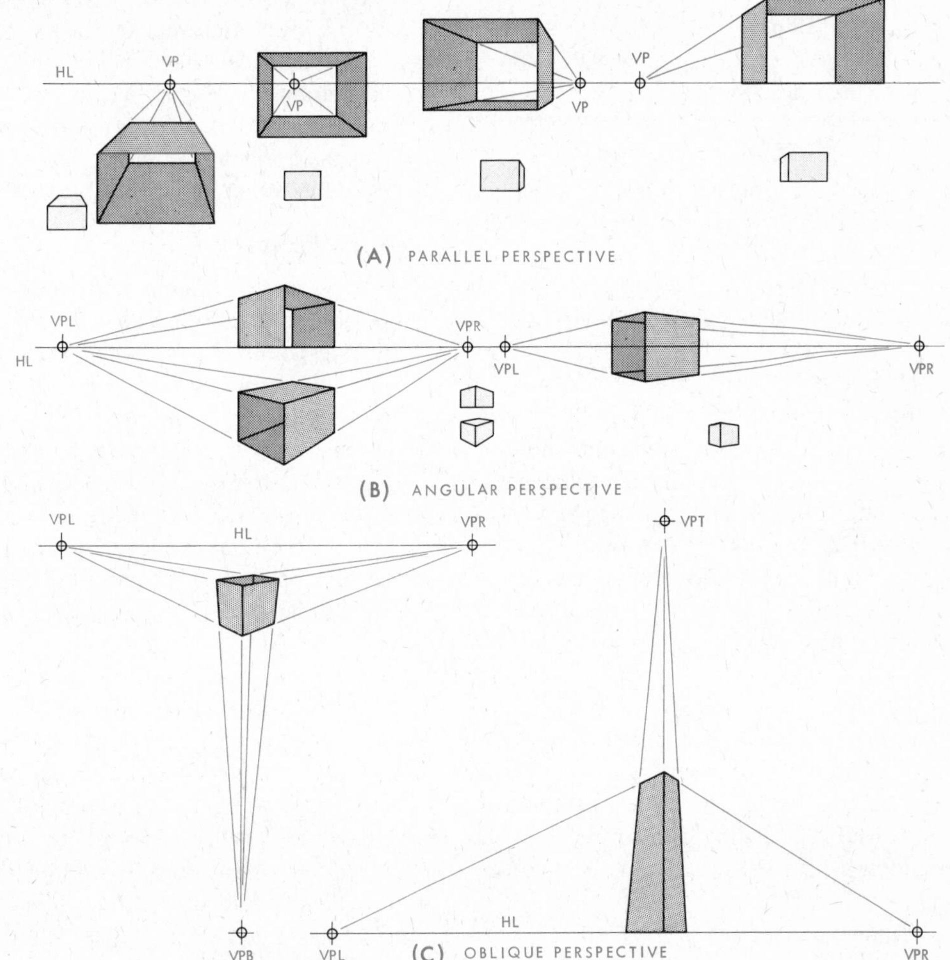

Fig. 14-3. These three categories of perspective show how the object lines converge at the vanishing point(s).

The following abbreviations are commonly used in discussing perspective:

Station Point	(SP)
Ground Plane	(GP)
Ground Line	(GL)
Picture Plane	(PP)

Horizon Line	(HL)
Vanishing Point	(VP)
Vanishing Point Left	(VPL)
Vanishing Point Right	(VPR)

Perspective Types

Perspective drawings may be classified into three categories: (1) *parallel* or one-point, (2) *angular* or two-point, and (3) *oblique* or three-point. Each type may be used to a particular advantage.

Parallel Perspective

Fig. 14-3 (top) illustrates parallel or one-point perspective. As its name implies, it has only one vanishing point. To achieve this characteristic, *two* of the principal axes of the object must be parallel to the picture plane, while the third is perpendicular to the picture plane. The axes of an object are width (horizontal), height (vertical), and depth (receding). Another way of describing parallel perspective is to say that the picture plane is parallel to one of the *faces* of the object. One-point perspectives are particularly suited for interiors showing three walls, the ceiling, and/or the floor (depending where the eye level is located).

Angular Perspective

Angular or two-point perspective has two vanishing points (Fig. 14-3, center). Note that only *one* axis (vertical) is parallel to the picture plane. The other two axes are at an angle to the picture plane. The angular perspective is highly adaptive to any type of object for any situation. Architecturally, the angular perspective may be used to describe exteriors and interiors of structures, as well as any detail for a presentation or display drawing. Depending on the nature of the object (solid or open) and the position of the horizon line, either two or three faces of the object may be visible.

Oblique Perspective

Oblique or three-point perspective (Fig. 14-3, bottom) has, as its name implies, three vanishing points. *No* principal axis is parallel to the picture plane: all three principal axes are at an angle. Theoretically this is the most correct type of perspective when the object is *placed above* or *below* the horizon line. As we view any object that is placed below or above our eye level (horizon line), either the top or the bottom of the object is closer to the eye. It should, therefore, be larger.

Three point perspective can best be illustrated by standing on the top of a high building and viewing an adjacent, lower building. The top of that building will appear to vanish to a point at the right and a point to the left. Also the vertical sides of the building will appear to converge to a point below. The same phenomena will be evident in reverse if the same tall building is viewed from the sidewalk. The use of three-point perspective is *usually* limited to aerial views of buildings. It is seldom used in residential renderings.

Picture Plane and Station Point

The general shape of the object drawn in perspective can be changed by moving the picture plane and changing the station point. In most instances for the sake of convenience, the designer, draftsman, or illustrator will place the picture plane between the object and the station point. (The object or objects may be placed in front of the picture plane but this poses additional manipulation of the visual rays.) When the object is in its usual position (immediately behind the picture plane), the perspective drawing is smaller than its actual size in the plan and elevation views. As the picture plane is moved farther away from the object, i.e., closer to the station point, the perspective becomes smaller. This is easily illustrated by forming a frame with the index fingers and thumbs (Fig. 14-4). Simply move the hands closer to and farther away from any object. You will observe that the object appears larger within the rectangle as the rectangle is moved closer to the object. Conversely, it appears smaller as the rectangle is farther away from the object.

To achieve the least amount of distortion in a perspective, the station point should be located at such a distance from the object that the visual rays will *include* the object and form an angle *not greater* than 30°. This angle (frequently called the *clear angle of vision*) will insure the elimination of distortion.

Fig. 14-5 shows the same object drawn from three different station points. The station point has been kept at the same elevation and in the same line with the object. However, its distance from the object has

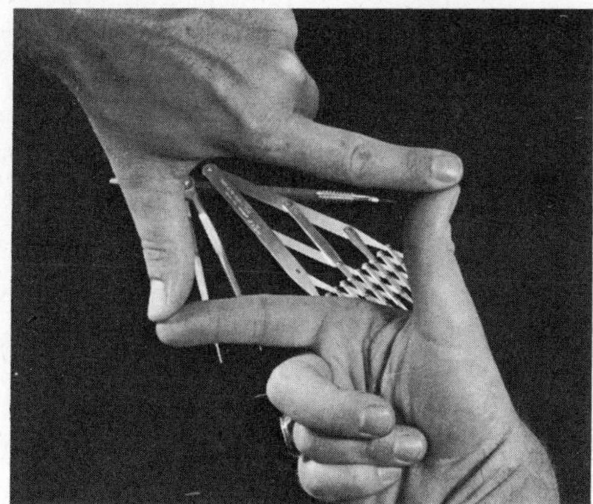

PHOTO: ALLAN STAMBERG.

Fig. 14-4. The principle of the picture plane may be simply demonstrated by forming a frame with the hands and moving it closer to and further away from the object.

been varied. As the station point has been moved closer to the object (as in position 1) the perspective drawing appears to be distorted. By taking a 30°-60° triangle and placing the 30° angle at the station point, note that the object is *not completely included* by the triangle's sides. In position 2 the station point is located properly so that the sides of the triangle just touch the extreme corners of the object. From this vantage point the distortion has been eliminated. Position 3 shows the cone of vision including *more* than the object. Here again, there is no distortion.

By placing the station point nearer to the picture plane the vanishing points are forced closer together and thus contribute to increased distortion. Placing the station point at the minimum distance, so the object is

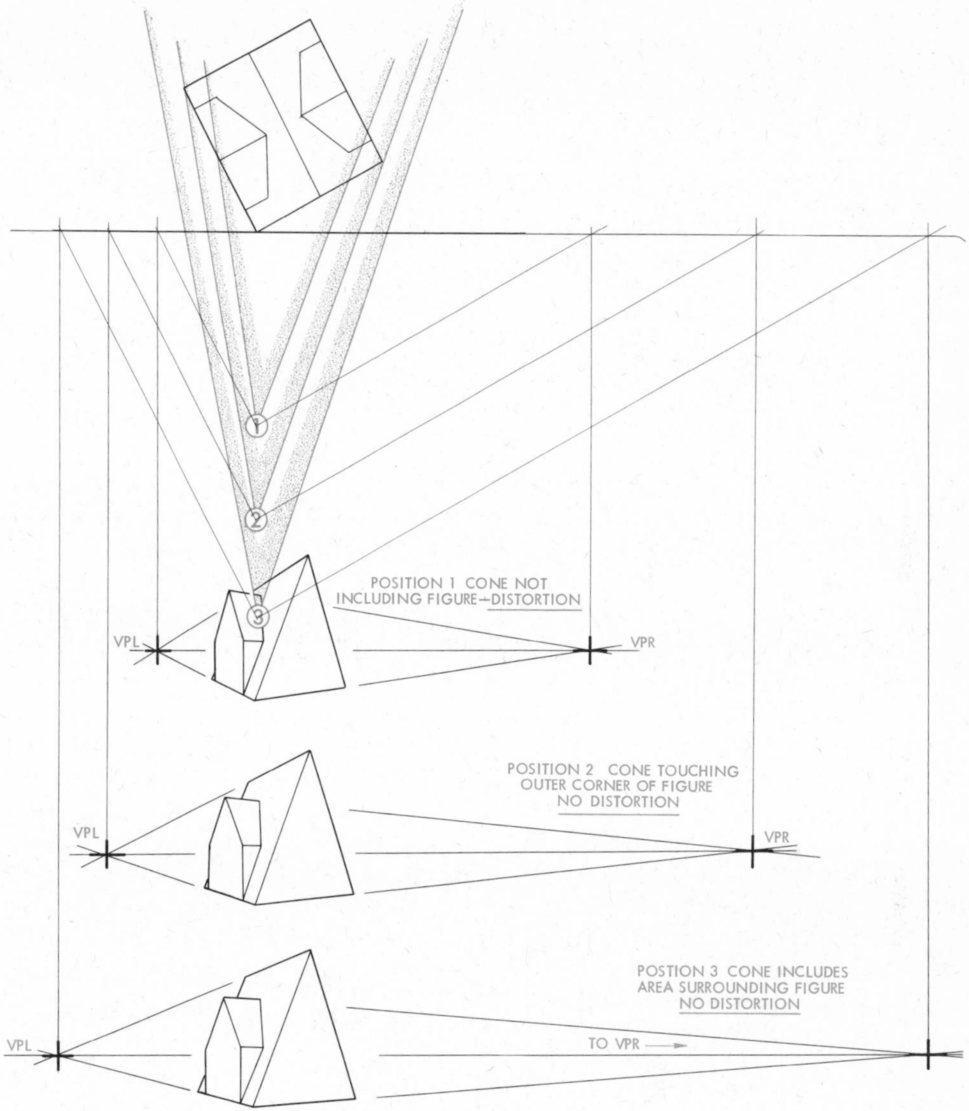

Fig. 14-5. This comparison of three perspectives shows the effects of the cone of vision.

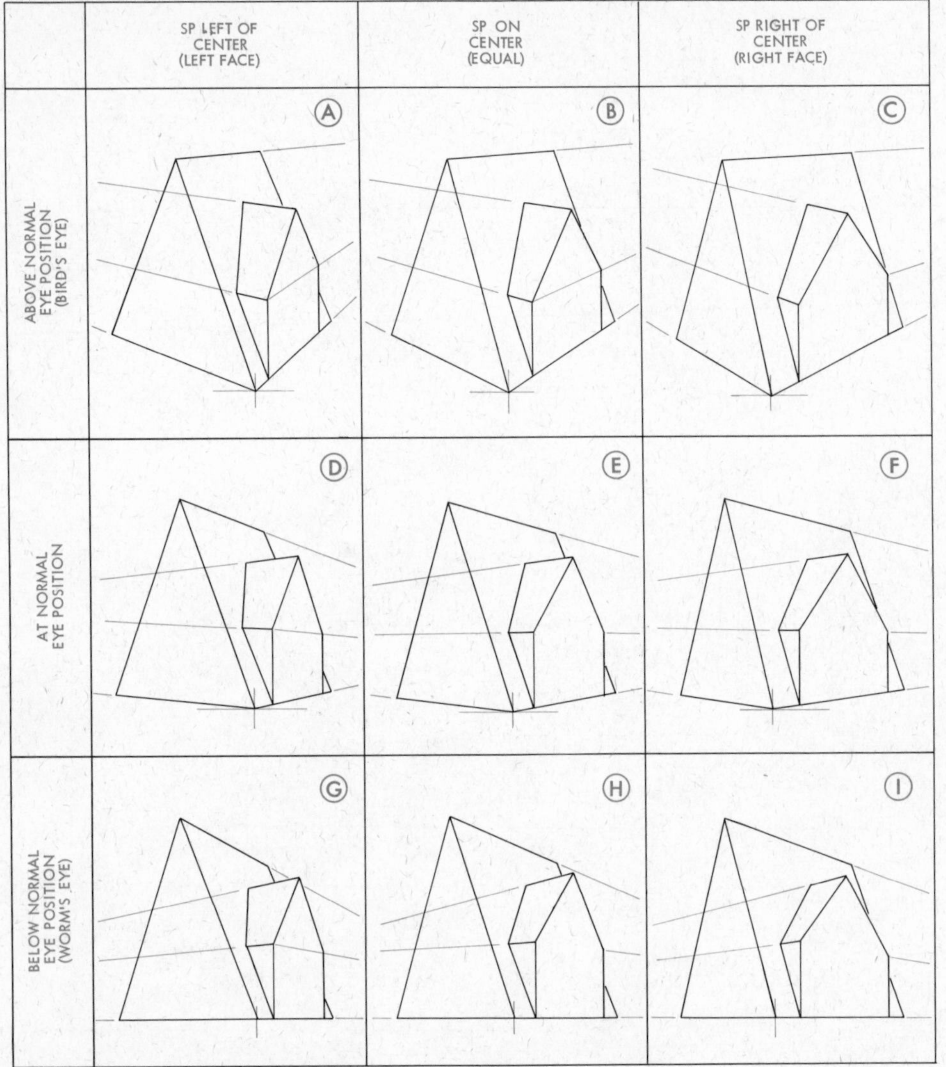

Fig. 14-6. Changing the vantage point changes the face of an object.

included by the 30° angle, will prove the best rule of thumb. There are occasions when the station point may be moved closer to purposely change or draw attention to a particular feature. A more complete discussion of this matter is presented in Morgan's *Architectural Drawing: Perspective, Light and Shadow, Rendering.*[1]

The station point may be moved to the left or right or up or down to achieve emphasis on a particular face or faces. Fig. 14-6 illustrates the effect of different station points. Observe the different effects that can be achieved.

Perspective Drawing

Each of the following types of perspective drawings are explained in a step-by-step procedure. Where plans and elevations are needed for drawing perspectives, it is suggested that a print of the plan and elevation be made so that a redrawing of these views is eliminated.

Parallel Perspective: Plan View Method

The *plan view method* of drawing a parallel perspective is one of several procedures currently used. In the architectural field the plan view method has proved the most successful for the beginning student. The following step-by-step procedure illustrates, along with Fig. 14-7, the plan view method of drawing a one-point perspective.

Step 1. Draw the top edge view of the

1. Sherley W. Morgan, *Architectural Drawing: Perspective, Light, and Shadow, Rendering* (New York: McGraw-Hill Book Company, Inc., 1950).

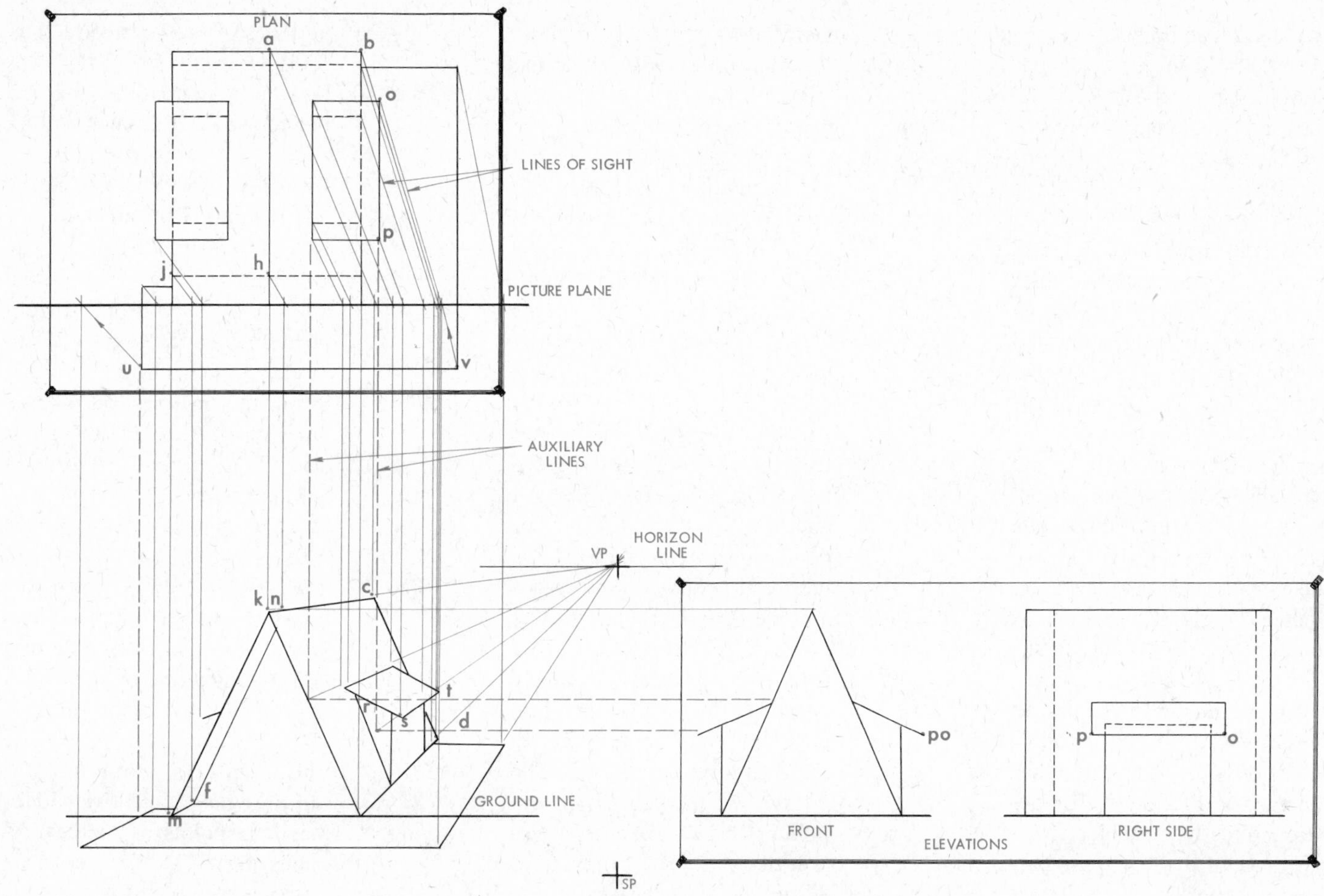

Fig. 14-7. The plan view method of drawing a parallel perspective is one of the most common.

picture plane (PP) near the top of sheet of detail paper. Cut out the plan and elevation views from a print. Tape the plan view along the horizontal PP line. The front edge of the object does not have to touch the PP. However, by placing it so that it does touch, it will reduce the number of points that must be carried to the station point (SP).

Step 2. Draw the horizon line (HL) below the plan view. The location of the HL is determined by the vantage point of the observer. If the object is to be viewed *below* the eye level, place the HL immediately below the plan view. If the object is *above* eye level, move the HL farther down.

Step 3. Draw the horizontal ground line (GL). The position of the ground line depends upon how far above or below the horizon line the object will be placed. Since all plans are in scale (¼″ = 1′-0″, for example) the distance between the HL and GL will be in the same scale. Tape the elevation view to one side of the perspective. Locate the elevation base *on* the GL.

Step 4. Locate the SP. To eliminate as much distortion as possible, *place the SP not closer than two times the width (length) of the object from the nearest point on the plan view.* The SP may be located at any position directly in center front, left or right. Unless some particular condition exists, it is perhaps most advisable to place the SP either to the left or right of center. Remember: the visual cone must include the object and the angle must not be *greater* than 30°.

Step 5. Locate the vanishing point (VP). Draw a vertical line from the SP to the HL. This intersection with the HL forms the VP.

Step 6. Project the width of the object from the plan view to the ground line.

Step 7. Draw the front face of the object. This will be true size and shape since the front is touching the PP.

Step 8. Project perspective depth of the object. Carry all visible edges from the front face to the VP. From the SP draw lines to the rear corners of the object in the plan view, points *a* and *b*. (See Fig. 14-7.) The points that are formed by the intersection of the lines of sight and the PP are the perspective *depths* of each feature viewed from that particular vantage point. Draw projectors from these points of intersection to the lines carried to the VP. The intersection of these lines form points *c* and *d*—the perspective length of these two visible edges.

Step 9. Draw recessed face. The only visible portion of the recessed front face is along the left and bottom. To locate this portion, as in Step #8, draw lines of sight from *h* and *j* to the SP. Where these intersect with the PP, drop projectors to the *k* VP and *m* VP respectively, thus forming points *n* and *f*.

Step 10. Locate those features that do not touch the PP, such as line *po*. To find the correct perspective of *po,* extend this line to the PP and drop an auxiliary line to the perspective. Project *po* from the *elevation* to the projection of *po* dropped from the PP, forming point *r*. Connect *r* to VP. Drop projectors from the intersection of the lines of sight (to *p* and *o*) and the PP to the *r* VP, forming points *s* and *t*.

Step 11. Add in remaining detail behind PP.

Step 12. Locate and draw any detail in front of the PP. Since points *u* and *v* appear in front of the PP, extend a line of sight from the SP through the points to the PP. Drop a projector from this intersection (on the PP) down to the perspective and locate the points as in the previous steps.

Angular Perspective: Office Method

Perhaps the best "teacher" of angular perspective is the *office method.* The following step-by-step procedure illustrates, along with Fig. 14-8, the office method of drawing a two-point perspective.

Step 1. Draw the edge view of the PP near the top of the paper.

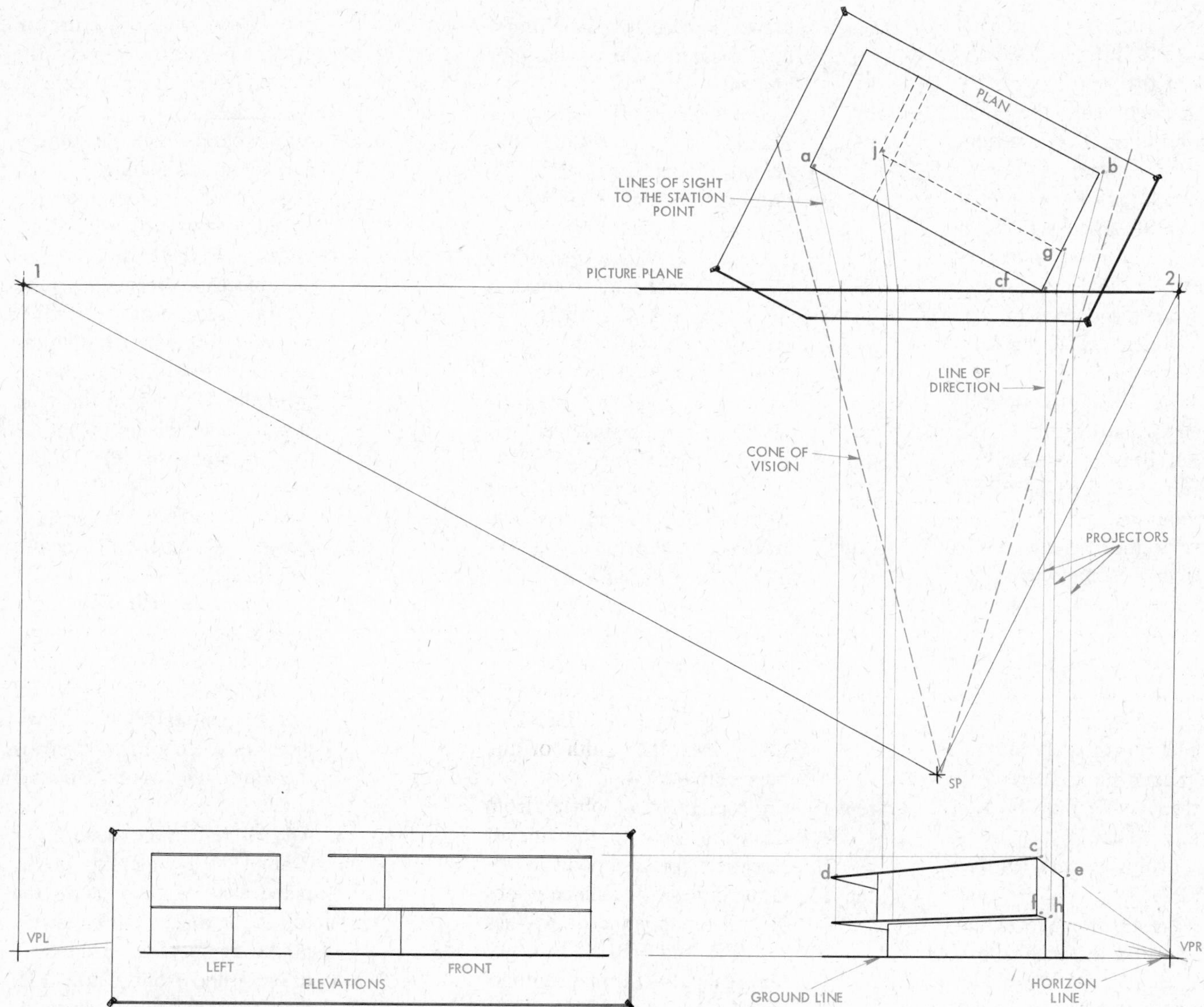

Fig. 14-8. Angular or two-point perspective is possibly the most used form of perspective.

Step 2. Orient the print of the plan view along the PP. Determine which face (s) of the object needs to be emphasized. Tape the print in this position. For drafting ease, allow a corner of the object to touch the PP.

Step 3. Locate the SP. The SP may be located at any position to the left, right, or "on" a line projected from the corner of the object. This is called the *line of direction* or *line of measure*. In this case (Fig. 14-8) the SP has been located to the left of the corner. Remember: the distance from the SP to the PP is the viewing distance (in scale) and the extreme corners (points *a* and *b*) of the object must be contained by the 30° cone of clear vision.

Step 4. Draw lines from the SP to the PP parallel to the sides of the object on the plan view. This forms the vanishing points in the PP (points 1 and 2).

Step 5. Draw the GL. It may be located below the SP (as illustrated) or midway between the SP and PP.

Step 6. Locate the HL or eye level line at the desired distance above the GL. (Fig. 14-6 shows the results of the movement of the eye level above and below the normal position.) The distance between these two lines must be the same scale as the plan and elevation. Normal viewing would place the HL 5′-6″ above the GL. In this illustration the HL is coincident with the ground line, thus resulting in a worm's eye view.

Step 7. Tape the elevation prints on the GL. These may be located on either side of where the perspective will be drawn. From these elevation views the various heights will be projected to the perspective.

Step 8. Locate the vanishing point left (VPL) and the vanishing point right (VPR). Drop verticals from points 1 and 2 to the HL. This gives VPL and VPR.

Step 9. Draw lines of sight from SP to exterior corners *a* and *b* in the plan view. Where the lines of sight pierce the PP, drop verticals to the ground line. This determines the width of the perspective view.

Step 10. Project height of object from elevation view to the line of direction, forming point *c*.

Step 11. Draw in basic box shape of object. From point *c* draw lines to VPR and VPL. The basic "box shape" is formed at points *d* and *e* where these lines have intersected with the first two projectors (from *a* and *b* in the plan view) that were drawn. These lines now represent the correct length *in perspective* of these edges.

Step 12. Add in basic detail. The undercut that appears along the front edge of the object may be added in next. Project height of undercut to the front corner of the object in perspective, point *f*. Draw a line from *f* to VPR. Next determine the depth of the undercut by drawing a line from the SP to *g* in the plan view. Where the line from SP to *g* intersects the PP, drop a projector to *f* VPR. This gives the depth (point *h*) in perspective of the undercut. Because the undercut is visible, draw a line from *h* to VPL. The length of this line is obtaned in the same way as line *fg*. Draw a line of sight from SP to *j*. Where this pierces the PP, drop a projector to line *h* VPL. This gives the width (length) of the undercut.

Step 13. Add in remaining detail. For example, the underside of the plane that extends along the top of the object will be visible in the perspective. Therefore, draw a line from *d* to VPR. Similarly, the point immediately below point *d* is carried to VPR. Determining what is vis-

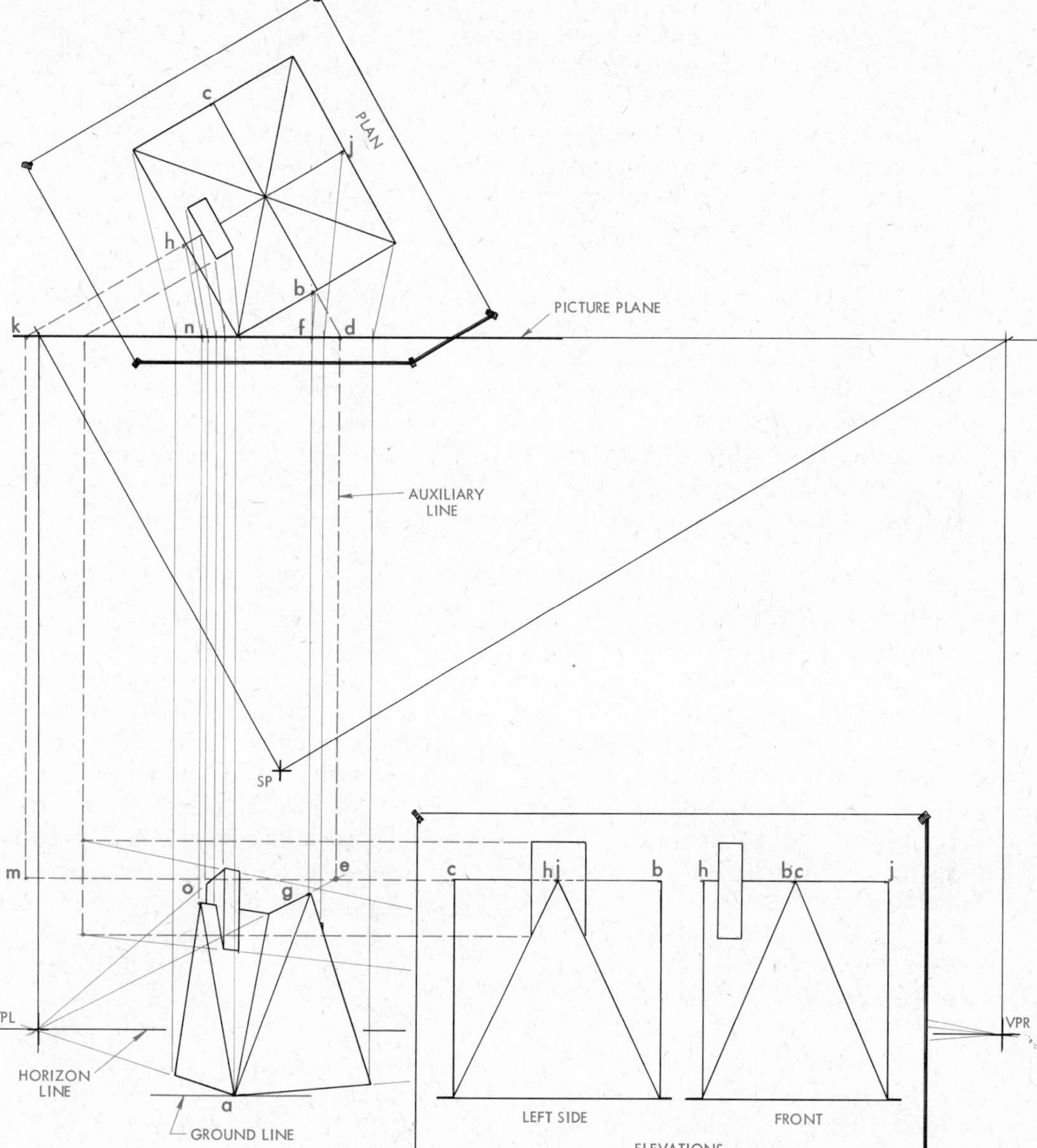

Fig. 14-9. An angular perspective of an object that has no edges touching the picture plane presents special problems.

ible in the perspective drawing primarily is a matter of projecting and drawing the correct lines and points. However, one's ability to perceive the object as it is viewed from the SP is almost as important. This will grow as more experience is gained with perspectives.

Angular Perspective: Recessed Objects

All objects do not assume a basic, simple shape as shown in Fig. 14-8. The measurements in this perspective were derived wholly or in part from heights projected from the elevations *to the corner* (located in the picture plane and on the line of direction) and from the plan view. Any height dimension that touches the picture plane will be shown in the perspective or picture plane *fundamentally* (that is, in true size) and may be used to derive other measurements, such as lines *ce, fh, cd,* etc., in Fig. 14-8. Many objects, however, are composed of lines that do not touch the picture plane. If a perspective can be drawn of any line, then a perspective may be drawn of any object regardless of its complexity or position behind the picture plane.

As the object in Fig. 14-9 is viewed, *no* height dimensions touch the picture plane. To obtain these heights their terminal points must be *extended* to the picture plane. The following is an outline of the procedure that is used (see Fig. 14-9) for finding the spatial position of lines which do not touch the picture plane.

Step 1. Draw PP.
Step 2. Orient print of plan view and tape in place.
Step 3. Locate SP relative to the 30° cone of clear vision.
Step 4. Draw lines from SP to PP parallel to sides of plan.
Step 5. Draw GL.
Step 6. Locate and draw HL.
Step 7. Tape print of elevations on GL.
Step 8. Locate VP's on the HL.
Step 9. Draw lines of sight from SP to the exterior corners in the plan view and drop projectors from these points of intersection with the PP.
Step 10. From the corner that touches the PP, drop a vertical to the ground line, point *a*. Carry point *a* to VPL and VPR.
Step 11. Locate and draw those lines which do not touch the PP.

a. Find the piercing point of line *bc* with PP.
   1. Extend line *bc* in the plan view to the PP—forming point *d*.
   2. Drop an auxiliary line from point *d* to the perspective.
   3. Extend line *bc* from the elevations until it intersects with the auixiliary line dropped from point *d* in PP. This forms point *e*. Point *e* represents the piercing point of line *bc* as it is extended to the PP.

b. Locate the height of point *b* in the perspective.
   1. Connect piercing point *e* with VPL. This is a perspective view of a line of infinite length containing line *bc*.
   2. Draw a line of sight from SP to *b*. Where this line intersects with the PP (at point *f*) drop a projector to line *e* VPL.
   3. The intersection of the projector from *f* and *e* VPL (point *g*), represents the terminal point *b* of line *bc* in perspective. (The usual student comment at this time is: "But the height of the object in perspective is not the same as it is in the elevations." It must be remembered that point b is behind the PP and not touching it; therefore, it appears smaller in height since it is farther from the SP.)

c. Find the piercing point of line *hj* with the PP.
   1. Extend line *hj* in the plan view to the PP, forming point *k*.
   2. Drop an auxiliary line from point *k* to the perspective.
   3. Extend line *hj* from the elevations until it intersects with the auxiliary line dropped from *k* in the PP; this forms point *m*. This is the piercing point of *hj* extended to PP.

d. Locate the height of point *h* in the perspective.
   1. Connect piercing point *m* with VPR. This line is the perspective

Fig. 14-10. A T-square perspective rendered in pencil is a quick method of producing a presentation drawing.

view of a line containing *hj*.

2. Draw a line of sight from the SP to *h*. Point *n* represents the intersection of this visual ray with the PP. Drop a projector from *n* to line *m* VPR.
3. The intersection of projector *n* and line *m* VPR (point *o*) represents the end point *h* of line *hj*.

e. The height of the prismatic projection and its intersection with the inclined surface is obtained in the same manner as lines *hj* and *bc*.

Step 12. Complete the remainder of the perspective.

T-Square Perspective

The term "T-square perspective" is misleading since this type of delineation is in no sense of the word "a perspective." A T-square perspective may be referred to as a presentation or display drawing. In essence the T-square perspective is a simple *elevation,* showing only *two* of the three principal dimensions, that has been dressed up to produce the illusion of depth — the third dimension. An example of this type of work is shown in Fig. 14-10. Obviously this delineation is quick and simple. Its basic purpose is to enable the client to visualize the building before it is constructed. Some consideration must be given to the appearance created in the foreground so that the building looks as natural as possible in the setting.

The step-by-step procedure for making a T-square perspective is illustrated in Fig. 14-11. Usually a front elevation is used for this work. Sometimes, however, a rear or side view may be used if it has a particular feature which should be illustrated.

Step 1. Place a sheet of vellum over the front elevation and trace the complete elevation, using light lines.

Step 2. Locate sidewalks and driveway. Try several angles for these. The sidewalk should vanish to a point just as in a parallel perspective.

Step 3. Locate shrubs. Keep the bases of shrubs and trees away from the house by dropping their bases slightly below the grade line on the elevation. Quickly rough in the outline of the plantings.

Step 4. Outline. Draw a heavy outline around the roof(s) intersecting roofs, projecting walls, and edges of the building.

Step 5. Determine shade. Select one source of light and use this as a basis for further shading. Frequently the light comes over the observer's left shoulder and will be indicated on the drawing by shadows to the right and below each projecting member on

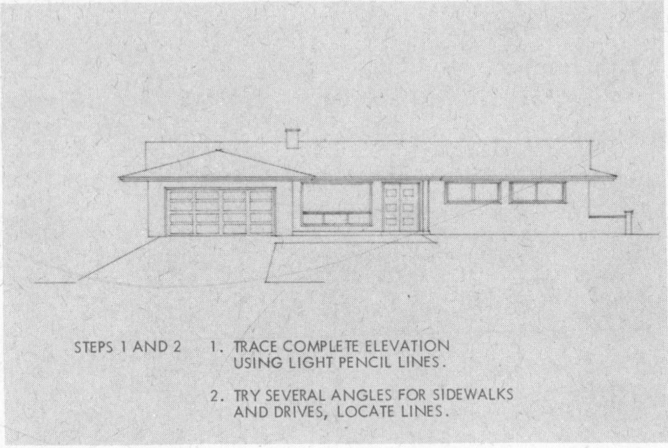

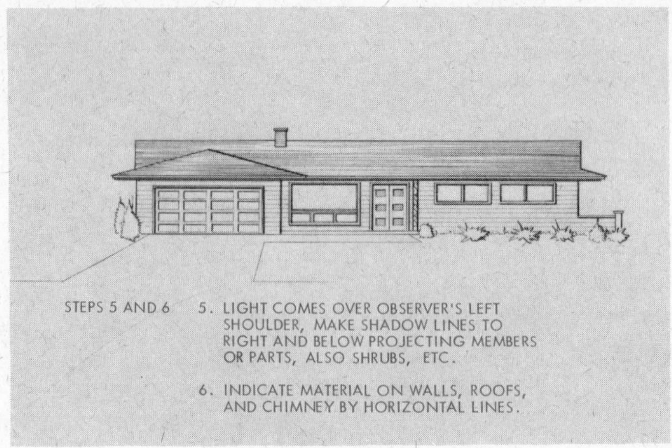

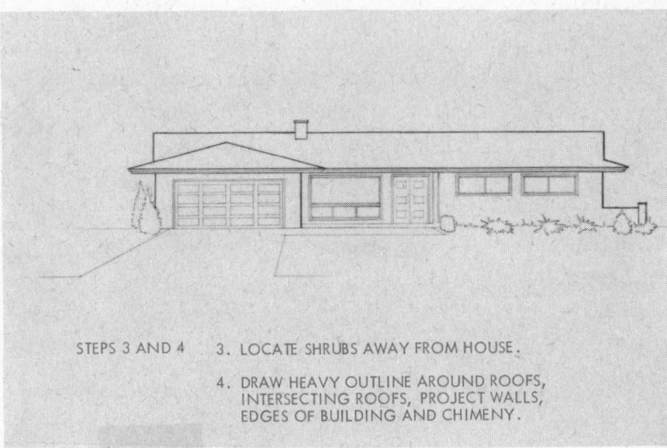

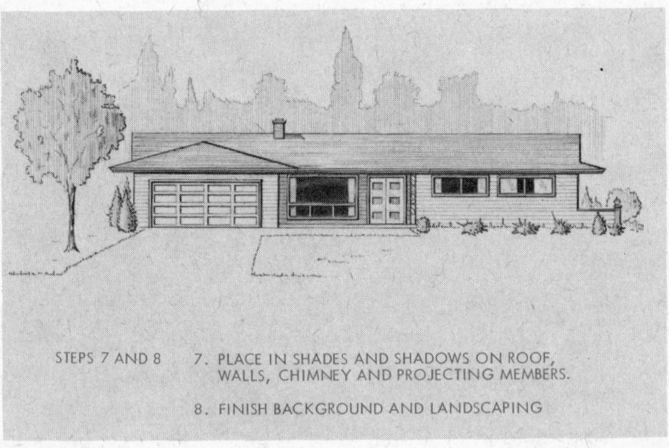

Fig. 14-11. Follow this step-by-step procedure in drawing a T-square perspective.

the chimney cap, eaves, gutters, casings, rails, sills, stiles, muntins, etc.

Step 6. Indicate building materials. Draw in the building materials such as siding, brick, stone, shingles, etc. Use horizontal lines spaced at the correct interval. An Ames Lettering Guide or Braddock-Rowe Lettering Triangle can be used for this very readily. Note: since the roof is an inclined surface the shingles will be foreshortened. They will appear much closer together than they actually are.

Step 7. Place in shades and shadows. The exact relation of surfaces can be indicated by a pattern of shades. Properly executed shadows give the drawing life and clarity. Surrounding trees, shrubs, walls, drives, structures, etc. should be a definite complement to the house. Complete this step by placing shades and shadows on roof, walls, chimney, and under all projecting members, shrubs, fold lines in drapes or curtains, etc. Note that where nothing is behind the window, such as a drape, the glass is black. This gives a more natural appearance to the rendering.

Step 8. Add finishing touches to the background and landscape.

Success in making a T-square perspective depends almost wholly upon contrasts created by variations of lights and darks. The pencil is one of the most flexible rendering mediums and lends itself to these different techniques. Always express the form and texture in the *simplest* way possible. A simple, direct drawing that immediately realizes the desired effect is preferable to one that is over rendered. When you are done—quit!

Mechanical Perspectives: Drawing Tips

Much time can be saved in drawing the visual rays from the station point and lines from the vanishing points by using a drafting tape and thumb tack. Draw two intersecting perpendicular lines on the non-adhesive side of a 1½″ piece of drafting tape (see Fig. 14-12) and push a thumb tack through the underside. Simply place the tape so the vertical and/or horizontal line coincides with the location of the lines forming the desired

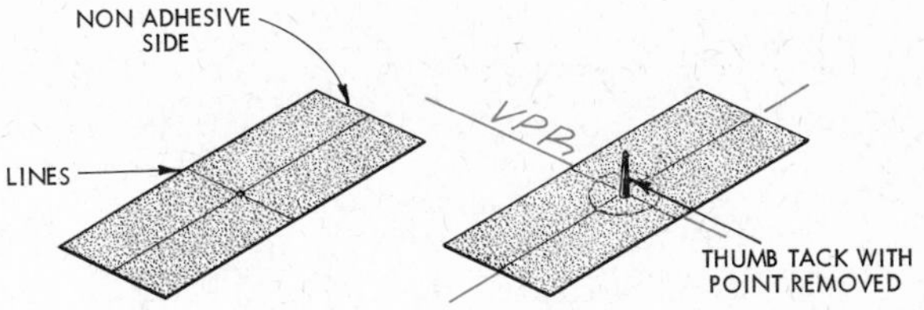

Fig. 14-12. A thumbtack attached to the board with drafting tape saves time in placing the straight edge on the vanishing points and the station point.

point. This will eliminate the constant repetition of placing the pencil at the vanishing point or station point to adjust the straight edge. To prevent any injury be sure to remove the tape and thumb tack and place a small piece of "Art Gum" eraser on the exposed portion of the thumb tack.

If a T-square is used as a straight edge, turn it over so the head will not interfere with the edge of the board. See Fig. 14-13.

If the perspective view is to be at the normal eye level, place the horizon line 5′-6″ to 6′-0″ above the ground line. For a bird's eye view, move the horizon line to 15′-0″ above the ground line. An elevation greater than this will lead to excessive distortion. A worm's eye view will necessitate a horizon line coincident with the ground line. If the structure is on a hill then the horizon line should be lower than the ground line.

Lay out the perspective with a hard pencil, 4H or 5H, and keep it pointed at all times. As lines are drawn rotate the pencil slightly. This will tend to keep the point conical rather than wearing it flat in one location. If a soft pencil is used it will wear quickly and have a greater tendency to smudge. Frequently, perspective layouts must be accurate. This is particularly true

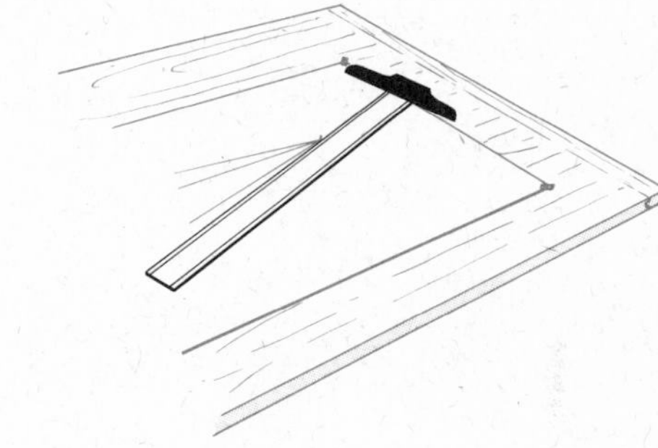

Fig. 14-13. By turning the T-square over the head will not interfere with the working edge of the board.

for plotting a curved surface or a series of offset points. A hard, well pointed pencil is good insurance for accuracy.

Perspective Sheets and Grids

Various types of perspective sheets and grids are available for drawing parallel, angular, and oblique perspectives. Some are more complicated to use than others.

Perspective Sheets

Few grids, however, offer the advantages of the Perspective Sheet since it is both simple and flexible.

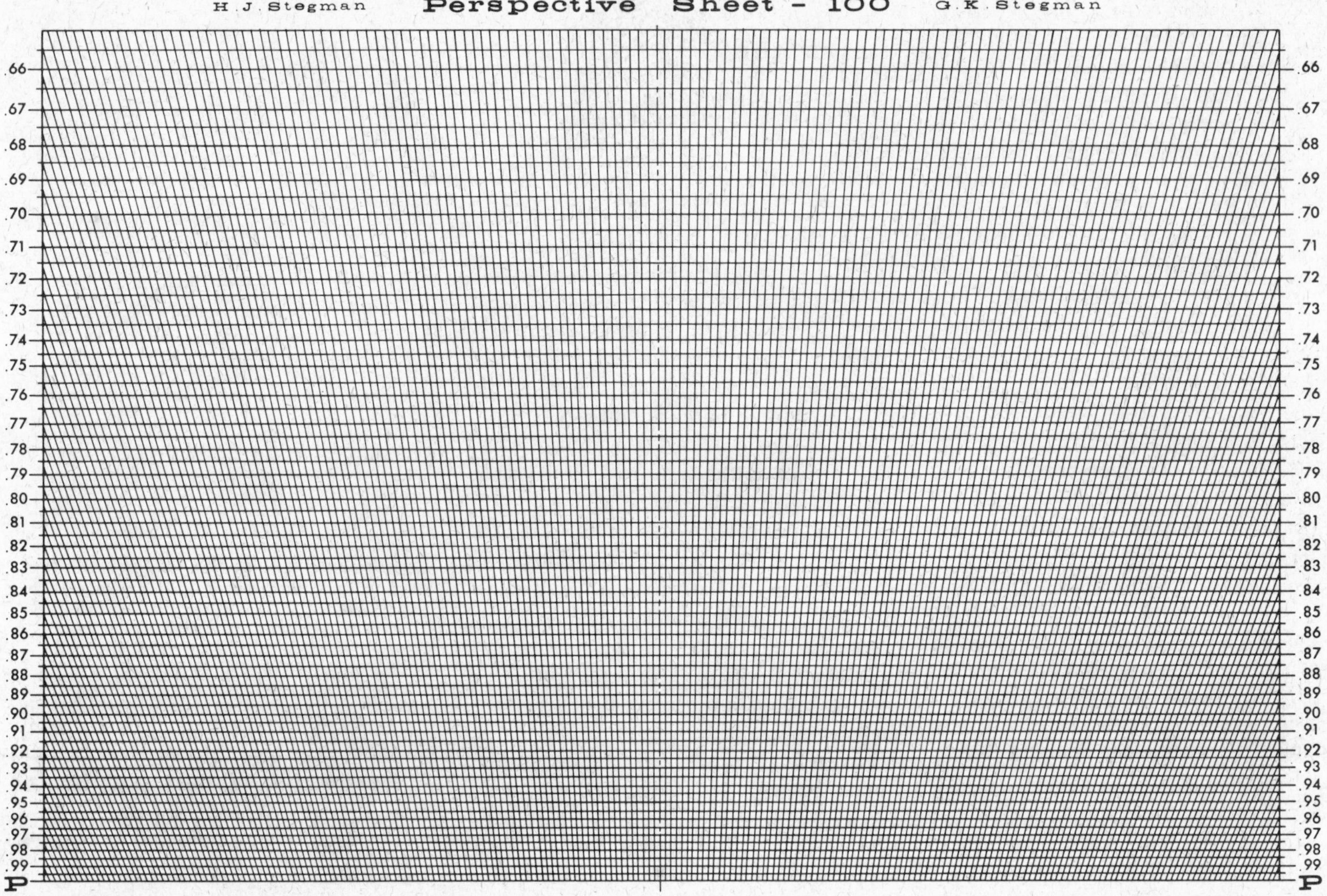

Fig. 14-14. The Perspective Sheet simplifies the mechanical perspective.

The Perspective Sheet (Fig. 14-14) first appeared, with modifications, under the name Calibron Perspective Paper. It was conceived by Theodore M. Edison and is used with his permission. The position of the object may be changed readily, thereby giving the draftsman a wider latitude of emphasis that may be placed on a particular face. The position relative to the horizon line, as well as the distance from the picture plane, is also more flexible. Perhaps the greatest asset of the Perspective Sheet is that an angular perspective *may be drawn completely* in as little space as 12″ × 16″. A normal mechanical angular perspective, drawn by the office method, may require a 2′ × 4′ to establish the station point and vanishing points. Observe in Fig. 14-14 that the upper part of the Perspective Sheet is ruled with converging lines which run to a station point below. These angular lines of sight terminate at the horizontal picture plane, and are the regular visual rays on which the plan view may be placed. The series of lines parallel to the picture plane, marked with reducing decimal values .99, .98, .97, .96, .95 etc., represent the diminishing height of vertical lines at each of these stations (horizontal lines) behind the picture plane. By placing a sheet below, as shown in Fig. 14-15, the *traces* (projectors) of the intersection of the visual ray and the picture plane may be drawn for any point on the plan view. If a point does not fall on one of the visual rays, simply interpolate its path to the picture plane. Fig. 14-15 shows the Perspective Sheet with a plan and perspective. The following is an outline of the step-by-step drawing procedure.

Step 1. Align and tape the perspective sheet on one end of a drawing board or place on a regular drawing table.

Step 2. Orient and tape plan view of the object in any desired position (place to the left or right of the center to emphasize a particular face, etc.).

Step 3. Tape a piece of detail paper or

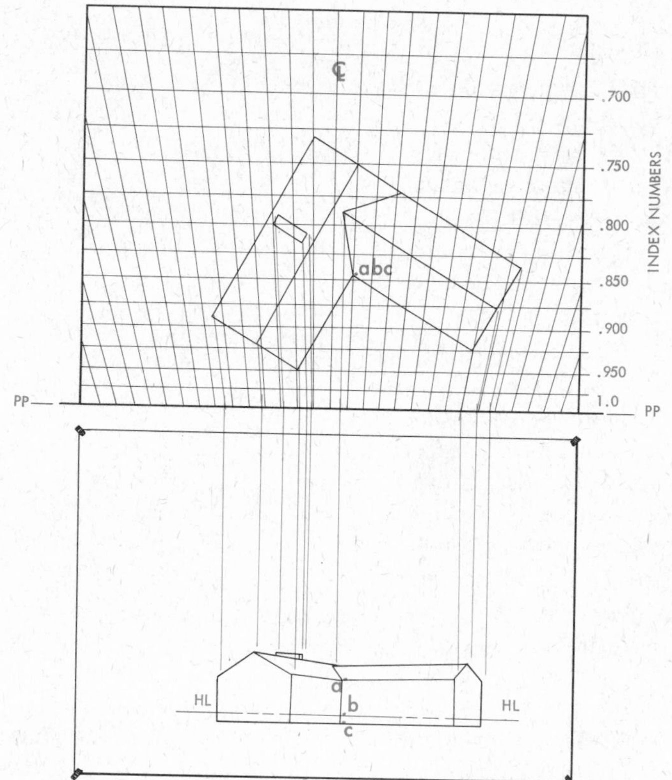

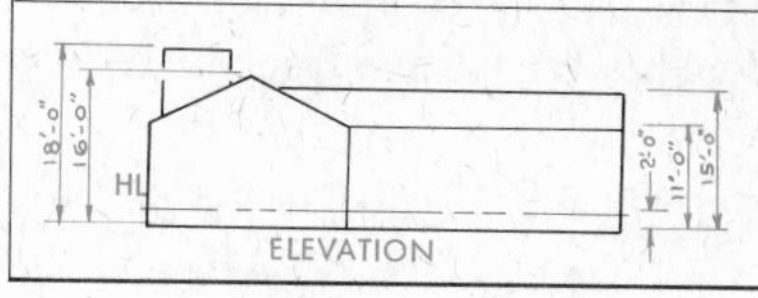

Fig. 14-15. The Perspective Sheet offers versatility and convenience when making an angular perspective.

vellum immediately below the perspective sheet.

Step 4. Draw the HL near the middle of the piece of vellum.

Step 5. Locate HL on a print of the elevation. Assume the grade line is the GL and measure from this point. All vertical distances are measured, in both perspective and elevation from the HL's.

Step 6. Locate various points on the perspective.

a. Heights are located in the perspective by multiplying the true distance or scale distance of the point above the HL by the given *index number* (numbered horizontal line) on which that point appears. Lay off the resultant value *above* the HL in the perspective on the trace of the visual ray.

b. The distance of that line below the HL is obtained in the same manner. Take the true or scale distance of the lower end of the line below the HL and multiply it by the index number. Lay off the resultant distance *below* the HL on the trace of its visual ray.

Example: To find the height in perspective of line *abc:* line *abc* falls on index line .845, therefore multiply *ab* (the portion of the line that is above HL, 9′-0″) by .845; 9′-0″ × .845 = 7′-7″. (The height 9′-0″ is taken from the elevation.) Step this distance (7′-7″) off *above* the perspective HL on the trace of this visual ray. Next multiply portion *bc* (the portion of the line that is below HL, 2′-0″) by .845; 2′-0″ × .845 = 1′-7″. Set this distance (1′-7″) off *below* the HL on the trace of the same visual ray.

Step 7. *The main outline of the object and the details are added in relation to the general mass of the object.*

Perspective Sheet Height Finder. The calculations to determine perspective heights may be eliminated by constructing a height finder. First draw a horizontal base line with a perpendicular at the left end. Step off a series of 6″ divisions *(in the same scale as the plan and elevation)* on the perpendicular. Mark off 10 equal divisions, ⅝″ *(full scale)* apart, on the horizontal; erect a perpendicular at this point.

The use of ⅝″ full scale divisions on the base line will permit easy sub-dividing. If a total of 20′ has been set off on the left perpendicular, step off 10′ on the right perpendicular. Connect the 20′ and 10′ graduations on the perpendiculars with a straight line and extend this angular line to the horizontal base line forming point *a*. Extend lines from each of the 6″ graduations on the left perpendicular to point *a*. Mark the graduations, beginning at the left end of the horizontal

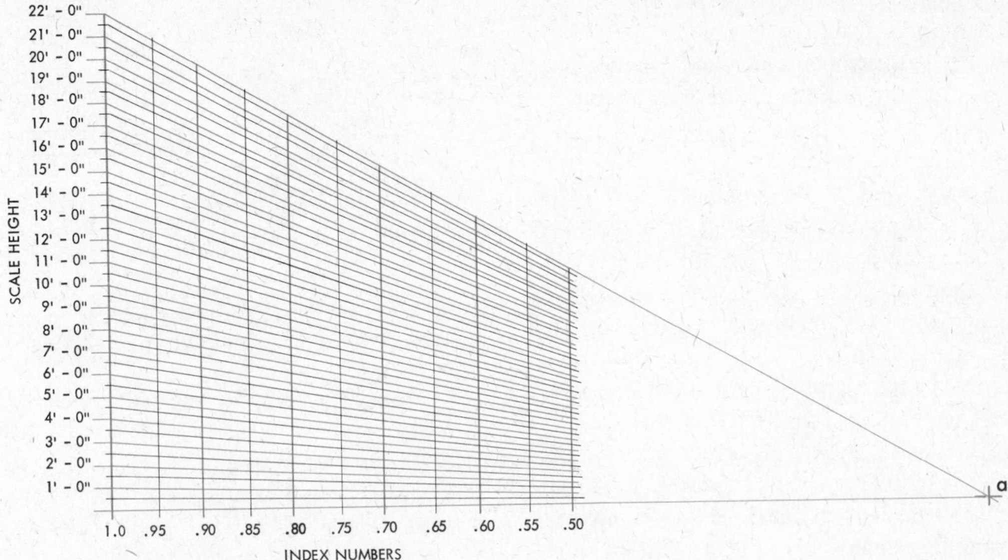

Fig. 14-16. A height finder may be easily constructed thereby eliminating the need of calculating when using the Perspective Sheet.

base line .95, .90, .85, .80, etc. These represent index numbers.

If it is desired, each of the ⅝″ graduations may be divided into ⅛″ graduations and the appropriate decimal value added to the existing calibrations—.99, .98, .97, .96, *.95,* .94, .93, .92, .91, *.90,* .89, etc. This technique will lend more accuracy to the perspective. Distances may be "picked off" by using the appropriate position on the index line and desired height. Fig. 14-16 illustrates a height finder scaled for 22′ on the left perpendicular.

Further information on the different series of Perspective Sheets and height finders may be obtained by writing to the authors.

Perspective Grids

Perspective grids differ from the perspective sheet in that most grids limit the angle of the object in relation to the picture plane. Notably, however, the *Gibby Optometric Perspective Grid* and the *Andersen Three-Point Oblique Perspective Chart* are easy to manipulate and will produce good results. (These copyrighted grids are available from The A. Lietz Co., P.O. Box 3633, San Francisco, California.) Fig. 14-17 illustrates these two grids. They may be used equally well for architectural or mechanical work.

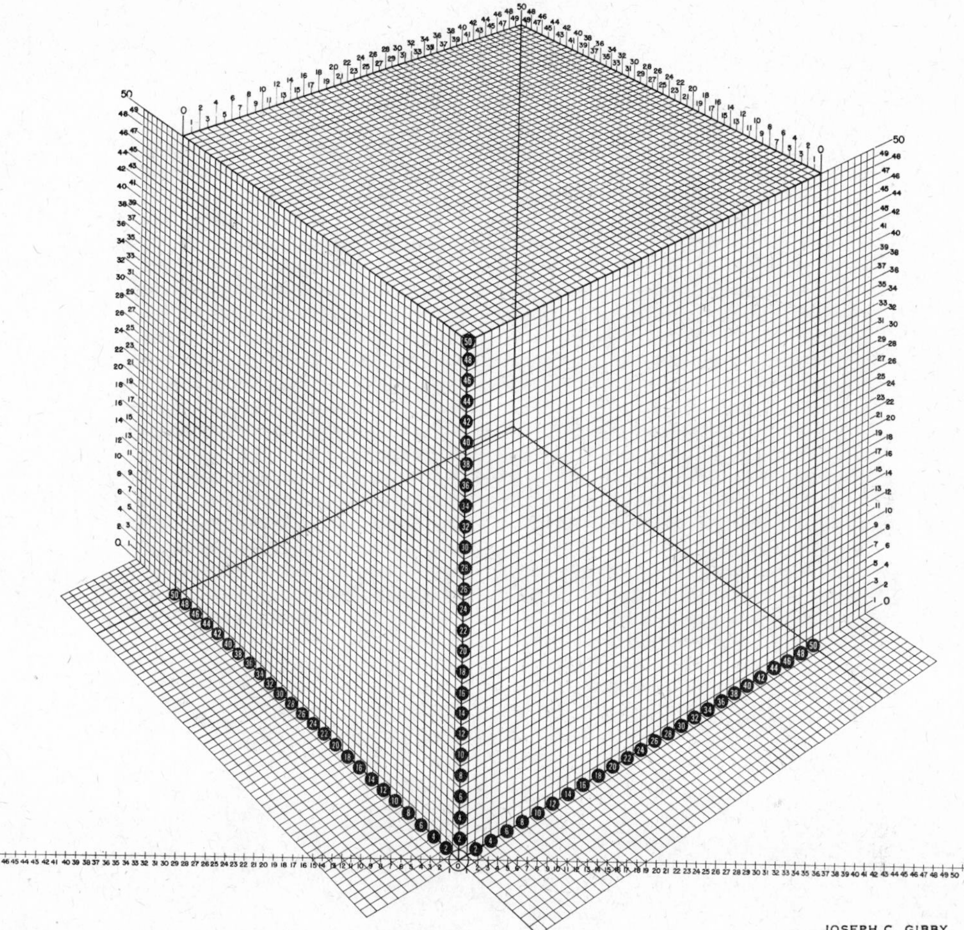

JOSEPH C. GIBBY.

Fig. 14-17. Grids may also be used in drawing the perspective. The Gibby Optometric Perspective Grid (above) uses black lines to show visible lines of an object and blue lines to show invisible lines. The Andersen Three-Point Oblique Perspective Chart is shown on the next page.

Perspective Rendering

Frequently, as a student looks enviously at a finished perspective rendering, he is overheard to remark, "How much art training do I need to make a drawing like that?"

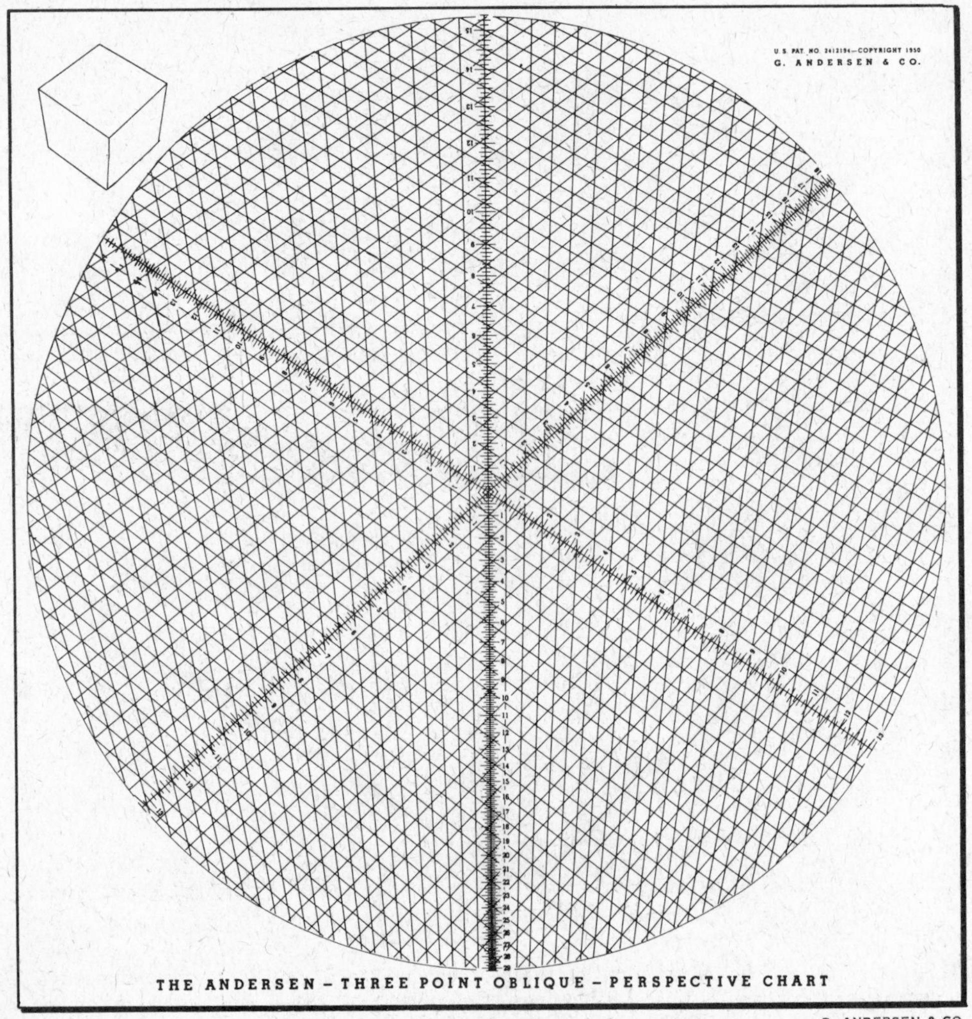

Fig. 14-17. Cont'd. (Andersen Three-Point Oblique Perspective Chart.)

The answer is three-fold. First, you do not have to be a Rembrandt or a Titian to make a good finished rendering. In fact, the student doesn't need any previous art courses. Second, it is necessary to have an interest in this type of drawing. Often a high degree of interest replaces a lack of innate ability. Each experience with a rendering can produce gratifying results. Third, and perhaps most important, the student must be willing to experiment and practice with different techniques, pencils, and papers. Each grade of pencil and each type of point will produce different surface qualities. Obviously, practice is important to develop any degree of skill in rendering. Many times students who have taken art courses find their results disappointing. This is frequently due to an overconfident feeling and an unwillingness to work and apply some of the basic principles that are suggested in this chapter. The student who has no previous background may well perform in an outstanding manner because of his willingness to experiment and practice.

Rendering, as in other creative endeavors, is based upon the ability to observe and experiment. This, in essence, is the basis for all learning—observation and experimentation. Notice how others have treated a particular surface or object or how they have produced a shadow effect without losing the detail. Study examples of style in rendering textures in the leading architectural and building magazines. Each illustrator expresses himself differently. One may give a particular treatment to limestone; another may render limestone in a different manner. Reprints of competition drawings and planning books provide good illustrations. Try copying a particular pencil style on a small sheet of paper (select a tree, window, shrub, entryway, etc.). Note critically the character

DESIGNED AND DELINEATED BY DONALD BROWN.

Fig. 14-18. Heavy pencil shading may be used to create an attractive presentation drawing.

of the pencil stroke and the type of pencil point used to create this effect. Figs. 14-18 through 14-20 give examples of rendering techniques.

Pencil Grade

The grade or hardness of a pencil will influence the tone of the line.

Fig. 14-21 illustrates a comparable analysis of pencil grades that are used in architectural renderings. A soft pencil will produce a granular effect when drawn on paper; by applying additional pressure the line will become deep black. A soft pencil will also give a deeper tone to a line than a medium. Sometimes this is highly desirable. As the pencil increases in hardness, the tone created becomes lighter. Each person uses a

Fig. 14-19. Light pencil shading may also create an effective rendering.

Fig. 14-20. Ink techniques, combined with commercially prepared shading sheets, are often used in rendering. Shading screens are shown on the shaded areas of the house (front windows, garage doors, etc.). These are cut and applied directly to the drawing.

pencil in a unique manner. This mainly depends on the amount of pressure. Some may obtain a dense, black, bright line with a 2B, while another person may find a 4B necessary to equal the same result. On the average, however, a *soft pencil* (B, 2B, 3B, 4B, 5B, 6B) will produce a black tone; a *medium pencil* (HB, F, and H) will give medium tones; and a *hard pencil* (4H, 3H, 2H) will render light tones. It is necessary to experiment with different grades of pencils to obtain the "feel" of the tone it will produce.

Pencil Point

The shape of the point will determine the kind of line that will be produced. Each type of point will give a specific character to the line. The types of points commonly used (illustrated in Fig. 14-22) are described below.

Conical. The conical point is the most utilitarian since it is used for many types of general purpose work. Sharpening the pencil with a pencil sharpener or a pencil pointer will produce a fine sharp point. When this fine point breaks, however, it will "nick" the paper, thus resulting in a blemish that will be difficult to erase. With the pencil held in the normal position, simply draw the point lightly over a piece of scrap paper. This small amount of pressure will cause the fine point to break. Repoint the pencil by rotating it on the paper.

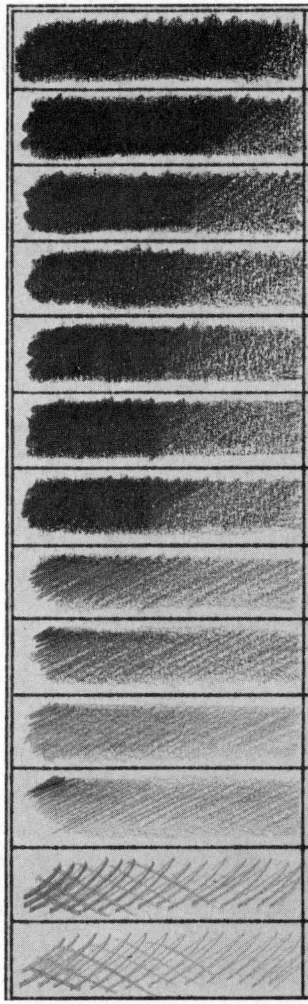

Pencil	Grade	Use
ExExB		for surfaces
ExB		for drawings and intense shadow
6B		for very light and soft drawings and for darkest shading
5B		for deep shadow
4B	Grade 1	for varieties of shading; for studies and sketching
3B	Grade 1	for clear outlines, especially suitable for sketches
2B		for clear and distinct hatching, down to deepest cast shadow; Superior Writing Pencil
B	Grade 2	for finer shading, soft toned drawings and plans; Popular Writing Pencil
HB	Grade 2	for outlines and finest shading; General Purpose Pencil
F	Grade 3	for architectural and technical plans, light cast shadow, for large lettering and heavy lines in photo-prints where edges and outlines are to be specially emphasized, also for drawings on wood and for wood engravings
H	Grade 3	
2H	Grade 4	
3H	Grade 4	for measurement indicating arrows, addressing, itemised lists, and for distinct, sharp outline drawings

J. S. STAEDTLER, INC.; MONTVILLE, NEW JERSEY.

Fig. 14-21. Each grade of pencil produces a different tonal value.

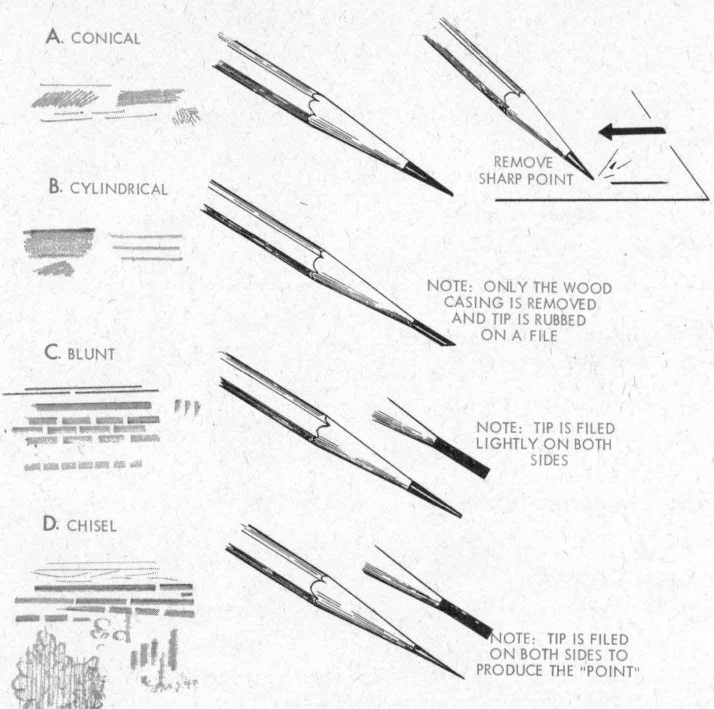

Fig. 14-22. Each specific type of pencil point produces a different line.

Cylindrical. The cylindrical point may be used for shading large areas with the flat face. By revolving the point 180°, a fine line may be produced. The wood casing is removed by a pocket knife or a draftsman's pencil sharpener. The exposed lead is then drawn across a file to produce a plane surface. Place the file on the table top and hold the pencil in the normal drawing position. Merely move the point along the file. The point will then be at the proper angle to produce a full broad line.

Blunt. By filing both sides of the exposed lead, yet allowing the tip to have some thickness, a broad, sharp, line may be obtained. This type of point is a time saver for drawing random bricks, shingles, lights, some types of trees, etc. Both the blunt and cylindrical point will produce a wide line. The blunt will tend to be sharper along the edges, whereas the cylindrical will be a bit fuzzy.

Chisel. The chisel point is similar to the blunt in general shape. The chisel, however, is sharpened to a fine edge. It will produce a broad crisp line similar to the blunt point, *but* it will also give a fine, thin line. In the softer leads the chisel point has a tendency to break easily. Wood cased pencils and mechanical lead holders having rectangular rather than cylindrical shaped leads are available in varying degrees of hardness. These are called "chisel-point" pencils.

Regardless of the type of point used in rendering, the point must be free of all graphite particles. Even the smallest amount of graphite will cause a smudge. To eliminate graphite granules, a 4″ or 6″ mill file or ignition file is recommended rather than abrasive paper or cloth for pencil pointing. A file may be readily cleaned by tapping it on a hard surface. Abrasive paper tends to hold the graphite. See Appendix A for a further discussion of abrasive paper and pencil points.

Tone Scale

One method of becoming familiar with each grade of pencil is to build a tone scale. See Fig. 14-23. Lay out several rectangles ½" × 2½" or 3". Begin at one end of the rectangle with the deepest value that the pencil will produce, then progress to the right, gradually decreasing the pressure until the value of the line is light gray. Try several tone scales with different pencil grades (the grade controls the intensity and quality of the tone). Experimentation will show that the softer pencils will produce a more granular effect than a medium or hard. Try both the continuous and non-continuous type tone scales. Since the value areas are not connected in the non-continuous tone scale, the separate areas of black and gray serve as a good comparison of the pressures required to produce a given value.

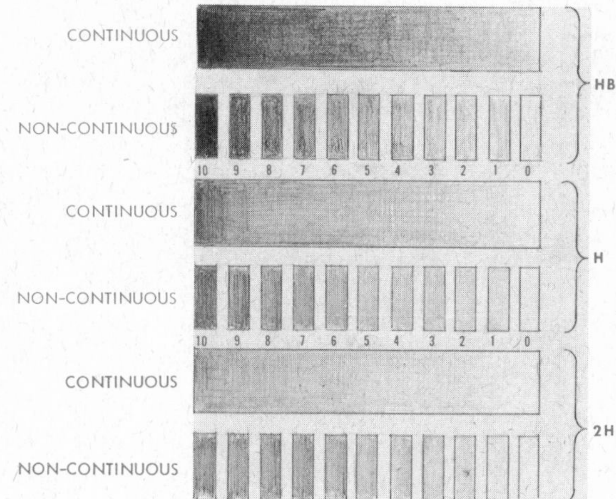

Fig. 14-23. Building a tone scale with different pencil grades helps to develop a feeling for the limitations of each pencil.

Paper

Grades and surface textures of paper have a distinct effect on pencil tones. A soft pencil on rough paper will yield a graying effect. A medium paper, however, will reduce the granular tone. For reproduction purposes, vellum is frequently used for renderings. The surface quality of vellum is considerably different than that of art papers or boards (such as Strathmore or Bristol boards). Many vellums have a "tooth" quality. This texture readily accepts pencil and will produce dense black values with a minimum amount of pressure. Before beginning a rendering, test several grades of pencils on the medium you intend to use. Though one may be familiar with a specific type of paper used for working drawings, the *touch* that is required for renderings may be different.

Entourage

An entourage (that is, the surroundings: shrubs, trees, people, etc.) is placed around the house to give a natural appearance. The perspective may be naturally enhanced by the addition of a simple human form on the sidewalk, driveway, or lawn. Some plantings must be placed around the structure to give it a finished, "lived-in" air. To draw a perspective of a dwelling and omit or sparsely plant the visible portions of the site would detract greatly from the building.

Fig. 14-24 shows some of the many possible shapes, kinds, and styles of trees and plantings that may be used in the foreground and background of the rendering. Look closely at each illustration—study the technique that was used to form the outline. Study particularly the tonal values that give a three-dimensional effect. These add zest to a rendering.

Fig. 14-24 also gives several examples of human figures. The addition of a simple stylized figure will bring the perspective to life. Note the very simple outline that has been used to produce the human shape. If the size of the figure is too large or detailed, or is placed in a prominent position, it may detract from the purpose of the rendering. The figures should compliment the structure; they should not attract attention away from the structure.

Ink Rendering

Though the medium and technique is different for ink, the general shape of the entourage is the same. Remember that the line produced with ink is a constant value,

Fig. 14-24. Additions of trees, shrubs, plantings, and/or human figures to the rendering give a professional touch.

and may not be grayed as with pencil. The illusion of grayed values is obtained by line width and spacing. As with pencil work, it is necessary to have several pens which will produce varying types of lines. Fig. 14-25 shows several examples of line techniques used to produce different tones. For those who have never sketched in ink, a Hunt #107 Hawk-quill pen is recommended. The nibs of the Hawk-quill are less flexible than the Hunt #102 or other fine nibbed pens. These nibs may be easily touched up with

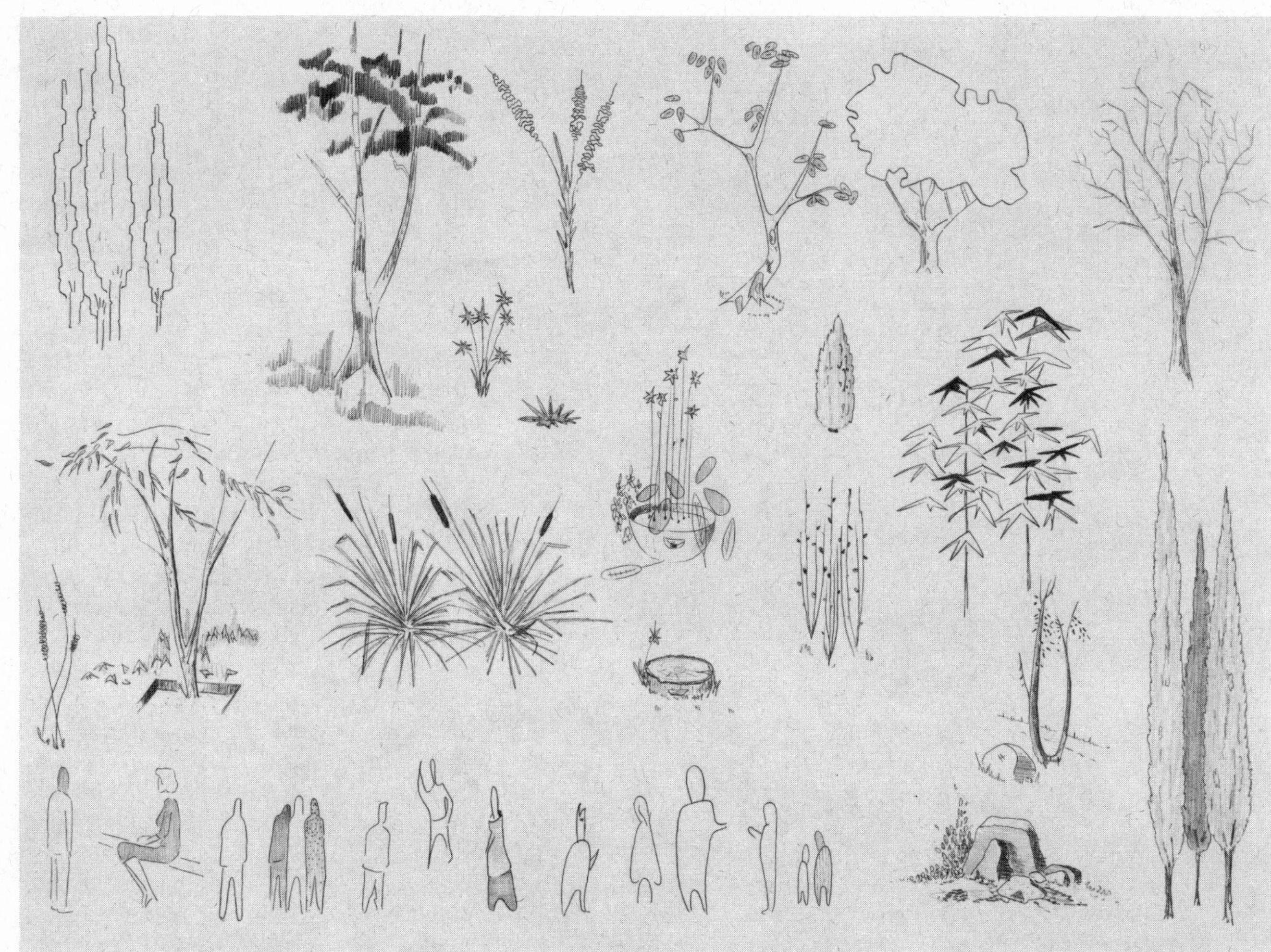

Fig. 14-24. Cont'd.

a hard Arkansas stone to change the line width. When testing the pen, hold it in a relaxed manner—not rigidly. Practice by making different types of strokes: horizontal side strokes made with the hand only, horizontal strokes with the arm, and vertical strokes with the fingers. Apply pressure with some strokes and ease up on others. More pressure causes the nibs of the pen to spread. This creates an interesting effect and may be used to good advantage for some types of foliage.

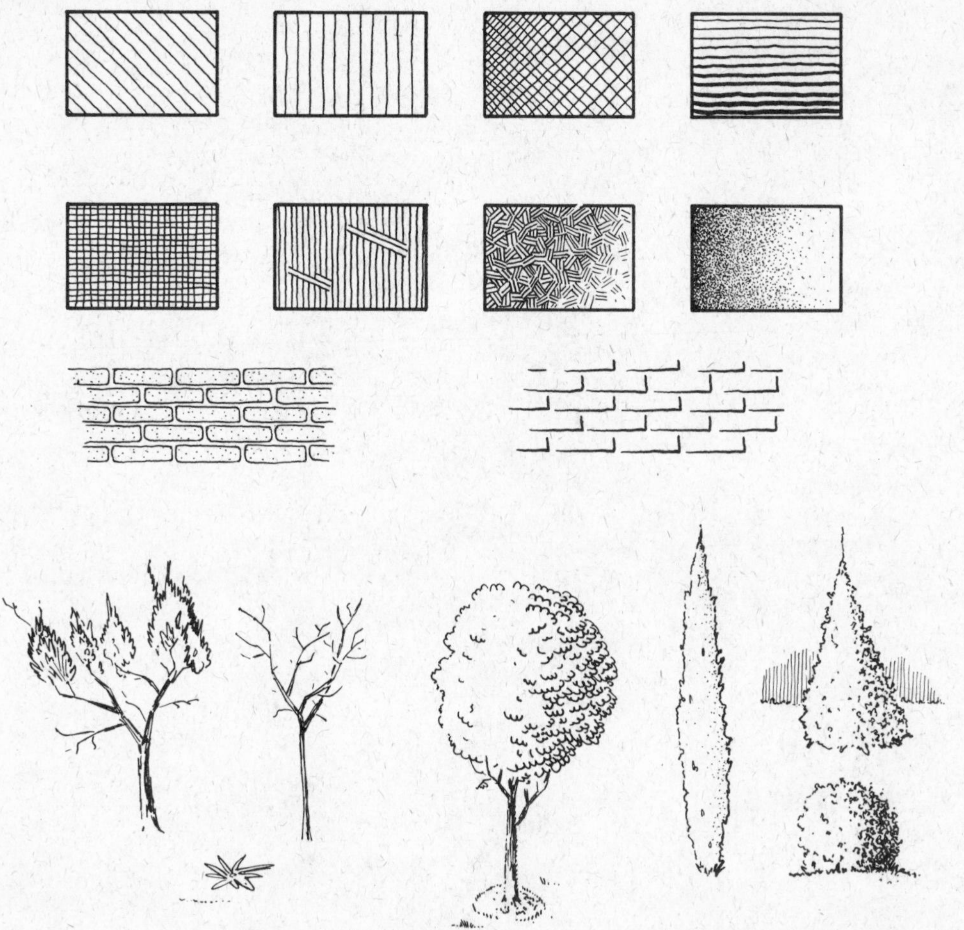

Fig. 14-25. Pen and ink technique differs from that required for pencil.

Once the perspective is laid out, place a piece of vellum over the sheet. With soft pencil lines block in various trees and shrubs at the sides and along the front of the house. Do not add in detail, simply indicate with a pencil line those portions that will be in shadow. Now begin to experiment with technique. For a single shrub several pens may be used to produce the appearance of foliage, light, and shadow.

Color

Pastel crayons and colored pencils are sometimes used on presentation drawings that will be displayed. The variety of effects and contrasts that may be obtained by combining pencil and color are almost limitless.

Pastel crayons offer the most promising results for the beginner since they may be easily erased if a mistake is made. Pastels may be used in two different manners.

In the first method, the crayon is rubbed on a piece of paper towel or other coarse paper to produce a crayon dust. The dust is applied to the drawing by "loading" a piece of cotton with the crayon dust and rubbing it on the paper. Several applications will intensify the value of the color. To bring the color to a line, a piece of detail or bond paper may be used as a mask, see Fig. 14-26. The cotton is moved from the mask to the drawing. This will prevent a build-up of crayon particles beneath the mask and will eliminate any smudges. Cotton wound on an orange stick or commercially prepared cotton swabs are especially handy for filling in corners, deepening color, or blending. Colors may be easily "mixed" or "grayed" by this method of application.

In the second method, which requires more experience, the crayon is applied *directly* to the paper and is then blended with a piece of cotton. Because the pastel is directly applied the color will be pure—that is, it will have the same value as the stick. The opportunity to obtain a delicate, realistic color is reduced when the crayon is applied directly. With the direct method of

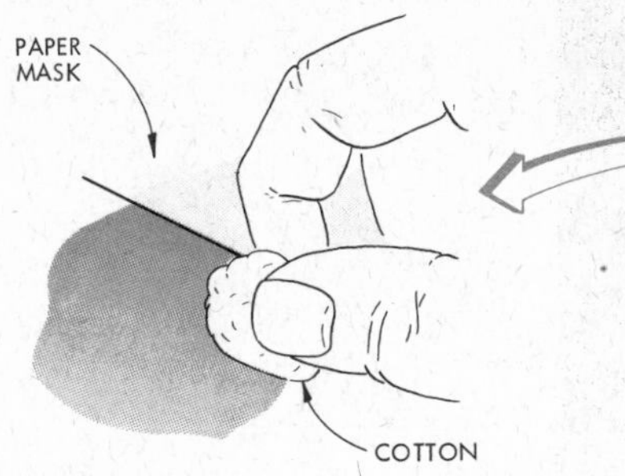

Fig. 14-26. Detail paper may be used as a mask to protect different colored areas of the rendering.

application, colors may be grayed or shaded, but care must be exercised not to apply too much black.

Colored pencils offer a convenient method of applying color to a rendering. Some brands of colored pencils are water soluble. After the desired colors have been applied, a brush dipped in clear water may be used to further blend the colors. Painting with colored pencils, as this is sometimes called, will tend to reduce the stiff appearance of the color and will give the effect of a water color. A word of caution: Thoroughly wash the brush before switching to another colored area. If water-color paper is unavailable, be sure to test the paper for its reaction to water.

Special Effects: Sepia

An interesting effect may be created by making a sepia print (this is sometimes referred to as an intermediate print) of a pencil or ink perspective rendered on vellum. A sepia print is made by the diazo reproduction processes. It is similar to a white print; however, rather than blue or black lines, the lines are a deep yellow-brown. Also, the sepia print is printed on a translucent paper. When a sepia print is made of a rendering, it should be run sufficiently fast to produce a slight amount of light brown background. The plain sepia print of a rendering is different and eye catching since it is a departure from the usual black on white. The monochromatic scheme of brown values from light to dark tones creates an impression of early evening. Further life may be added by "coloring in" the trees, shrubs, grass, building, etc., with colored pencils directly on the sepia print. The intensity of the light brown background may be increased to produce a later evening effect by decreasing the exposure time.

Sepia Pencils. A departure from colored pencil or pastel crayon may be achieved by rendering the perspective with a sepia pencil. As the name implies, the lead is a medium brown color. The single color produces a decidedly striking effect. The pencil is "worked" as an ordinary art pencil. Most pencil manufacturers produce the sepia pencil in only one grade with two values of brown. These pencils are used mainly on white Strathmore paper. However, a tinted paper (such as ivory, buff, light gray, light brown, or light blue) offers a new avenue for renderings.

Questions and Problems

1. Build a collection of pencil or pen illustrations of entourages that may be used as examples for rendering perspective.
2. Select a published drawing in an architectural, building trades, or popular home magazine and analyze it according to the tone scale in Fig. 14-23.
3. Make a white print of the front elevation of a home you have designed. Place a piece of vellum over the print and make a T-square perspective. Place the light source so it originates over your left shoulder.
4. Make an angular perspective of a home you have designed. Carefully select the face which must be emphasized. Position the station point in relation to the face.
5. Choose one particular exterior feature of the home you have designed, such as the front entryway, sun porch, patio, etc. Make an angular perspective. Place the horizon line 10′-0″ above the ground line. Render this drawing to create the effect of the sun coming over observer's left shoulder.
6. Select one of the rooms or the main entryway of one of your house plans and draw a parallel perspective with horizon line 5′-0″ above the ground line.

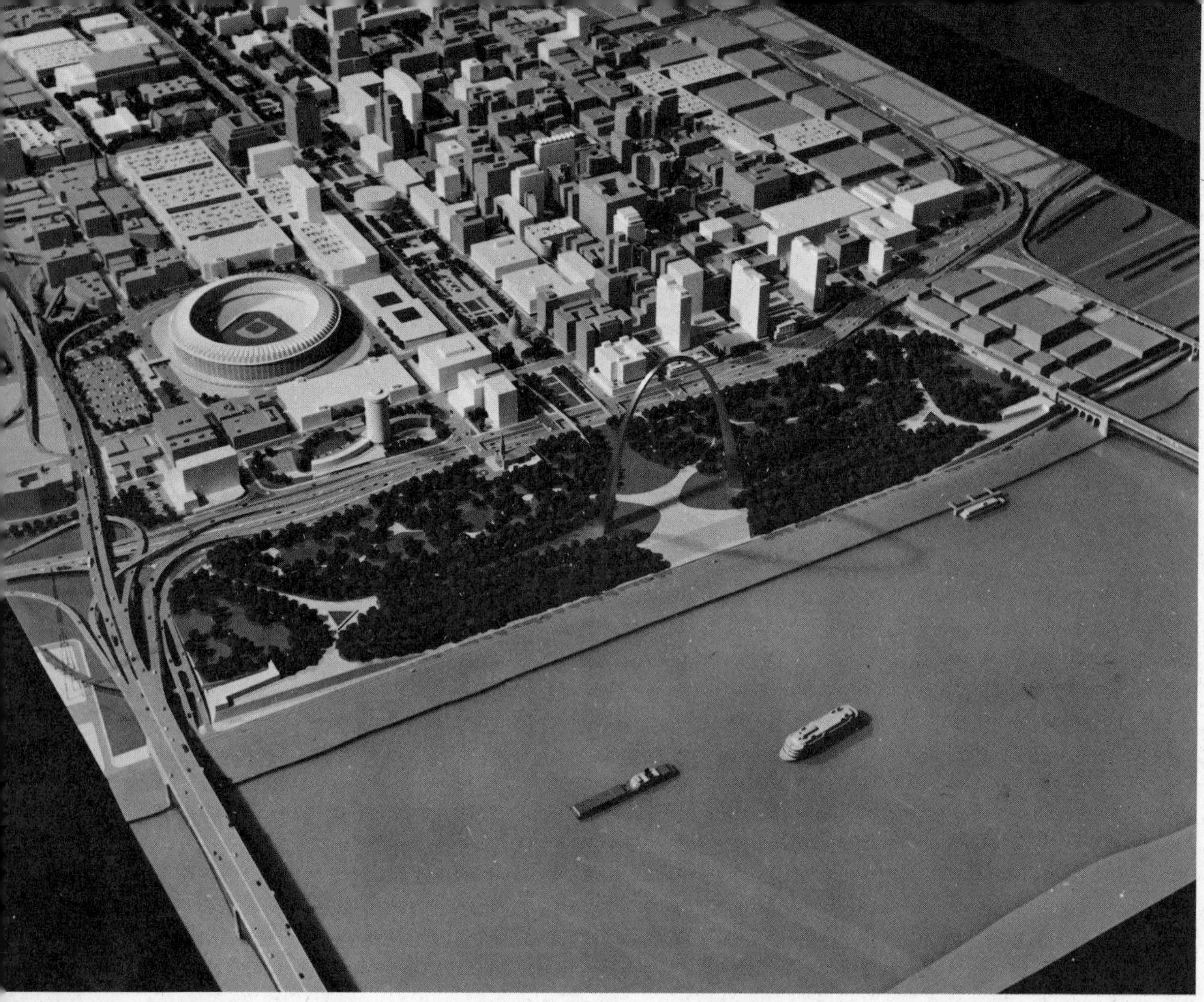

COURTESY: CALLAGHAN-SEILAR; SOUTH HAVEN, MICHIGAN.

Models are used not only for residences, but also for city planning. This is a scale model ($1'' = 100'$) of downtown St. Louis, Missouri.

House Models 15

Models are a supplementary means of checking the graphical description shown on the plan, elevations, and perspective. They aid in the visualization of the finished appearance of the proposed structure and its room arrangement. Usually, models are built to a small scale and incorporate as much detail as possible to achieve a realistic effect. The realism achieved in a model sometimes may be very deceiving. Close inspection of photos of landscaped homes often reveal that they are merely a cleverly camouflaged photo of a model superimposed on a photograph of the actual site. Models frequently serve to spark a new idea in the design of a structure. Even the most accomplished designer, on occasion, has difficulty visualizing the completed project. The time and effort expended to construct a model is more than repaid if it can help to eliminate costly changes while the building is under construction. Some architects and designers employ models to study proposed changes or additions to an existing building.

Models have the distinct advantage of showing the **completed** structure from any angle. A presentation or perspective drawing, however, reveals the basic three dimensions of the building from only a single vantage point. Models are the only way the structure may be shown in the third dimension. In the eyes of the client, many mysteries hidden on the plan and elevation are solved by the model.

House Models

Model making uses numerous tools and materials for purposes for which they were not originally intended. The use of matches, hat trim, bird gravel, sandpaper, marbles, sawdust—in fact anything that will result in the desired effect—is fair play in model making.

Probably one of the most important features in model making is the finish which is applied. Poor painting or staining can ruin an otherwise excellent model. The more realism that is provided in the model, the more interesting it will become. Attention must be given to all the details on the exterior of the model.

The equipment required for model making is not extensive. However, several pieces of equipment are necessary to the basic kit of tools. These are: model maker's knife or

MODEL BY RICHARD TETZLAFF.

Fig. 15-1. The preliminary study model shows mass and form relationships. It is a simple and quick method that may be used to illustrate the general shape of the structure.

Fig. 15-2A. This figure shows a display model of the Oakland County Courthouse, Michigan. Note the use of scale model figures and automobiles.

a single edge razor blade, 1 sheet of No. 320 abrasive paper, T-square or an old 45° or 30°-60° triangle, ½″ square × 6″ sanding block, thumb tacks, straight pins, airplane or model cement, rubber cement, and a pair of scissors.

Models are not limited only to building exteriors. Industry uses models to show various processes, flow of materials and goods, circulation patterns, production sequences, plant layout, and the spacing of equipment.

The scale of the model is dependent upon the size of the structure. Many commercial buildings are modeled ⅛″, 1/16″ or 1/32″ to 1′-0″. Most residential models are made to the scale of ¼″ = 1′-0″. Smaller residential structures also sometimes use a scale of ⅜″ = 1′-0″.

Models fall into two classifications: Preliminary study and display. They may be constructed from either cardboard or balsa wood.

Preliminary study models are most frequently made from flat, white poster board (sometimes called show card board). No finish is added. The prime purpose of these models is to aid in the analysis of mass, space, and general form. No attempt is made to dress the model with an entourage. Fig. 15-1 shows a preliminary study model of an A-frame summer house.

Display models show the proposed structure as it will appear in its completed form. Scale figures, sidewalks, trees, shrubs, automobiles, etc., are added to give realism. By placing the model in its intended surroundings the client is better able to understand the theme the architect has planned in harmonizing man, nature, and materials. The quantity of entourage incorporated in the

O'DELL, HEWETT, AND LUCKENBACH ASSOCIATES,
ARCHITECTS; BIRMINGHAM, MICHIGAN.
PHOTO: LENS-ART; DETROIT, MICHIGAN.

Fig. 15-2B. This figure shows a photo of the actual building taken from the hexagonal structure.

O'DELL, HEWETT, AND LUCKENBACH, ASSOCIATES,
ARCHITECTS; BIRMINGHAM, MICHIGAN.

Fig. 15-3. The topographic features may be represented by cutting the contours from wallboard and placing them in their proper relationship.

model must be carefully planned. Fig. 15-2 illustrates a large building with a discrete amount of foliage. Note the photo of the completed building (Fig. 15-2B).

Entourage Detail

The following paragraphs give suggestions for several methods of making the entourage. These suggestions are by no means definitive. There is no limit to the materials that may be used. Individual creativeness should suggest many possibilities.

Earth Contour

The contours (earth forms) of the site may be simulated by using blotting paper, papier maché, air hardening clay, water putty, plaster of Paris, plastic-type wood filler, or other similar, easily molded, materials. Changes in the site's topography can be made by placing these materials over rough cardboard contours, a wire screen, balled burlap, or by modeling the cement directly on a flat base. Wallboard may be cut to the various contour outlines, cemented, and nailed together to form the rough shape of the site. See Fig. 15-3. The stepped outline of the contours may be used to show the changes in elevation, or they may be further modeled with a wood rasp and sandpaper to produce a smooth surface flow.

Plant Forms and Trees

Interesting trees and shrubs may be fabricated from pipe cleaners, copper wire (bare or insulated), picture wire, sawdust, cork, paper, sponges, etc. For example, a deciduous tree may be formed by twisting several pieces of picture wire together and splaying the ends to form branches. Actual twigs and tips of various species of bushes may be used to form large trees. See Fig. 15-4. Foliage may be simulated by trim-

MODEL BY RICHARD TETZLAFF.

Fig. 15-4. Twigs of trees and bushes may be used to form trees. The foliage used on these twigs is lichen. (This is a display model. Fig. 15-1 shows the same house as a preliminary model.)

ming a piece of steel wool or sponge (natural or man-made) to desired shape, then spraying it with green paint and highlighting the foliage with a lighter or darker shade of green. The bare limbs of a twig may be brushed with glue and then dipped in sawdust, paper confetti, 1/16″, 1/8″, or 3/16″ diameter plastic foam spheres, or sponge particles. This produces an unusually attractive tree. These may then be sprayed lightly with a contrasting shade of green. Tree trunks may be dipped or painted with glue and then covered with fine shredded sponge to produce a unique appearance. Dried plants and weeds will also make excellent trees. For instance, the golden rod plant when dried and placed adjacent to a model will appear to be a miniature elm tree. Shrubs may be fashioned from sponge by trimming with a shears to the proper shape. Hedges also may be easily made from rubber sponges by trimming or cutting to the proper shape. Bushes may be simulated by cutting 36 to 60 (depending upon weight and ply) 1½″ pieces of yarn and tying them tightly at the base with thread. The loose ends are fluffed to lend a realistic appearance. Small shrubs and low spreading evergreens are sometimes made from balls of plastic-type wood filler. These are molded to the approximate shape and then covered with glue and rolled in finely ground dyed sponge or sawdust. They may then be painted if desired.

Flowers

Often, due to their minute size, flowers are omitted from the model. If they are desired, however, yarn may be looped (similar to a hooked rug) through a cardboard template and sized with starch. When dry the stiffened yarn is removed from the template and small bits of paper or material are cemented to the yarn tips. The flowers are then cemented in place.

Vines

Some model makers employ vines in conjunction with other plantings to give variety to the surroundings. Vines may be painted on the side of the structure with a No. 3 sable brush. Yarn, heavy coat and button thread, string, or wire may be carefully formed, painted, and cemented to the wall or structure. Small pieces of green paper may be used to represent the leaves.

Grass

Probably the most effective material that may be used to represent grass on a *flat site* is painted burlap. Other materials such as green colored felt, velvet, or blotting paper will also give the illusion of grass. Green flock or sand applied to wet shellac or paint will provide a realistic looking lawn. If green colored sand is not available, ordinary sand may be painted after it has been applied to the base coat and has had sufficient time to dry. Probably the most economical way to represent grass on the model is to use sawdust that has been dyed green with diluted food coloring. This is attached to the terrain by glue, rubber cement, or shellac.

Roads, Sidewalks, and Crushed Stone

Roads and sidewalks may be made from long strips of fine (No. 00 or 100) abrasive paper. This is cut to the proper width and length and glued in the desired location. Never cut abrasive paper or cloth on a paper cutter or with drafting shears because this will quickly dull the cutting edges. A coating of sand or bird gravel sprinkled on a coat of quick drying cement or shellac will produce the effect of crushed stone.

Water

Water may be represented by a plain or colored mirror. Patterned glass may be used for wave effects and distorted reflections. Colored cellophane or acetate cemented to the top of the mirror surface will also give the effect of waves.

Figures

Scale automobiles or human figures may be used to give the model "life." Frequently commercially made models of automobiles and figures specify the scale. If this is not indicated, measure the object to be sure it will fit with the house model. Neglect of this seemingly insignificant matter may throw the appearance out of scale. Measure carefully! Figures are also used in models of commercial structures to supply a visual scale of the approximate size. A simple, stylized figure cut from cardboard (similar to the ones shown in Fig. 14-24) may be used for this purpose. The most critical point in making the figure is to have the correct height. The average height of the individual is 5′-10″ to 6′-0″. Simply cut the figure from a piece of poster board, apply a coat of black paint or india ink, and cement in place on the sidewalk or on the steps of a building.

Building Material Details

As with the entourage, building details may use many different materials. Again, individual invention should be used to produce a realistic effect.

Brick, Rock, and Stone

Often these masonry materials are simulated by grooving cardboard or balsa wood with a spent ballpoint pen or mimeograph stylus. The mortar joints may be painted in with a brush and the face of the brick or masonry material may be painted by rolling the paint on with a linoleum block brayer. (A linoleum block brayer is a 4″ or 5″ wide rubber covered roller with a handle perpendicular to the axis of the roller. Its primary purpose is to apply ink to the face of a linoleum block for block printing.) Stone may also be made by using pieces of masking tape pre-cut to the desired shape and pressed on the wall.

Vertical or Horizontal Siding

Strips of detail or heavy paper may be cut and then cemented in place on the wall. (Remember to allow the correct amount to be laid to the weather.) When siding is made from separate strips and applied in an identical manner to regular beveled siding, the result will be strikingly realistic. If balsa wood is used for the model, the siding may be represented by using a stylus or spent ballpoint pen and making indentations in the wood to represent the joints. If board and batten siding is to be used on the model, separate pieces representing the batten strips may be fastened to the walls.

Stucco

Plaster of Paris, patching plaster, or Keene Cement mixed to a consistency of heavy cream and dipped on the wall with a No. 3 or larger sable brush, will produce a stucco effect. If it is desired that the stucco be colored, water colors or tempera paint may be applied to the stucco after it has thoroughly dried.

Roofing

Roof shingles may be made by cutting a series of long strips of detail paper slightly wider than the width to be laid to the weather. Stack 36 or 40 of these strips and secure the ends with rubber bands or thumb tacks. To simulate shingles, make ⅛″ deep cuts approximately ¼″ O.C. with a bandsaw or hack saw. Fig. 15-5 illustrates this procedure. Attach each strip to the roof: begin at the eaves then stain with water color, diluted ink, or food coloring. Do not saturate the paper with the coloring agent.

Rolled roofing or tar and gravel roofing may be simulated by using sheets of abrasive paper, such as aluminum oxide (tan), garnet (red), flint (gray), or emery cloth and wet or dry abrasive paper (black). Apply these materials on the roof with rubber or model cement.

Wrought Iron and Metal Work

Wrought iron work may be made by using copper bell or iron stove pipe wire bent into the desired shape. This can be soldered to the supports (if these are metal) or cemented to strips of balsa wood. They then are sprayed with a flat enamel. Other metal work on the model may be formed by using nails, brads, or wire. In some instances metal work, such as muntins, may be ruled with acetate ink on a sheet of plastic.

Flashing and Sheet Metal Work

Copper tooling foil or heavy duty kitchen aluminum foil may be used for flashing around chimneys, roof valleys, etc. Aluminum foil will be satisfactory for any other

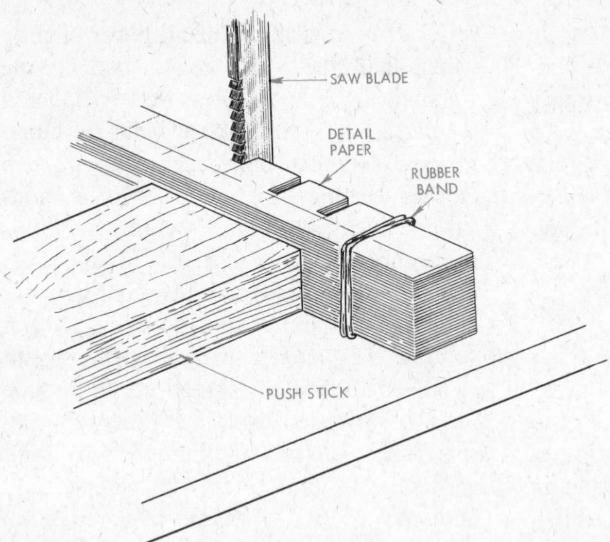

Fig. 15-5. Roof shingles may be readily made by cutting detail paper with a band saw.

areas that require sheet metal. Always have the dull side of the aluminum foil exposed.

Windows

Many house models are spoiled by omitting window lights. Window lights may be represented by attaching sheets of acetate or plastic on the inside. To give a more realistic effect, a small piece of colored cloth may be applied to the back side of the window to serve as a curtain or drape. Do not forget to cement vertical and/or horizontal pieces of balsa wood across the window to represent the rails.

Doors

Most doors used in homes built today are flush. A plain piece of cardboard cut to the desired shape can represent a flush door. If a panel door is called for, the panels may be built up by adding additional pieces of cardboard.

Window and Door Trim

To produce an attractive model, trim must be placed around the windows and doors. The easiest method is to use a 1/16″ or 1/8″ square strips of balsa wood. This is cemented around the window and door openings. Fig. 15-6 lilustrates the use of balsa wood strips. A strip of cardboard may also be used to represent the trim. Probably the most efficient method is to use a strip of balsa wood since it is uniform in thickness and is easily molded, if this is desired, by sanding.

Prepared Materials

Several manufacturers specialize in model

MODEL BY STEVE FREDERICKSON.

Fig. 15-6. Balsa wood strips, 1/16″ or 1/8″ square, may be used to trim windows and doors.

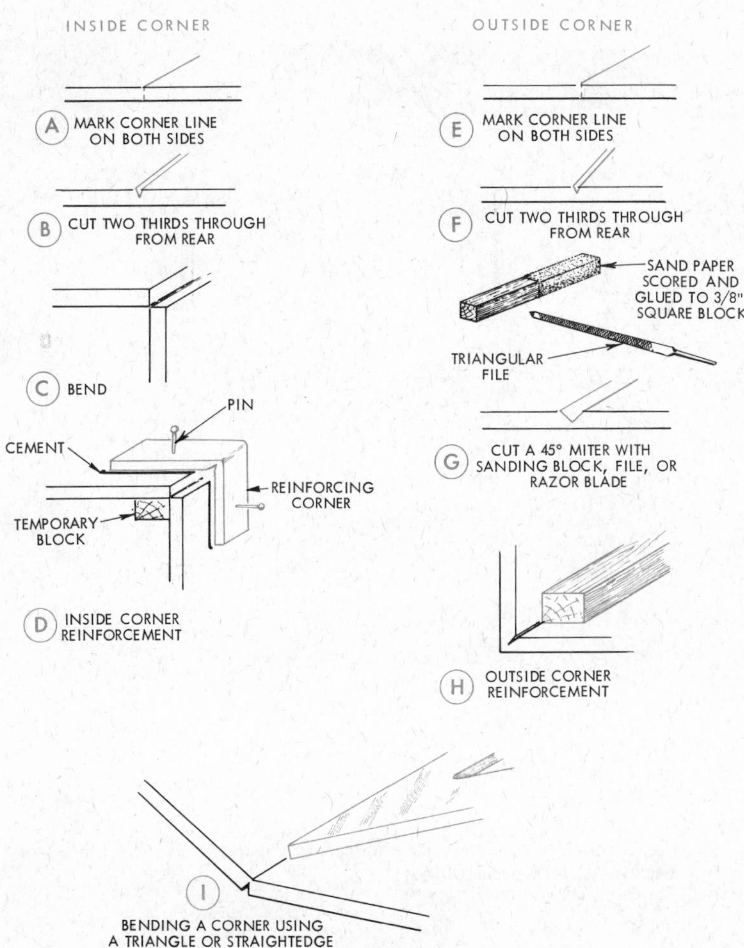

Fig. 15-7. Folded-Corner Construction.

building materials. They produce (to scale) dimensioned lumber; printed sheets representing brick, stone, siding, and roofing; as well as various types of windows and doors. Several firms produce kits that may be used to construct any style of house. These kits have the advantage of being quick and easy to assemble. They do not, however, have the finished appearance that a well-built architectural model will give.

Model Construction Details

As mentioned earlier, architectural models can be constructed from either balsa wood or cardboard. Frequently models are fabricated from a combination of both of these materials. The following gives some of the methods used in constructing model details from cardboard. Poster board (show card board) is used.

Figs. 15-7 and 15-8 show the step-by-step

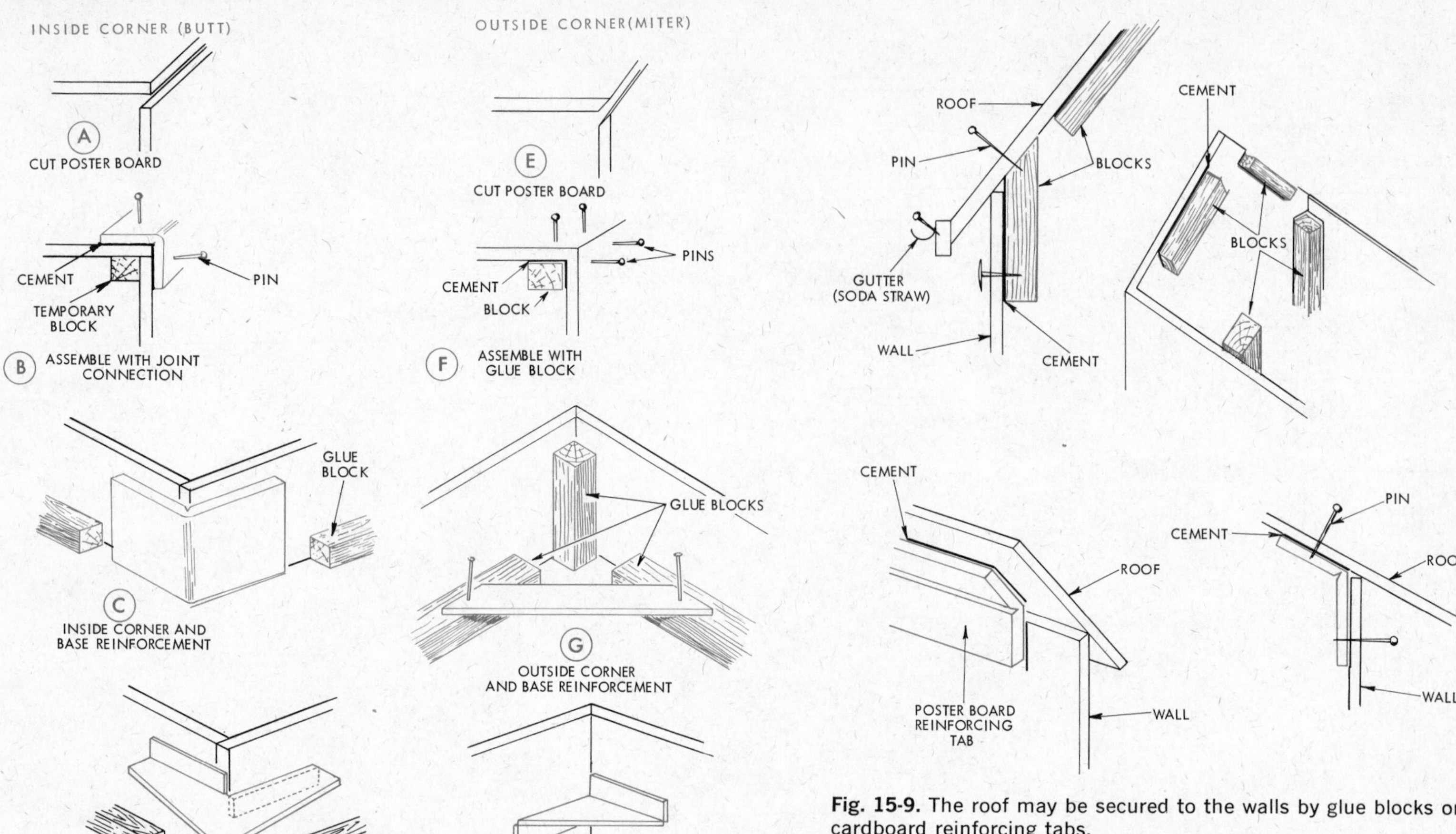

Fig. 15-8. Corner-Construction: Miter and Butt Joint.

Fig. 15-9. The roof may be secured to the walls by glue blocks or cardboard reinforcing tabs.

procedure in constructing inside and outside corners. To construct either an inside or outside *folded* corner. a mark is placed on both sides of the board and then a cut is made. For the inside corner (see Fig. 15-7B), a cut is made approximately ⅔ of the depth from the rear side. (When cutting, use an old magazine or a piece of hard board to protect the work table or desk.) The piece is bent along the cut and a cardboard reinforcing corner is placed inside to give added support and rigidity. For the outside folded corner (see Fig. 15-7C). a 45° miter cut from the rear side is made with a razor blade, triangular file, or a piece of sandpaper glued to a 3/8" strip of soft wood. The poster board is bent along the cut so a sharp edge will result. A balsa or soft wood block is then glued on the inside of the corner for support.

Frequently the model maker will find that it is necessary to join *separate* pieces for the corner. Either a miter or a butt joint may be used. Fig. 15-8 shows methods used in making these two types of joints.

Figs. 15-7 and 15-8 also show methods of reinforcing inside and outside corners. These methods may be used for either cardboard or balsa wood. NOTE: In many cases thumb tacks or pins are shown. These are used to hold temporary blocks and to support the corner. Once the cement has dried, the pins or tacks are removed.

Fig. 15-9 (top) illustrates one method of securing a roof to the side walls. Placing the glue blocks in this position will permit a larger bonding surface for the roof. Additional strength may be obtained by placing a frieze board at the junction of the exterior wall and the roof. Fig. 15-9 (bottom) illustrates how to secure a roof using cardboard reinforcing tabs.

The easiest method to join two intersecting roofs that form a valley is to provide a tab on one of the members as shown in Fig. 15-10A. The dormer may be attached by using a glue block (Fig. 15-10B). A spring clothespin may be used as a clamp to hold two pieces as the cement dries.

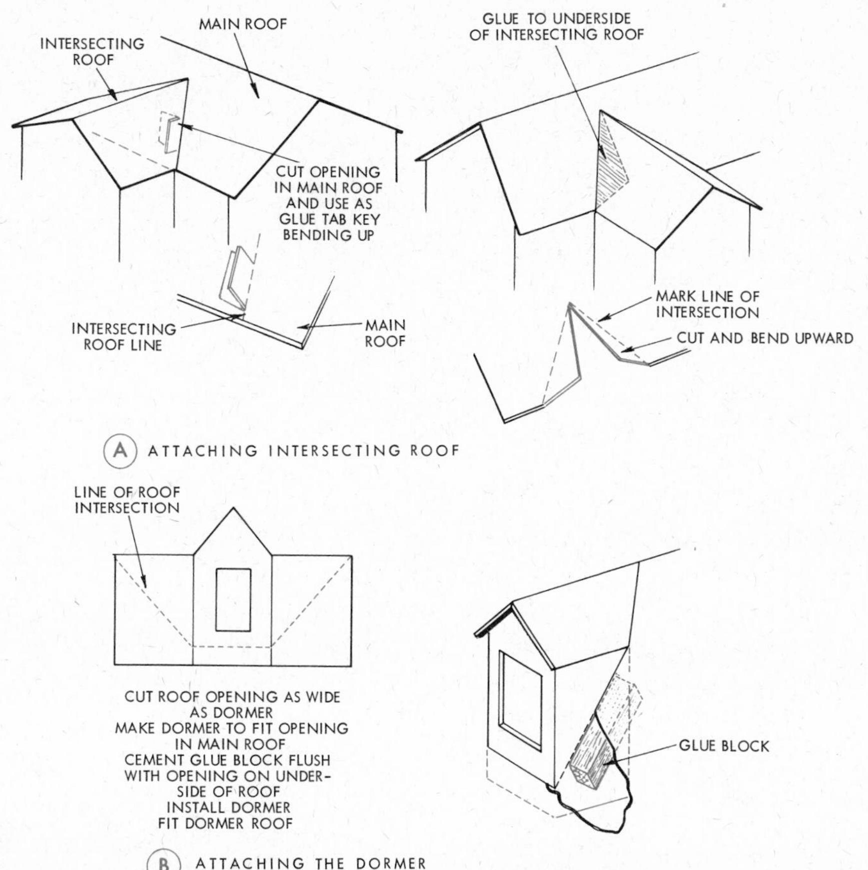

Fig. 15-10. These methods may be used for fastening intersecting roofs and dormers.

Poster Board Models

Preliminary Study Models

The purpose of a preliminary model is simply to show the relationship of the structural masses. Usually no window or door openings are shown in this type of model. The following procedure outlines the step-by-step method that is used in constructing a preliminary model.

(1) Study plans and elevations for the proper layout.

(2) Lay out walls, with light pencil lines, in the proper sequence on poster

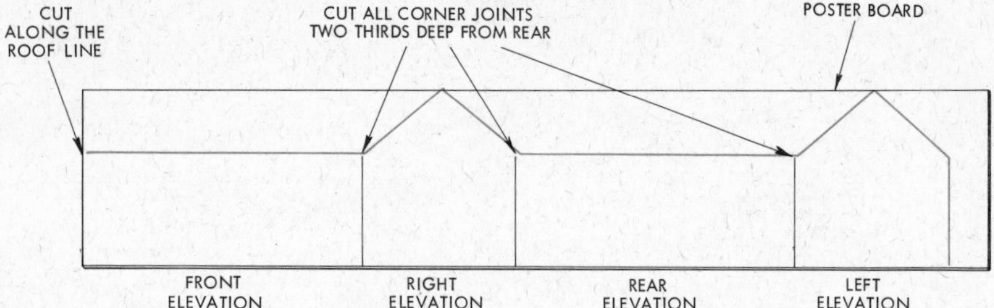

Fig. 15-11. When outlining the walls, keep the layout in the proper sequence.

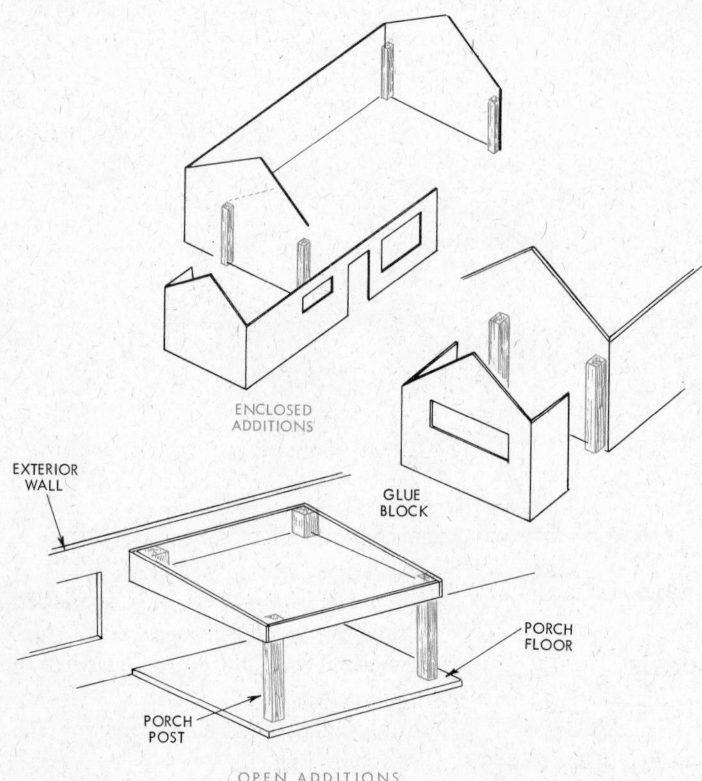

Fig. 15-12. Several methods may be used for attaching additions.

board. Keep the layout in line: the front elevation hinged to the right elevation, the right elevation hinged to the rear elevation, the rear elevation hinged to the left elevation. See Fig. 15-11. If the plan deviates from the rectangular or square form, any projections or offsets (such as a porch or garage) may be laid out and added separately. See Fig. 15-12.

(3) Cut along the roof line.

(4) Cut all corner joints ⅔'s deep.
   A. Cut inside corners from rear.
   B. Cut outside corners from rear; cut miters with the sanding block.

(5) Carefully fold the walls to form the proper angles. To insure a sharp corner, place a triangle on the bend line to act as a "break."

(6) Place folded walls over the plan of structure to make certain the model will be square. To prevent movement, pin walls to the plan as shown in Fig. 15-13.

(7) Reinforce corners with poster board or wooden blocks.

(8) Study the shape of the roof and layout in light pencil lines. NOTE: Obtain the true size of the roof from any two adjacent elevations, i.e., the front and right or rear and left elevations. This will give the eave length and slant length of the roof.

(9) Cut joints for the ridges ⅔'s deep from rear, cut miters with the sanding block.

(10) Fold roof to form proper shape. Use

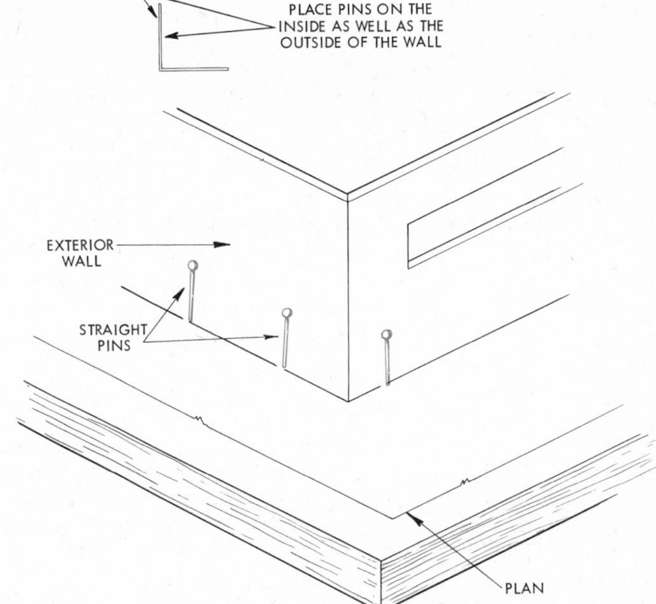

Fig. 15-13. Pinning the walls to the plan will insure a squared house.

a triangle as in step No. 5. Secure the under side of the roof with cardboard reinforcement. Some roofs because of their length will require a balsa wood strip, cemented on the underside, to act as a stiffener.

(11) Place glue blocks on inside walls flush with top edge.

(12) Cement roof in place.

(13) Place model on a piece of felt, blotter, or dark colored material and study relation of masses and general exterior appearance.

Display Models

Many of the steps in constructing a display model are similar to those required to fabricate a preliminary study model. Of course more detail is added. The following steps outline a procedure that may be used in the construction of a poster board display model.

(1) Study the plans and elevations for the proper layout.

(2) Lay out the walls, doors, and window openings, with light pencil, in their

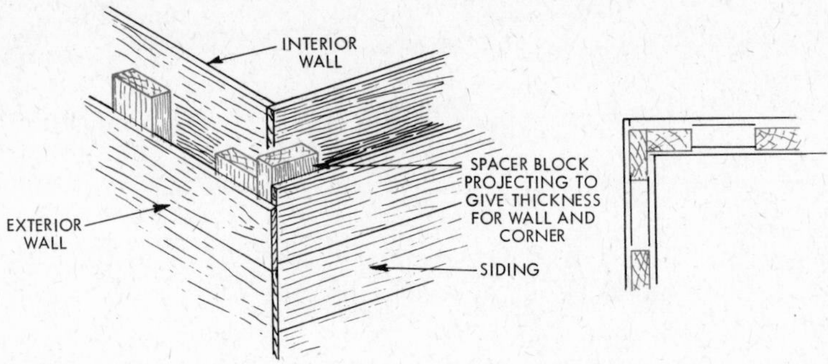

Fig. 15-14. These two methods may be used when constructing walls with balsa wood.

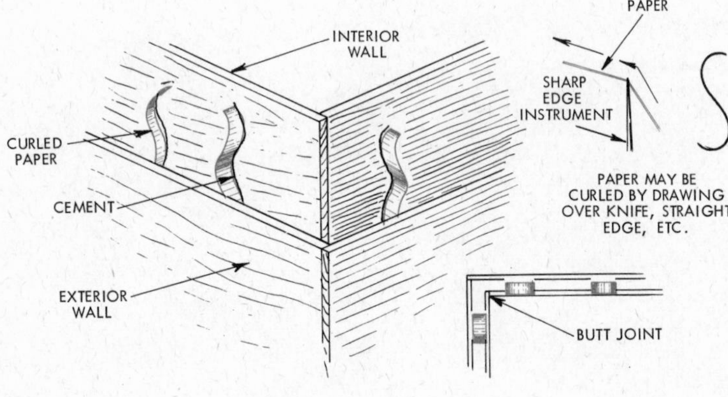

proper sequence, on a sheet of poster board. Any projections will be added after the basic form of the model has been erected.

(3) Cut out window and door openings.

(4) Cut along the roof line.

(5) Cut joints ⅔'s deep.

  A. Cut inside corners from rear.

  B. Cut outside corners from rear; cut miters with the sanding block.

(6) Fasten a print of the floor plan to a piece of plywood or other level surface.

(7) Carefully fold the exterior walls to their proper angle and pin to plan.

(8) Place reinforcement at all corners to insure square corners.

(9) Place glue blocks at roof edges and along the base of the model. Keep glue blocks at least ⅛" away from window openings to prevent them from being seen.

(10) Study roof for proper layout.

(11) Cut out and assemble roof. If support strips are necessary, cut to length and glue in place.

(12) Cut out chimney, dormers, etc.

(13) Glue chimney, dormers, etc., to model.
(14) Paint roof and walls or apply roofing materials and siding or brick materials to walls.
(15) Add window and door trim around all openings.
(16) Paint all trim.
(17) Lay out window lights and fasten to the back of openings.
(18) Cut out and secure curtains, draperies, etc.; cement to the rear of all windows.
(19) Cut out doors and fasten to openings with tape.
(20) Glue roof to model.
(21) Secure model to the building site and lay out location of walks, drive, etc.
(22) Apply all materials for walks and drives. Construct and fasten grass, trees, shrubs, hedges, and flowers.

Balsa Wood Display Models

Instead of using cardboard-type materials, the model may be constructed from balsa wood. Some model makers feel that balsa wood gives them more freedom and flexibility. Obviously, the walls cannot be laid out consecutively as with the cardboard-type model. Each wall is laid out and cut separately and then glued in place. (Corner reinforcement for a balsa wood model is the same as that used in cardboard models.) Otherwise, the general procedure is identical. Small bits of detail may be more readily added since balsa wood is easily shaped with a razor blade and abrasive paper. Siding materials, such as wood siding or masonry veneer and roofing materials, are applied in a manner identical to the cardboard model.

Removable Roofs

Some display models are designed so that the roof may be removed to view the interior of the model. Models of this type are usually used for commercial display purposes, such as development homes, building and loan association displays, home shows, exhibits, etc. All exterior features and appointments of the model are the same. The method of constructing corners will of necessity be altered. Several methods of construction are shown in Fig. 15-14. Many of the plumbing fixtures (sink, lavatory, bath tub, water closet) and appliances (refrigerator, stove, washer, dryer, etc.) can be carved from soap. Furniture, such as sofas, chairs, or beds, may be constructed from cardboard and covered with a solid or print material. Quilted chintz material adds the illusion of padding. Tables, coffee tables, etc., can be constructed from balsa wood, veneer, or "thin wood." One of the advantages of the "open" type of model is that various color schemes may be shown in their proper relationship.

Questions and Problems

1. Construct a presentation model of one of the house plans that was designed in Chapter 4. Compare the model with the elevations. Has the impression created by the plans and elevations changed after the completion of the model?
2. What types of changes could be recommended in the plans after analyzing the mass relationships of the model?
3. How many different uses are there for a display model?

PHOTO BY ALLAN STAMBERG.

The specifications give information not found on the working drawings.

Specification Writing 16

One of man's greatest problems stems from his inability to communicate adequately. One of the most precise methods of conveying technical information is through a technical drawing. However, supplemental information (specifications) must frequently be added for further clarification of materials, methods, etc. In the field of architectural drawing, specifications are an integral part of planning and designing a structure.

Specifications

The working drawings for a structure give only the shape and size. To be complete they must be accompanied by a set of specifications. Specifications give an explanation of the quality and kind of materials, colors, finishes, and fabrications. The quality of workmanship may also be given.

Specifications amplify and supplement the set of working drawings. They also give much of the information that cannot adequately be presented on each sheet of the set of drawings. If all the information contained in the specifications were to be placed on the drawing, it would be too scattered and difficult to find. Directions for various aspects of the building would have to be repeated many times. Using specifications, directions are given only once.

Only information which cannot be easily placed on plans is incorporated in the specifications. This should be presented in language that is clear, simple, and concise. In addition, specifications include information such as the legal responsibilities, methods of purchasing equipment, and the insurance requirements on the building.

Basically, the set of specifications serves three purposes. (1) It is a legal document that gives instructions for bid advertisement, bid invitations, owner-contractor agreement, and bond forms that are necessary. Before any specifications are written, the laws, building codes, the requirements of the state, and the ordinances of the local community should be consulted and used as guidelines. (2) Specifications serve as a guide for the contractor or sub-contractor who is bidding for the work. The specifications enable him to make an intelligent estimate of the costs that will be involved in the installation and/or construction. (3) Specifications also give technical descriptions and directions for fabricating and erecting the materials.

The specifications may be divided into several sub-divisions: scope of work, mate-

VA Form VB4-1852
FHA Form 2005
Jan. 1955

For accurate register of carbon copies, form may be separated along above fold. Staple completed sheets together in original order.

Form approved.
Budget Bureau No. 63-R055.10.

Plan 329 (includes 2 car garage)

☐ Proposed Construction

DESCRIPTION OF MATERIALS

No. .... (To be inserted by FHA or VA)

☐ Under Construction

Property address .... *City* .... *State* ....

Mortgagor or Sponsor .... (Name) .... (Address)

Contractor or Builder .... (Name) .... (Address)

INSTRUCTIONS

1. For additional information on how this form is to be submitted, number of copies, etc., see the instructions applicable to the FHA Application for Mortgage Insurance or VA Request for Determination of Reasonable Value, as the case may be.

2. Describe all materials and equipment to be used, whether or not shown on the drawings, by marking an X in each appropriate check-box and entering the information called for in each space. If space is inadequate, enter "See misc." and describe under item 27 or on an attached sheet.

3. Work not specifically described or shown will not be considered unless required, when the minimum acceptable will be assumed. Work exceeding minimum requirements cannot be considered unless specifically described.

4. Include no alternates, "or equal" phrases, or contradictory items. (Consideration of a request for acceptance of substitute materials or equipment is not thereby precluded.)

5. Include signatures required at the end of this form.

6. The construction shall be completed in compliance with the related drawings and specifications, as amended during processing. The specifications include this Description of Materials and the applicable Minimum Construction Requirements.

1. EXCAVATION:

Bearing soil, type Sand and Gravel

2. FOUNDATIONS:

Footings: Concrete mix 2500 # .... Reinforcing ....
Foundation wall: Material Poured Conc. 8" .... Reinforcing ....
Interior foundation wall: Material .... Party foundation wall ....
Columns: Material and size 3" adj. Post .... Piers: Material and reinforcing ....
Girders: Material and sizes 1 Beam 7" at 15.3 # .... Sills: Material ....
Basement entrance areaway .... Window areaways ....
Waterproofing Tar .... Footing drains ....
Termite protection Shield at Brick
Basementless space: Ground cover .... Insulation .... Foundation vents ....
Special foundations ....

3. CHIMNEYS:

Material Face Brick .... Prefabricated (*make and size*) ....
Flue lining: Material Vitrified Clay .... Heater flue size 8 x 12 .... Fireplace flue size 12 x 12
Vents (*material and size*): Gas or oil heater 5" G. I. .... Water heater 3" G. I.

4. FIREPLACES: OPTIONAL

Type: ☒ Solid fuel; ☐ gas-burning; ☐ circulator (*make and size*) .... Ash dump and clean-out 10
Fireplace: Facing Brick ....; lining Fire Brick ....; hearth Ceramic ....; mantel None

5. EXTERIOR WALLS:

Wood frame: Grade and species Cedar #2 .... ☒ Corner bracing. Building paper or felt 15# Felt
Sheathing Asphalt impregnated Fiberboard; thickness ½"; width 4 x 8; ☒ solid; ☐ spaced ...." o. c.; ☐ diagonal; ....
Siding Aluminum ....; grade ....; type ....; size ....; exposure 8" "; fastening Nailed
Shingles ....; grade ....; type ....; size ....; exposure ...."; fastening Per Mfg.
Stucco ....; thickness ....". Lath ....; weight .... lb.
Masonry veneer Face Brick $60/M .... Sills Lime Stone .... Lintels ....

rials to be used, fabrication and erection, and guarantee. The specifications are also often divided into trade divisions, such as excavation, fill and grading, concrete, masonry, structural steel and iron, carpentry and millwork, general metal, roofing, electrical, plumbing, heating, lathing and plastering, insulation, finish hardware, painting, special equipment, landscaping, planting, and finish grading.

The specifications spell out the *scope of work* that is to be performed by the contractor. He is told precisely what work he is to do—the labor, materials, and equipment he is to furnish. The *work not included* is also spelled out. Some facets of work in the various building trades are closely related and it becomes necessary to tell the contractor what is *not* to be included in a specific area. When workmanship is specified, this tells the workmen or sub-contractor how to do the work. For example, they may state how many coats of paint and what colors are to be applied to the interior and

Masonry: Facing ; backup thickness ". Bonding
Door sills Window sills Lintels
Interior surfaces: Dampproofing, coats of ; furring
Exterior painting: Material Exterior lead and oil ; number of coats 3
Gable wall construction: ☐ Same as main walls; ☐ other Aluminum siding in gable

6. FLOOR FRAMING: 2 x 10 - 16" o.c.
Joists: Wood, grade and species #2 Fir ; other ; bridging 1 x 3 ; anchors
Concrete slab: ☒ Basement floor; ☐ first floor; ☐ ground supported; ☐ self-supporting; mix 5 sk. ; thickness 3";
reinforcing ; insulation ; membrane
Fill under slab: Material Sand ; thickness 4".

7. SUBFLOORING: *(Describe underflooring for special floors under item 21.)*
Material: Grade and species 1/2" plyscore ; size 4 x 8 ; type Plyscore
Laid: ☒ First floor; ☐ second floor; ☐ attic sq. ft.; ☐ diagonal; ☐ right angles. Solid

8. FINISH FLOORING: *(Wood only. Describe other finish flooring under item 21.)*

Location	Rooms	Grade	Species	Thickness	Width	Bldg. Paper	Finish
First floor	Liv. Rm. Bedrooms Hall	#1	Oak	25/32	2½	Slaters	Felt Bruce
Second floor		Common	Shorts				
Attic floor	Family Rm. sq. ft.		Oak	Ranch	Plank		Prefinished

VA Form VB4–1852
FHA Form 2005 1 DESCRIPTION OF MATERIALS

DESCRIPTION OF MATERIALS

9. PARTITION FRAMING:
Studs: Wood, grade and species Cedar #2 Size and spacing 2 x 4 16" o.c. Other

10. CEILING FRAMING:
Joists: Wood, grade and species Trusses 24" o.c. Other Bridging

11. ROOF FRAMING: Fir 24" o.c.
Rafters: Wood, grade and species Trusses 24" o.c. Roof trusses (see detail): Grade and species

12. ROOFING:
Sheathing: Grade and species Fir Plyscore 3/8" ; size 4 x 8 ; type C. D. ; ☒ solid; ☐ spaced " o.c.
Roofing Asphalt shingles ; grade C ; weight or thickness 235 ; size 12x36; fastening Mfg. specs.
Stain or paint Underlay
Built-up roofing ; number of plies ; surfacing material
Flashing: Material 26 G. I. ; gage or weight ; ☐ gravel stops; ☐ snow guards

13. GUTTERS AND DOWNSPOUTS:
Gutters: Material G. I. ; gage or weight 24 ; size 4" ; shape O. G.
Downspouts: Material G. I. ; gage or weight 24 ; size 3" ; shape Rect. ; number
Downspouts connected to: ☐ Storm sewer; ☐ sanitary sewer; ☐ dry-well. ☒ Splash blocks: Material and size Concrete 12 x 24

14. LATH AND PLASTER:

Lath ☐ walls, ☐ ceilings: Material ; weight or thickness Plaster: Coats ; finish ~~Tape cement~~

Dry-wall ☒ walls, ☒ ceilings: Material Gypsum ; thickness 1/2 ; finish Smooth ; joint treatment ~~and sand~~

Rust proof metal corners, back block ceiling joints

15. DECORATING: *(Paint, wallpaper, etc.)*

Rooms	Wall Finish Material and Application	Ceiling Finish Material and Application
Kitchen		
Bath		
All Rooms	Alkyd Resin stipple-2 coats	Same - 2 coats

16. INTERIOR DOORS AND TRIM:

Doors: Type Flush and folding ; material Birch, Pine ; thickness 1-3/4 & 1-3/8

Door trim: Type Casing 1-3/4; material W.P. Base: Type Wood ; material W. P. ; size 2-1/4

Finish: Doors Flush-Seal and Varnish ; trim W. P.

Other trim *(item, type and location)*

17. WINDOWS:

Windows: Type Dble. Hung ; make Grand Rapids ; material W. Pine ; sash thickness 1-3/8

Glass: Grade SS ; ☐ sash weights; ☐ balances, type Spring ; head flashing

Trim: Type Casing ; material W. P. Paint Enamel ; number coats 2

Weatherstripping: Type Friction ; material SS Storm sash, number

Screens: ☐ Full; ☒ half; type Alum. ; number 9 ; screen cloth material alum.

Basement windows: Type 2-lite ; material steel ; ☐ screens, number 0 ; ☐ Storm sash, number 0

Special windows Wood picture - per elev.

18. ENTRANCES AND EXTERIOR DETAIL:

Main entrance door: Material W. P. ; width 3' ; thickness 1-3/4" Frame: Material Wood ; thickness 5/4"

Other entrance doors: Material W. P. ; width 2'8" ; thickness 1-3/4" Frame: Material W. P. ; thickness 5/4"

Head flashing Galv. Weatherstripping: Type Friction ; saddles Aluminum

Screen doors: Thickness "; number ; screen cloth material Storm doors: Thickness "; number

Combination storm and screen doors: Thickness 1 "; number 2 ; screen cloth material Aluminum

Shutters: ☐ Hinged; ☒ fixed. Per Elev. Railings Louvers 2 - 14 x 20 metal

Exterior millwork: Grade and species 1 - W. P. Paint Exterior Grade ; number coats 3

19. CABINETS AND INTERIOR DETAIL:

Kitchen cabinets, wall units: Material Birch W. P. ~~XXXXX~~ Sp. feet of shelves 25 ; shelf width 12"

Base units: Material Birch W. P. ; counter top 16 sp. ft. ; edging Formica

Back and end splash Ceramic full Back Splash Finish of cabinets Stain and Varnish ; number coats 3

Medicine cabinets: Make Miami Carey 621 ; model Ideal 501

Other cabinets and built-in furniture 48" Formica Vanity

20. STAIRS:

Stair	Treads		Risers		Strings		Handrail		Balusters	
	Material	Thickness	Material	Thickness	Material	Size	Material	Size	Material	Size
Basement	Fir	2 x 10			Fir	2 x 10	W. P.	1-3/4	Round	
Main										
Attic										

Disappearing: Make and model number

2

exterior of the house. Since the specifications serve as a contract, all reference to what the contractor must do is commonly introduced by the word *"shall"*; all reference to what the owner must do is commonly introduced by the word *"will."*

Specifications can also be used in appraising a building for the purposes of loan evaluation. In some instances, lending institutions will ask for the specifications on an existing building so they may more adequately assess the value. Specifications call out the materials that have been used in the building and not merely those materials which are visible.

The architect or designer usually prepares the specifications for a set of drawings. This way there is less chance a misunderstanding will occur about the material to be used in the building. In some cases the architect will indicate that no substitutions may be made for a particular item. If, however, a substitute is permitted, the words *"or equal"* or *"or similar"* are used. Preparing specifica-

21. SPECIAL FLOORS AND WAINSCOT:

	Location	Material, Color, Border, Sizes, Gage, Etc.	Threshold	Base	Underfloor
Floors	Kitchen &	Dining area - Vinyl Tile		W.P. 2¼	5/8 Ply.
	Bath	Ceramic	Marble	Ceramic	Cement
	½ Bath	Vinyl Tile			5/8 Ply

	Location	Material, Color, Border, Cap, Sizes, Gage, Etc.	Height	Height at Tub	Height at Shower
Wainscot	Bath	Ceramic Tile in Mastic with bull nose			
		Tub recess only		6'	6'

Bathroom accessories: ☐ Recessed; material ________; number ____; ☒ attached; material Ceramic; number 9

22. PLUMBING:

Fixture	Number	Location	Make	Mfr's Fixture Identification No.	Size	Color
Sink	1	Kitchen	Townsend	Steel enamel Dble compartment	32 x 21	Colored
Lavatory	2	Bath	Rheem Richmond	Roundell & Richeleu	18" & 19x17	Colored
Water closet	2	Bath	Rheem Richmond	G2210		Colored
Bathtub	1	Bath	Rheem Richmond		5'	
Shower over tub*	1		Chrome pltd.Brass			
Stall shower**						
Laundry trays	1	Basement	Mustee-single	Compartment fiberglass	24 x 24	

*☒ Curtain rod **☐ Door ☐ Curtain rod

Water supply: ☒ Public; ☐ community system; ☐ individual (private) system.★

Sewage disposal: ☐ Public; ☐ community system; ☒ individual (private) system.★

★*Show and describe individual system in complete detail in separate drawings and specifications according to requirements.*

House drain (inside): ☐ Cast iron; ☐ tile; ☒ other ~~copper~~ House sewer (outside): ☐ Cast iron; ☒ tile; ☐ other ________

Water piping: ☐ Galvanized steel; ☒ copper tubing; ☐ other ________ Sill cocks, number 2

Domestic water heater: Type Automatic; make and model Republic

recovery 25.2 gph. 100° rise. Storage tank: Material ________; capacity 40 gallons.

Gas service: ☒ Utility company; ☐ liq. pet. gas; ☐ other ________ Gas piping: ☒ Cooking; ☒ house heating.

Footing drains connected to: ☐ Storm sewer; ☐ sanitary sewer; ☐ dry well. Sump pump ________

23. HEATING:

☐ Hot water. ☐ Steam. ☐ Vapor. ☐ One-pipe system. ☐ Two-pipe system.

☐ Radiators. ☐ Convectors. ☐ Baseboard radiation. Make and model ________

Radiant panel: ☐ Floor; ☐ wall; ☐ ceiling. Panel coil: Material ________

☐ Circulator. ☐ Return pump. Make and model ________; capacity ________ gpm.

Boiler: Make and model ________ Output ________ Btuh.; net rating ________ Btuh.

Warm air: ☐ Gravity. ☒ Forced. Type of system Perimeter

Duct material: Supply Sht.Metal; return Sht. Metal Insulation ________, thickness ________ ☐ Outside air intake.

Furnace: Make and model Lennox Input 120,000 Btuh.; output 96,000 Btuh.

☐ Space heater; ☐ floor furnace; ☐ wall heater. Input ________ Btuh.; output ________ Btuh.; number units ________

Make, model ________

Controls: Make and types Minneapolis-Honeywell Automatic

Fuel: ☐ Coal; ☐ oil; ☒ gas; ☐ liq. pet. gas; ☐ electric; ☐ other ________; storage capacity ________

tions is becoming more involved and exacting every day. New material and new methods of construction require close investigation by the architect or designer. It is imperative that all features of the "specs" be made clear so that there is no misunderstanding.

Specifications may have errors. Some errors to guard against are: (1) unfair and ambiguous clauses, (2) a difference between the drawings and specifications, (3) unclear specifications of materials, and (4) an omis-

Firing equipment furnished separately: ☐ Gas burner, conversion type. Stoker: ☐ Hopper feed; ☐ bin feed.
Oil burner: ☐ Pressure atomizing; ☐ vaporizing
Make and model .... Control ....

Electric heating system: Type .... Input .... watts; @ .... volts; output .... Btuh.

Ventilating equipment: Attic fan, make and model ....; capacity .... cfm.
Kitchen exhaust fan, make and model ....
Other heating, ventilating, or cooling equipment Rangpire Model 523 Ductless

24. ELECTRIC WIRING:
Service: ☒ Overhead; ☐ underground. Panel: ☒ Fuse box; ☐ circuit-breaker 100 amp.service Number circuits 7 x 1
Wiring: ☐ Conduit; ☐ armored cable; ☒ nonmetallic cable; ☐ knob and tube; ☐ other ....
Special outlets: ☐ Range; ☐ water heater; ☐ other Furnace-Laundry circuit
☒ Doorbell. ☐ Chimes. Push-button locations Front and Rear Doors

25. LIGHTING FIXTURES: 11 up
Total number of fixtures 5 down Total allowance for fixtures, typical installation, $ 100.00
Nontypical installation ....

3 DESCRIPTION OF MATERIALS

DESCRIPTION OF MATERIALS

26. INSULATION:

LOCATION	THICKNESS	MATERIAL, TYPE, AND METHOD OF INSTALLATION	VAPOR BARRIER
Roof			
Ceiling	3"	Blown in fiberglass	
Wall	1/2	Asphalt impregnated fiberboard & 1-1/2 fiberglass with vapor barrier	
Floor			

27. MISCELLANEOUS:
(Describe any main dwelling materials, equipment, or construction items not shown elsewhere):

Birch Cabinets
Brush Coat Basement
Double Compartment Sink
Built-in Range and Oven
48" Formica Vanity
Formica Edged Countertops
Miami-Carey Sliding Mirrors
Hood and Fan
Aluminum Siding
Flush Birch Closet Doors

100 Ampere Service
Screens
Family Rm. Paneled with Abitibi
Gun Stock
Glass Doorwall

HARDWARE: *(Make, material, and finish)* Front and Rear - Quikset 400 Std.
Passage - Reliant 700
Bath Passage - Chrome 710

sion of necessary clauses that should be included for the owner's protection.

The buyer of a new home that has been built speculatively, or the buyer who has contracted to have a house built, should ask to read the specifications. Any questions concerning the content or interpretation of the specifications should be clarified immediately. Remember, specifications are a part of a legal document and, combined with the drawings, may be used in court as binding evidence in the event of a litigation.

SPECIAL EQUIPMENT: *(State material or make and model.)*

Venetian blinds .... Number .... Automatic washer ....
Kitchen range Westinghouse .... Clothes drier ....
Refrigerator .... Other ....
Dishwasher ....
Garbage disposal unit ....

PORCHES:

Floating slabs, post hole footings on large porch elev.

TERRACES:

42 x 42 on ground slab

GARAGES:

19 x 20 Garage, 16' Taylor Door, 42" footing-
Brick front one side, over half, drywall sidewall, & Ceiling trusses 24 o.c., aluminum
siding on end and rear; 12 x 19 Family Room rear of Garage

WALKS AND DRIVEWAYS: 16' at Garage, 16' at street

Driveway: Width .... Base material Sand; thickness 4". Surfacing material Concrete; thickness 4"
Front walk: Width 3 Material Concrete; thickness 4". Service walk: Width 2 Material Conc.; thickness 4"
Steps: Material ....; treads ...."; risers ....". Cheek walls ....

OTHER ONSITE IMPROVEMENTS:

(Specify all exterior onsite improvements not described elsewhere, including items such as unusual grading, drainage structures, retaining walls, fence, railings, and accessory structures.)

Finish grade entire lot

LANDSCAPING, PLANTING, AND FINISH GRADING:

Topsoil 4" thick: ☐ Front yard; ☒ side yards; ☒ rear yard to rear of lot feet behind main building.
Lawns *(seeded, sodded, or sprigged)*: ☒ Front yard ....; ☒ side yards ....; ☐ rear yard ....
Planting: ☐ As specified and shown on drawings; ☐ as follows:

1 Shade trees, deciduous, 1-1/2" caliper.
.... Low flowering trees, deciduous, ...' to ....'
.... High-growing shrubs, deciduous, ...' to ....'
.... Medium-growing shrubs, deciduous, ...' to ....'
.... Low-growing shrubs, deciduous, ...' to ....'
.... Evergreen trees, ...' to ....', B & B.
.... Evergreen shrubs, ...' to ....', B & B.
.... Vines, 2-year ....

IDENTIFICATION.—This exhibit shall be identified by the signature of the builder, or sponsor, and/or the proposed mortgagor if the latter is known at the time of application.

Date .... Signature ....

Signature ....

4

VA Form VB4–1852
FHA Form 2005

U. S. GOVERNMENT PRINTING OFFICE : 1961 O -619988

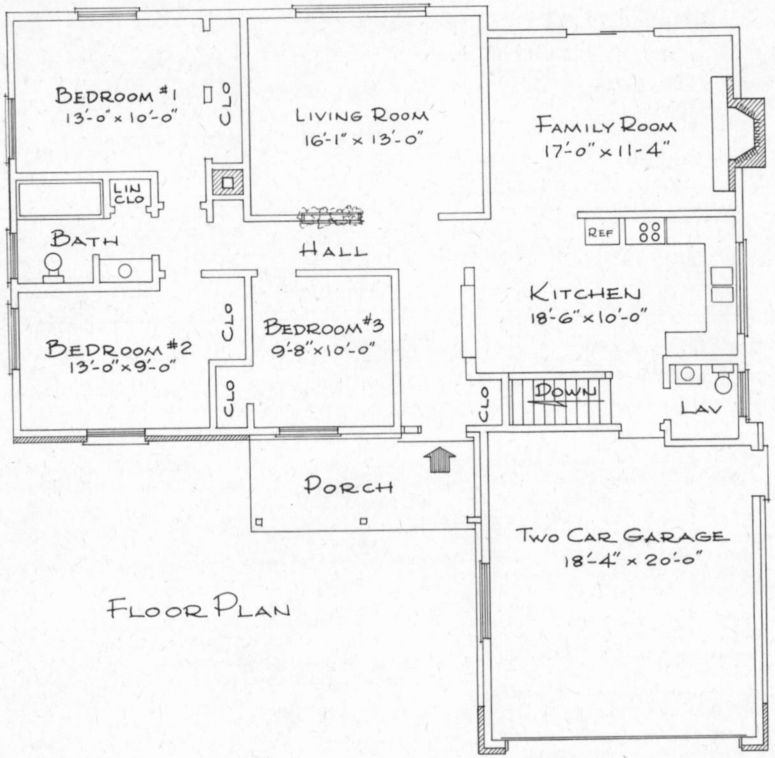

BEDROOM #1
13'-0" x 10'-0"
CLO
LIVING ROOM
16'-1" x 13'-0"
FAMILY ROOM
17'-0" x 11'-4"
LIN CLO
BATH
HALL
REF
KITCHEN
18'-6" x 10'-0"
CLO
BEDROOM #3
9'-8" x 10'-0"
BEDROOM #2
13'-0" x 9'-0"
CLO
CLO
DOWN
LAV
PORCH
TWO CAR GARAGE
18'-4" x 20'-0"
FLOOR PLAN

Fig. 16-1. This floor plan is used with the FHA specifications.

Fig. 16-2. Use this perspective with the FHA specifications.

Specification Forms

Specifications, for the most part, are similar in form and content. Materials used in the construction of a frame house will, of course, be different from the materials used in a brick veneer house with concrete block backing. However, the *form* is the same.

Specifications are rarely completely written from the beginning. Most designers have a basic form which they use for all residential building. Fill-in forms are available in all major construction classifications. All that must be added to the fill-in or completion form is a description of the exact size, material quantity, type, or catalog number of the material. These forms are usually available from office supply houses.

The specification form shown is supplied by the U.S. Government Printing Office for builders who are seeking a FHA or GI appraisal for loan purposes. The floor plan and perspective of the one-story residence given in the specification is also shown. See Figs. 16-1 and 16-2.

Another specification form is shown in Appendix C. This is a basic form used by a planning service.

A careful estimate and responsible, informed financing assures the security of the home.

Estimating and Financing 17

To approach home design and home selection on an intelligent basis, both the architect and the prospective buyer must have some knowledge of the estimated value of the home and the standard procedures used in the purchase transaction. There is a direct relationship between the financial condition of a prospective home owner and the value of the home he can afford. Given the financial condition of a prospective buyer, it is possible to determine the price range of homes he may reasonably consider. Knowing this, the architect is able to design house plans to fit within the buyer's price range. In addition to this, the architect may be expected to advise the client on financial questions.

Home Estimating

Estimating the cost of a building represents the expenditures required to cover the *entire* cost of building, or the *entire* cost of remodeling. For the contractor or builder, it represents *all* the required material and labor costs for *each* item forming the completed structure. The smallest items, such as lock sets for doors, door stops, removal of dirt from the excavation, etc., must be included in the estimate to insure an accurate cost analysis.

Besides material and labor costs, the contractor, in submitting a bid, must *also* consider operating expenses, equipment depreciation, and profit.

The seemingly limitless number of items which enter into the cost of any building will vary widely with the locality, climate, labor, and market condition. It is imperative, therefore, that the prospective builder make a careful estimate in order to intelligently assess the cost of the building and the approximate number of man hours needed to successfully complete the job.

Rough Estimates

Square Footage

Probably the quickest and most simple method of computing a *rough estimate* (for purposes of comparing similarly constructed houses) is to figure the square footage. This simply involves the two principle dimensions of the house, *length* (width) and *depth*. (Note: dimensions are taken from the *outer* surfaces of the *outside* walls.)

It should be emphasized that the square footage method is of value only when comparing *similar* construction built with *similar* prices for *labor, materials,* and *design.* For example, the price per square foot of a plain frame, ranch-type house with minimal appointments *cannot* be used to estimate the cost of a two-story brick veneer colonial with above average fixtures and appointments. A multi-level dwelling will, in the long run, tend to be slightly less per square foot than a one-story, all factors being approximately equal. If the cost for a multi-level dwelling is to be estimated by the square footage method, a similar type home should be used for comparison.

Estimating the construction cost of a home may be accomplished on the square foot basis by reference to such manuals as Boeckh's *Manual of Appraisals* or Wenzlick's *Residential Appraisal Manual.* These manuals contain cost per square foot figures which must be multiplied by a factor (predicated on the location of the building in the United States) to arrive at the cost in a particular locale. The square footage method should *not* include open or closed porches, attached garages, or basements.

Take, for example, a one-story slab house, 40′ × 28′. Using the square footage method (length times depth), the house would contain 1120 sq. ft. Let us say that similar houses in the same locality cost on the average of $15.50 per sq. ft. The square footage method would give a rough estimate of $17,360 for the house (1,120 sq. ft. times $15.50). Any unusual or expensive features would, of course, cause this estimate to be too low. Conversely, using a lower grade of material or omitting common features would cause this estimate to be too high.

Cubic Footage

A more refined method (compared to the square foot method) of arriving at a *rough estimate* is by computing the *cubic footage* of the house. (Sometimes cubic footage is referred to as *cubic content.*)

This calculation takes into consideration all three principal dimensions: *length, depth,* and *height.* The cost per cubic foot is similarly dependent upon the type and quality of building materials and on the wages paid to workers. These, of course, will vary from locality to locality. Again, only *similar* houses may be compared.

The cubic content is often used before the working drawings or specifications have been completed for a cost approximation. To obtain the total cubic footage, multiply the total square footage (length × depth) in the floor plan by the height of the building. The height of the structure is measured from the floor (*underside* of concrete slab) to the plate, plus one-half the distance from the plate to the ridge (outside of roof). Non-enclosed porches and attached garages may be figured at *one-half* volume; basements at *two-thirds* volume. The total cubic footage is multiplied by the average cost per cubic foot for similar houses.

Take the same one story slab house (40′ × 28′) used in the previous section. Assume the height from *under* slab to top plate is 8′-6″. The cubic footage for the main part of the house would be 9,520 cu. ft. (1,120 sq. ft. times height 8′-6″). Assume the height from top plate to the ridge (outside measurement) is 6′, and that a symmetrical gable roof is used. The attic volume would be 3,360 cu. ft. (one-half distance from eave line to ridge, 3′, times 1,120 sq. ft.). The total cubic footage would be 12,880 cu. ft. Assume the average cost for similar houses in the same locality is $1.45 per cu. ft. The cubic footage method would give a rough estimate of $18,670 for the house (12,880 cu. ft. times $1.45).

Exact Estimate

The most accurate method used to determine an estimate is by actually making a quantity survey of materials, labor, time, etc., needed to construct the house. All the information necessary for these calculations is taken directly from the working drawings. Information relative to the kind, quantity, and quality of materials is obtained from the written specifications. Excavation information is derived from the floor plans (or the foundation plan if a basement is planned) and the plot plan. There are many forms and procedures for taking off materials from the plans and specification. However, a successful estimate depends basically upon the practical experience and knowledge gained from long familiarity with house construction.

JOHN M. ANDERSON, AIA, ARCHITECT. BELL & VALDEZ, BUILDERS; BELLEVUE, WASHINGTON.

Fig. 17-1. This well-designed and well-planned L-ranch house has a sheltered lanai and adjoining patio with a direct access to the living room and family room.

Estimating List

An estimating list, if organized systematically, is an asset in assuring that all items have been accounted for. For convenience, the estimating list may be broken into the following categories.

1. Earth excavation and grading
2. Concrete construction and finish
3. Brick and block construction and veneer
4. Wall paving and floor paving
5. Lumber framing and construction
6. Sheet metal work
7. Wood, exterior and interior, millwork
8. Gypsum board, ceiling and wall
9. Floor and wall tiling, vinyl and ceramic
10. Metal finish hardware
11. Finish, interior and exterior paint
12. Bathroom accessories
13. Plumbing system and fixtures
14. Heating system and fixtures
15. Electrical system and fixtures

The order in which the estimating categories are presented is generally the same as that followed in the specifications. The sequence follows the order in which the various trades work on the job. Plumbing, heating, and electrical work, however, are traditionally put at the end.

To show exactly how the preceding list may be used, Fig. 17-1 illustrates a home built in the Seattle, Washington area at a cost of $22,900 in late 1963 by Bell and Valdez Builders.[1] Fig. 17-2 depicts the floor plan, elevations, and details of this highly functional, three bedroom basementless home. The following estimating materials inventory lists all of the items and considerations necessary for construction.

House Area.	
Livable floor area	1585 S[2]
Garage floor area	465 S
Lanai floor area	240 S
Lanai storage floor area	55 S
Earth Excavation & Grading.	
Topsoil 6″ grade exc. & pile	7545 S
Earth floor leveling	2345 S
Earth foundation exc. & B′ fill	310 C[3]
Earth hand footing exc. & f′fill	600 C
Gravel 4″ floor sub-fill	790 S
Concrete Construction & Finish.	
2500# Conc. chim. pier & wall footing	330 C
2500# Conc. chim. pier & wall footing forms	540 S

1. "Well-planned 'L' Wins Honors in A/B Contest," *American Builder,* XXCVI (March, 1964).
2. S = square feet.
3. C = cubic feet.

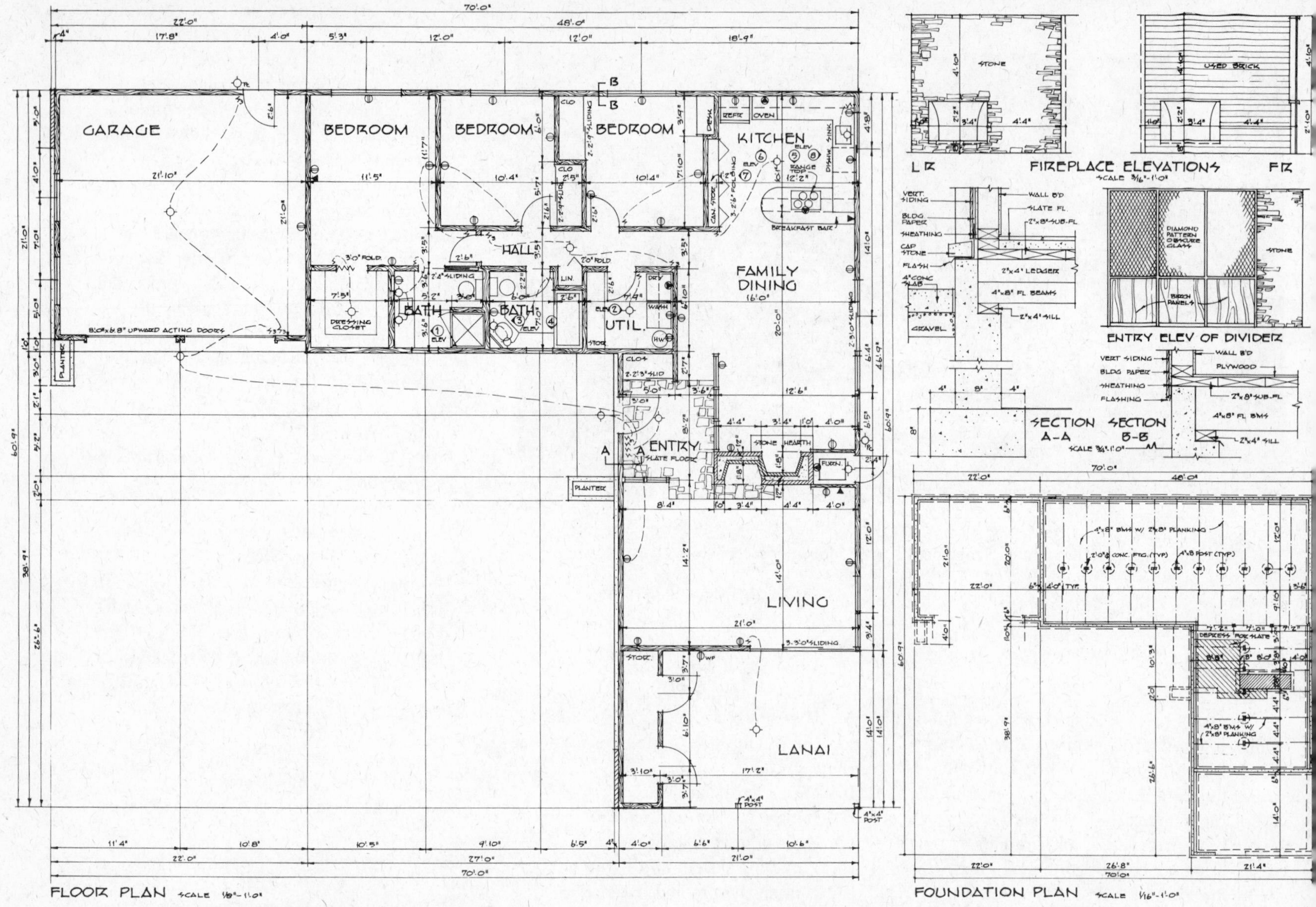

Fig. 17-2. These working drawings show plan, elevations, and details of the L-ranch house. (Drawing not to scale, reduced to fit page.)

JOHN M. ANDERSON, AIA, ARCHITECT. BELL & VALDEZ, BUILDERS; BELLEVUE, WASHINGTON.

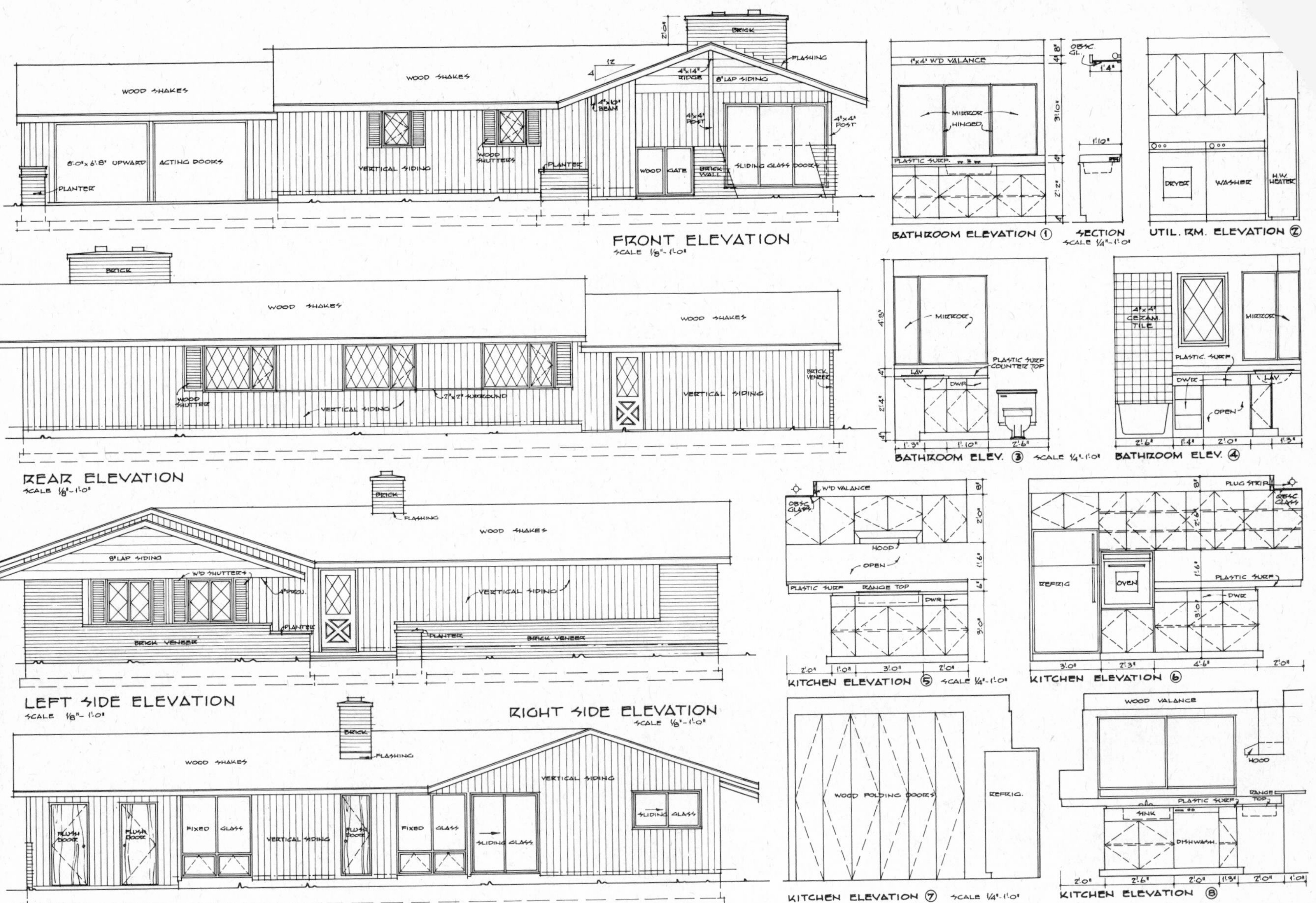

Fig. 17-2. Cont'd.

2500# Conc. foundation walls	385 C
500# Conc. foundation walls forms	1440 S
2500# Conc. 4″ floor slab O.G.	790 S
2500# Conc. 5″ × 1″ wall cap & forms	20 L[4]
P. C. Conc. 4″ × 2½″ wall sills	40 L
P. C. Conc. 4″ chimney cap	25 S
Monolithic floor wd. float finish	790 S
Kraft paper floor wd. prot. & cure	790 S

Brick & Block Construction & Veneer.

Face brick 4″ ext. wall veneer	255 S
Face brick 4″ ext. chim. wl. veneer	90 S
Face brick 4″ planter & retain. walls	135 S
Sel. com. brick 4″ fireplace veneer	90 S
Fire brick 4″ f. p. floor paving	10 S
Fire brick 4″ f.p. wall lining	30 S
Conc. block chimney construction	215 C
Vitr. T. C. 12″ × 12″ chim. flue	25 L
Acid & mortar expose brick clean & point	610 S
Metal 12″ × 36″ F. P. dampers	2 U[5]
Metal 4″ × 8″ cleanout doors	2 U
Metal 3″ × 4″ × ¼″ F. P. lintels	8 L

Stone Wall Facing & Floor Paving.

Fieldstone 4″ f.p. wall facing	90 S
Slate 2″ hearth & floor paving	85 S
Brush & water facing & pave cleaning	175 S

Lumber Framing & Construction.

4″ × 14″ wood drs. roof ridge	15 L
4″ × 10″ wood doors roof beams	30 L
4″ × 8″ wood floor beams	370 L
4″ × 8″ wood 24″ floor beams post	18 U
4″ × 4″ wood drs. structural post	18 L
2-2″ × 10″ wood O.H. door lintel	20 L
2-2″ × 8″ wood door & wind. lintel	95 L
2″ × 8″ wood roof ridge	105 L
2″ × 8″ wood valance blocking	30 L
2″ × 8″ wood 16″ oc ceiling joists	1535 S
2″ × 8″ wood floor planks	1510 S
2″ × 6″ wood 16″ oc ceil. joists	465 S
2″ × 6″ wood 16″ oc roof rafter	3230 S
2′ × 6″ wood 16″ oc part. studs	75 S
2-2″ × 6″ wood partition sills	10 L
2″ × 6″ wood partition plates	10 L
2″ × 6″ wood o'head door bucks	30 L
2″ × 4″ wood 16″ oc part. studs	1250 S
2″ × 4″ wood 16″ oc wall studs	2165 S
2-2″ × 4″ wood studs sill	415 L
2″ × 4″ wood studs plates	415 L
2″ × 4″ wood floor ledger	45 L
2″ × 4″ found. fir. beam sills	100 L
1″ × 6″ wall lining	1760 S
1″ × 6″ roof lining	3230 S
Plyscore ½″ floor lining	1510 S
15# felt roof insulation	3230 S
15# felt wall insulation	1760 S
15# felt floor insulation	1510 S
Wood roof shakes	3230 S
Wood ext. vertical siding	1405 S
Wood ext. lap siding	100 S

Metal Sheet Work.

16 oz. copper chimney flashing	35 S
16 oz. copper wall sill flashing	40 S
16 oz. copper roof valley flashing	45 S
16 oz. copper cap & base flashing	30 S
16 oz. copper found. wall flashing	200 S

Wood Exterior & Interior Millwork.

Wood 8″ × 6′-8″ o'Head door & acc.	2 U
Wood 3′ × 6′-8″ ext. door, F&T	2 U
Wood 2′-4″ × 7′ ext. door, F&T	1 U
Wood & glass 3′ × 7′ ext. door, F&T	1 U
Wood & glass 2′-6″ × 7′ ext. door, F&T	1 U
Wood & glass 6′ × 7′ ext. sldg. door, F&T	1 U
Wood & glass 9′ × 7′ ext. sldg. door, F&T	1 U
Wood 2′-6″ × 6′-8″ int. door, F&T	4 U
Wood 2′-2″ × 6′-8″ int. door, F&T	1 U
Wood 2′-4″ × 6′-8″ int. sldg. door, F&T	1 U
Wood 2-2′ 3″ × 6′-8″ int. sldg. door, F&T	1 U

4. L = lineal feet.
5. U = units(s).

Wood 2-2′ 9″ × 6′-8″ int. sldg. door, F&T 1 U
Wood 2′ × 6′-8″ fldg. door, F&T 1 U
Wood 3′ × 6′-8″ fldg. door, F&T 1 U
Wood 3-2′-6″ × 7′ fldg. door F&T 1 U
Wood & glass 6′ × 2′-8″ sldg. wind. F&T 1 U
Wood & glass 6′ × 7′ comb. F&P wind. F&T 2 U
Wood & glass 6′ × 3′-6″ F&Case. wind. F&T 3 U
Wood & glass 2′ × 2′-6″ casem. F&T 2 U
Wood & glass 3′-6″ × 3′-6″ fixed wind. F&T 2 U
Wood 1′-6″ × 3′-6″ wind. shutters 6 U
Wood 1′-6″ × 3′ wind. shutters 4 U
Wood 1″ × 8″ ext. fascia 310 L
Wood ⅜″ soffit boarding 755 S
Wood 2″ × 2″ ext. moulding 12 L
Wood 5′ × 4′ lanai gate & acc. 1 U
4″ wd. & glass 8′ int. divid. walls 12 L
Wood 1″ × 24″ closet shelving 15 L
Wood 1″ × 12″ storage shelving 35 L
Wood 1″ × 18″ storage shelving 30 L
Wood 1″ × 16″ closet shelving 17 L
Wood 1″ × 2″ shelving cleats 97 L
Wood 1″ d. closet poles 32 L
Wood 1″ × 8″ wall valance 30 L
Wood & glass 1″ × 16″ lt. fixt. screen 7 L
Prefin. wood 6′-6″ × 1′-8″ × 2′-6″ van. base cab. 1 U
Prefin. wood 7′ × 2′ × 2′-6″ van. corn. base cab. 1 U
Prefin. wood 4′-6″ × 2′-6″ × 1′ util. wl. cab. 1 U
Prefin. wood 3′ × 1′-6″ × 2′-6″ desk 1 U
Prefin. wood 2′ × 3′ kit. base cabinet 17 L
Prefin. wood 2′-6″ × 1′ kit. wall cabinet 12 L
Prefin. wood 3′ × 3′ kitchen island base cabinet 6 L
Prefin. wood 2′ × 1′ kit. island wall cabinet 8 L

Gypsum Board Ceil. & Wall Boarding.

Gypsum board ½″ T. J. ceil. boarding 1535 S
Gypsum board ½″ T. J. gar. ceil. boarding 465 S
Gypsum board ½″ T. J. wall ceil. boarding 3250 S
Gypsum board ½″ wall lining 130 S

Vinyl & Ceramic Floor & Wall Tiling.

Vinyl ⅛″ floor tiling 1425 S
Vinyl 4″ wall base 475 L
Gypsum board ½″ wall lining 130 S

Metal Finish Hardware.

Metal ext. cylinder locks 5 U
Metal ext. sldg. dr. locks 2 U
Metal int. sldg. dr. locks 1 U
Metal int. door locks 5 U
Metal int. fldg. dr. locks 3 U
Metal int. door hinges 10 U
Metal ext. door hinges 15 U
Metal int. sldg. dr. hardware set 2 U
Metal ext. sldg. dr. hardware set 2 U
Metal window sldg. dr. hardware set 10 U

Paint Ext. & Int. Finish.

Paint ext. millwork 3 coats 2950 S
Paint int. millwork 3 coats 600 S
Paint wood doors 3 coats 1525 S
Paint wood sash 3 coats 400 S
Paint gyp. bd. ceil. 2 coats 2000 S
Paint gyp. bd. wall 2 coats 3250 S

Metal & Glass Toilet Room Accessories.

Metal & Glass 3′ × 7′ shower encl. door 1 U
Metal & glass medicine cabinet 2 U
Chrome metal toilet paper holders 2 U
Chrome metal soap dish & grab bar 1 U
Chrome metal tumbler & tooth-brush holder 2 U
Chrome metal 24″ towel bar 4 U
Chrome metal 5′ shower curtain rod 1 U
Metal & glass 3′-6″ wall mirror & acc. 12 U

Plumbing System & Fixtures.

Water service connection & piping 1 U
Sanitary service connection & piping 1 U
Gas service connection & piping 1 U
Gas furnace connection & piping 1 U
Washer connection & piping 1 U
Dishwasher connection & piping 1 U
Dryer connection & piping 1 U
Hose bibb connection & piping 2 U
Vanity sinks connection & piping 2 U
Bath tub connection & piping 1 U
Water closet connection & piping 2 U
Shower head connection & piping 1 U
Shower drain connection & piping 1 U
Kitchen sink connection & piping 1 U

Heating System & Fixtures.

Gas hot air furnace & accessories	1 U
Gas hot air temp. control equip.	1 U
Metal ducts & registers	14 U

Electrical System & Fixtures.

Electric service connection	1 U
Electric service panel & switch	1 U
Telephone service connection	1 U
Gas furnace connection & wiring	1 U
Range top, connection & wiring	1 U
Built-in oven connection & wiring	1 U
Dishwasher connection & wiring	1 U
Clothes washer connection & wiring	1 U
Exhaust fan, connection & wiring	1 U
Range hood, connection & wiring	1 U
Elec. H. W. htr., connection & wiring	1 U
Single switch, outlet & wiring	11 U
3-way Switch, outlet and wiring	7 U
Conv. recept. outlet & wiring	28 U
Telephone recept. outlet & wiring	3 U
Conv. Recept. W. P., outlet & wiring	1 U
Entr. P. button, outlet & wiring	2 U
Ceil. light outlet & wiring	7 U
Wall light outlet & wiring	5 U
Ext. wl. light outlet & wiring	4 U
Ceiling fixtures & bulbs	7 U
Wall fixtures & bulbs	5 U
Wall W. P. fixtures & bulbs	4 U

So that an accurate estimate may be obtained, the total man-hour cost for skilled and semi-skilled craftsmen and laborers must also be computed.

Reliable estimates based on the various areas of the United States are given in the *Building Construction Cost Data* book (published by the Robert Snow Means Co., Duxbury, Mass.). This publication is revised yearly and gives estimating information (by geographical area) on materials and labor costs.

Home Financing

In buying a home, no obligation should be assumed that does not take into consideration emergencies which may arise. A close relationship must exist between the mortgage payments and the family's income.

Yearly and Monthly Income

Frequently, a "rule of thumb" is used to determine roughly the amount one can afford for a house. Perhaps the most popular is 2½ times the total yearly gross income of the chief wage earner. Another "rule of thumb" is to take ¼ to ⅕ of a month's salary, *or* one week's pay out of each month's salary for *housing expenses.* Housing expenses are based on the monthly payment for principal and interest to retire the loan, *plus* 1/12 annual fire insurance premium (this is required), *plus* 1/12 annual property tax, *plus* 1/12 annual mortgage insurance premium (if desired by the home owner.) These figures give only rough estimates of how much can be devoted to housing. For some these guidelines may be followed with safety, for others it may only spell disaster. For example: a family could easily use these guidelines if they purchased a home in an established area where the schools were debt-free, the taxes low, and the house located close to the chief wage earner's employment. If, on the other hand, this same family were to purchase a home in a *new development* located some distance from the city, with no paved streets, sidewalks, etc., they would have to pay considerably more taxes, eventual assessments, and greater transportation costs. Yet, in both cases, the factors would indicate the family could afford the house.

The figures shown in Table 17-1 can be used to determine the approximate amount that can be spent for housing. These figures are based on what most families can afford to pay, namely about ⅕ of the monthly or annual income. To assess the probable cost which the family can assume, simply read across. If, for example, a family earns approximately $416.00 per month, they could adequately purchase a $12,000 house. If the family has one or two children, then take the figure in the preceding row; if there are three or more children, then two figures above. For example, if there are two children and the head of the family earns $8,-000, they can purchase a $16,500 home. A family having the same income with three or four children can afford a $14,500 home. If a family has extraordinary expenses (such as anticipated high taxes, many installment payments, large educational bills, high food costs, entertainment, travel, medicine, or doctor bills) the price of the house must be lowered. If these circumstances prevail, the house cost must be additionally lowered one figure.

TABLE 17-1

APPROXIMATE HOUSE COST IN RELATION TO INCOME

INCOME*		TOTAL HOUSE COST
MONTH	YEAR	
$ 333	$ 4,000	$ 9,100
416	5,000	12,000
500	6,000	14,500
583	7,000	16,500
666	8,000	19,700
750	9,000	22,500
833	10,000	25,500
916	11,000	27,500
1,000	12,000	30,000
1,250	15,000	35,000

*Gross income or income before deductions.

Housing Income

A more reliable method for calculating the amount available for housing is listed by the U. S. Savings and Loan League, *What You Should Know Before You Buy a Home.*

1. List the total take-home income. This is the *spendable* income derived from the total salary or wages *minus* all deductions for income taxes, social security, hospitalization, retirement, etc. Note: The wife's income or children's income *should not* be included since this is usually temporary when compared to the life of the mortgage. Include any income derived from dividends or interest if this is permanent.
2. List *all expenses,* including money for food, clothing, medical and dental care, life insurance, education, recreation, utilities and fuel, transportation, monthly savings, contributions, dues, and installment purchases. Total these.
3. Subtract total expenses (#2) from the total take-home income (#1). The result gives the housing income, or the amount that can be spent on housing. This determines, in part, the size of mortgage the prospective home owner can adequately carry.

Table 17-2 gives the approximate loan amounts (based on housing income) which may be borrowed. These amounts are calculated for 10, 15, and 20 year mortgages at different rates of interest.

If, for example, it has been determined that the total amount available for housing is $125.00 a month or $1,500 per year, the approximate loan amount can then be determined. Using the approximate loan amounts in Table 17-2, it may be assumed, for example, that a $14,425.00 home loan could be safely undertaken at 5½ per cent interest for a 20 year period. According to the U. S. Savings and Loan League, this represents what one would be able to finance from current income. The loan amounts given in Table 17-2 *do not* include costs of maintenance or upkeep which vary with age, size and construction of the home. These figures also *do not* include the down payment required by all lending institutions. By adding the amount available for a down payment to $14,425.00, a basic figure will be obtained which the family can afford.

Other variables may enter into the total picture and thereby affect the over-all housing cost and mortgage size. Some lending institutions consider the present income and potential income of the prospective borrower, size of the down payment, mortgage terms, present and projected taxes, utility costs, time payments on appliances, commuting costs, ability to save, number of children, and existing or potential basic improvements in the community (schools, public buildings, streets, etc.).

Home Loans

Basically, three types of home loans are currently available to the public: (1) Private conventional loans, which are assumed by a private lender, such as a bank, savings and loan association, or commercial mortgage house; (2) GI Loans, wherein the government *guarantees* the loan; and (3) FHA (Federal Housing Administration) government insured loans, wherein the money is borrowed from a private source, but the loan is *insured* by the federal government.

The conventional loan is available for financing both old and new homes. The availability of the GI and FHA loans for both new and old homes is governed by the supply of home mortgage money, demand for mortgages, level of interest rates, and other related factors. The conventional loan can easily adjust to the varying needs of the people and to changed financial conditions. The GI and FHA loan can not readily adjust because the terms are fixed by the Congress of the United States.

TABLE 17-2
APPROXIMATE LOAN AMOUNTS BASED ON MONTHLY INCOME FOR HOUSING*

INCOME FOR HOUSING		AT 5 3/4%			AT 5%		
MONTHLY	ANNUAL	10 YR	15 YR	20 YR	10 YR	15 YR	20 YR
$ 40	$ 480	$ 3, 265	$ 4, 210	$ 4, 850	$ 3, 245	$ 4, 140	$ 4, 800
50	600	4, 080	5, 265	6, 060	4, 055	5, 170	6, 000
60	720	4, 900	6, 315	7, 275	4, 865	6, 205	7, 200
80	960	6, 530	8, 420	9, 695	6, 485	8, 275	9, 600
100	1, 200	8, 165	10, 525	12, 120	8, 110	10, 345	12, 000
125	1, 500	10, 205	13, 160	15, 150	10, 135	12, 930	15, 000
150	1, 800	12, 245	15, 790	18, 180	12, 160	15, 520	18, 000
175	2, 100	14, 285	18, 420	21, 210	14, 190	18, 105	21, 000
200	2, 400	16, 325	21, 050	24, 240	16, 215	20, 690	24, 000
225	2, 700	18, 365	23, 685	27, 270	18, 245	23, 275	27, 000
250	3, 000	20, 405	26, 315	30, 300	20, 270	25, 860	30, 000

		AT 5 1/2%			AT 6%		
MONTHLY	ANNUAL	10 YR	15 YR	20 YR	10 YR	15 YR	20 YR
$ 40	$ 480	$ 3, 180	$ 4, 035	$ 4, 615	$ 3, 115	$ 3, 935	$ 4, 485
50	600	3, 975	5, 040	5, 770	3, 895	4, 920	5, 605
60	720	4, 770	6, 050	6, 920	4, 675	5, 900	6, 730
80	960	6, 360	8, 070	9, 230	6, 235	7, 870	8, 970
100	1, 200	7, 950	10, 085	11, 540	7, 790	9, 835	11, 215
125	1, 500	9, 935	12, 605	14, 425	9, 740	12, 295	14, 020
150	1, 800	11, 920	15, 125	17, 310	11, 690	14, 755	16, 820
175	2, 100	13, 910	17, 650	20, 190	13, 635	17, 215	19, 625
200	2, 400	15, 895	20, 170	23, 075	15, 585	19, 670	22, 430
225	2, 700	17, 880	22, 690	25, 960	17, 530	22, 130	25, 235
250	3, 000	19, 870	25, 210	28, 845	19, 480	24, 590	28, 035

From: U. S. Savings and Loan League. WHAT YOU SHOULD KNOW BEFORE YOU BUY A HOME.

*Taxes have been estimated at $18 annually and insurance at $3 annually for every $1, 000 loaned on the house.

Conventional Loans

Private conventional loans are construed to include all loan plans in which the federal government *does not participate,* either as a *guaranteeing* or as an *insuring agent.* The loan is given by a bank, savings and loan association, insurance company, mortgage house, or by any one who wishes to lend the necessary amount. The lending institution advances its own money to the borrower, and if for some reason he is unable to repay, the lender stands the loss. The rate of interest charged on the private conventional loan is usually higher (ranging between 5 to 7 per cent) and the length of time for repayment is usually shorter (10 to 20 years) than the GI or FHA loans. The down payment required for the conventional loan may be as low as 10 per cent, or may range up to 40 per cent of the purchase price. The down payment is usually less for a new home than for an old home.

GI Loans

The GI loan is for veterans only. The maximum interest rate and the terms of the loan are controlled by the federal government. The down payment is less than other types of loans and the terms are longer. The government guarantees the lending institution a greater part of the loan in case of default. Private lending institutions make the loan; *the government does not lend the money.*

FHA Loans

An FHA loan is *insured by the government* against default. As with the GI loan, a private lending agency grants the loan, but the federal government insures that the *lender* will not lose on the loan. The loan is only insured when *both* the credit standing of the borrower and the construction standards of the house are satisfactory. (The construction is checked periodically by an inspector from the FHA.) These standards enable much larger loans (higher loan to value ratio) to be granted by the lender because of the protection against loss. Thus, smaller down payments are required. The borrower pays an insurance premium of ½ of 1 per cent computed monthly, on the outstanding principal. In addition an application fee is charged by the FHA. Both "government type" loans take much longer to obtain due to the extensive investigative measures which must be conducted.

Mortgages

The type, size, and location of a house is important. But just as important, however, is the economic status of the purchaser and his credit rating. These two features play an important role in the decision of the lending institution to grant a mortgage.

The closer the purchaser meets the borrowing standards of the lending institution, the higher (within reasonable limits) the mortgage. That is: the higher the loan will be in comparison to the value of the property. This feature is especially true when qualifying for a low interest mortgage. Usually all lending institutions will view the purchaser from the following vantage points.

His ability to pay:

1. Purchaser's income must be sufficient to support the monthly mortgage obligation. The monthly income (before deductions) should be four or five times greater than the mortgage payment.
2. Purchaser's income after deductions should be sufficient to allow for minimal size installment payments.
3. Purchaser's record of employment should be steady. One year in present position is desirable.

His willingness to pay:

1. Purchaser's credit record should be good. All lending institutions will investigate the purchaser's credit rating. It is sound business to establish a credit rating.
2. Purchaser's credit record should not contain any judgments or bankruptcies unless they can be justifiably explained.

Mortgage Contract Features

The mortgage contract may include some or all of the following features. Their inclusion makes home ownership less costly, more pleasant, and more convenient.

1. *Package Provision.* This enables the borrower to finance certain appliances and other necessary items as part of the original loan.
2. *Open End Provision.* This allows the borrower to apply for additional funds, before the mortgage is paid off, with repayment *amortized* (spread) over the term of the loan.
3. *Additional Payment Privilege.* This allows the borrower, without penalty, to make additional payments over the regular monthly payment. These additional payments apply strictly to the principal.
4. *Full Prepayment Privilege.* This permits the borrower to repay the balance of the loan prior to the maturity date. The note should be checked, since some may be prepaid in as short a period as 91 days without any service charge. With other notes, the period may range between 3 to 5 years.
5. *Loan Modification Agreement.* This permits adjusting the terms of the original mortgage in accordance with a change in the borrower's financial status.
6. *Taxes and Insurance Provision.* This allows taxes and insurance to be paid over a 12 month period.
7. *Transfer Privilege.* This allows the property to be sold with only a nominal charge for service.
8. *Mortgage Redemption Insurance.* This assures the surviving family a debt-free home in event of the home owner's death. The small amount paid for mortgage insurance is wise protection for the family.
9. *Skip-a-payment Plan.* This grants the borrower the right, in case of emergency or financial hardship, to skip one monthly payment per year. The mortgage is extended, however, and the necessary interest is added to meet the increased length of time.

Second Mortgage

The more money that can be used for the down payment, the better chance a prospective home owner has of purchasing a more costly home. And the more money that is used for a down payment, the smaller the amount that needs to be borrowed. Consequently, less total interest will be paid over the life of the loan. The greater the *equity* (the value of the property minus liens and the unpaid balance), the greater the incentive a purchaser has to achieve full ownership. However, if the buyer does not have sufficient funds for the down payment, the seller may arrange for a *second mortgage*. The risk is great.

The second mortgage may be obtained through private or conventional sources for the difference between the prospective home owners fund and the largest available first mortgage. (The first mortgage may cover only 60 to 70 per cent of the purchase price.) With a second mortgage (as with the conventional, GI, or FHA loan) the buyer retains the legal title to the property.

Monthly Payments

Most loans will be repaid on a monthly basis over a period of years. The figures shown in Table 17-3 represent the monthly amount paid to retire the mortgage for each $1,000 borrowed. These figures represent both principal and interest. If, for example, a loan was assumed for $13,000 at 5½ per cent interest for 20 years, the monthly payment, exclusive of insurance and taxes, would be $6.88 × 13 = $89.44. A more complete financial picture may be obtained by adding $3.00 per month per $1,000 borrowed to account for insurance, taxes, and upkeep for the home. In this instance, an additional $39.00 would be added to the $89.44, making the total $128.44 per month. Taxes vary between towns and suburban areas just as insurance rates vary; therefore, the figure of $3.00 per $1,000

TABLE 17-3

MONTHLY PAYMENT NECESSARY TO AMORTIZE EACH $1,000 BORROWED FOR HOME OWNERSHIP

LOAN LENGTH YEARS	MONTHLY PAYMENT REQUIRED TO AMORTIZE $1,000							
	4 1/2%	4 3/4%	5%	5 1/4%	5 1/2%	5 3/4%	6%	6 1/4%
10	10.37	10.49	10.61	10.73	10.86	10.98	11.11	11.23
11	9.62	9.75	9.87	9.99	10.12	10.25	10.37	10.50
12	9.01	9.13	9.25	9.38	9.51	9.63	9.76	9.89
13	8.48	8.61	8.74	8.86	8.99	9.12	9.25	9.38
14	8.04	8.17	8.29	8.42	8.55	8.68	8.82	8.95
15	7.65	7.78	7.91	8.04	8.18	8.31	8.44	8.58
16	7.32	7.45	7.58	7.71	7.85	7.98	8.12	8.26
17	7.03	7.16	7.29	7.43	7.56	7.70	7.84	7.98
18	6.77	6.90	7.04	7.17	7.31	7.45	7.59	7.73
19	6.54	6.67	6.81	6.95	7.08	7.22	7.37	7.51
20	6.33	6.47	6.60	6.74	6.88	7.03	7.17	7.31
21	6.15	6.28	6.42	6.56	6.70	6.85	6.99	7.14
22	5.98	6.12	6.26	6.40	6.54	6.69	6.84	6.98
23	5.83	5.97	6.11	6.25	6.40	6.54	6.69	6.84
24	5.69	5.83	5.97	6.12	6.27	6.41	6.56	6.72
25	5.56	5.71	5.85	6.00	6.15	6.30	6.45	6.60
26	5.45	5.59	5.74	5.89	6.04	6.19	6.34	6.50
27	5.34	5.49	5.64	5.78	5.94	6.09	6.24	6.40
28	5.24	5.39	5.54	5.69	5.84	6.00	6.16	6.31
29	5.15	5.30	5.45	5.61	5.76	5.92	6.08	6.24
30	5.07	5.22	5.37	5.53	5.68	5.84	6.00	6.16

Compiled from IMPROVED PAYMENT TABLE FOR MONTHLY MORTGAGE LOANS (Boston: Financial Publishing Co., 1961).

borrowed may be high or low, depending upon the area.

Home Cost Considerations

Interest

Various means exist by which the cost of a house may be reduced. For example, not all lending institutions charge the same amount of interest. The interest rates of the local savings and loan association, bank, insurance company, and Veterans Administration (GI Loan) may very well differ ½ per cent. Shop for a loan—borrow the money as cheaply as possible.

Long Term Mortgage—Extra Payments

A long term mortgage (20 to 30 years) may benefit the prospective buyer more than it may appear on the surface. With this type of mortgage, thousands of dollars may be saved by making extra or additional payments. These additional payments are deducted directly from the principal, without any portion being used for interest, taxes, insurance, or escrow fund. That portion of each payment devoted to interest, particularly on a long term loan, may be used as a deductible feature on income tax. This offers a distinct advantage. The long term loan also offers lower monthly rates. It is wise to inspect the loan agreement to be sure that extra payments can be made and are deducted from the principal.

Interest Rates and Loan Length

Table 17-4 draws an interesting comparison of varying interest rates for a loan of $12,500. For example, the monthly payment, based on 5¼ per cent, for 15 years is $100.49. At the same interest rate for 30 years, the monthly payment is $69.03. Compare the difference, however, in the total amount paid in the 15 year term, $18,-088.20, with the total amount on the 30 year term, $24,850.80. The lender pays $6,-762.60 for the additional 15 years use of the unpaid balance. Contrary to popular opinion the difference of ¼ per cent in the interest rate does not make an appreciable difference in the monthly payment; however, on loans over 20 years the difference in total payment is significant.

TABLE 17-4

A COMPARISON OF INTEREST RATES AND LOAN LENGTH BASED ON A LOAN OF $12,500

INTEREST RATE	PAYMENT	LENGTH OF LOAN IN YEARS			
		15	20	25	30
5 1/4%	MONTHLY	100.49	84.24	74.91	69.03
	TOTAL	18,088.20	20,217.60	22,473.00	24,850.80
5 1/2%	MONTHLY	102.14	85.99	76.77	70.98
	TOTAL	18,385.20	20,637.60	23,031.00	25,552.80
5 3/4%	MONTHLY	103.81	87.77	78.64	72.95
	TOTAL	18,685.80	21,064.80	23,592.00	26,262.00
6%	MONTHLY	105.49	89.56	80.54	74.95
	TOTAL	18,988.20	21,494.40	24,162.00	26,892.00

Compiled from IMPROVED PAYMENT TABLE FOR MONTHLY MORTGAGE LOANS (Boston: Financial Publishing Co., 1961).

Owner Construction

If the prospective owner is a "do-it-yourself man," and if the contractor or builder will permit, some work may be contracted by the owner (such as painting, landscaping, laying tile, building terraces, patios, planting grass, etc.). In some instances the prospective owner is not fully aware of the enormity of his responsibility when contracting to paint the entire house inside and outside, to grade and landscape the site, or to trim the inside. For some, these contracts resolve themselves into frustrating hours, weeks, and even months of lost time.

Building Economy

Frequently, if the lending institution or guaranteeing agency (FHA) will permit, substitutions may be made at a savings to the purchaser. Frequently, for example, vinyl tile may be substituted for hardwood flooring, dry wall (sheet rock) for plaster, or a lavatory for an extra full bath.

Elimination of fancy and costly details obviously result in savings. Proper perspective of the funds available will aid in planning. Plan so that details may be added after the initial financial burden has passed. For example, building the garage or finishing the basement or attic can be done at a later date.

Additional Costs

A word of caution is extended at this point. Do not exhaust all savings for the sake of the down payment. Some reserve funds should be set aside for emergency use. Remember additional cash will be needed for:

1. Closing costs (including appraisal fees and loan charges), fees for recording the mortgage or deed, legal fees, and/or fees for title insurance or evidence of clear title to the property.
2. Repairing, decorating, and modernizing in the case of an existing home; and landscaping for a new home.
3. Drapes and fixtures, or carpeting to make the home more livable.
4. Moving costs.

5. New appliances and furnishings that may be considered necessary in purchasing a home.

Transaction Closure

Services of a competent attorney should be secured in completing the purchase of the house to insure that all statements relative to the title, deed, loan, contracts, etc., are correct. In any event, the prospective owner should be familiar with certain essentials and the terms involved in the final transaction. The architect may be expected to act as a counselor in advising and assisting the client.

Once the house plans, lot, and contractor have been selected, or the house has been selected, the usual procedure is then to make a payment of approximately 1 per cent of the purchase price to the contractor or realtor. This payment is generally referred to as *earnest money* and indicates the buyer intends to purchase the property or to build the house. Following this, the buyer files a formal mortgage loan application with the institution who will lend the money. This loan application requires rather detailed information concerning personal income, savings, debts, credit references, property appraisal, and the amount of money to be borrowed. The information given on this form will be carefully checked and evaluated by the lending institution. If the lender is satisfied with the qualifications of the prospective borrower and the property is a good risk, he will give the loan. The borrower than receives notification verifying the acceptance of the loan application. The terms of the mortgage will be drawn and a date set for "closing the transaction." At this date the buyer, seller (or his agent), representative of the mortgage lender, and the attornies involved will be present.

At the loan closing the buyer presents the lender with an amount of money equal to the down payment, *plus* closing costs and *less* the earnest money previously paid. The seller will then present the deed to the property with evidence of clear title to the buyer. The seller then receives a check (from the mortgagee) for the balance of the sale price (less the seller's expenses). (The seller's expenses include: cost of abstracting, drafting of deed, payment of existing lien balances and assessments, real estate sales commission, and his share of pro-rated taxes for the current year.) The buyer then signs the mortgage.

Real Estate and Mortgage Terminology

The following lists some general terms encountered in home financing.

Real Estate

1. *Deed* is the legal instrument that transfers the title of property from one person to another.
   a. *Warranty Deed* is a guarantee by the seller that the title is flawless.
   b. *Quit Claim Deed* guarantees nothing—it merely undertakes to transfer the title. The deed has (or presumes to have) properly described the property.
2. *Title* is that which gives the right of ownership.
3. *Appraisal* is an evaluation of property in order to determine its value.
4. *Abstract* is the legal description of the property and history of previous ownerships.
5. *Certificate of Title* is the assurance that the title to the property is unmistakably in the purchaser's name.
6. *Title Search* is an investigation conducted to see that the ownership of house is free of liens.
7. *Title Insurance* insures against any defects that may exist in the title prior to the time the title is passed. These defects may come to light at a future transaction.
8. *Earnest Money* is a deposit given by a prospective buyer to the seller as evidence he is in earnest about buying the property.
9. *Purchase Agreement* contains all essential terms and conditions of the sale, and the memorandum of agreement between seller and purchaser. This is executed pending examination of the title and performance of other conditions affecting the transfer of property.
10. *Recording* of deeds with the registrar (for the county in which land is located) is the best insurance against loss

of agreements affecting transfer of ownership.

11. *Escrow* is money and papers held by a third party until the conditions in the contract are fulfilled.
12. *Equity* is the increasing portion of the house the buyer owns as the mortgage is paid off.
13. *Depreciation* is the decline in value of a house from wear and age.

Mortgage

1. *Mortgage* is the pledge of property (in the case of housing) as security for payment of a debt.
2. *Straight Mortgage* comes due all at once at a specific date (that is both the interest and the principal).
3. *Amortized Mortgage* is a systematic loan reduction plan. Monthly payments are made that retire the mortgage. These payments include interest, payment on principal, taxes, assessments, and insurance premiums.
4. *Second Mortgage* is made on property where a first mortgage already exists. The risks are greater and interest rates are higher. In the case of foreclosure, the holder of the second mortgage cannot collect until the first mortgage holder has been satisfied.
5. *Mortgagee* is the one who gives the mortgage or the lender who puts up the money for the mortgage.
6. *Mortgagor* is the home buyer who has signed the mortgage. He makes out the mortgage to the mortgagee (the lender uses the mortgage as security).
7. *Lien* is in effect a mortgage. A lien may be filed by anyone who has a claim for labor or material costs against the property.
8. *Note or Bond* is a written promise to repay the money borrowed.
9. *Interest* is the *rent* paid for money borrowed.
10. *Closing Costs* are paid by the buyer as a fee charged by the lenders for making the mortgage.
11. *On Schedule* refers to payments which fall periodically on a set date.
12. *Foreclosure:* After a certain number of mortgage defaults, the mortgagee, under the terms of the contract has the right to sell the property in public auction to regain his investment.

Questions and Problems

1. Assume that the average cost for building an "L" ranch house in your area is $14.75 per sq. ft. Using the square footage method, what would be the rough estimate for the house shown in Fig. 17-2? Do not include the square footage of the garage or the lanai (exclusive of storage space). Measure from outside walls (walls are 8″ thick).
2. Using the same plan (Fig. 17-2), estimate the rough cost using the cubic footage method. Assume $1.80 per cubic foot. Use one-half volume for the lanai and the garage.
3. A prospective home owner is able to finance a house costing $20,000. He wishes to buy an "L" ranch house. At $1.20 per cu. ft., what is the total volume he can afford? How does this knowledge aid the plan designer? How does this aid the buyer in selecting a house?
4. A prospective home owner has $3,500 for a down payment on a piece of property. This represents 25% of the purchase price. He can obtain a 6% loan over a 20 year period. How much of his income should be set aside each month to take care of housing? What is the value of the property he will own?
5. How much could be afforded for a house if the prospective buyer earned $7,000 per year, had 2 children, and had exceptional medical expenses?
6. How much could be saved on a $14,000 loan at 5½% interest for 15 years as compared to the same amount for 25 years?
7. A prospective owner wants to buy a piece of property for $16,000. He has $4,000 for a down payment and will borrow the rest for 15 years at 6% interest. How much must he pay per year to cover the cost of ownership? Insurance, taxes, and upkeep must be included.
8. A prospective home buyer earns $450 monthly. How much can he afford to borrow on a 6%, 20-year loan? He has $3,000 for a down payment. What would be the total home expenditure?

RILCO LAMINATED PRODUCTS.

Commercial architecture must take into account the use to which the structure will be put. This supermarket is located in Virginia.

Light Commercial Buildings 18

There are two basic differences between light commercial and residential buildings. First, the commercial structure is planned for investment purposes. Second, the commercial plan must be concerned with the flow of material goods as well as personnel. Coupled with these two main differences are numerous other features which play an important role in arriving at a workable, attractive plan. No single chapter could completely cover all of the aspects of light commercial architecture. This chapter is presented as a basis for planning and as a springboard into the multi-faceted commercial field.

Commercial Classifications and Activities

Business may be grouped together into three general classifications: *servicing, merchandising,* and *manufacturing*. A partial list representative of each group is given below. Light commercial architecture also falls into these three general groups.

1. *Servicing:* Repair, laundry, dry cleaning, insurance, brokerage, medical, dental, bookkeeping, barber, beauty, motel, gas station, branch bank, appliances, general office, etc.
2. *Merchandising:* hobby, toy, florist, dry goods, men's wear, women's wear, grocery, hardware, variety, drug, bakery, home furnishings, auto sales, restaurant, shoe, etc.
3. *Manufacturing:* sheet metal, machine shop, tent and awning, tailor, plastics, mill work, print shop, etc.

It is evident that some businesses fit poorly into any one category, or fit into more than one category. However, there are certain *activities* which are common to all types of light commercial architecture. Depending upon the building and its intended use, areas must be planned for these activities. However, not all of these may be common to any one building. The outline below gives the major activities that must be considered in planning.

1. Merchandising
    a. Sales
    b. Display
    c. Customer reception
2. Material Goods Handling
    a. Receiving
    b. Routing
    c. Storage
    d. Shipping
3. Work Areas
    a. Preparation for manufacture
    b. Manufacture
    c. Fabrication

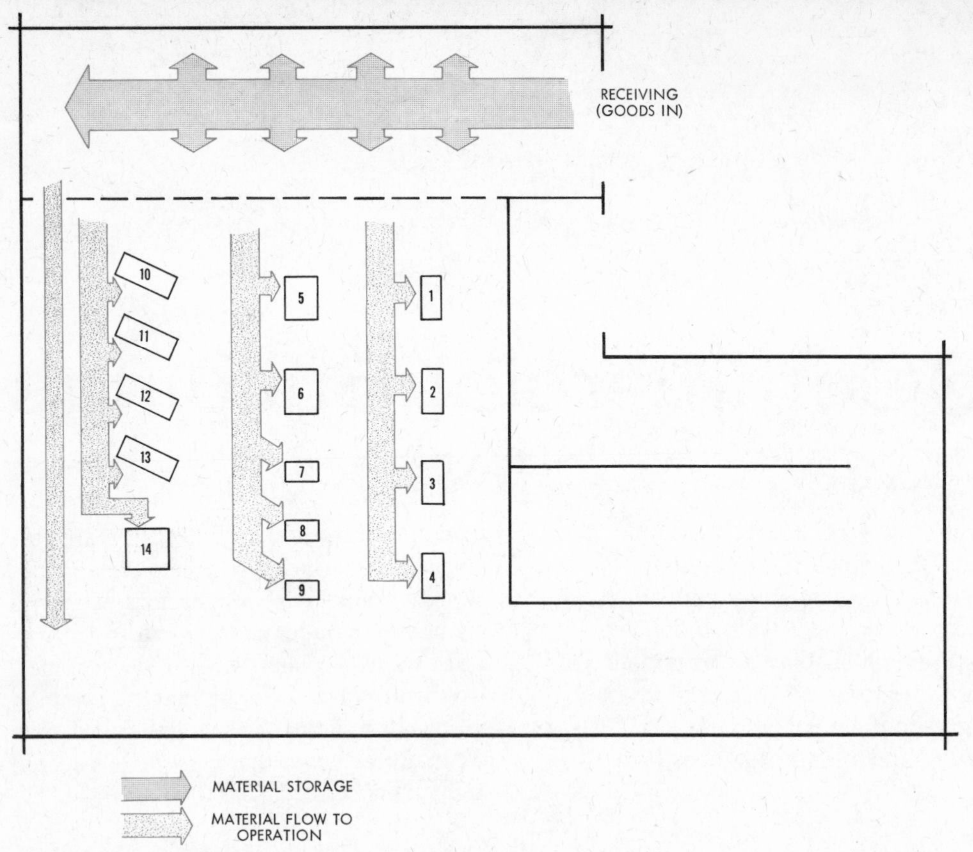

Fig. 18-1. Material Flow in a Commercial Structure.

d. Check out area
e. Clerical
f. Service
4. Sanitation and Rest
a. Customer
b. Employees
5. Maintenance and Power

Planning Points

Using the common business activities outlined above, a series of planning points may be derived for light commercial structures.

Material Flow. All businesses must have provision for an orderly flow of materials from the *receiving dock or facility, to storage and/or dispersing area.* The flow of materials should be planned so it will not interfere with other activities of the building.

Consideration must be given to the amount and kinds of material received and the frequency of delivery. Provision must also be made for convenient and adequate storage, and for aisleways for material flow and personnel circulation. Fig. 18-1 illustrates typical material flow in a commercial structure.

Merchandising. Space must be set aside for *display, sales,* and *stock storage.* The type of business will determine the space devoted to merchandising. Obviously an apparel store or small super market would require much more display area than that of a light manufacturing concern. The type of merchandise offered for sale, the importance of the display location, and the area allotted for customer circulation, will frequently dictate the arrangement of the merchandising area. In the selling area, the merchandise should be separated according to the needs of the customers. For example:

1. Staple articles—those items which the customer intends to purchase.
2. Convenience articles — those goods which the "looking customer" may purchase, and which may lead to other purchases.
3. Luxury goods—those articles that are high profit but not necessarily high priced. These items have eye appeal that may draw customers.

Often, luxury items are placed to attract the customer's attention and to guide him to areas where he may make a purchase. Fig. 18-2 shows a customer flow pattern for a men's haberdashery. The customer flow of traffic is generally to the right and all service features should be related to this. Most businesses are designed to handle many customers. Ample space, therefore, should be provided to permit traffic flow.

Servicing. Servicing may take many forms. Depending upon the type of service offered, considerations must be given to waiting

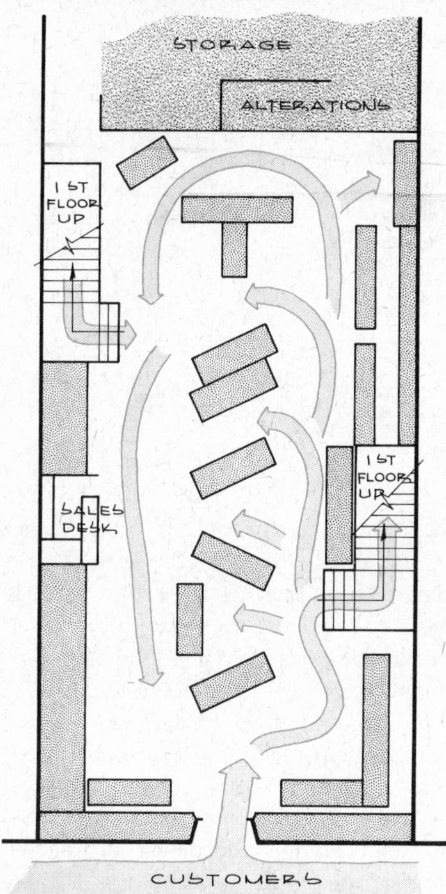

Fig. 18-2. Customer Circulation in a Men's Haberdashery.

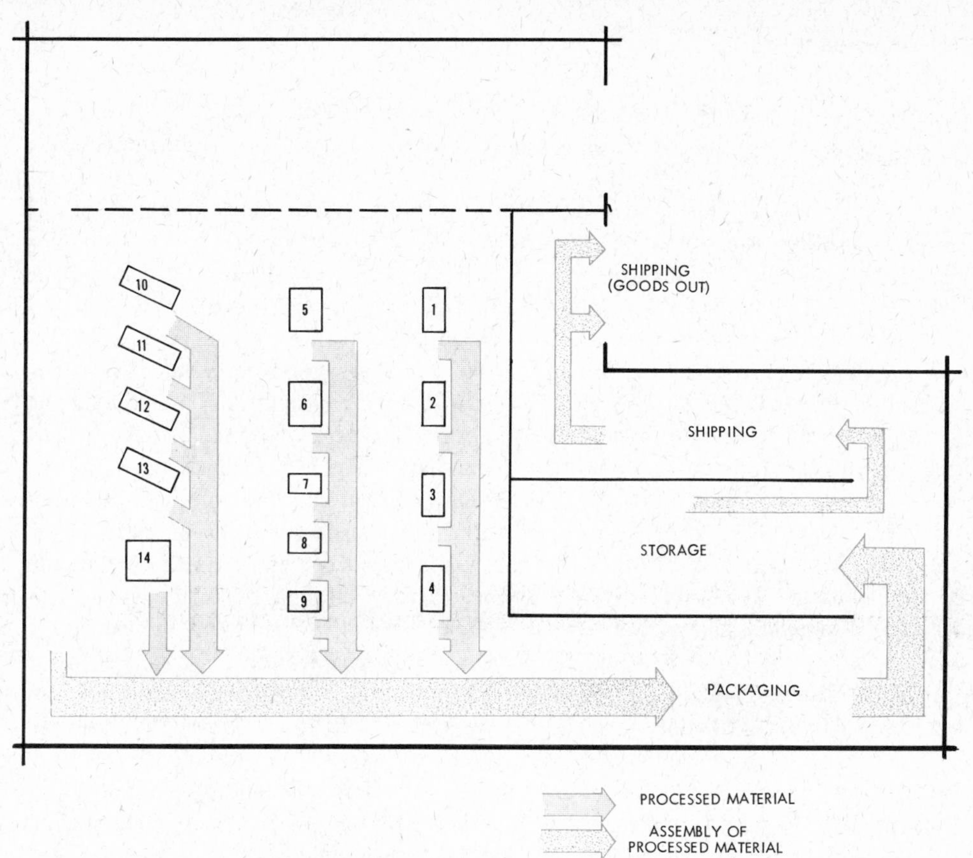

Fig. 18-3. Manufacturing Flow Diagram.

areas, eating areas, lounge areas, etc. If the business offers repair and adjustment, adequate space must be allocated for this work area. Space requirements for the necessary service equipment must be analyzed to allow for adequate movement of personnel.

Manufacturing. If light manufacturing is planned, a *flow diagram* of the steps of manufacture or fabrication should be drawn. This aids in the identification of necessary work stations and personnel areas. See Fig. 18-3. (Compare this figure to the material flow in Fig. 18-1.) It may be wise to bring in consulting groups.

After the production flow has been outlined, equipment requirements (amount, size, weight, etc.) must be checked so the structure will carry the imposed loads. In addition, space must be allocated for packaging of the finished product.

Office Space. Virtually every commercial structure includes some type of provision for business transactions, conferences, etc. These areas should be away from the noise and distractions of the business itself. Many buildings include one or more offices that will provide the necessary privacy.

In some instances commercial structures

are planned with a second floor or with a portion of the main level as rental office space. Frequently, contractors or developers will plan an entire building based on leased office space. Whether one portion or the entire structure is devoted to offices, the following items should be considered: (1) *reception area* (2) *waiting and display area,* (3) *main offices* (if a suite of offices is planned), (4) *subsidiary offices,* (5) *work areas for personnel,* and (6) *storage facilities.* The designers must consider sound proofing and office acoustics, as well as artificial and natural lighting.

Flexibility. The interior should be planned for flexibility. This is usually accomplished by designing on a modular basis and using movable, non-load bearing interior partition walls. Commercial buildings constructed in this flexible manner give the owner a wider possibility of meeting the potential needs of the lessee. Small businesses must consider flexibility and expansion as the business grows. The question must be asked "How could this plan be expanded at a later date with the least expense and disruption."

Floor Space. To be most useful, floors should be as free as possible from supporting columns. This permits greater traffic movement and utilization of space. Columns should not be spaced less than 13 ft. center to center. If a series of stories are to be built side by side, a module for column spacing is selected based on the number of stores or shops planned. The span module selected should permit flexibility so that the stores may be enlarged or reduced as business may dictate. Once again—movable, acoustically sound partitions may be used to divide the shops. Remember: the amount of usable floor space is an important factor in any plan (generally about 70 per cent of the gross floor area). Approximately 17 per cent of the gross area is given to stairs, elevators, toilet facilities, rest areas, shafts, etc.

With the increased use of prestressed and precast structural concrete forms, greater spans are possible than ever before. Roof trusses of steel and laminated wood beams offer a wide range of design possibilities. Manufacturers of these trusses or beams will supply technical data, and will custom manufacture their product to fit the particular design and specifications.

Ceiling Heights. All store, shop, and office ceiling heights are specified by local building codes. These should be checked before any design is begun.

Table 18-1 gives recommended light commercial store heights.

TABLE 18-1
RECOMMENDED FLOOR HEIGHTS FOR LIGHT COMMERCIAL STRUCTURES

FLOOR	HEIGHT
BASEMENT	8'-0" MINIMUM
FIRST FLOOR (NO MEZZANINE)	12'-0" MINIMUM
FIRST FLOOR TO MEZZANINE	8'-0" MINIMUM
MEZZANINE TO CEILING	8'-0" MINIMUM
SECOND FLOOR	12'-0" MINIMUM

Elevators. Frequently, rental accommodations may be on the second floor. In this case, the builder may consider installing an elevator. In comparison to its use, the cost of an elevator for most small buildings is prohibitive. If a structure rises above two levels, and if the estimated probable traffic would be sufficient, it may be a wise investment. However, most light commercial structures do not have more than three floors. A stairway offers the most economical solution to the problem.

Entryway and Lobby. The design of a entryway and lobby will have a definite effect on the rentability of the building. The lobby and stair area should give the feeling of openness and freedom so the customer is invited to walk up to the second floor. If this is not provided, the second floor area will be difficult to rent. The lobby and stairway shown in Fig. 18-4 is an example of good design and planning. The success of a building is dependent upon the appeal it has for the customers, tenants, and employees.

Store or Office Front. Attractive fronts and display windows are means of inducing customers to enter the structure. Display windows may be opened to show the interior of the shop or closed to give the customer privacy. Location of the door and the flow of pedestrian traffic may determine the interior plan. Some means of advertising or displaying the firm's name is important in many businesses.

Site. Commercial lot frontage may be small. This will present orientation problems—particularly with regard to the glare and heat from the sun. If a northern or eastern exposure is impossible, double glaz-

Fig. 18-4. An attractive lobby and stairway invites the customer to walk up to the second floor.

ing, heat resistant glass, gray or bronze tinted glass, screens, draperies, or louvered awnings must be included in the design to provide as much comfort as possible. Access must also be provided for delivery and shipment of goods without causing traffic congestion.

Parking. Communities (through zoning or code restrictions) will require a given amount of parking space per square foot of office or business space. Parking space must be provided for employees and customers. Where land values are high, the cost of parking space is increased greatly. The solution is to provide some parking facilities *in* or *under* the building. This results in pushing the building upward. Where land values are low, the shape of the building will tend to be horizontal. In this case, off-street parking should be considered.

With the increased number of cars, lack of parking spaces has spelled doom in the central city core for many small shops and office buildings. The trend is now towards decentralization away from the downtown area.

Location. As communities grow, the local businessman is faced with expansion and/or relocation. Frequently it becomes necessary to build on another location in a newly developing area of the community. Forward-looking cities have surveys conducted by professionals to determine in which direction and to what extent the community can be expected to grow in the future. The small businessman must evaluate the community's growth prior to making a large property and building investment. All property should be investigated for zoning restrictions and the future possibilities of zone changes. A light commercial establishment in a heavy industrial zone is not usually a profitable venture. For example, a millinery shop located near heavy steel industries has a poor prospect of success.

Climatic Conditioning. Air conditioning has become an accepted fact for commercial establishments. A lack of this feature may hamper the rental or sale of the property. Humidity, heat, and dust present problems for various types of products. Air conditioning, in part, can aid the control of these problems.

Planning Procedure

Prior to the preliminary layout of any light commercial structure, some basic research must be carried out on the type of business and the building in question. The extent of the research will be reflected in the final plan. Many sources are available upon which the designer may draw prior to planning.

Architectural Magazines. Architectural and building magazines periodically devote entire issues to commercial architecture. The building magazines are frequently concerned with light commercial and low rise buildings. Be sure to read the advertisements for new and existing products and materials.

Architectural Planning Books. Many fine architectural books are available that are concerned with: planning problems, construction data, examples of new construction techniques, design of specific types of construction, etc. A wealth of information awaits the reader. Investigation of books and magazines frequently leads the designer to new solutions to problems—not by copying, but by an amalgamation of ideas. A list of architectural publications may be found at the end of the book (Appendix D).

Professional or Trade Journals. Magazines or journals of a particular type of business frequently publish new material and ideas that will help the designer in producing the most efficient plan.

Financial Papers and Journals. Financial papers and journals should not be overlooked since the trends of many businesses are reported. Many feature articles on merchandising products, manufacture, etc., are published and may be of definite value to the designer.

Similar Businesses. An analysis of competing businesses, from the standpoint of layout and design, will affect the plan. This is usually carried out by observation.

Consulting Firms. Frequently the client, upon the recommendation of the designer, will bring in a consulting firm to analyze the existing business procedure. The firm's recommendations may result in a more efficient organization of the business or manufacturing procedures. This new organization will be reflected in the design of the building.

Market Analysis. Investigation into the needs, habits, and buying potential of the public in the field which the structure will serve is a must for a successful business. The designer must also determine if any changes in traffic flow are anticipated in the proximity of the proposed building site. A factor not to be overlooked is an analysis of the customer's buying habits—particularly the amount and kind of purchases.

Clients. The designer must, of course, consult with the client as to his needs and desires in the building. It is important to determine what type of products and/or services he wishes to offer his customers. Frequently the designer must diplomatically unearth through conferences with his client, what strengths and weaknesses exist in the present business. This will allow the designer to anticipate building needs.

Questions and Problems

1. Review the special issues of *Architectural Forum, Architectural Record,* and *American Builder* that exclusively covered commercial architecture. What kind of problems did the designer encounter in designing the building and how were they solved? What kind of an alternate solution could you suggest?
2. Visit several new stores in your community and analyze the kinds of mer-

chandise which have been placed nearest the front or main entrance, and the kinds placed farther to the rear of the store. What reasons exist for placing these goods in that particular location?

3. Borrow from the local library or a local businessman several professional, trade, or retailing journals. Search each one carefully for any new innovations in servicing, merchandising, handling of goods, etc., that might effect a designer's building layout for a particular business.
4. Contact the local Chamber of Commerce or the local city government to determine if any demographic (population) surveys have been conducted in your community. Using this information or personal observation, in what direction has the population been moving? Based on this expansion, what areas have been zoned for light commercial businesses? How many commercial zoning classifications does your city have?
5. Select a site zoned for small business establishments and plan a two-story office building having a total of 15,000 sq. ft. Each floor has three suites of offices; one suite on each floor has not been rented. The owner of the building has obtained 10-year leases from the following four tenants:

A. Creative drafting service. This is a free lance drafting and illustrating firm. At present it employs three men, plus the owner.

B. Consulting marketing service. This firm is owned by two market consultants and they employ one office girl.

C. Letter and telephone answering service. A small company employing three typists, one duplicating (offset) machine operator, and two women handling the telephone answering service. In addition, plan one executive office for the owner.

D. Credit Bureau Office. This office employs three office girls, and has two men working in the field who use the office as a communications center.

PHOTO BY ALLAN STAMBERG.

To eliminate error, a check list is used for checking the working drawings.

House Plan Check List 19

The purpose of any check list is to aid in producing, to the greatest degree possible, an omission-free document, procedure, or plan. Essentially, the "House Plan Check List" logically groups the myriad of details that may be forgotten. The inclusion or omission of a title, symbol, note, call-out, size, etc., will represent the difference between a complete set of working drawings and those which are hastily and carelessly drawn.

Check List Use

The items listed in the "Check List" represent the chief features that are to be placed on a *complete* set of working drawings. Every effort has been made to make this list as comprehensive as possible for the average single-family dwelling. Each category or division of the check list may be used as an aid in determining those items that will be pertinent to the drawing at hand, such as a specific detail, elevation, plot plan, etc. The check list may be used in checking a partially completed set of plans to be sure that all features are included. Depending upon the situation, each item identified in the "Check List" may not appear in the complete set of working drawings. For example, in the case of a basementless house, plumbing features would not be shown on the basement plan.

It should be noted that the "Check List" contains a division for the lower level and main level. If an upper level or second floor is to be drawn, the items listed for the main level should be used as a guide in checking the plan. The section listed as "Elevations" should be used for *every elevation drawn.* All elevations, garage included, should be checked against the items enumerated under elevations.

Some architect's and designer's offices use standardized, prepared drafting sheets. These may be purchased commercially, or they may be drawn in the drafting room, reproduced, and inserted in the set of drawings. For example, some offices use a standard sheet for the plot plan already laid out with all the necessary call-outs and information. The draftsman fills in the details for each particular job. Also some offices (operated in association with construction or development companies, or lumber dealers) use standard sheets showing stair construction, cornice, and/or sill construction.

A set of *working drawings* is included with the "Check List." They may be used as a supplementary reference.

Check List Organization

Each division or section of the "Check List" represents a complete sheet or a portion of a sheet belonging to the plans.

Usually the door, window, and room finish schedules are placed on a single sheet. In some instances, however, schedules are placed on the floor plans. Similarly if interior elevations are shown, these may be placed on the sheet with the first floor plan. This is usually the case when interior elevations are used to show the kitchen cabinets. Frequently the detail of the footing and portion of the foundation wall will be shown on the basement or lower level plan. Truss details, or soffit or bulkhead details, will be shown on the same sheet with a section through the house. Some sets of plans will show all elevations grouped on the same sheet, while others will have the front and rear elevations on one sheet, and the right and left elevations shown on another. Frequently, the deciding factor in the grouping or separation of features is the sheet size standard to a particular office.

The outline of the "Check List" presentation is as follows:

- I. Presentation Drawings
- II. Working Drawings
  - A. Plot Plan
  - B. Basement (Lower Level) or Foundation Plan
  - C. First Floor (Main Level) Plan
  - D. Elevations
  - E. Interior Elevations
  - F. Wall or Structural Sections and Details
  - G. Fireplace Details
  - H. Stair Detail
  - I. Schedules (Window, Door, and Room Finish)
  - J. Joist Framing Plan
  - K. Roof Framing Plan
- III. Sheets in a Set of Working Drawings

To list all details for all types of dwellings would be impractical. If the draftsman will check each detail he believes necessary against the appropriate section, he can be fairly certain that he has included everything that will aid the contractor in estimating the cost, ordering materials, scheduling work, and constructing the building.

Some enumeration appearing in one section of the "Check List" are duplicates of items appearing in other sections. This is deliberate so that some key items will not be overlooked.

The success of the plans lies in the question: "Are the plans complete enough so that this house can be built?"

Presentation Drawings

1. Pictorial view with entourage
   a. Perspective (1 or 2 point)
   b. T-square perspective
2. Pictorial view of special features
   a. Approach to entryway
   b. Patio
   c. Interior of entry hall
   d. Living room with fireplace
   e. Any other outstanding features
3. Floor plan (to scale)
   a. Basement or lower level
   b. First floor or main level
   c. Second floor or upper level, etc.
4. Proper title for each plan view
5. Proper title for each perspective
6. Room names
7. Room sizes (13′-6″ × 19′-0″) below name
8. Overall length and depth
9. Balanced layout of sheet
10. Indicate scale
11. Border line
12. Designer's name, draftsman's name, firm's name, etc.
13. Owner's name
14. Sheet number

Working Drawings

A. **Plot Plan.**

1. Outline of lot—single line
2. Outline of house—single line (fill in with hatching)
3. Outline of porch—single line
4. Outline of patio—single line
5. Outline of garage—single line (fill in with hatching)
6. Outline of driveway—single line
7. Outline of public and private side walks—single line
8. Outline of other features (such as swimming pools, private wells, individual sewage systems, etc.)
9. Indicate curb line
10. Center line of street(s) and name(s)
11. Dimensions of lot
12. Dimension of each feature (house, garage, patio, sidewalk, etc.) from lot lines

13. Dimension of each feature
14. Call out each feature
15 Indicate and call out grade elevations at corners of house
16. Indicate and call out grade elevations at corners of lot
17. Indicate and call out grade elevations at center of street
18. Call out house number and street.
19. Call out lot number
20. Call out block number.
21. Call out sub-division name
22. Call out city, county, and state
23. Indicate north
24. Indicate title
25. Indicate scale
26. Border line
27. Draftsman's name, firm's name, etc.
28. Owner's name
29. Sheet number

B. **Basement (Lower Level) or Foundation Plan.**

1. Outline of footings—broken line
2. Outline of foundation and pilasters
3. Outline of post or column footings—broken line
4. Outline of porch footings — broken line
5. Outline of porch foundation
6. Indicate soil pipe and vents
7. Indicate drainage provision (footing, storm, sanitary)
8. Indicate floor drains and clean outs
9. Indicate sump provisions
10. Indicate heating plant
11. Indicate oil tank if applicable
12. Indicate water heater
13. Indicate water closet and lavatory
14. Indicate laundry tubs
15. Indicate hose bibs
16. Indicate basement windows
17. Indicate window wells
18. Indicate outside entrance
19. Call out window and door symbols (from window and door schedules)
20. Indicate waterproof foundation wall
21. Outline of fireplace footing
22. Outline of fireplace foundation
23. Indicate fireplace cleanout
24. Outline of stairs (with directional arrow)
25. Indicate ceiling outlets
26. Indicate wall convenience outlets
27. Indicate switches and arrangements (curved dashed line from switch to outlet)
28. Indicate special appliance outlets
29. Outline any built-in features
30. Specify type and thickness of floor
31. Indicate and call out concrete floor reinforcement
32. Dimension foundation from outside to outside
33. Dimension thickness of wall
34. Dimension location of post or column
35. Dimension location of door(s) and windows from outside of foundation wall to their centerlines.
36. Check building code against plan
37. Indicate each room or area
38. Indicate each feature
39. Indicate title
40. Indicate scale
41. Border line
42. Designer's name, draftsman's name, firm's name, etc.
43. Owner's name
44. Sheet number

C. **First Floor (Main Level) Plan.**

1. Outline of outside walls — (nominal thickness)
2. Outline of partition walls—(nominal thickness)
3. Outline of patio
4. Indicate outline of roof overhang—broken line
5. Indicate window openings
6. Indicate door openings with swings
7. Outline of front porch or stoop
8. Outline of rear porch or stoop
9. Outline of fireplace and flues
10. Outline of chimney
11. Indicate stairs with number and sizes of treads and risers (show directional arrows)
12. Indicate stairwell handrail
13. Indicate kitchen
14. Indicate living room
15. Indicate dining room or area
16. Indicate family room
17. Indicate bedroom(s)
18. Indicate bathroom(s) (show fixtures; detail tiling)
19. Indicate lavatory(s)
20. Indicate mud room
21. Indicate laundry
22. Indicate work area
23. Indicate entryway
24. Indicate closets
25. Indicate sizes of closet clothes pole and shelf

26. Indicate garage, if applicable
27. Indicate other features, such as range, refrigerator, sink, washer and dryer, water softener, cabinet, shelves, etc.
28. Indicate ceiling outlets
29. Indicate wall convenience outlets
30. Indicate bells, buzzers, TV outlets, fans, etc.
31. Indicate valance lighting
32. Indicate undercabinet lighting
33. Indicate special appliance outlets
34. Indicate quartz zone or ceiling heater for bathrooms
35. Indicate weatherproof convenience outlets
36. Indicate yard lighting
37. Indicate switches and arrangement
38. Indicate electrical service entrance
39. Indicate service disconnect, panel board, branch control centers
40. Indicate all plumbing fixtures (bathtub, shower, lavatory, water closet, etc.)
41. Indicate soil pipe
42. Indicate hose-bibs
43. Indicate gas outlets
44. Call out window symbols (from window schedule)
45. Call out door symbols (from door schedule)
46. Dimension window location from outside stud face to center of window and center to center
47. Dimension door locations from outside stud face to center of door
48. Dimension overall from outside of stud face to outside of stud face
49. Dimension partition from outside of stud face to stud faces of partion or to center of partition
50. Dimension partition wall thickness
51. Dimension exterior wall thickness
52. Indicate arches and/or cased openings
53. Indicate girder or I-beam with proper symbol and call out size
54. Indicate joist size, O.C. spacing and directional arrow
55. Indicate type of floor (vinyl tile, ceramic tile, slate, carpet, etc.) below room title
56. Indicate type of wall finish (plaster, dry wall, textured panel, etc.) below room title
57. Indicate type of ceiling (plaster, dry wall, textured, panel, acoustical plaster, etc.) below room title
58. Indicate type of heating unit in each room
59. Indicate garage drain, if applicable
60. Indicate title
61. Indicate scale
62. Border line
63. Designer's name, draftsman's name, firm's name, etc.
64. Owner's name
65. Sheet number

D. **Elevations.**

1. Indicate footing (broken line)
2. Indicate foundation wall (broken line)
3. Indicate basement floor (broken line)
4. Indicate and call out grade line
5. Indicate and call out water table or drip cap
6. Indicate basement windows
7. Indicate and call out screened vents for crawl space
8. Indicate and call out finish floor(s) (heavy center line)
9. Indicate and call out finish garage floor, if applicable (heavy center line)
10. Indicate porch railings, steps, columns, or posts
11. Indicate bay — veneer materials and roofing
12. Indicate dormer — veneer materials and roofing
13. Indicate doors
14. Indicate door trim
15. Indicate windows
16. Indicate window trim
17. Indicate and call out finish ceiling (center line)
18. Indicate siding or veneer in patches
19. Call out siding or veneer on *each* elevation
20. Indicate and call out exterior lights
21. Indicate and call out weatherproof convenience outlets
22. Indicate and call out conductor pipe (leader) (size, type, and material)
23. Indicate gutter and call out type and material
24. Indicate fascia and call out size
25. Indicate and call out corner trim
26. Indicate flashing and call out material and gauge
27. Indicate roofing material in patches and call out type
28. Indicate gravel stop and call out gauge and material

29. Indicate chimney and call out material
30. Indicate pitch triangle
31. Indicate gable end louvers and call out amount of net free air square area
32. Indicate roof vents and call out amount of net free air (square area) for ventilation.
33. Call out window symbols (from window schedule)
34. Call out door symbols (from door schedule)
35. Dimension from footing to finish grade
36. Dimension from finish grade to finish floor
37. Dimension from finish floor to finish ceiling
38. Dimension from ridge to top of chimney
39. Indicate title for each elevation
40. Indicate scale
41. Border line
42. Designer's name, draftsman's name, firm's name
43. Owner's name
44. Sheet number

E. **Interior Elevations.**

1. Indicate true width of wall
2. Indicate true width of window
3. Indicate true width of doors or openings
4. Indicate door swing with broken lines
5. Indicate true width or length of stairs
6. Indicate typical section through soffit, wall cabinet, and base cabinet
7. Indicate cabinets with drawers
8. Indicate counter
9. Indicate shelves with broken line
10. Indicate closets with shelves and clothes pole
11. Indicate plumbing fixtures
12. Indicate towel bars
13. Indicate soap dish and grab bar
14. Indicate vanity
15. Indicate medicine cabinet
16. Indicate mirror
17. Indicate shower door
18. Indicate obscure or pattern glass
19. Indicate stove
20. Indicate range hood or counter top unit
21. Indicate oven
22. Indicate refrigerator
23. Indicate dishwasher
24. Indicate incinerator
25. Indicate fireplace
26. Indicate bookcase
27. Indicate wall materials (tile, brick, stainless steel, wood paneling, etc.)
28. Indicate textures of surface materials
29. Indicate toe space
30. Indicate heat supply registers
31. Indicate cold air returns
32. Indicate convenience outlets
33. Indicate special outlets
34. Indicate wall switches
35. Indicate wall fixtures
36. Indicate air conditioning registers
37. Indicate direction of sliding doors and windows with arrow
38. Indicate base and shoe
39. Indicate ceiling trim, cove, or molding
40. Indicate true slope of ceiling
41. Indicate sloping ceiling
42. Indicate exposed beams
43. Dimension from finish floor to top of counter
44. Dimension from top of counter to underside of wall cabinet
45. Dimension from underside of wall cabinet to top of wall cabinet
46. Dimension over-all height from finish floor to underside of soffit
47. Dimension from finish floor to mirror
48. Dimension from finish floor to clothes pole in closet
49. Dimension from finish floor to fixed shelves in closet
50. Dimension from finish floor to top of vanity
51. Dimension from finish floor to top of wainscoting
52. Indicate name of each wall elevation (living room, kitchen, hall, etc.)
53. Indicate compass direction of each wall elevation
54. Indicate scale of each interior
55. Border line
56. Designer's name, draftsman's name, firm's name, etc.
57. Owner's name
58. Sheet number

F. **Wall or Structural Section and Details.**

1. Indicate where section has been taken on plan(s)
2. Indicate footing with reinforcing rod
3. Indicate footing drain tile
4. Indicate foundation wall with reinforcing

5. Indicate method of waterproofing and call out material and size
6. Indicate sill construction and call out component members and sizes
7. Indicate anchor bolt and call out size and spacing O.C.
8. Indicate studs and spacing O.C.
9. Indicate insulation material
10. Indicate sheathing and call out type and thickness
11. Indicate siding or veneer material and size
12. Indicate perimeter insulation if applicable
13. Indicate floor joists and call out material and size
14. Indicate sub-floor and call out material
15. Indicate finish floor and call out material
16. Indicate double plate
17. Indicate partition wall
18. Indicate blocking or horizontal bridging
19. Indicate ceiling joists and call out material, size, and spacing O.C.
20. Indicate typical window or sliding glass door
21. Indicate lintel over window or sliding glass door and call out material and size
22. Indicate ceiling insulation and call out thickness and type
23. Indicate finish ceiling and call out material, thickness, and finish
24. Indicate roof rafters and call out material, size, and spacing O.C.
25. Indicate collar beams and call out material, sizes, and spacing
26. Indicate roof knee braces and call out material, size, and spacing
27. Indicate roof sheathing or boards and call out size
28. Indicate roofing and call out type and thickness
39. Indicate gravel stop and call out material and gauge
30. Indicate fascia and call out material and size
31. Indicate nailing block and call out typical size
32. Indicate soffit and call out material, and amount of net free air (square area) for ventilation
33. Indicate molding at underside of soffit and wall and call out type and size
34. Indicate gutter and call out material, gauge, and size
35. Indicate pitch triangle and call out rise and run
36. Indicate ridge and call out material and size
37. Indicate ridge vent
38. Indicate roof vent
39. Dimension from footing to finish grade
40. Dimension from finish grade to finish floor
41. Dimension amount siding overhangs foundation wall
42. Dimension from finish floor to finish ceiling
43. Dimension from finish floor to top of exterior wall plate
44. Dimension from finish floor to top of interior wall plate
45. Dimension rafter length
46. Dimension amount of overhang
47. Dimension head height of typical window or door
48. Indicate typical plate detail(s) with necessary call outs and sizes
49. Indicate typical ridge detail(s) with necessary call outs and sizes
50. Indicate typical cornice detail(s) with sary call outs and sizes
51. Indicate typical sill detail(s) with necessary call outs and sizes
52. Indicate typical threshold detail(s), call out manufacturer's name, model number, and size
53. Indicate truss detail(s) with necessary call outs and sizes
54. Indicate typical soffit or bulk head detail(s) with call outs and sizes
55. Indicate any other details that may be necessary to clarify the drawings
56. Indicate title—each section and detail
57. Indicate scale—each section and detail
58. Border line
59. Designer's name, draftsman's name, firm's name, etc.
60. Owner's name
61. Sheet number

G. **Fireplace Details.**

1. Elevation (full or half) of fireplace
2. Plan section (full or half) of fireplace
3. Full section from basement to flue
4. Indicate and call out facing material and bond, if brick

5. Indicate and call out fire brick
6. Indicate and call out outside facing material
7. Indicate flue tile and call out size
8. Indicate damper and call out manufacturer, model number, and size
9. Indicate angle iron and call out size
10. Indicate mantel and call out material and size
11. Indicate ash dump and call out manufacturer, model number, and size
12. Indicate clean-out door and call out manufacturer, model number, and size
13. Indicate molding
14. Indicate front hearth and call out material and size
15. Indicate spark arrestor and call out size
16. Indicate type of brick design over opening (jack arch, rowlock, soldier course, etc.)
17. Indicate construction over front hearth
18. Dimension width, height, and depth of fire chamber
19. Dimension angle or flare of fire chamber
20. Dimension width and depth of throat
21. Dimension angle of smoke chamber
22. Indicate smoke chamber fillet
23. Dimension length and bearing of angle iron
24. Dimension height of mantel and projection
25. Dimension overall size of front hearth
26. Dimension location of molding
27. Dimension interior facing of fireplace
28. Indicate and dimension fireplace foundation
29. Indicate and dimension fireplace footing
30. Indicate other necessary dimensions for any additional features (built-in wood box, decorations, etc.)
31. Indicate title (each section and detail)
32. Indicate scale (each section and detail)
33. Border line
34. Designer's name, draftsman's name, firm's name, etc.
35. Owner's name
36. Sheet number

H. **Stair Details.**

1. Elevation of stairs in section, including portion of floors
2. Plan of stairs
3. Indicate edge of sloping ceiling
4. Hand rail(s)
5. Typical riser and tread section
6. String board
7. Shoe rail
8. Shoe fillet
9. Indicate newel post and call out material and size
10. Indicate balusters and call out material and size
11. Dimension clear head room
12. Dimension height of hand rail
13. Dimension width of stairs
14. Dimension height from finish floor to finish floor
15. Dimension horizontal length of stair.
16. Dimension tread from front face of riser to nosing
17. Dimension riser from top of tread to top of tread
18. Dimension nosing
19. Dimension hand rail and call out material
20. Indicate title—each section and detail
21. Indicate scale—each section and detail
22. Border line
23. Designer's name, draftsman's name, firm's name, etc.
24. Owner's name
25. Sheet number

I. **Schedules.**

I. Window
   1. Code Symbol—letters and number of each type of window used
   2. Quantity
   3. Sash size (W × H)
   4. Thickness
   5. Rough opening (if desired)
   6. Material (wood, aluminum, steel)
   7. Manufacturer's name
   8. Catalog number
   9. Glazing (obscure, pattern, wire, D.S., plate, etc.)
   10. Remarks (custom, pair w/mullion between)

II. Door
   1. Code symbol
   2. Quantity
   3. Size (W × H)
   4. Thickness

5. Rough opening (if desired)
6. Type (flush-hollow, flush-solid, panel, full louver)
7. Material (wood-birch, mahogany, oak, metal)
8. Manufacturer
9. Catalog number
10. Finish (varnish, enamel)
11. Jamb (wood, metal, flush, etc.)
12. Remarks (single, pair, jamb in pocket, bi-fold, by-pass, etc.)

III. Room Finish
1. Key to finish (natural finish, gloss enamel, semi-gloss enamel, flat paint, stain, natural finish, prefinished, exterior stain, exterior latex, exterior sash, and trim, etc.)
2. Room
   a. Floor
      (1) Oak flooring
      (2) Carpet
      (3) Tile
      (4) Concrete
      (5) Slate
   b. Base and Shoe
      (1) Hardwood
      (2) Softwood
      (3) Tile
   c. Walls—North, South, East, West
      (1) Plaster
      (2) Gypsum board
      (3) Wood paneling
      (4) Unfinished
   d. Ceiling
      (1) Plaster
      (2) Gypsum board
      (3) Acoustical tile
   e. Cabinets and doors
   f. Trim

J. **Joist Framing Plan.**
1. Indicate outline of foundation wall—broken line
2. Indicate sill plate and call out size
3. Indicate sill header and call out size
4. Indicate girder(s) or I-beam and call out size
5. Indicate girder posts and call out size
6. Indicate joists and call out typical size
7. Indicate cantilever framing and call out size
8. Indicate porch(s) framing
9. Location of bridging and call out
10. Indicate location of plywood subflooring panels
11. Indicate double header and trimmer around openings (chimney, fireplace, stairwell, etc.)
12. Note all structural members

13. Indicate title
14. Indicate scale
15. Border line
16. Designer's name, draftsman's name, firm's name, etc.
17. Owner's name
18. Sheet number

K. **Roof Framing Plan.**

1. Indicate outline of exterior walls—broken line
2. Indicate outline of bearing wall—broken line
3. Indicate outline of roof (including overhang)—solid line
4. Indicate location of supporting beams or members for roof-center line
5. Indicate posts or columns that support beams and call out size, material, and/or manufacturer and model number
6. Indicate location of breaks in roof surface (valleys, ridges, and hips) and call out size
7. Indicate rafters with solid lines and call out material, size, and spacing O.C.
8. Indicate fascia board and call out size and material
9. Indicate double header and trimmer around openings
10. Indicate and call out hangers, straps, plates, plywood gussetts, rings
11. Indicate any additional details necessary to complete plan
12. Indicate title
13. Indicate scale
14. Border line
15. Designer's name, draftsman's name, firm's name, etc.
16. Owner's name
17. Sheet number

Sheets In a Set of Working Drawings

1. Plot plan
2. Basement or lower level plan
3. First or main level plan
4. Second or upper level plan
5. Front and rear elevations
6. Right and left elevations
7. Interior elevation
8. Wall or structural sections and details
9. Fireplace details
10. Stair details
11. Schedules
12. Joist framing plans
13. Roof framing plans

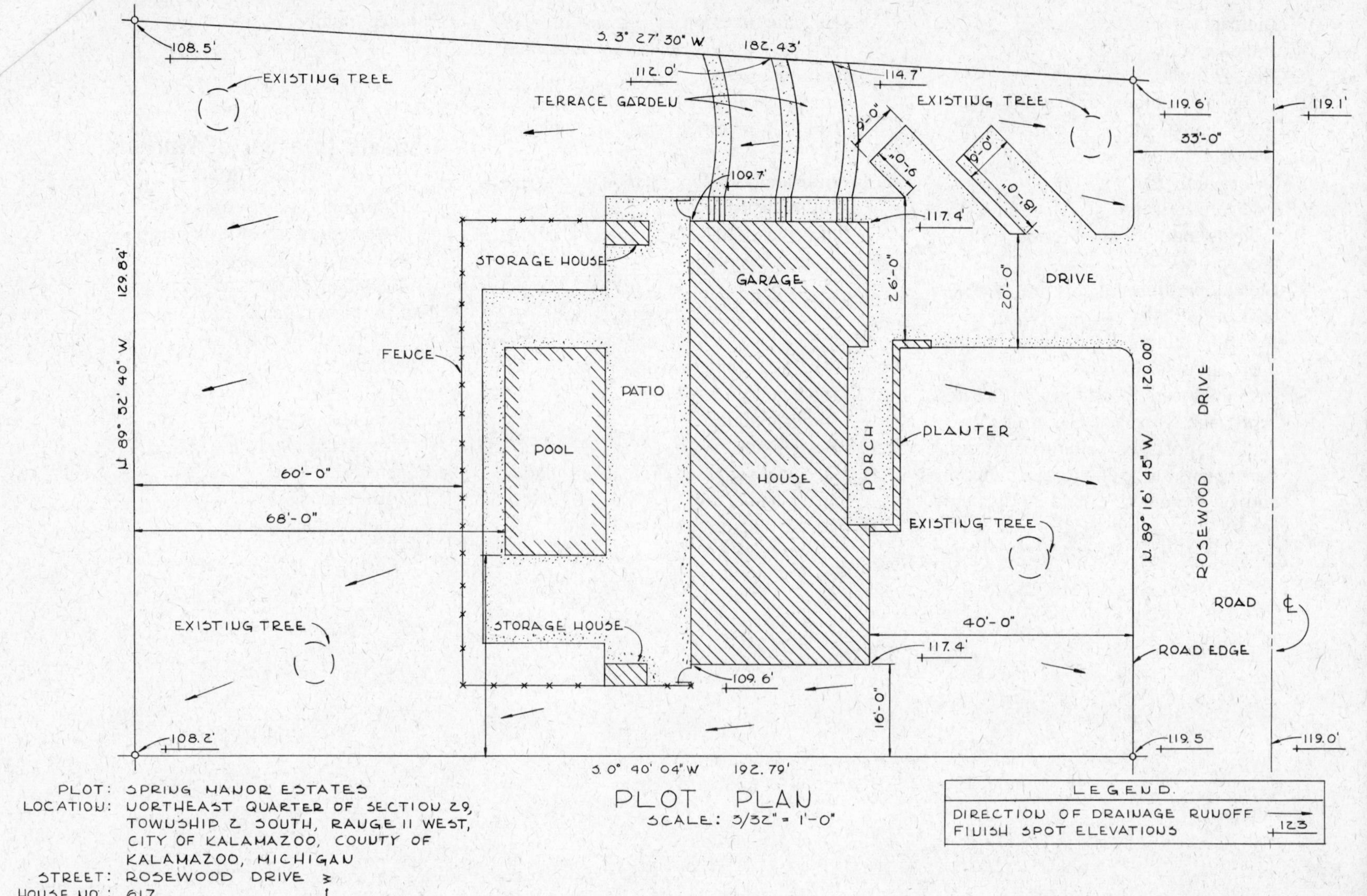

PLOT PLAN

SCALE: 3/32" = 1'-0"

PLOT: SPRING MANOR ESTATES
LOCATION: NORTHEAST QUARTER OF SECTION 29, TOWNSHIP 2 SOUTH, RANGE 11 WEST, CITY OF KALAMAZOO, COUNTY OF KALAMAZOO, MICHIGAN
STREET: ROSEWOOD DRIVE
HOUSE NO.: 617
LOT NO.: 5
BLOCK NO.: 2

W
S — N
E

LEGEND.	
DIRECTION OF DRAINAGE RUNOFF	→
FINISH SPOT ELEVATIONS	123

THE RESIDENCE OF
DR. & MRS. ROBT. PUTNAM
617 ROSEWOOD DRIVE KALAMAZOO., MICH.
PARAMOUNT DESIGN INC.
KALAMAZOO., MICHIGAN
5-17-65
DESIGN BY: H. OLSEN & W. PALM, JR. DRAWN BY: W. PALM, JR.

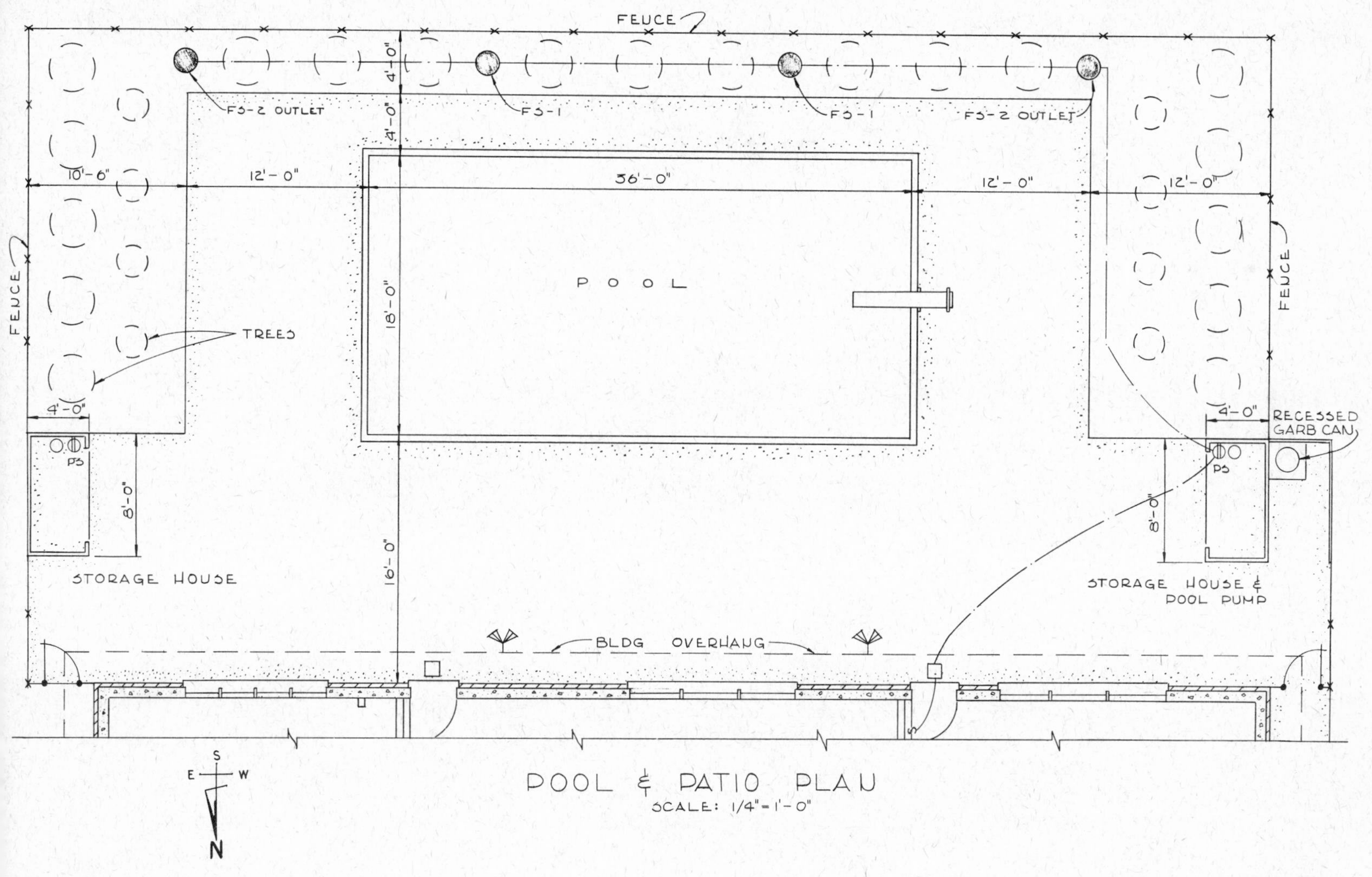

POOL & PATIO PLAN
SCALE: 1/4" = 1'-0"

THE RESIDENCE OF
DR. & MRS. ROBT. PUTNAM
617 ROSEWOOD DRIVE KALAMAZOO, MICH.
PARAMOUNT DESIGN INC.
KALAMAZOO, MICHIGAN
5-17-65
DESIGN BY: H. OLSEN & W. PALM, JR. DRAWN BY: W. PALM, JR.
2
6515

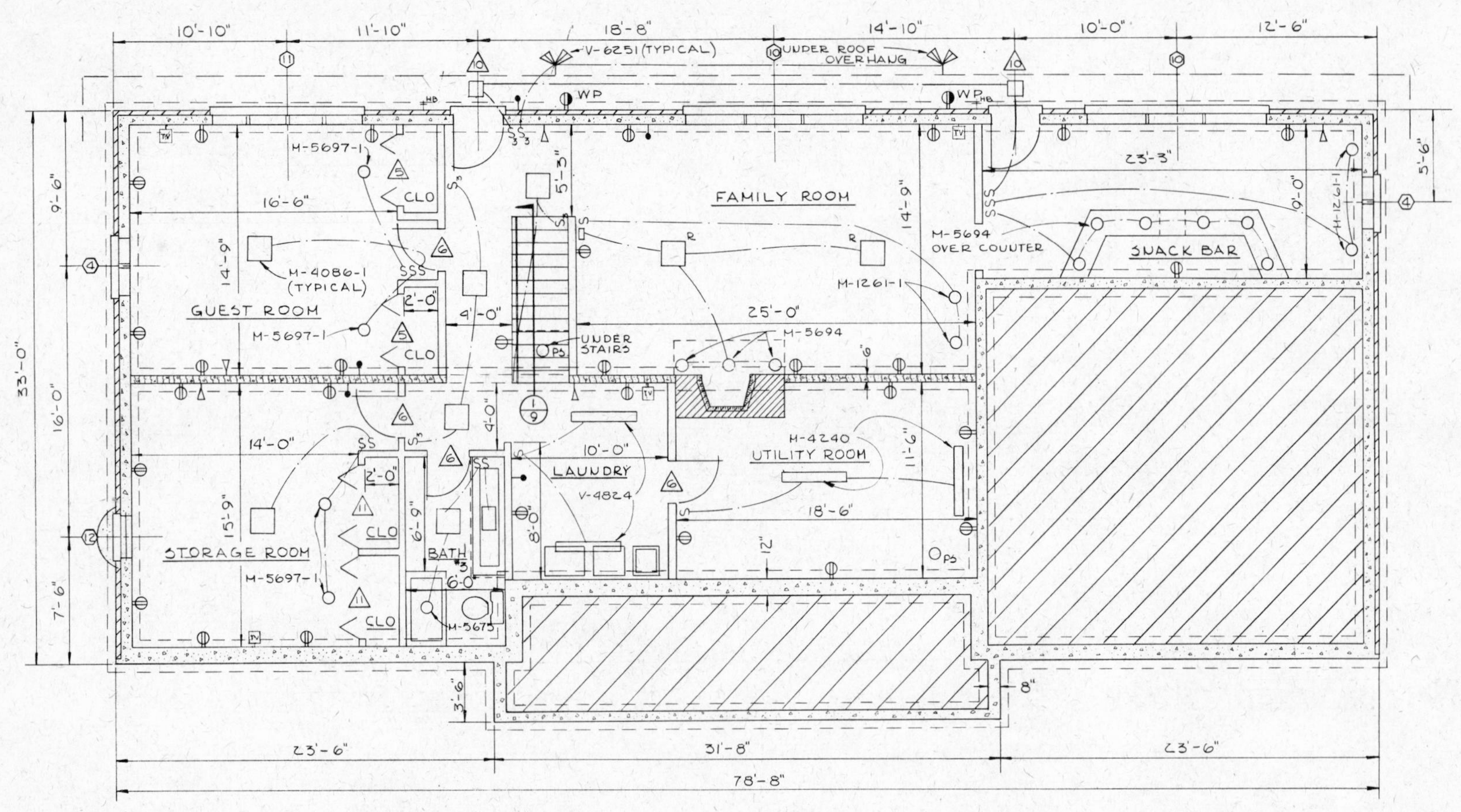

FOUNDATION & ELECTRICAL PLAN

SCALE: 1/4" = 1'-0"

THE RESIDENCE OF
DR. & MRS. ROBT. PUTNAM
617 ROSEWOOD DRIVE KALAMAZOO, MICH.
PARAMOUNT DESIGN INC.
KALAMAZOO, MICHIGAN
3-17-65
DESIGN BY: H. OLSEN & W. PALM, JR. DRAWN BY: W. PALM, JR.

3

6515

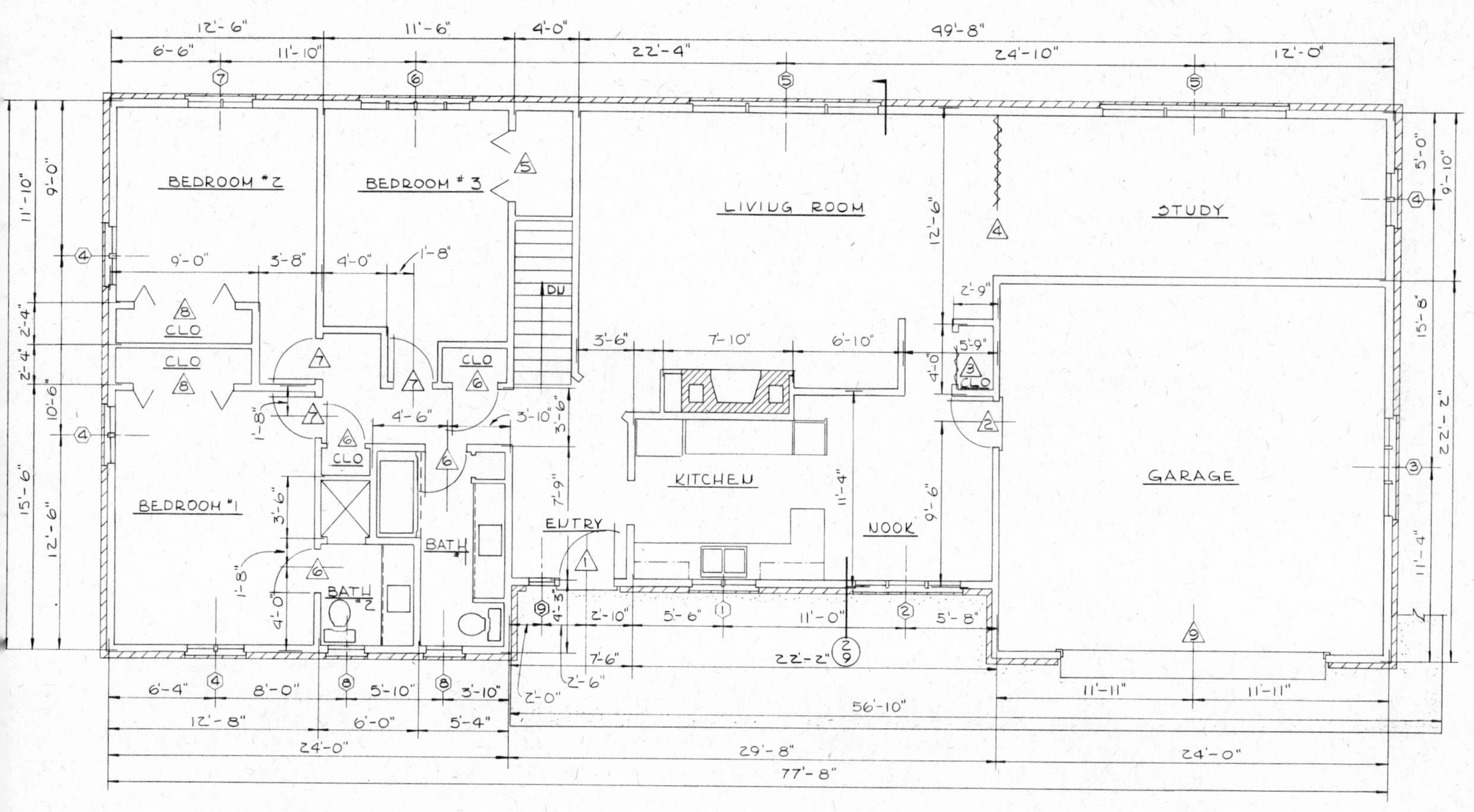

FIRST FLOOR PLAN
SCALE: 1/4" = 1'-0"

THE RESIDENCE OF
DR. & MRS. ROBT. PUTNAM
617 ROSEWOOD DRIVE KALAMAZOO, MICH.
PARAMOUNT DESIGN INC.
KALAMAZOO, MICHIGAN
DESIGN BY: H. OLSEN & W PALM, JR. DRAWN BY: W. PALM, JR. 5-17-65

4

6515

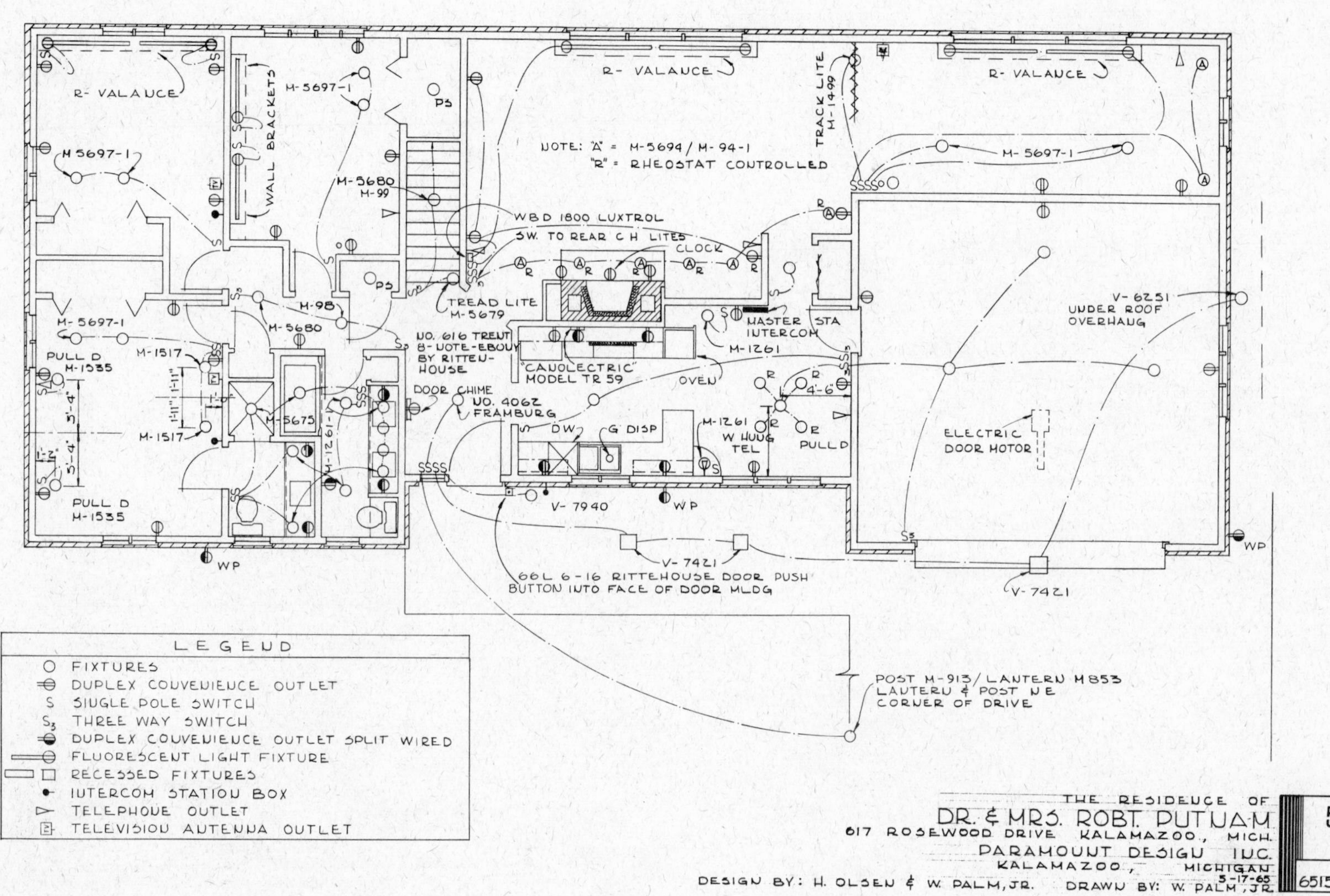
FIRST FLOOR ELECTRICAL PLAN
SCALE: 1/4" = 1'- 0"
NOTE: "A" = M-5694 / M-94-1
"R" = RHEOSTAT CONTROLLED
R- VALANCE
WALL BRACKETS
M-5697-1
M-5680
M-99
WBD 1800 LUXTROL
SW. TO REAR C H LITES
CLOCK
TRACK LITE M-1499
TREAD LITE M-5679
M-98
NO. 616 TRENT 8-NOTE-EBONY BY RITTEN-HOUSE
"CANOLECTRIC" MODEL TR 59
MASTER STA INTERCOM
M-1261
OVEN
DOOR CHIME
NO. 406Z FRAMBURG
DW
G DISP
W HUNG TEL
PULL D
M-1535
M-1517
M-5675
V-6251
UNDER ROOF OVERHANG
ELECTRIC DOOR MOTOR
V-7940
WP
V-7421
66L 6-16 RITTEHOUSE DOOR PUSH BUTTON INTO FACE OF DOOR MLDG
POST M-913/LANTERN M853
LANTERN & POST NE CORNER OF DRIVE
LEGEND
FIXTURES
DUPLEX CONVENIENCE OUTLET
S SINGLE POLE SWITCH
S_3 THREE WAY SWITCH
DUPLEX CONVENIENCE OUTLET SPLIT WIRED
FLUORESCENT LIGHT FIXTURE
RECESSED FIXTURES
INTERCOM STATION BOX
TELEPHONE OUTLET
TELEVISION ANTENNA OUTLET
THE RESIDENCE OF
DR. & MRS. ROBT. PUTNAM
617 ROSEWOOD DRIVE KALAMAZOO., MICH.
PARAMOUNT DESIGN INC.
KALAMAZOO, MICHIGAN
5-17-65
DESIGN BY: H. OLSEN & W. PALM, JR. DRAWN BY: W. PALM, JR.
5
6515

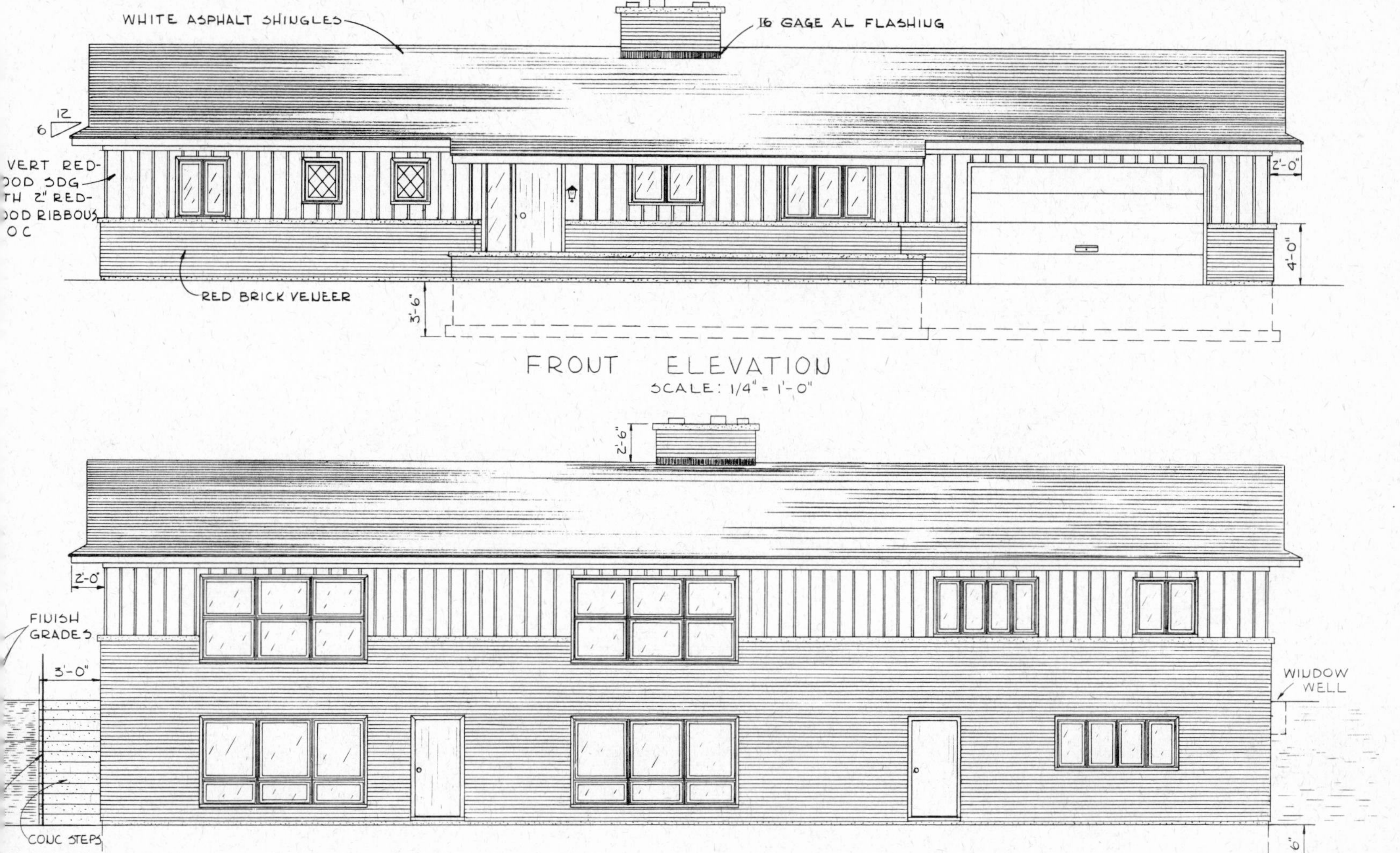

THE RESIDENCE OF
DR. & MRS. ROBT. PUTNAM
617 ROSEWOOD DRIVE KALAMAZOO, MICH.
PARAMOUNT DESIGN INC.
KALAMAZOO, MICHIGAN
5-17-65
DESIGN BY: H. OLSEN & W. PALM, JR. DRAWN BY: W. PALM, JR.
6
6515

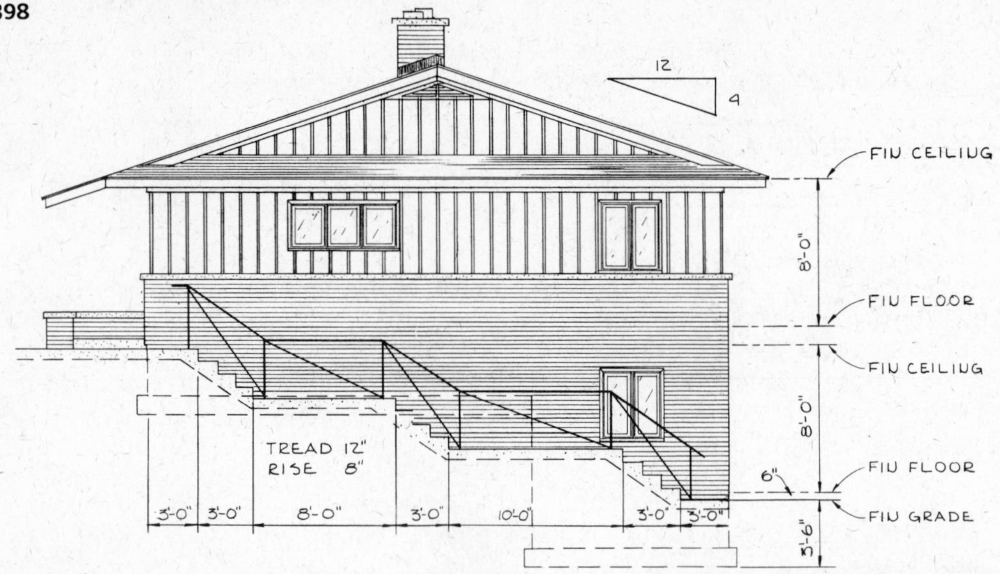

RIGHT ELEVATION
SCALE: 1/4" = 1'-0"

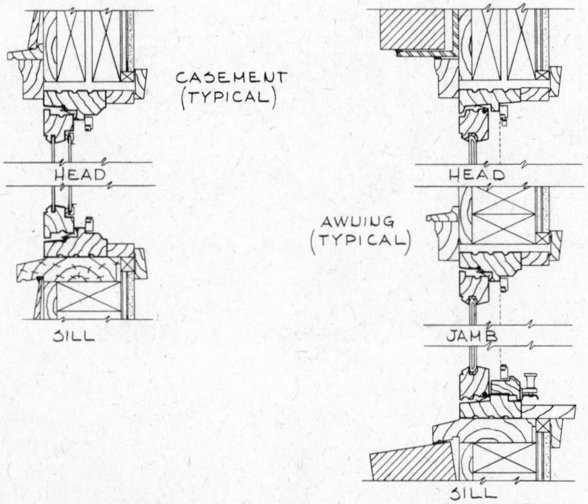

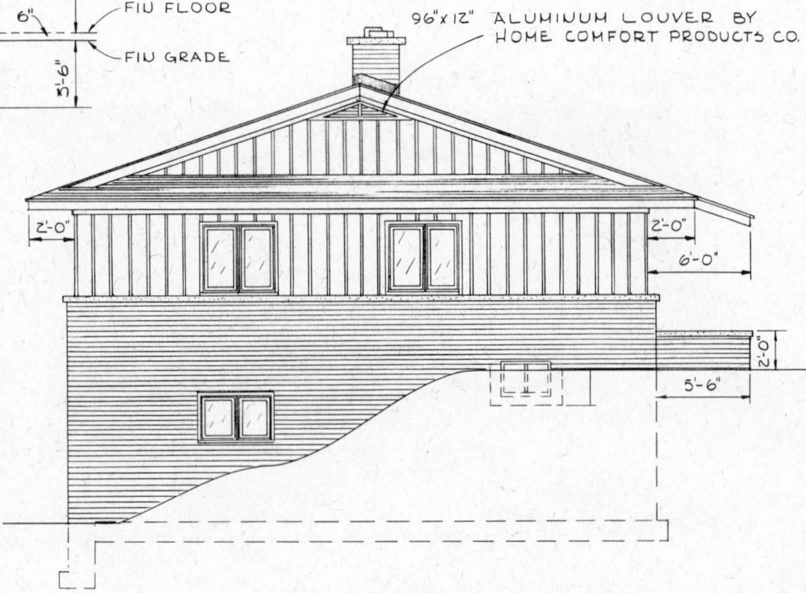

LEFT ELEVATION
SCALE: 1/4" = 1'-0"

WINDOW SECTION DETAILS
SCALE: 3" = 1'

THE RESIDENCE OF
DR. & MRS. ROBT. PUTNAM
617 ROSEWOOD DRIVE KALAMAZOO, MICH.
PARAMOUNT DESIGN INC.
KALAMAZOO, MICHIGAN
5-17-65
DESIGN BY: H. OLSEN & W. PALM, JR. DRAWN BY: W. PALM, JR.

7

6515

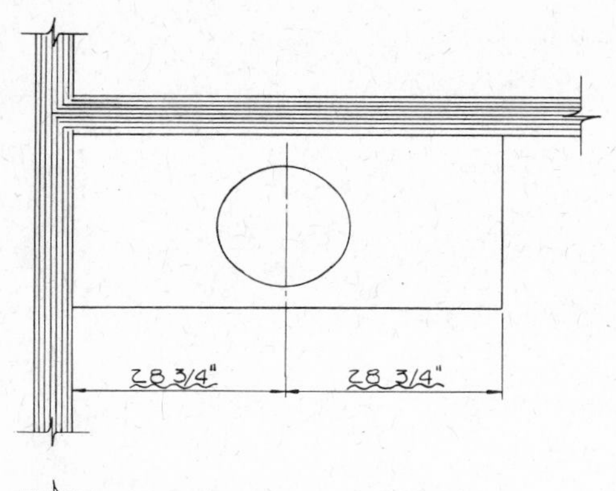

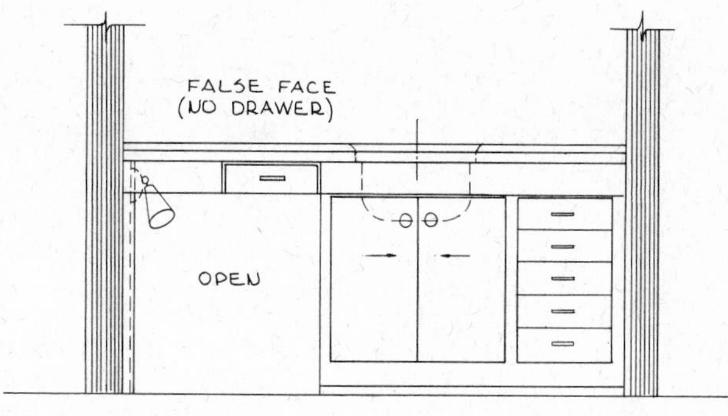

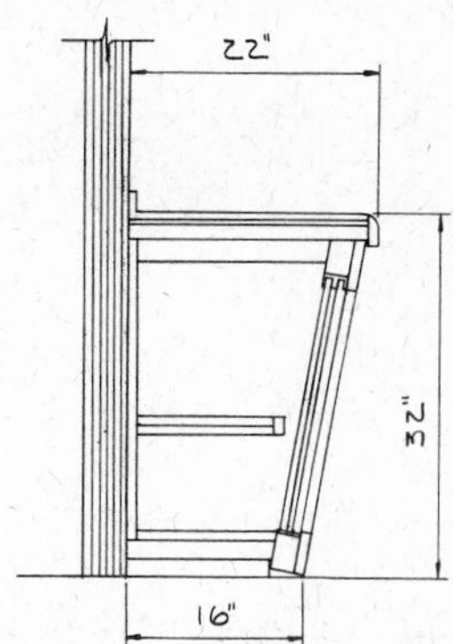

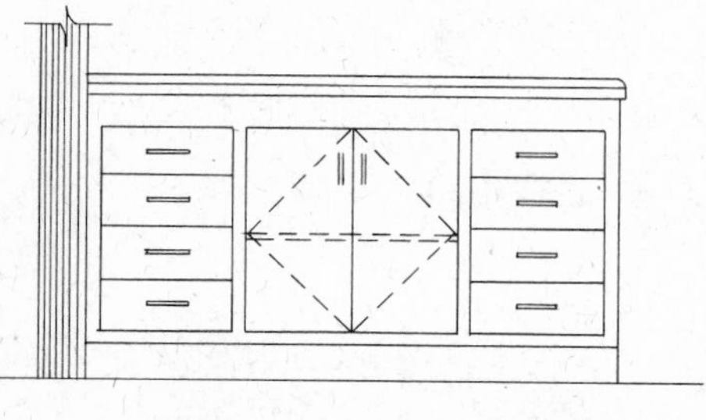

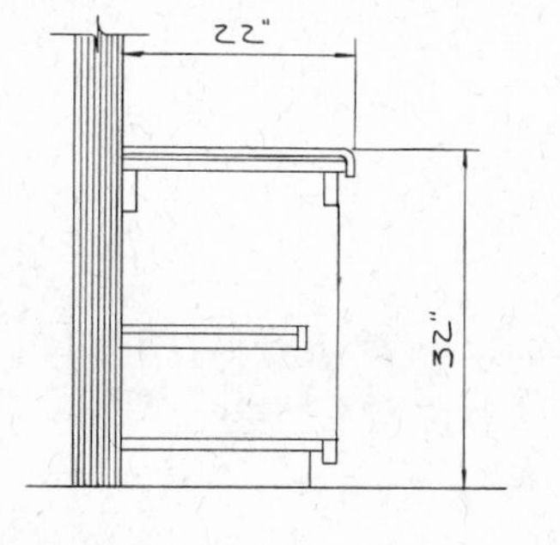

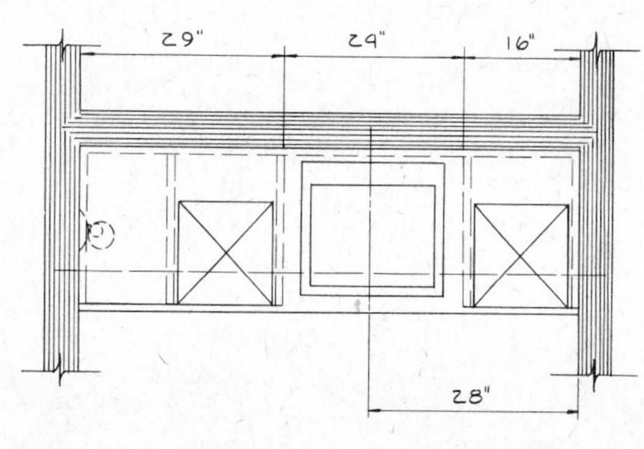

MASTER BEDROOM BATH

BASEMENT BATH

INTERIOR DETAILS

SCALE: 1" = 1'-0"

THE RESIDENCE OF
DR. & MRS. ROBT. PUTNAM
617 ROSEWOOD DRIVE KALAMAZOO, MICH.
PARAMOUNT DESIGN INC.
KALAMAZOO MICHIGAN
5-17-65
DESIGN BY: H. OLSEN & W. PALM, JR. DRAWN BY: W. PALM, JR.

8

6515

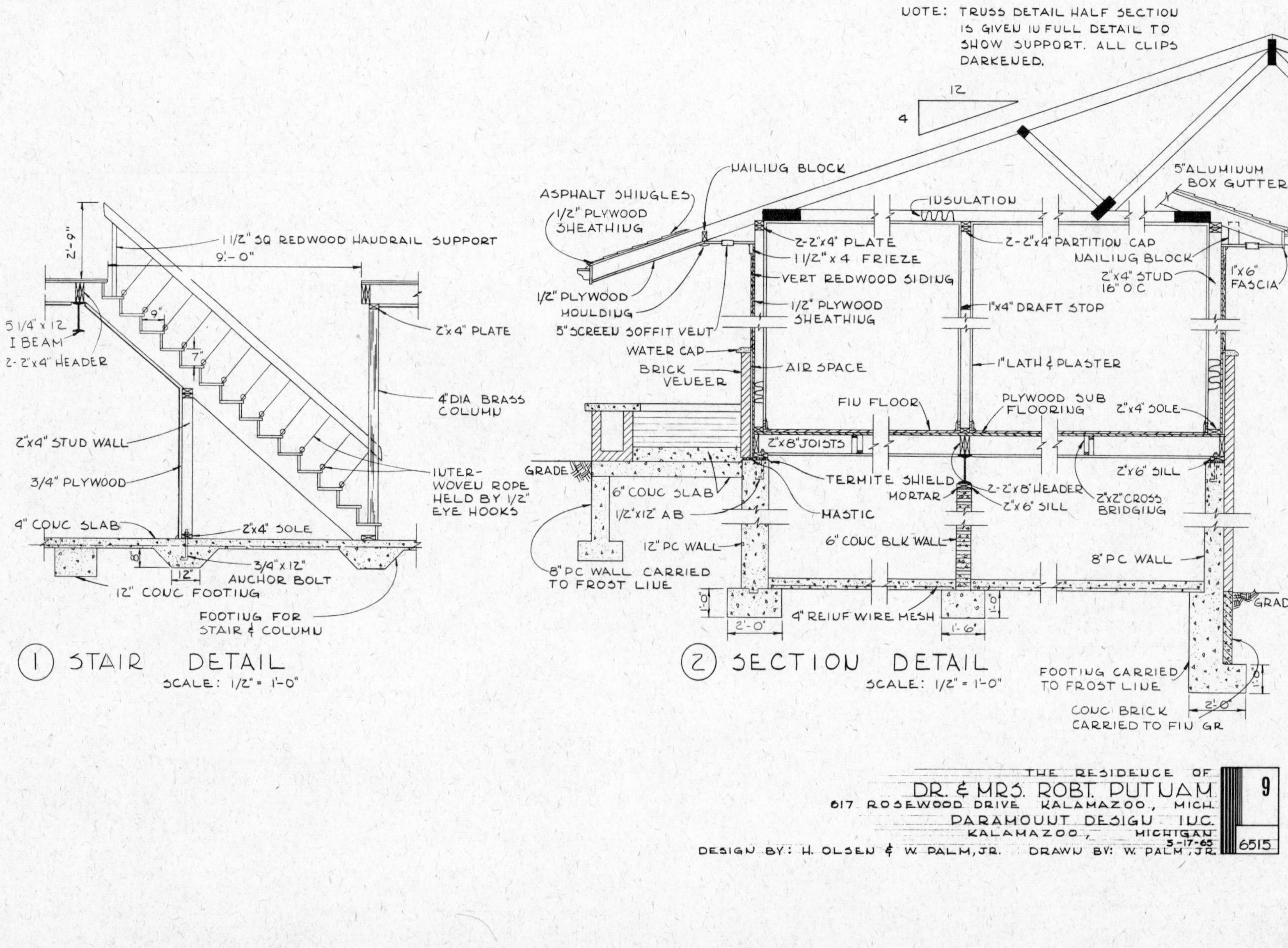

NOTE: TRUSS DETAIL HALF SECTION
IS GIVEN IN FULL DETAIL TO
SHOW SUPPORT. ALL CLIPS
DARKENED.

12
4

NAILING BLOCK
5" ALUMINUM
BOX GUTTER
ASPHALT SHINGLES
INSULATION
1/2" PLYWOOD
SHEATHING
2-2"x4" PLATE
2-2"x4" PARTITION CAP
1 1/2" x 4 FRIEZE
NAILING BLOCK
VERT REDWOOD SIDING
2"x4" STUD
16" O C
1"x6"
FASCIA
1/2" PLYWOOD
MOULDING
1/2" PLYWOOD
SHEATHING
1"x4" DRAFT STOP
5" SCREEN SOFFIT VENT
WATER CAP
BRICK
VENEER
AIR SPACE
1" LATH & PLASTER
FIN FLOOR
PLYWOOD SUB
FLOORING
2"x4" SOLE
2"x8" JOISTS
GRADE
TERMITE SHIELD
2"x6" SILL
6" CONC SLAB
MORTAR
2-2"x8" HEADER
2"x6" SILL
2"x2" CROSS
BRIDGING
1/2"x12" AB
MASTIC
12" PC WALL
6" CONC BLK WALL
8" PC WALL
8" PC WALL CARRIED
TO FROST LINE
1'-0"
2'-0"
4" REINF WIRE MESH
1'-6"
1'-0"
GRADE
FOOTING CARRIED
TO FROST LINE
1'-0"
2'-0"
CONC BRICK
CARRIED TO FIN GR

2'-9"
1 1/2" SQ REDWOOD HANDRAIL SUPPORT
9'-0"
9"
5 1/4" x 12
I BEAM
2-2"x4" HEADER
7"
2"x4" PLATE
4" DIA BRASS
COLUMN
2"x4" STUD WALL
INTER-
WOVEN ROPE
HELD BY 1/2"
EYE HOOKS
3/4" PLYWOOD
4" CONC SLAB
2"x4" SOLE
8"
3/4" x 12"
ANCHOR BOLT
12"
12" CONC FOOTING
FOOTING FOR
STAIR & COLUMN

(1) STAIR DETAIL
SCALE: 1/2" = 1'-0"

(2) SECTION DETAIL
SCALE: 1/2" = 1'-0"

THE RESIDENCE OF
DR. & MRS. ROBT. PUTNAM
617 ROSEWOOD DRIVE KALAMAZOO., MICH.
PARAMOUNT DESIGN INC.
KALAMAZOO., MICHIGAN
3-17-65
DESIGN BY: H. OLSEN & W. PALM, JR. DRAWN BY: W. PALM, JR.
9
6515

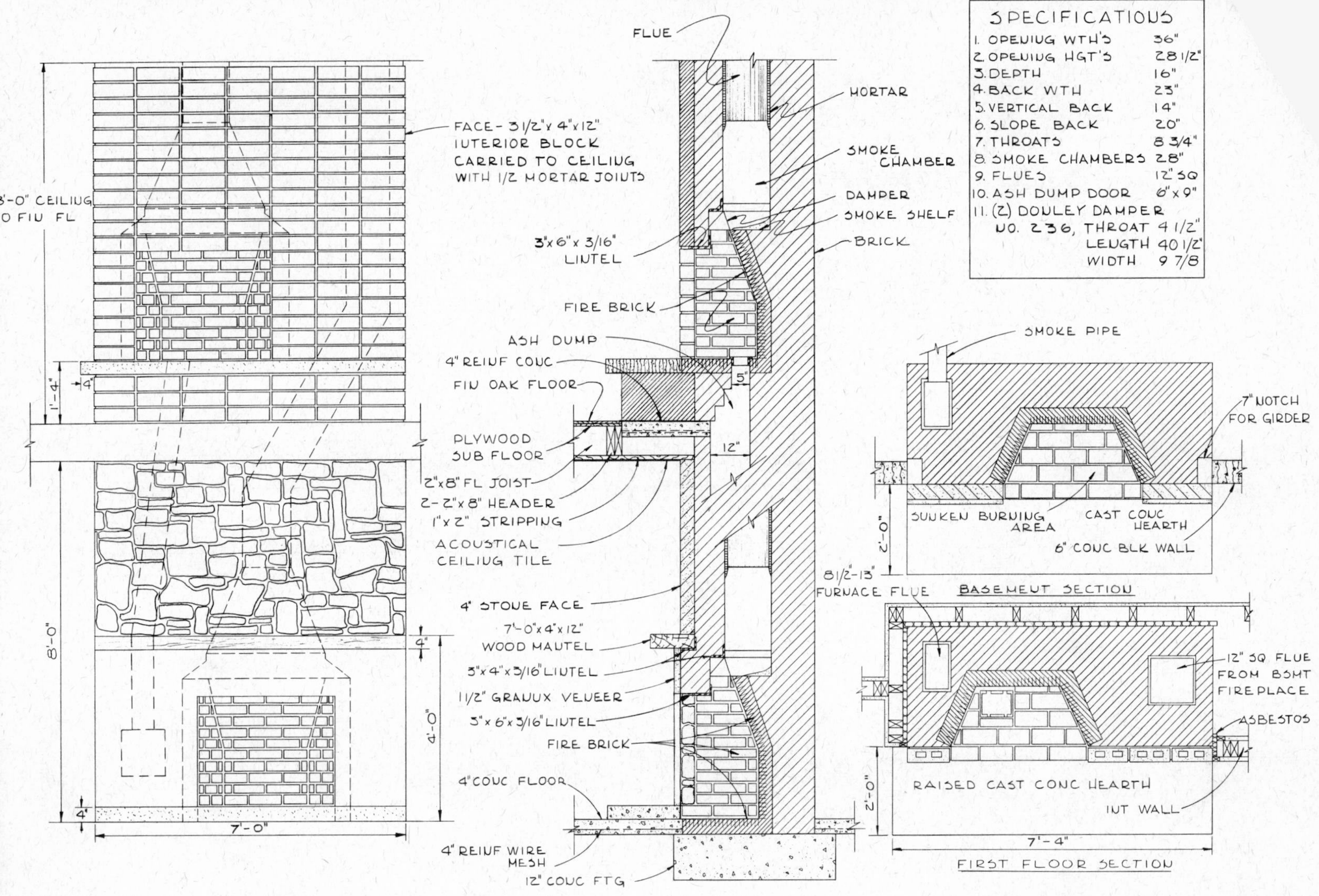

FIREPLACE DETAIL
SCALE: 3/4" = 1'-0"

THE RESIDENCE OF
DR. & MRS. ROBT. PUTNAM
617 ROSEWOOD DRIVE KALAMAZOO, MICH.
PARAMOUNT DESIGN INC.
KALAMAZOO, MICHIGAN
3-17-65
DESIGN BY: H. OLSEN & W. PALM, JR. DRAWN BY: W. PALM, JR.

10

6515

		TYPE	MANUFACTURE & CATALOG NO.	MATERIAL	REMARKS
		CASEMENT	PELLA # 3228C2	WESTERN PINE	
		↓	↓ # 4424C3	↓	
			# 3224C3		
		↓	# 4420C2		
		AWNING	# 4432A32		
	9 3/4"	CASEMENT	# 4420C4		
	4 x 3'-9 3/4"	↓	# 4424C2		
	-4 3/4" x 2'-9 3/4"	↓	↓ # 3228C1		GLAZED, WITH DIAMOND MUNTIN
9	1'-6" x 6'-8"	FIXED	JOB MADE		CUSTOM SIZE
10	11'-0 3/4" x 5'-9 3/4"	AWNING & FIXED	PELLA #4448A4420A32		
11	8-0 3/4" x 3'-9 3/4"	CASEMENT	↓ # 4424C4		
12	2'-6" x 2'-0"	FIXED	RIMCO # 2814	↓	

WINDOW SCHEDULE

SYM. △	SIZE WTH & HGT	THK	TYPE	MANUFACTURE & CATALOG NO.	MATERIAL	FINISH	JAMB	REMARKS
1	3'-3" x 6'-8"	1 3/4"	FLUSH-SOLID	CURTIS C 1341	PINE	NATURAL	WOOD	
2	2'-6" x 6'-8"	↓	↓	↓ C 1091	↓			
3	3'-0" x 6'-8"	3/8"	FOLDING	PELLA	WALNUT			
4	9'-3" x 8'-0"				↓	↓		CUSTOM
5	4'-0" x 6'-8"	↓	↓	↓	PINE	PAINTED		
6	2'-6" x 6'-8"	1 3/8"	FLUSH HOLLOW	CURTIS C 1042				
7	2'-3" x 6'-8"	↓	↓	↓				
8	6'-1" x 6'-8"	3/8"	FOLDING	PELLA	↓			
9	16'-0" x 7'-0"	↓	OVHD GARAGE	"FILUMA" FIBERGLAS GARAGE	ALUMINUM			FIBERGLASS FACE SKIN
10	3'-0" x 6'-8"	1 3/4"	FLUSH SOLID	CURTIS	PINE			
11	3'-2 1/2" x 6'-8"	3/8"	FOLDING	PELLA	↓	↓	↓	

DOOR SCHEDULE

THE RESIDENCE OF
DR. & MRS. ROBT. PUTNAM
617 ROSEWOOD DRIVE KALAMAZOO, MICH.
PARAMOUNT DESIGN INC
KALAMAZOO, MICHIGAN
3-17-65
DESIGN BY: H. OLSEN & W. PALM, JR. DRAWN BY: W. PALM, JR.

11

6515

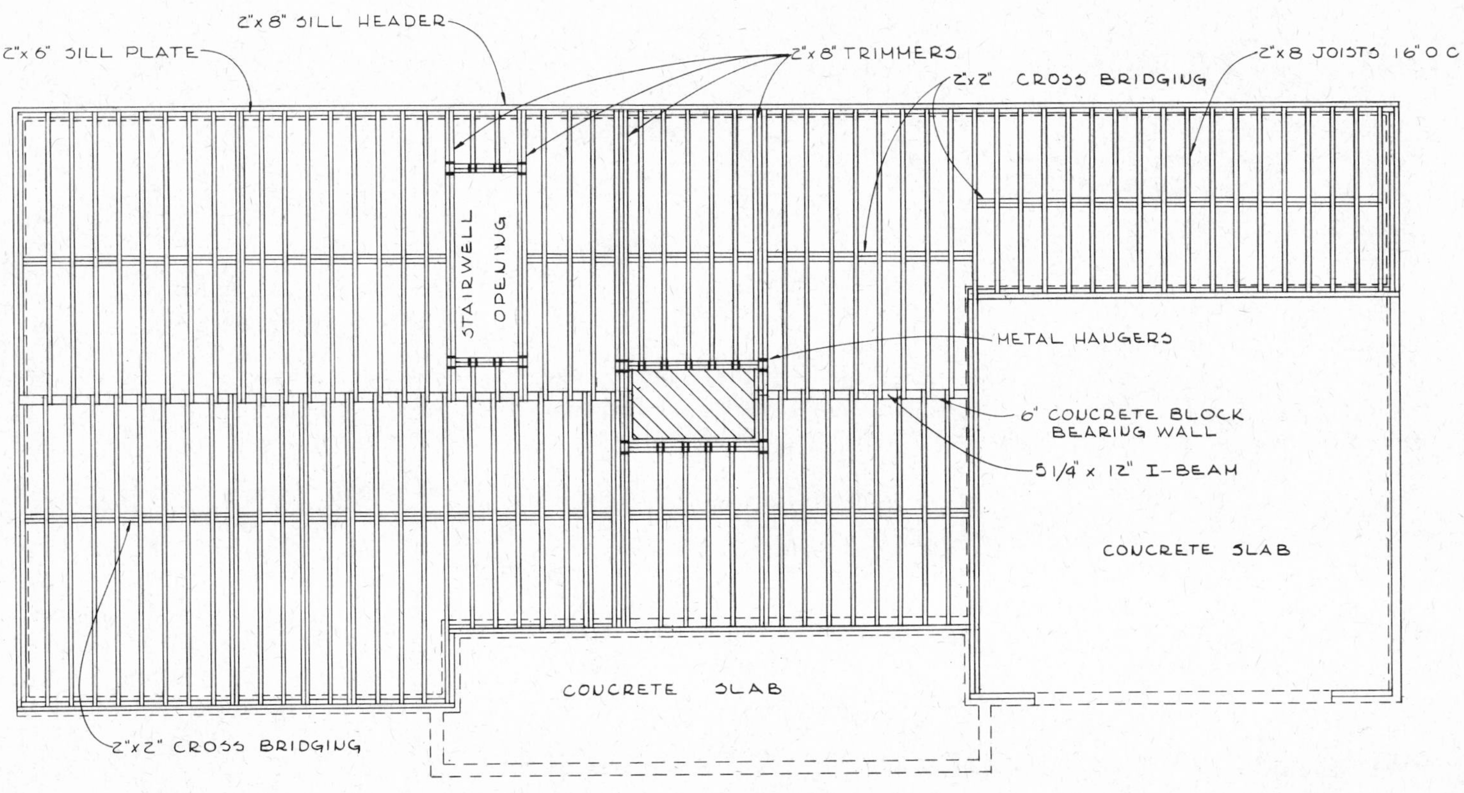

JOIST FRAMING PLAN

SCALE: 1/4" = 1'-0"

THE RESIDENCE OF
DR. & MRS. ROBT. PUTNAM
617 ROSEWOOD DRIVE KALAMAZOO, MICH.
PARAMOUNT DESIGN INC.
KALAMAZOO, MICHIGAN
5-17-65
DESIGN BY: H. OLSEN & W PALM, JR. DRAWN BY: W. PALM, JR.

12

6515

g Instruments d Techniques A

Graphical methods and instruments, almost as old as man himself, have changed very little compared to other modern technical accomplishments. Changes certainly have been made in the idioms of the graphical language, but sweeping changes have not occurred in the basic form of delineation. Drawing is said to be the universal language of the world. Drawings made by an architect, engineer, designer, or draftsman in Seattle are understood equally well by another technically trained person in New York, London, or Rome.

One of the best ways to learn the "how" of drafting is not merely to read about it, but to actually become involved in the drawing. To become skilled in the expression of this language, one must master the technique of handling the tools, equipment, and materials. The draftsman's and designer's success depends not only upon his knowledge of the various facets of home planning and construction, but also upon the facility in which he uses the tools and materials of his craft.

As with the master craftsman, good work demands good tools and equipment. When these are carefully selected and given proper care, they will last a lifetime. Whenever possible, the student should attempt to purchase the best grade of equipment; there is no compromise for quality.

In any craft there are certain recognized instruments fundamental for the beginner. These and other items are illustrated and explained in the succeeding paragraphs. Those items that are considered essential for the architectural drawing student are identified with an *asterisk*.

Equipment and Techniques

Drawing Boards

*Drawing boards** and tables come in a variety of sizes. The most common board size is approximately 18″ × 24″. Other available sizes are: 20″ × 24″, 20″ × 26″, 23″ × 31″, 24″ × 36″, and 31″ × 42″. These boards are made of narrow strips of basswood or other soft wood glued together with a cleat across either end to prevent warping. See Fig. A-1. Cleats form the right and left working edges of the board. To serve as a guide for the T-square the end cleats should be straight and firmly fastened to the board. Some drawing boards are provided with metal, rather than wood, end cleats. This has the advantage of not being subjected to wear or denting by careless treatment.

Straight Edge Devices

T-squares. The *T-square** (Fig. A-2) is

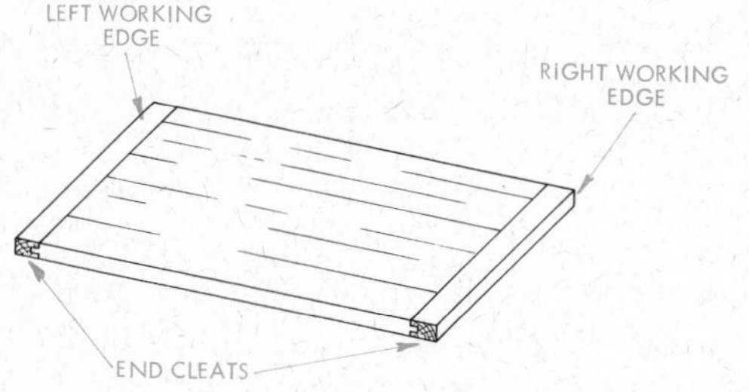

Fig. A-1. Drawing boards are usually made of basswood and are available in various sizes.

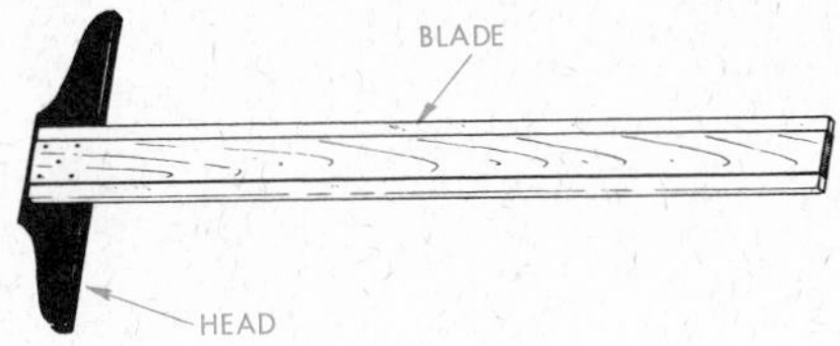

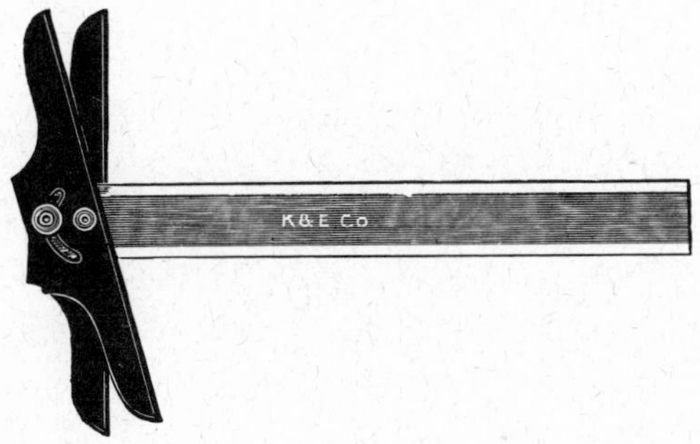

KEUFFEL & ESSER CO.; HOBOKEN, NEW JERSEY.

Fig. A-2. T-squares serve as a guide for triangles and for drawing horizontal lines. They are made with fixed and adjustable heads and are available with different length blades.

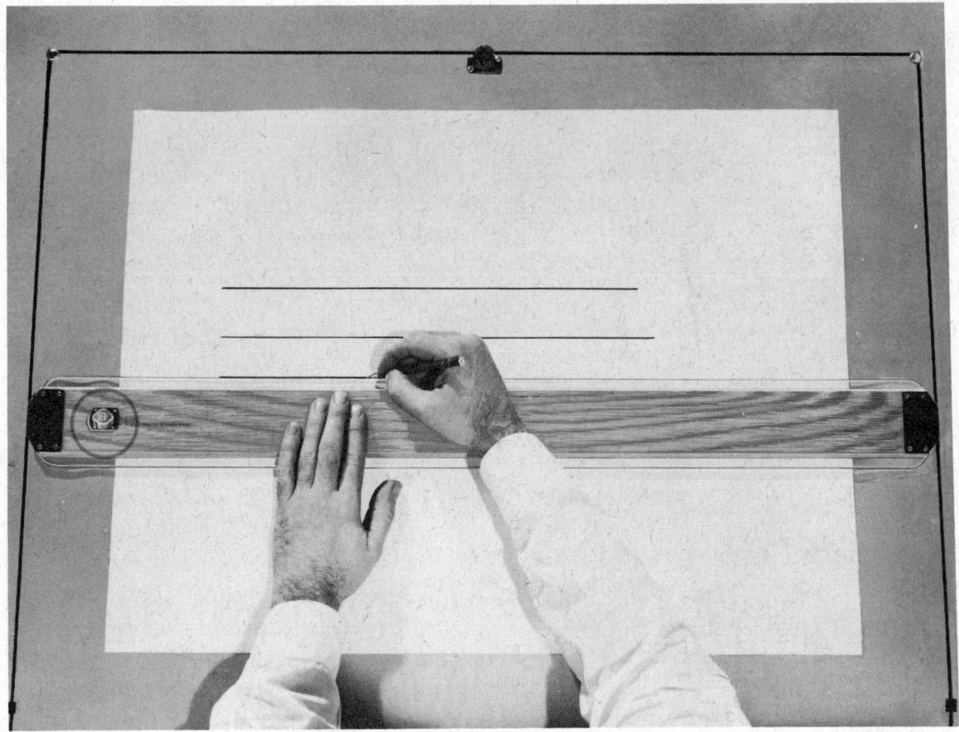

KEUFFEL & ESSER CO.; HOBOKEN, NEW JERSEY.

Fig. A-3. The sliding parallel straight edge simplifies the matter of drawing lines since the blade always moves in a parallel path. Some straight edges may be locked in position to eliminate constant pressure to prevent movement (see circle).

used for drawing horizontal and parallel lines. It is also used as a guide for triangles in drawing vertical and inclined lines. Two types of T-squares are available: the fixed head and the adjustable head. The fixed head is used in most situations. The adjustable head T-square is also designed to be used as a fixed head T-square for drawing horizontal lines. By rolling the T-square over so the adjustable portion of the head is against the working edge, parallel inclined lines may then be drawn to any desired angle. Horizontal lines are always drawn from the top edge of the blade, while the head is held firmly against the working edge of the board. T-squares vary in length from 18″ to 60″. All lengths are available with either a plastic edged wood blade or

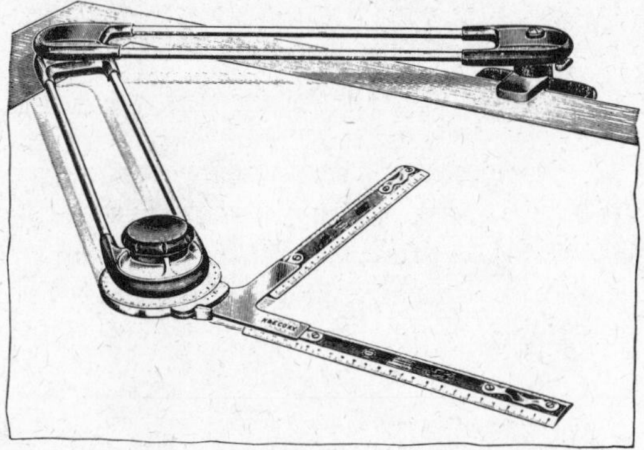

KEUFFEL & ESSER CO.; HOBOKEN, NEW JERSEY.

Fig. A-4. The drafting machine is useful for doing large blueprints and drawings.

an all-wood blade. The plastic edge is the most widely used of these two types because lines that are beneath the blade are visible.

Sliding Parallel Straight Edge. The T-square has its limitation in long line drawings because it must be held firmly against the edge of the board. Today the sliding parallel straight edge (sometimes called the parallel rule), is usually used in all architectural offices in place of the T-square. See Fig. A-3. The parallel straight edge has an advantage over the T-square since it is supported at both ends. The support at either end causes the rule to move in a parallel path and it may be held in position with a minimal amount of effort.

Drafting Machine. The drafting machine (Fig. A-4) is used in some architectural drafting offices. However, the parallel straight edge is preferred by most architectural draftsmen. The drafting machine combines the T-square, triangles, protractor, and scales.

Drawing Mediums

Tracing Paper and Vellum. Almost all architectural drafting offices prepare every drawing, including preliminary sketches, studies, working drawings, etc., on tracing paper or *vellum.** In past years all drawings were first made on opaque paper and then were traced in ink on transparent paper or cloth. Advances in paper technology have produced highly transparent mediums that have eliminated the necessity of inking to produce a quality print. Frequently the terms "tracing paper" and "tracing vellum" are used synonymously. There is, however, a difference. Tracing paper is a thin transparent paper called *natural tracing paper.* When tracing paper is impregnated with a transparentizing fluid it is then called tracing vellum. Vellums are characterized by their highly transparent quality, yet are very durable and non-yellowing. They are further characterized by the fact that they "take" pencil very well and have excellent erasing qualities. Vellums are manufactured from 100 per cent rag stock.

Rendering. Paper for rendering should be of sufficient weight, quality, and grain (tooth) so that it will "take" pencil in line and shade and will erase with ease.

Fastening Paper To the Board

The drafting medium is secured to the board with *drafting tape,** staples, or thumb tacks. Tape is probably the most widely used because it does not damage the drawing. In fastening the paper to the board: (1) Position the paper about 3″ or 4″ from the top and left edge (left-handers should use the right edge) of the board. See Fig. A-5. If the drawing is to be large it may be necessary to alter these distances. (2) Place the T-square

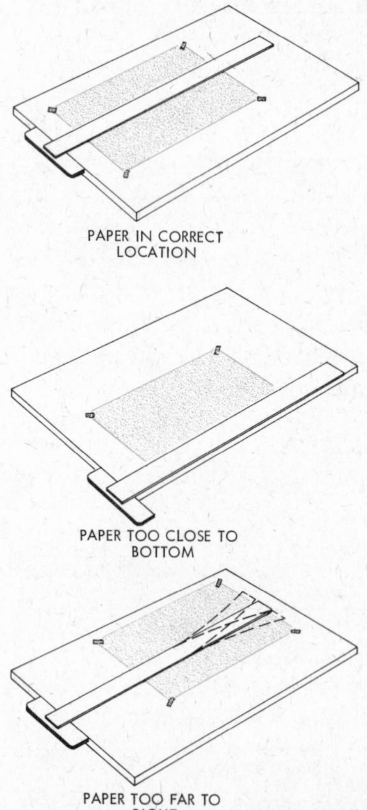

Fig. A-5. The paper must be located to avoid inconvenience and the possibility of error.

on the board with the head tight against the left edge (right edge for left-handers). (3) Align the top edge of the paper with the upper edge of the T-square blade so there is approximately $\frac{1}{32}''$ of paper exposed above the blade. It is much easier to gauge the parallelness of these two by observing the white space between the blade and the paper than if they both coincide. Hold the paper in the center, slide the T-square downward several inches. (4) Fasten paper to the board in the two upper corners. (5) Move the T-square upward to check alignment. (6) Secure the lower corners to the board by stretching the medium diagonally. And (7) burnish the tape with the fingernail to insure that it is firmly adhered to the drawing sheet and board. If the tape is not secure, it will roll under the T-square blade and triangles, causing "drag" as these instruments are moved. Small amounts of the adhesive material may also be deposited on the under side of the T-square. This small amount of adhesive will collect dirt and graphite and is one of the main causes of dirty drawings.

Pencils

A pencil* is the usual means of recording information on the drawing medium. Pencils are graded by hardness. This is indicated by a number and a letter stamped on one end of the pencil. Fig. A-6 shows pencils in their general hardness classifications with line samples of different pencil grades. It is rather difficult to state specifically which grade of pencil should be used for a particular job since several factors enter into consideration: (1) touch, (amount of pressure applied by each individual is different); (2) tooth of the drawing medium; (3) atmospheric conditions (when it is exceedingly humid, a softer pencil may be required); and (4) brand of pencil (all pencils of the same grade, as an example 2H, are not necessarily the same degree of hardness). Pencils used by the draftsman or designer are either wood-cased or held in mechanical lead holders (Fig. A-7). Probably the main advantage of the mechanical lead holder is that the weight and length of the pencil is always the same.

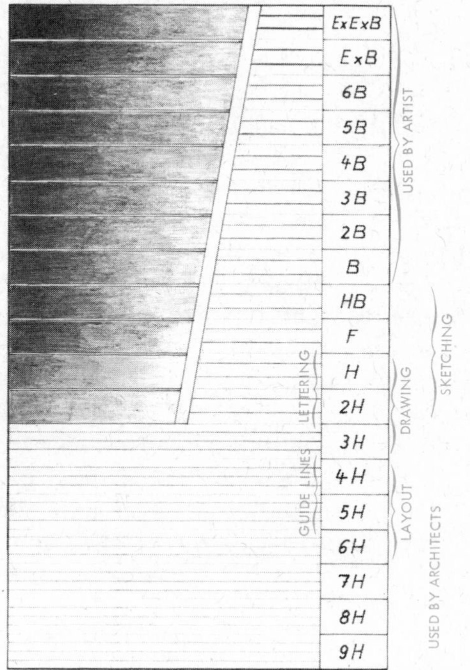

J. S. STAEDTLER, INC.; MONTVILLE, NEW JERSEY.

Fig. A-6. Different pencil grades produce different line widths. The harder the pencil the thinner the line.

KOH-I-NOOR; BLOOMSBURG, NEW JERSEY.
THEO. ALTENEDER & SONS; PHILADELPHIA, PENNSYLVANIA.

Fig. A-7. Mechanical lead holders eliminate the pencil sharpening problem. The two basic types, spring chuck (top) and screw chuck (bottom), are shown above.

Two types of pencil points, Fig. A-8, are commonly used by draftsmen: the conical point and the wedge or chisel point. The conical point is probably the most widely used but it does require pointing more frequently than the wedge.

To sharpen a wood pencil, for either a

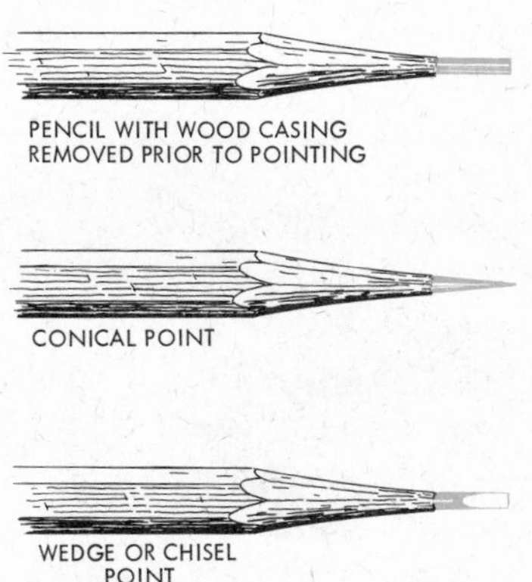

Fig. A-8. Two basic pencil points are commonly used by draftsmen.

KEUFFEL & ESSER CO.; HOBOKEN, NEW JERSEY.

Fig. A-9. A mechanical pencil pointer saves the draftsman considerable time.

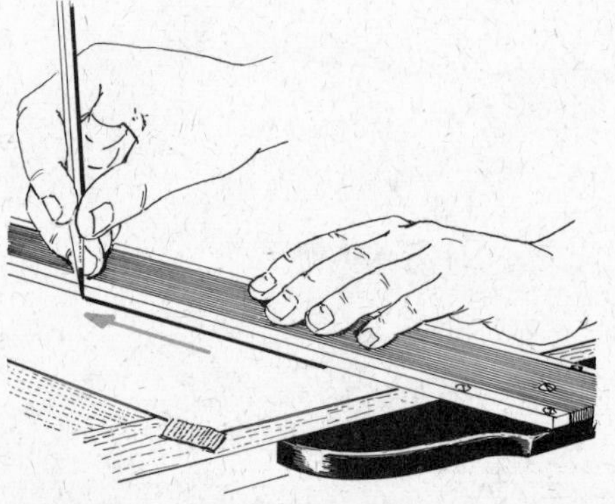

Fig. A-10. When drawing lines the pencil is inclined in the direction of travel and is rotated slightly.

conical or wedge point, remove the wood casing at the unmarked end with a pocket knife or a draftsman's pencil sharpener until ¼" to ⅜" of the lead is exposed. To obtain a conical point, draw the exposed portion of the lead across a 6" bastard or ignition file, or a commercially available pencil pointer, with long rotating strokes. Sandpaper is not recommended for pointing the pencil since the pieces of abrasive will tend to cut concentric rings in the point and weaken the point. It is wise to remove the excess graphite particles by tapping the file on a hard surface. Graphite particles may not be readily "knocked out" of the abrasive paper because it has a tendency to hold the graphite dust. The wedge point is produced by holding the pencil at a slight angle and drawing the exposed lead along the file until a ⅜" flat surface is obtained. Rotate the pencil 180° and file the opposite side in a similar manner. The wedge point will give a more constant line weight than the conical point. Pencil pointers, both electrically and mechanically operated, do the job much faster. See Fig. A-9.

Drawing Lines. When drawing any line with a straight edge as a guide, the pencil is inclined slightly in the direction of travel. See Fig. A-10. To eliminate constant repointing of the pencil, it should be rotated slightly as the line is being drawn. This slight rotation will produce a uniform line width and preserve the point shape. When a series of horizontal lines are being drawn, the upper line is drawn first. The succeeding lines are drawn from top to bottom.

EBERHARD FABER, INC.; NEWARK, NEW JERSEY.

Fig. A-11. Erasers may be either stick or prismatic in form.

Erasers

*Erasers** (Fig. A-11) are a necessary part of the draftsman's equipment. They are available in the prismatic form or in the stick variety. Probably the stick type is the most convenient for the majority of jobs. All errors must be erased and corrected. The number of erasers required by the draftsman depends upon the type of drawing. Usually three kinds of erasers are used: hard, soft, and gum. The soft eraser removes light lines, smudges, etc., while the harder eraser (no grit) removes heavy, stubborn lines. The gum type eraser is especially suited for removing construction lines, smudges, or finger prints. Before attempting to remove a line, clean the eraser by rubbing it on a piece of clean paper to remove any graphite smudges or body oil that may be deposited on the eraser tip. This will eliminate the red or pink smudge on the drawing that is almost impossible to remove.

When erasing, stretch the paper by holding it with the thumb and middle finger. This will prevent the paper from wrinkling or tearing. Frequently when a tracing must be corrected, considerable erasing will be required to remove the line. This may be accomplished most speedily by placing a triangle under the vellum. The triangle provides a hard non-resilient surface.

Erasing Shield. Often an erasing shield (Fig. A-12) is used to protect adjacent lines or a portion of a line from being erased. Erasing shields are made of nickel silver or stainless steel. Select the opening in the erasing shield that is slightly larger than the portion of the line to be eradicated. Hold the erasing shield tightly and erase through the opening. If the eraser has been used considerably and is rounded, it may be difficult to erase up to the opening. A new eraser edge can be cut with a pocket knife. If an erasing shield is not available, or a special shaped opening is required, use a piece of vellum or detail paper as a shield.

Dusting Brush

The *dusting brush** (Fig. A-13) is a valuable accessory for removing eraser crumbs, dust, and graphite particles from the drawing surface. When using the brush, do not scrub the drawing, but lightly draw it across the surface. If any graphite particles are adjacent to a line they will not be ground into the vellum.

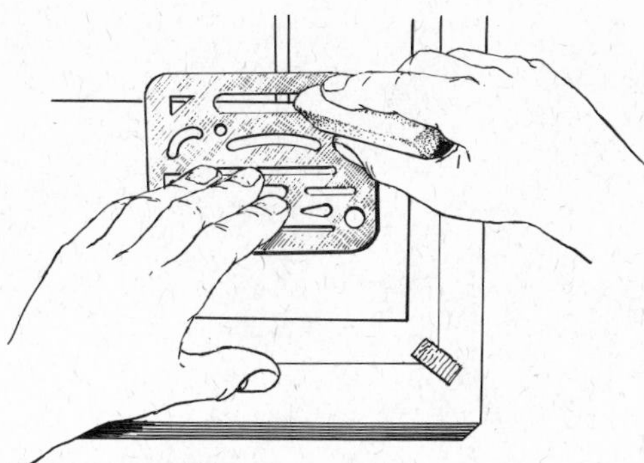

Fig. A-12. The erasing shield is used to protect adjacent lines.

KEUFFEL & ESSER CO.; HOBOKEN, NEW JERSEY.

Fig. A-13. The dusting brush is a desirable accessory for the draftsman.

Triangle

Triangles* (Fig. A-14) are manufacured in two standard types—the 45° and the 30°-60°. These are used for drawing vertical and sloping lines. They may be used singly or in combination with each other. The most frequently used sizes of the 30°-60° triangle are the 8″, 10″, or 12″; for the 45° triangle 6″, 8″, or 10″. Usually the 45° triangle is 2″ smaller than the 30°-60°. Triangles are sized by measuring the longest side of the right angle.

Fig. A-14. Triangles are used for drawing vertical and inclined lines. The 45° triangle should be 2″ shorter than the 30°-60° triangle.

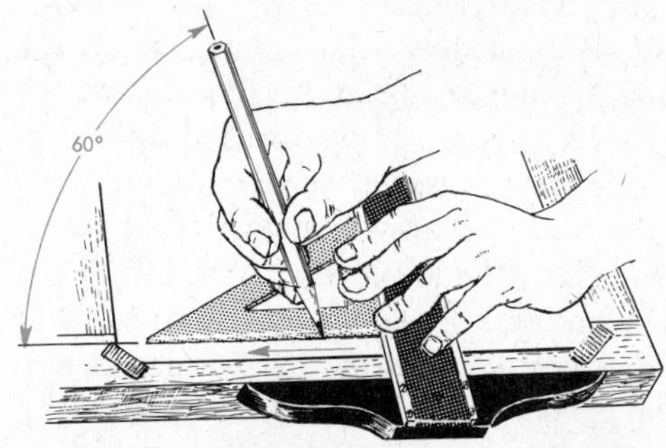

Fig. A-15. When drawing vertical lines the pencil is moved away from the blade. The pencil should be inclined in the direction of travel and rotated slightly.

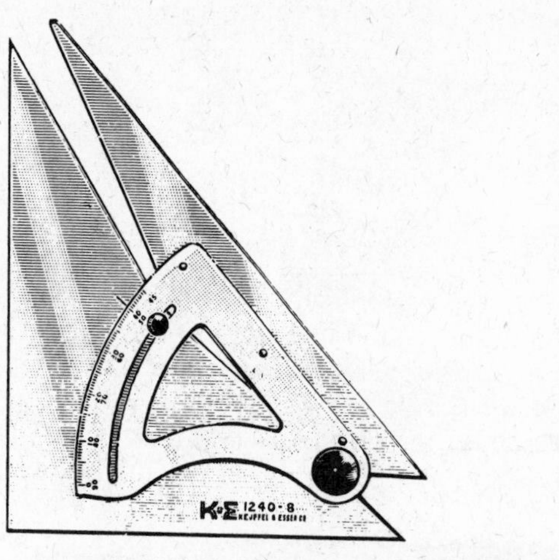

KEUFFEL & ESSER CO.; HOBOKEN, NEW JERSEY.

Fig. A-16. The adjustable triangle is used to draw any angular line from 0° to 90°.

Drawing Lines. The best method of drawing lines with the triangle is to hold the T-square head against the working edge of the board. The triangle(s) is slid into position and held securely with the fingers of the same hand, see Fig. A-15. The vertical or inclined lines are drawn away from the T-square. When drawing vertical lines the leftmost line is drawn first, then proceed to the right. (The left-hander will start at the right and proceed to the left.) Vertical lines are always drawn from the bottom to top; the pencil is inclined in the direction of travel. Often, angles other than those obtainable with the triangle or combinations of triangles are made by using either the adjustable triangle or the protractor.

Adjustable Triangle. The adjustable triangle is used to draw lines from 0° to 90° by adjusting the protractor device to the desired angle. See Fig. A-16. The movable side of the triangle is held in place by the clamp nut which may also be used as a convenient handle for lifting.

Templates

Many templates are available for use in architectural drafting. Two of the more common types are shown in Fig. A-17. These are used for lines, circles, symbols, fixtures, furniture, etc. in both plan and elevation. Templates save time and simplify much drafting. When using any template, always hold the pencil perpendicular to the face of the drawing. Do not incline and push the pencil point into the template opening and do not move the pencil in a circular motion. This will result in graphite powder being deposited on the drawing surface.

Guide Line Devices

The *Ames Lettering Guide* or the *Brad-*

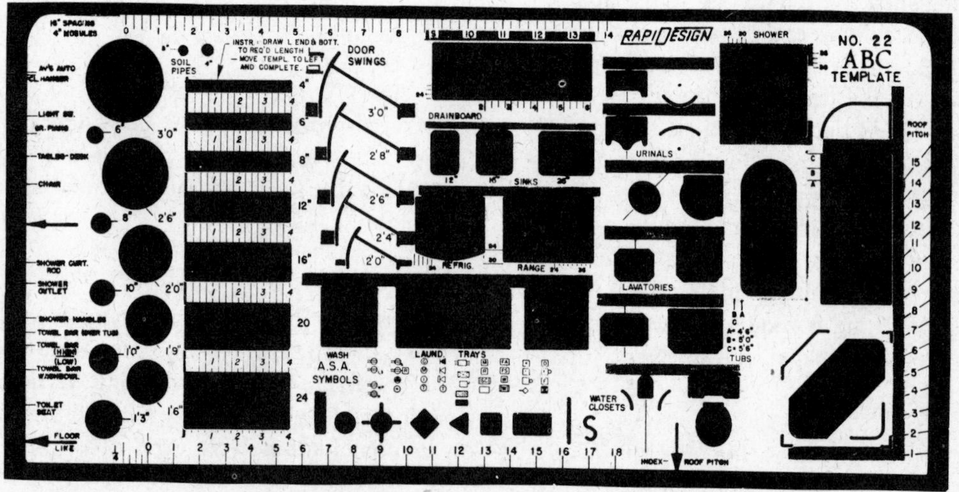

EUGENE DIETZGEN COMPANY; CHICAGO, ILLINOIS.

Fig. A-17. Templates aid the draftsman and designer in drawing circles, fixtures, symbols, etc.

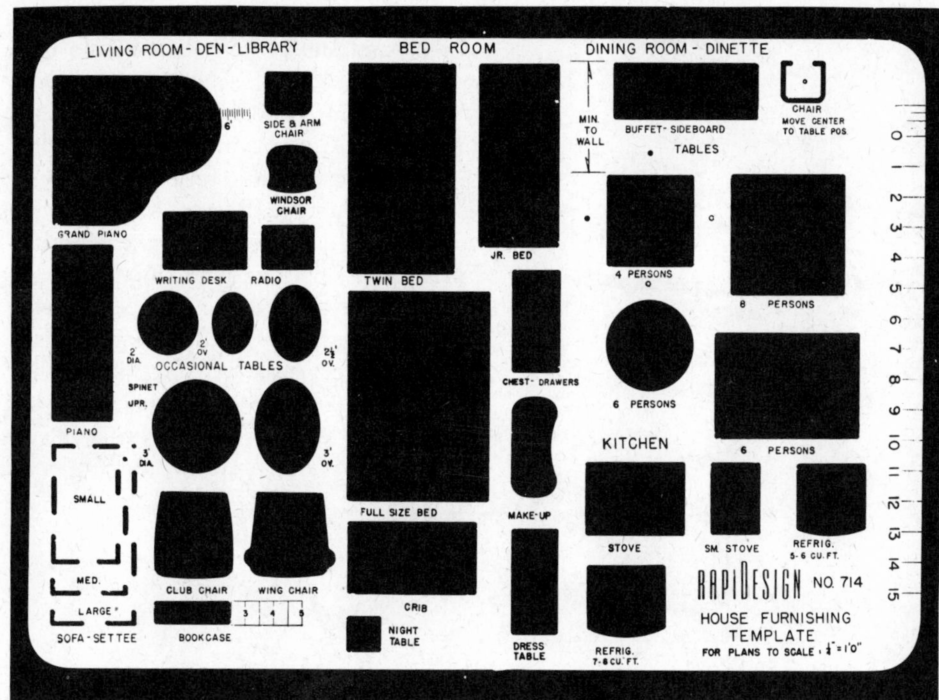

Fig. A-17. Contd.

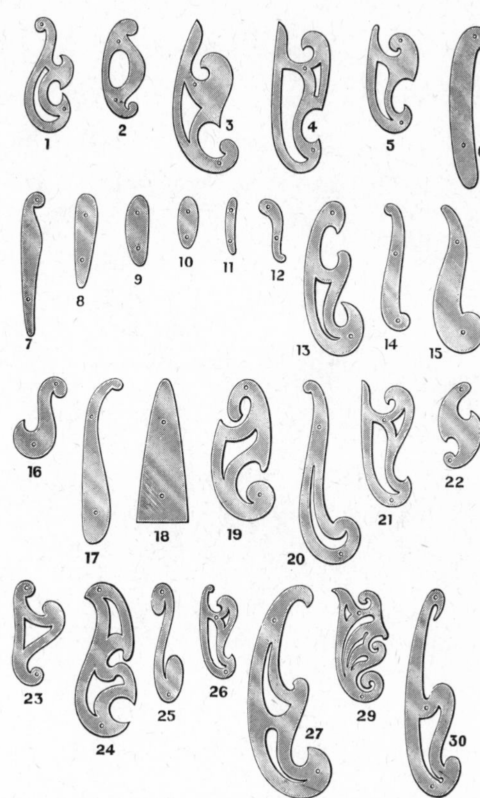
KEUFFEL & ESSER CO.; HOBOKEN, NEW JERSEY.

Fig. A-18. Irregular curves are available in many shapes and sizes to draw any curve.

dock-Rowe Lettering Triangle (see Fig. 5-6 in Chapter 5) will prove to be a time-saving device for drawing guide lines for lettering or for drawing a series of lines a uniform distance apart.

Irregular Curves

Irregular or French curves, see Fig. A-18, are used for drawing curves which cannot be made readily with a compass. Irregular curves come in a variety of sizes and shapes to produce practically every kind of curve.

Flexible curves, shown in Fig. A-19, may be bent to fit any *long* curve. These are not designed to be used for small curves.

Scales

The architect's scale, see Fig. A-20, is used for measuring distances full size, as well as laying out distances to scale. The term "laying out" or "drawing to scale" indicates that an object may be drawn on the sheet full size, enlarged, or reduced. Almost all scales have from two to eleven graduated faces that enable the draftsman to reduce or enlarge a distance to fit within the limits of the drawing sheet. Scales may be open divided with units marked (Fig. A-21, top) along the entire length of the face of the scale, but with only the end units subdivided into inches and fractions of an inch. A fully

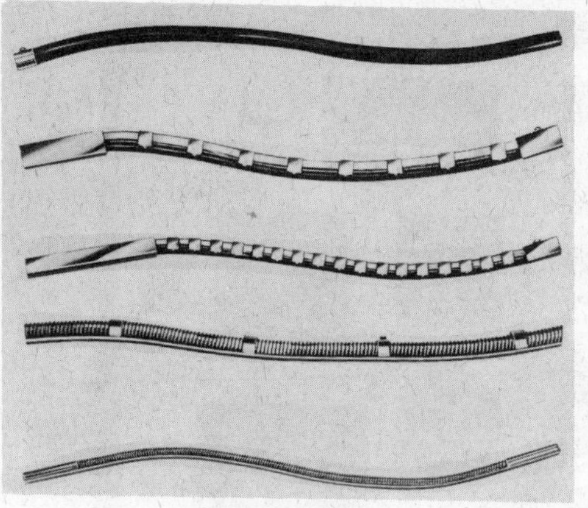

FREDERICK POST CO.; CHICAGO, ILLINOIS.

Fig. A-19. Flexible curves may be adjusted for any long curve.

divided scale (Fig. A-21, bottom) has equal divisions and subdivisions carried the full length of the scale face with continuous numbering. Only one kind of a division can be made on a face.

Scales are made in a variety of shapes. Fig. A-22 shows five different scale shapes. The flat scales are preferred by the majority of draftsmen since the graduations on the face are easier to read and the scale is less difficult to handle than a triangular scale.

The architect's scale may take any of the five shapes just shown. The usual shape of the architect's scale, however, is triangular;

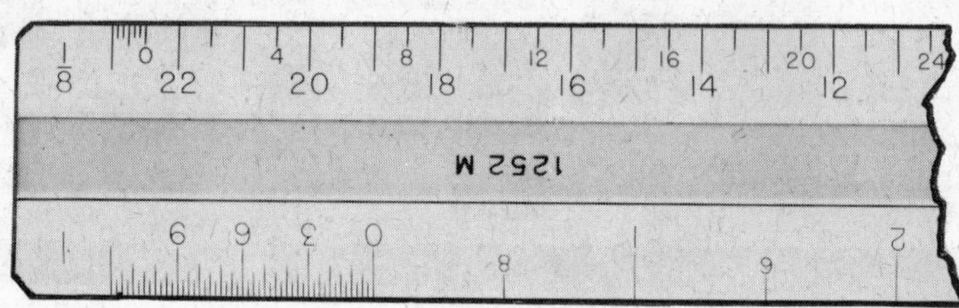

OPEN DIVIDED

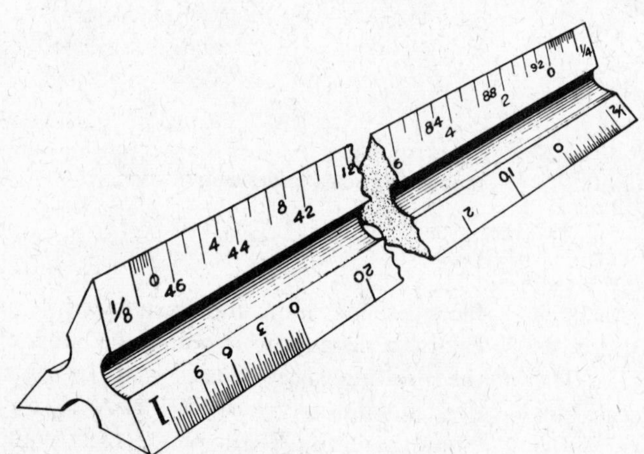

Fig. A-20. The triangular architect's scale is made in 6″ and 12″ lengths.

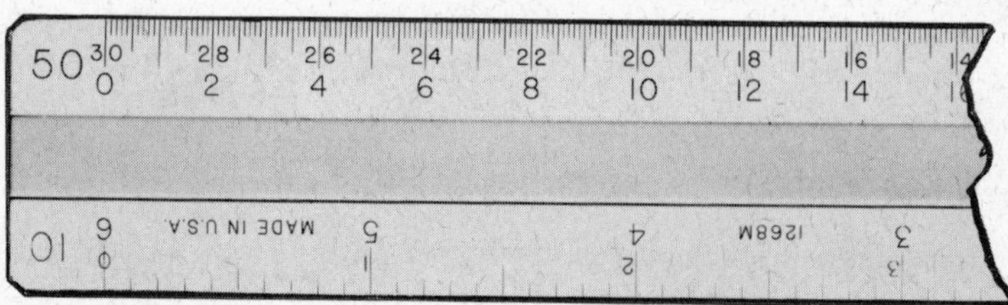

FULLY DIVIDED

FREDERICK POST CO.; CHICAGO, ILLINOIS.

Fig. A-21. Scale graduations may be open or fully divided.

		DESCRIPTION
	TWO BEVEL	Wide base with complete visibility of both faces.
	OPPOSITE BEVEL	Easy to lift by tilting.
	FOUR BEVEL	Four faces for four scales.
	REGULAR TRIANGULAR	Permits full face contact with drawing.
	CONCAVE TRIANGULAR	Only edges of bottom scales are in contact with drawing.

FREDERICK POST CO.; CHICAGO, ILLINOIS.

Fig. A-22. Personal choice guides the draftsman, designer, or architect in the selection of scales from any of the above styles.

TABLE A-1

STANDARD SIZES COMMONLY USED ON ARCHITECTURAL DRAWINGS		
WHEN DRAWING IS:	TO PRODUCE A DRAWING IN WHICH:	INDICATION ON SCALE FACE IS:
FULL SIZE	12" ON DRAWING EQUALS 12" ON OBJECT	12"
1/4 SIZE	3" ON DRAWING EQUALS 12" ON OBJECT	3"
1/8 SIZE	1 1/2" ON DRAWING EQUALS 12" ON OBJECT	1 1/2"
1/12 SIZE	1" ON DRAWING EQUALS 12" ON OBJECT	1"
1/16 SIZE	3/4" ON DRAWING EQUALS 12" ON OBJECT	3/4"
1/24 SIZE	1/2" ON DRAWING EQUALS 12" ON OBJECT	1/2"
1/32 SIZE	3/8" ON DRAWING EQUALS 12" ON OBJECT	3/8"
1/48 SIZE	1/4" ON DRAWING EQUALS 12" ON OBJECT	1/4"
1/64 SIZE	3/16" ON DRAWING EQUALS 12" ON OBJECT	3/16"
1/96 SIZE	1/8" ON DRAWING EQUALS 12" ON OBJECT	1/8"
1/128 SIZE	3/32" ON DRAWING EQUALS 12" ON OBJECT	3/32"

this has eleven different types of graduations. Ten of these different graduations are open-divided scales that appear on five of the six faces. Two different scales, one a multiple of the other, are placed on each of the five faces. For example, one face of the scale may be graduated using ⅛″ = 1′-0″ on one end and ¼″ = 1′-0″ on the other. Another face may be graduated using 3/32″ = 1′-0″ on one end, while the other will have 3/16″ = 1′-0″. The full scale is on a separate face and is fully graduated. Table A-1 gives the most commonly used standard scales found on the architect's scale. Almost any combination of scales can be obtained with divisions suitable to the work at hand.

Laying Off Dimensions. When pointing off measurements, look directly down on the point where the measurement is to be made. If a scale other than full size is used, the number of inches and feet are measured in one step. First read the number of feet on the scale either to the right or left of 0; then the inches are read from the subdivided

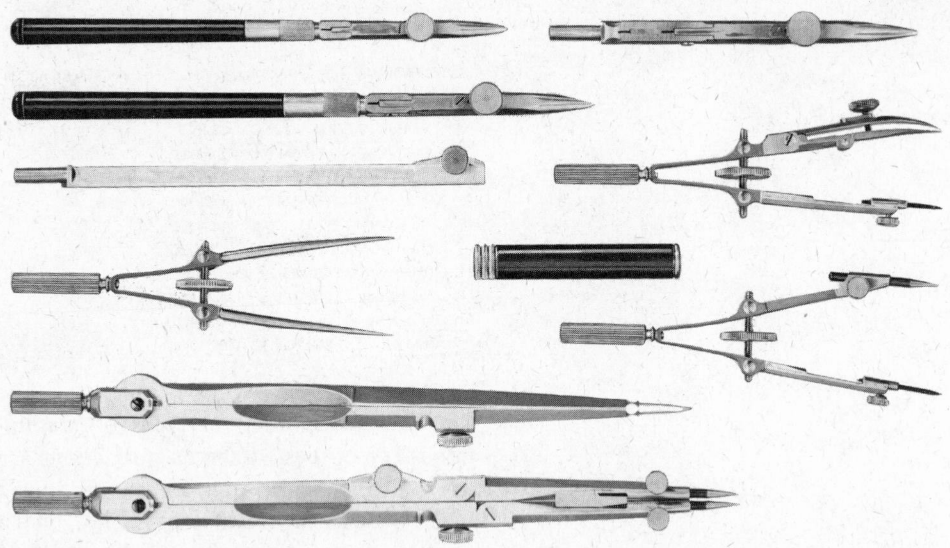

THEO. ALTENEDER & SONS; PHILADELPHIA, PENNSYLVANIA.

Fig. A-23. A basic set of drawing instruments will last a life time when properly cared for.

KEUFFEL & ESSER CO.; HOBOKEN, NEW JERSEY

Fig. A-24. The large divider is an essential piece of equipment.

unit (based on the normal divisions of one foot-inches) on the end. Indicate the specific location by a short dash or, preferably, make a small mark, rotating the pencil slightly, directly opposite the graduation. Do not transfer the measurements by dividers. This practice tends to dim the graduations on the scale and to introduce additional error.

Drawing Instruments

Drawing instruments are available in many sizes and qualities. It is not necessary to purchase an entire set of instruments. Probably the wisest choice is to purchase several basic, good quality items. Fig. A-23 shows a basic set of excellent quality drawing instruments. The most commonly used instruments are the *dividers,** Fig. A-24, which are used for dividing, transferring, and stepping off distances. The hair spring adjustment on one of the legs will permit greater accuracy in setting the dividers. The *large bow compass** (Fig. A-25) with the center adjusting screw is preferred over a friction head type construction. The compass is used for drawing circles. Many compasses are equipped with an interchangeable pencil or inking leg. Care must be taken in drawing a circle to incline the compass slightly in the direction the circle is drawn.

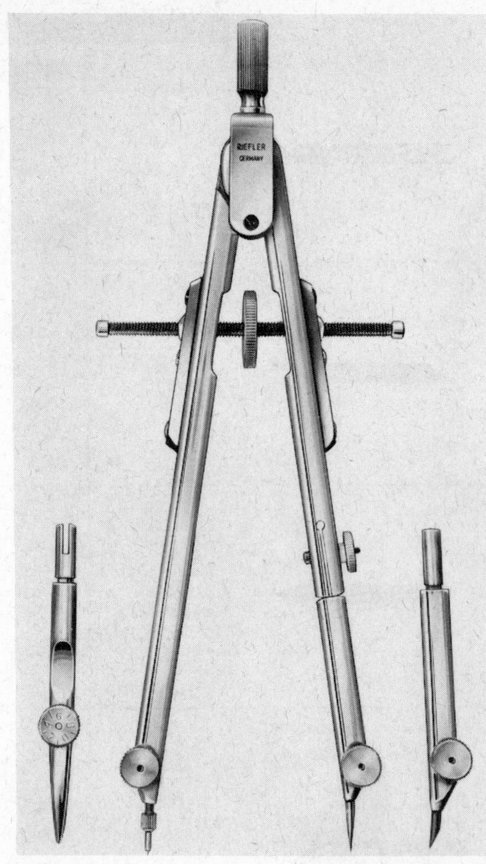

GRAMERCY GUILD GROUP, INC.; DENVER, COLORADO.

Fig. A-25. This large center-adjusting bow compass has an interchangeable pencil, ink, and divider leg.

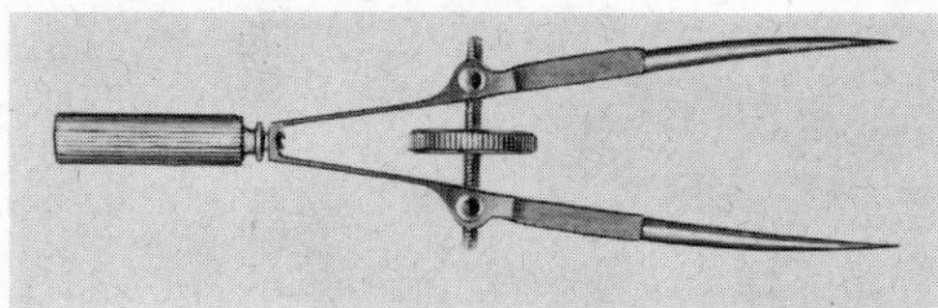

THEO. ALTENEDER & SONS; PHILADELPHIA, PENNSYLVANIA.

Fig. A-26. The small, center-adjusting bow divider is an essential piece of equipment for the draftsman.

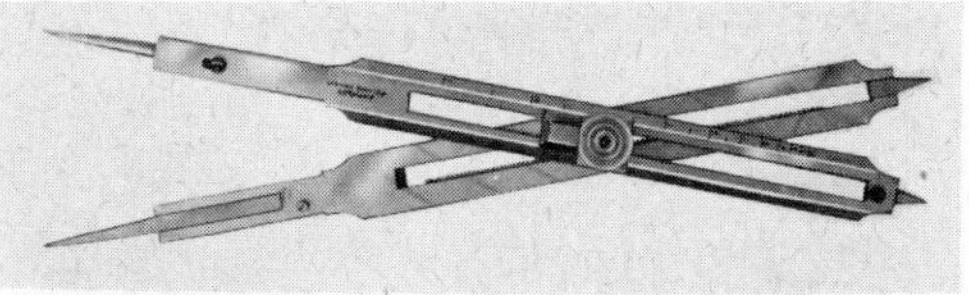

GRAMERCY GUILD GROUP, INC.; DENVER, COLORADO.

Fig. A-27. Proportional dividers are helpful for quickly enlarging, reducing, or dividing distances.

The needle point of the compass should be adjusted approximately 1/32″ longer than the pencil or pen point. The lead should be sharpened to a chisel point. Often a small, *center-adjusting bow divider** (Fig. A-26) may be desired for small detail work.

A ruling pen which is used for drawing lines in ink is included in many drawing sets. Frequently the draftsman is required to do a certain amount of inking. Care and practice is necessary before one gains any proficiency in handling a pen. It is suggested the student study any of the standard engineering drawing texts listed in Appendix D for additional information on inking technique.

Proportional Dividers

Proportional dividers, see Fig. A-27, may be used for enlarging or reducing line or for dividing any distance into a number of equal points. One side of the dividers are marked to obtain the desired number of divisions for lines. Circles may also be divided. The series of divisions for circles are marked 'circle'.

Guidance Information B

The basic purpose of including guidance information is to answer many questions that come from students and teachers regarding educational requirements and working conditions in the various crafts and professions associated with the field of architecture. It is hoped that the following information will assist the architectural drafting student in understanding the role that other fields play in their contribution to architecture.

A knowledge of architectural drafting not only serves those who are interested in continuing on in the field, but it also is a definite asset for those who are interested in pursuing the trades or professions examined in the following paragraphs. Each occupational area is examined in detail relative to the nature of the work, qualifications, returns, working conditions, and opportunities. The procedure for entering a particular profession or craft is also given.

Job Hunting

Job hunting calls for an exact plan of procedure. The applicant should not just look for a *job*—he should look for a *career*. To find a career suited to each individual's abilities and interest, research and salesmanship are necessary. Study any good book on salesmanship. A salesman usually uses a series of steps in selling a customer. These are: preparation, approach, interview, arousing interest, creating a desire, and securing a decision. Obtaining a job is selling yourself.

Every job applicant should observe the following rules:

1. Be modest, but don't develop an inferiority complex. Admit you know very little about the business but are willing to learn and start at the bottom.
2. Have an idea of what kind of job you want.
3. Show the employer your eagerness to go to work. Convince him that you are sure of what you want to do, even though you don't know how to do it.

Employment Possibilities

There are several ways in which to locate job prospects. (1) Let your friends and relatives know you are looking for a job; enlist their aid in getting your foot in the door. (2) Call at the state unemployment office and fill out the required forms. (3) Call at company employment offices and fill out an application for a job. (4) Write to several companies to see if there is an opening. (5) Answer help wanted ads. (6) Apply at employment agencies. (7) Contact your school guidance office.

Discover employers in your line of work and select those which seem to be most desirable. Look for an employer rather than a job. Start in your local area—after exhausting these possibilities try farther away.

Do advanced studying of the employer's business—study particularly the commodity in which it deals and the nature of the job you hope to get. This information may be obtained from the employees, from observing the concern, and from the local library in books like *Who's Who, Who's Who in Commerce and Industry, Reader's Guide,* etc. This will enable you to answer questions which may be asked in an interview. A helpful suggestion in the form of an original observation will indicate to the employer an interest in the concern's business or its problems.

If you obtain a letter of introduction from an influential friend or relative, this will give you the chance for an interview. You may also write and ask for an interview. Writing a letter of application for a job must be a sales letter. It must attract attention. Be frank and truthful. Try to inspire interest and confidence—incite the employer to action.

When filling out an application blank, fill it out very carefully: write clearly, spell correctly, be sure answers are accurate, and follow directions carefully.

It is a good idea to prepare a sales talk so as not to hesitate when the time comes. What would you want to know if you were the employer? You will qualify for a position if your past conduct, personality, and appearance are satisfactory.

The prospective applicant in architectural drafting or in some allied areas, will be expected to present a portfolio (collection) of architectural drawings. *The student, therefore, should take care to save samples of his best work.*

Each specialized field has its own particular qualifications and working conditions. The following sections examine in detail several fields associated with architecture.

Guidance Information: Professions

The architectural draftsman should be familiar with the allied professions and construction trades. This is especially true if he wishes to advance to a senior position or to start his own drafting firm. This general knowledge is needed if the draftsman is to assist in planning. It is also essential that the senior draftsman (along with the contractor and the architect) have an understanding of the particular qualifications and working conditions of each associated discipline. Conversely, many of the allied professions and trades have a direct need for a detailed understanding of architectural drafting. In some professions (such as landscape architecture, urban and city planning, and interior decorating), a study of architectural drafting may be required.

The following sections give detailed guidance information on professions associated with architectural drafting.

Architects

Nature of Work. An architect designs buildings and other structures and supervises their construction. These buildings and structures are designed so they are safe, useful, and pleasing in appearance. He determines, after consultation with the client, the methods of construction, cost, kinds and sizes of materials, and the equipment to be used in the proposed building. He also plans the interior (including lighting, heating, ventilating, wiring, decorating, etc.) in the most effective and efficient manner.

Qualifications. Anyone who can draw and visualize, and who possesses not only imagination but a good business sense, will enjoy this type of work. Mathematical ability, salesmanship, and an interest in the allied arts are also qualities useful to the architect. Five years of college training is necessary in most schools for a Bachelor of Architecture. Three years of practical experience is also necessary before becoming a qualified architect.

In most states a high school graduate may qualify to take the state examinations for his license by working for twelve years in the office of a registered architect.

An architect must have a state license in order to practice.

Returns. Architecture is very rewarding in that the architect can bring beauty, efficiency, and comfort into the lives of people. A great deal of satisfaction is gained in seeing one's own ideas developed into the finished product.

An architect's annual income is around $9,000 to $10,000 per year, although many exceed this figure.

Working Conditions. The architect's offices for the most part are light and airy and are generally equipped with reference materials and labor saving devices. Most architects work for a large organization; however, some individuals have considerable success by themselves.

No two jobs are ever the same, even though they may be used for the same purpose. Each assignment offers a new challenge with different solutions.

Opportunities. Population shifts, industrial expansion, relocation, improvement in living standards, and suburban development are all creating more job opportunities for architects. Reconstruction, obsolescence, fire losses, slum clearance, and modernization account for still more opportunities.

How to Enter. The student should consider working for an architect or construction firm during summer vacation. This will give an opportunity to gain experience in the field and may also open the way to a better job when he finishes school.

For information, contact colleges or universities offering architecture. Also contact:

American Institute of Architects
1735 New York Avenue, N.W.
Washington, D.C. 20006

Landscape Architects

Nature of Work. A landscape architect plans the arrangement of outdoor areas, parks, gardens, scenic roads, housing projects, campuses, and country clubs. Depending upon the client's wishes and the funds available, he may plan the entire arrangement of the site, supervise grading, construction and planting, *or* he may do only the basic planning.

Qualifications. The landscape architect should have a basic understanding of plant life. A good foundation in mathematics, art, and mechanical drawing is required by many schools. A Bachelor's Degree in Landscape Architecture may take four or five years, depending upon the institution. Some schools offer a Master's Degree. A few states (six or seven) require a license. It should also be noted that about 10 per cent of the landscape architects are women.

Returns. Salaries are between $8,000 to $10,000 per year. Those who have their own practice often earn more, but earnings fluctuate with the ability to get contracts.

Working Conditions. Ordinarily, hours are regular, except for planting time—then long hours may be expected.

Opportunities. Opportunities open up as the metropolitan areas grow causing a greater need for parks and recreation areas, housing projects, etc. Landscape architecture is closely tied in to city and regional planning.

How to Enter. The student should consider working for a landscape architect or a landscape contractor during summer vacation. This will give an opportunity to gain experience in the field and may also open the way to a better-than-average job when he finishes school.

Additional information can be obtained from schools offering landscape architecture or from:

American Society of Landscape Architects, Inc.
2000 K Street, N.W.
Washington, D.C. 20006

Urban or City Planners

Nature of Work. Urban planners develop master plans for over-all and long range developments of communities and cities. They also develop plans for the rehabilitation of slum areas, reconstruction of business buildings, and construction of highways. They also recommend rules and regulations to guide in the use of land and to guide in routing traffic.

Qualifications. Most employers desire two years of graduate work; however, young persons with an A.B.S. Degree (Bachelor of Science in Architecture) often work in governmental agencies. One must be able to speak and write well and must be able to visualize the effect of their plans and designs.

Returns. Beginning salaries are $6,500 to $7,500 and range upwards to more than $15,000 annually. Consultants are usually paid on a fee basis.

Working Conditions. Beginners will spend much of their time in drafting, field survey, and compilation of statistics. The senior members write reports, prepare construction standards, and spend much of their time in meetings with officials, addressing groups, etc.

Opportunities. This continues to be a field of opportunity for those with professional training. Many act as consultants to government agencies. Many cities have at least one planner, and many more are turning to urban planners as cities continue to spill into neighboring communities.

How to Enter. Information can be obtained from planning agencies in most cities, from the U.S. Civil Service Commission, and from schools offering degrees in planning. Information concerning employment opportunities may be obtained from:

American Institute of Planners
917 15th Street, N.W.
Washington, D.C. 20005

American Society of Planning Officials
1313 East 60th Street
Chicago, Illinois 60637

For Government positions (U.S.):
U.S. Civil Service Commission
Washington, D.C. 20415

Interior Decorators

Nature of Work. Interior decorators plan the color schemes; plan the selection and arrangement of furniture, draperies, and floor coverings; and supervise the work involved. They also plan decorations for offices, stores, theatres, schools, etc., and work on sets for motion pictures, television, and theatres.

Qualifications. An interior decorator must possess artistic talent and creative ability in order to be successful. He must be artistic—at the same time he must have practical skills.

Formal training is becoming increasingly important for entrance into this field. The minimum educational requirement is a two or three year course in an art school specializing in interior decorating and design, or a four year college course leading to a Bachelor's Degree in Fine Arts with a major in interior design and decoration.

Returns. Many experienced interior decorators earn only moderate incomes; others, usually designers, earn more than $25,000 yearly. Some work on commission plus salary.

Working Conditions. The hours are sometimes long and irregular. The work day is usually adjusted to suit the needs of the clients, often including evenings or week ends.

Opportunities. Interior decorators usually work with clients to determine needs and preferences. Many interior decorators have their own establishments, often selling upholstering, drapery materials, furniture, etc.

The older person has a distinct advantage in this field. Department and furniture stores continue to employ large numbers of trained decorators.

How to Enter. Further information may be obtained from:

American Institute of Decorators
673 Fifth Avenue
New York, New York 10022

Commercial Artists

Nature of Work. Commercial artists prepare illustrations designed to catch the eye of the reader and to stimulate interest in a particular product. These illustrations are usually found in newspapers, magazines, and other publications. They also create television and movie cartoons, fashion illustrations, greeting card illustrations, packaging and wall paper designs, etc.

Qualifications. Those with an above average ability in art are best suited for this occupation. Extensive training in fine arts, painting, sculpture, and architecture provides a good foundation, not only in obtaining employment but also in qualifying for promotion.

Some courses of study which grant a certificate require only two or three years. Many schools, particularly those associated with universities, require four years or more of study and confer a Bachelor of Fine Arts degree.

Beginning artists usually need a certain amount of on-the-job training before becoming a commercial artist.

Returns. There is a certain amount of satisfaction in being able to point with pride and say "I did that job."

The pay is unusually good, but the scale varies.

Working Conditions. The work week is 35 to 40 hours; however, hours are often longer in order to meet deadlines. The free-lance artist's work day is often affected by the amount of art work sold. This type of work is confining and tiring on the eyes.

Opportunities. Many commercial artists leave salaried employment for free-lance work. This is only advisable for those artists that are talented, creative, and have considerable experience.

Any adverse effect on the economy may result in a drastic reduction in advertising. This would naturally decrease the demand for commercial artists.

How to Enter. For information on art training and employment trends contact:

National Society of Art Directors
115 E. 40th Street
New York, New York 10016

For schools offering highly specialized courses in art and design contact:

National Association of Schools of Art
50 Astor Place
New York, New York 10003

Draftsmen

Nature of Work. Practically every phase of American life is dependent upon draftsmen. Everything that is built (houses, factories, skyscrapers, roads, bridges, machines, aircraft, appliances, etc.) needs detailed plans giving dimensions and specifications. A draftsman may make these drawings from preliminary sketches and general specifications; or, before drafting, he may have to calculate strengths, sizes, and costs, and determine suitable materials and processes to be utilized.

Most draftsmen are specialists in delineating various phases of work i.e., electrical, electronics, mechanical, sheet metal, structural, architectural, automotive, map making, model making, etc.

Qualifications. Anyone who likes drawing and is able to visualize would enjoy this work. Some mechanical aptitude and a neat and systematic working procedure (with a strict attention to details) is also necessary. Good eyesight is important.

Returns. A beginner receives $300 to $350 monthly, while top draftsmen receive $700 to $800 per month. Those in supervisory positions receive $1,000 per month.

There is a lot of personal satisfaction in helping to develop something useful from the beginning to the finished stage. On the other hand, a draftsman often devotes a great portion of his time to tedious work. This sometimes results in eye strain and poor posture from standing or sitting.

Working Conditions. Most large drafting rooms are well lighted. Drafting aids and devices are located at each desk.

Opportunities. The demand for draftsmen has been growing rapidly. In addition to those working in American industry, many thousands are employed by local, state, and federal governments; public utilities; engineering and architectural firms; and construction companies.

Opportunities for advancement are excellent. The more education one has the faster he progresses. There is very little chance of losing out to automation, despite tape controlled drafting machines and photo reproduction. Some of the routine tasks may be eliminated. With substantial increases in defense spending, public works programs, and space exploration, continued expansion in employment is likely.

How to Enter. The applicant should start as an apprentice draftsman, taking required courses at night school, community colleges, technical institues, colleges, or universities. An excellent background may be obtained from a two year post high school course in drafting and design technology.

Additional information may be obtained from:

American Federation of Technical Engineers
900 F Street, N.W.
Washington, D.C. 20004

Surveyors

Nature of Work. A surveyor locates land boundaries and collects information for maps, charts, etc. They keep data on physical characteristics, verify the accuracy of survey data, and prepare sketches, maps, and reports.

Surveyors have job titles which identify their specialty, some of which are: highway, land, geodetic, topographic, photogram metric, magnetic, hydrographic, mine, oil well, directional, pipeline, construction, or railroad.

Qualifications. A person entering this field should have an ability in algebra, geometry, trigonometry, calculus, and drafting. He should have successfully completed courses in these upon graduation from high school. Colleges and universities offer four year courses in surveying. The usual way of entering this field is by taking a number of extension courses while at the same time gaining on-the-job experience. A state license is required.

Returns. Beginning surveyors receive about $400 per month. Federal government positions depend upon the qualifications of the entrant.

Working Conditions. A surveyor must be in good health and have good eyesight. He must also like the outdoors and be able to stand for long periods of time in all kinds of weather. The work day is usually longer during summer months because conditions at that time are best for surveying.

Opportunities. Due to population growth, expanding economy, rapid growth of urban areas, housing developments, federal and state highway and expressway plans, etc., many new surveyors will be needed.

How to Enter. Information on surveying and its requirements may be obtained from:

American Congress on Surveying and Mapping
Woodward Building
Washington, D.C. 20005

On photogrammetry from:

American Society of Photogrammetry
44 Leesburg Pike
Falls Church, Virginia 22040

Industrial Arts Teachers

Nature of Work. Industrial Arts is a phase of education that offers students an insight into our industrial society through laboratory-classroom experiences in the areas of graphic arts, wood, metal, electricity, and transportation.

Qualifications. Everyone who wants to teach must hold at least a bachelor's degree with a major in the subject taught. A certificate issued by the state department of education is necessary. Certain other requirements, such as certificates of health, citizenship, and an oath of allegiance, are necessary in many areas.

Returns. Salaries vary: Industrial arts teachers are on the same schedule as teachers of other subjects. Credit is given for each year of teaching, armed forces service, higher degrees, etc. In some larger cities school teachers are receiving as high as $11,000 per year.

Teacher fringe benefits are many: vacations, sick leave, sabbatical leave, pension, etc. This makes teaching very attractive. There is also a great deal of personal satisfaction in helping and guiding students.

Working Conditions. Teachers are respected and often sought for advice. Employment isn't usually affected by changes in business conditions.

The summer recess and Christmas vacation enable the industrial arts teacher to work in his field of specialization (drafting, machine tool, etc.). Many teachers take additional courses for advancement and salary increases.

Opportunities. Growing enrollments in public schools and the large number of vacancies created by teachers retiring swell the number of teachers needed. Most schools encourage further study leading to a Master's Degree in order to strengthen their program.

A department chairmanship or some other administrative appointment is a possible advancement.

Income may be supplemented by adult education classes, evening school, or other part-time work.

How to Enter. Talk with your industrial arts teacher about the courses offered in high school that are required for entrance to a college offering industrial arts teacher education. Write to several colleges that offer industrial education degrees. Study their curriculum requirements, procedures, facilities, offerings, costs, etc. In addition, further information may be obtained from:

U.S. Dept. of Health, Education, and Welfare
U.S. Office of Education
400 Maryland Avenue, S.W.
Washington, D.C. 20202

National Education Association
1201 16th Street, N.W.
Washington, D.C. 20006

American Vocational Association
1025 15th Street, N.W.
Washington, D.C. 20005

Guidance Information: Construction Trades

The trades involved in construction may also benefit from practical experience in architectural drafting. It is *imperative* that the members in each of these occupations be able to *accurately* read and understand blueprints. Beyond this, an understanding of architectural drafting better qualifies the construction tradesman for his particular job. Architectural drafting experience also gives the tradesman a general understanding of the over-all situation in which he works. Advancement in each of these trades depends to a great extent on a general knowledge of the construction field.

To become qualified for a managerial position (foreman or higher) in the construction field, a working knowledge of drafting methods is necessary. This is true not only in a particular trade but also in the area of actual contracting and building. It is obvious that a builder, contractor, or developer must thoroughly understand architectural drafting methods and procedures. Without this basic understanding it is impossible to make sound business decisions based on architectural plans and specifications. A knowledge of building construction and architectural drafting practices are also essential if the tradesman wishes to become a specialized estimator within his own trade.

For the tradesman who someday intends to own his own business, practical experience in architectural drafting is essential. The independent contractor or builder may be expected not only to *read* architectural drawings but also to actively assist in *planning* and *designing* construction projects. A knowledge of drafting for the small, independent contractor or builder may mean the difference between profit or loss, success or failure.

The following sections are designed to give guidance information on the trades associated with construction.

Carpenters

Nature of Work. A carpenter is a craftsman who erects wooden building frames; installs interior and exterior trim; lays floors; and builds concrete forms, chutes, and scaffolds.

A rough carpenter erects wood framework, scaffolding, studs and rafters, and partitions; lays sub-flooring, sheathing, and floor joists; installs heavy timbers; and builds concrete forms.

A finish carpenter installs molding, panelling, cabinets, windows, doors, hardware, etc.; builds stairs; and lays floors. Some carpenters specialize in a particular type of work.

Qualifications. A carpenter must be in good health, physically strong, possess good manual dexterity, and be able to work in high places. A grade school diploma and high school training in mathematics is advisable. A carpenter should be 17 to 24 years old.

An apprenticeship of four years is the best way to enter the trade; however, it may be acquired informally by serving as helper or handy man for many years.

Returns. The hourly wage rates paid carpenters are generally higher than those paid to skilled workers in other trades.

Working Conditions. A carpenter's work is active and sometimes strenuous — much outdoor work is required. Prolonged climbing, squatting, and standing is often necessary.

A carpenter risks injury from slips, falls, and contact with rough materials, sharp tools, and power equipment.

Opportunities. The rising volume of construction causes an increasing need for carpenters. Carpenters are also needed for maintenance services in factories, commercial establishments, and governmental agencies. Remodeling, repairing, and altering require more men every year. Factory prefabrication of parts and building components are likely to increase the job prospects.

How to Enter. Carpenter contractors, union officials, the Bureau of Apprenticeship Training (U.S. Dept. of Labor), and the local office of the state employment service will provide information on carpenter apprenticeship or work programs.

Bricklayers

Nature of Work. The bricklayer works with brick, structural clay tile, refractory brick, facing tile, terra cotta, ceramic veneer, and concrete cinder and glass block. These building units are laid according to a predetermined pattern or bond, and are formed into walls, partitions, fireplaces, chimneys, and other structures.

Qualifications. A bricklayer must have a high degree of manual dexterity and be in good physical condition. The ability to work as a team in building is also required. He should be 17 to 24 years old and possess a high school diploma or its equivalent. He must serve a three to four year apprenticeship in order to become a journeyman.

Returns. Bricklayers are high on the building trade wage scale. There is also the satisfaction of saying "I helped build that building."

Working Conditions. This work period varies from 35 to 40 weeks a year. It is not as seasonal as it was years ago because of improved construction conditions and methods. When good, safe scaffolding is provided by contractors, hazards are at a minimum.

Opportunities. Employment prospects are bright for years to come; brick research is finding new methods and techniques.

How to Enter. Anyone desiring to become a bricklayer should make an application to the Bricklayer Joint Apprentice Committee in his locality. This contact can be through a local mason, contractor, the union, vocational guidance counselor, or a representative of the Bureau of Apprenticeship Training (U.S. Dept. of Labor). A prospective apprentice is first given pre-job training lasting from six to eight weeks. This is an excellent way to select qualified apprentices and also gives an opportunity to learn the correct fundamentals at the same time.

Stone Masons

Nature of Work. Stone masons build stone exteriors of structures using natural cut stone such as marble, granite, limestone, and sandstone; or artificial stone which is made to order using cement and marble chips or other masonry materials. In areas where there are no stone masons this work is done by bricklayers.

Qualifications. Applicant must be in good physical condition. He should be 17 to 24 years old with a high school diploma or its equivalent. A three year apprenticeship is required.

Returns. Wages are among the highest among the skilled building trades. However, these workers lose considerable time because of weather conditions and the short duration of many jobs.

Working Conditions. A major part of the work of a stone mason is done outdoors; it is somewhat strenuous as it involves lifting moderately heavy materials.

Opportunities. Modern office buildings have simple lines, little ornamentation, and large window areas. Little use of stone masonry is made. Consequently, job opportunities are relatively small.

How to Enter. (See bricklayers).

Cement Masons (Cement and Concrete Finishers)

Nature of Work. A cement mason is a skilled craftsman whose principal work is finishing exposed concrete surfaces, such as floors, walls, streets, sidewalks, and driveways. Finish is needed to make them strong and durable and, if necessary, watertight. Concrete finishing is done by hand and/or finishing machines.

Qualifications. The prospective cement finisher should be 18 to 25 years old with an education above grade school. He must be in good health and possess manual dexterity. The apprenticeship is three years. Many workers obtain these skills by working on construction jobs as laborers and helping cement masons. Credit toward an apprenticeship is frequently given for knowledge and skill gained in this manner.

Returns. The hourly wage rates paid cement finishers are above the average for building trade workers. Because of the nature of the material, concrete must be finished when poured. This often results in overtime.

Working Conditions. A lot of the work is done out of doors. Stooping, bending, or kneeling is required much of the time. Because of the seasonal nature of the work considerable time is lost.

Opportunities. More employment opportunities for cement finishers are expected with the increased use of cement. However, finishing machines may have some adverse effect upon employment prospects.

How to Enter. Anyone interested in the cement finishing trade should contact cement finishing contractors in his area, the union, local joint union-management apprenticeship committees, the local office of the Bureau of Apprenticeship and Training (U.S. Dept. of Labor), or the local state employment service.

Iron Workers

Nature of Work. Iron workers are craftsmen who install, erect, or assemble fabricated structural metal products used in the construction of industrial, commercial, or residential buildings. Structural workers erect the steel framework of bridges, buildings, and other structures, including metal storage tanks and overhead crane runways. Reinforcing ironworkers (rodmen) set steel bars in concrete forms to reinforce concrete structures. Ornamental iron workers install metal stairways, ladders, gratings, catwalks, metal window sashes, grilles, metal cabinets, and safety deposit boxes, etc.

Qualifications. The applicant should have a high school education or its equivalent, must be in good physical condition, and should be from 18 to 30 years old. The apprenticeship lasts three years.

Returns. The hourly rates are among the highest in the building trades. This is often increased by overtime work.

Working Conditions. Much time is lost by inclement weather. Rodmen are out of work intermittently because of the short duration of the job.

Safety devices, such as nets and scaffolding, have reduced accidents considerably.

Many structural workers spend considerable time traveling from job to job in order to be constantly employed.

Opportunities. This is one of the fastest growing of the skilled building trades. More opportunities are being created in this field because of the increased use of ornamental panels attached to buildings and the increased use of metal frames to hold large exterior glass installations.

How to Enter. Further information concerning apprenticeship or work opportunities may be obtained from the local contractor; the Bureau of Apprenticeship and Training (U.S. Dept. of Labor); the local state employment service; or:

International Association of Bridge, Structural and Ornamental Iron Workers
Suite 300
3615 Olive Street
St. Louis, Missouri 63108

Operating Engineers

Nature of Work. An operating engineer operates and maintains various types of power driven construction machines, such as cranes, bull dozers, pile drivers, paving machines, and power shovels.

Qualifications. Apprenticeships of three or four years are available in some localities. However, many men with mechanical aptitude enter this occupation by working as oiler job helpers to the heavy equipment repairmen.

Returns. Wage scales vary, even on the same machine. Much depends upon how many machines the individual can operate and maintain.

Working Conditions. Work is performed out of doors; employment, therefore, is influenced by weather. Because of the movement of some machines, the operator should be in good condition in order to take the shakes and jolts.

Opportunities. A continued rise in employment is anticipated due to the rise in construction. Increased mechanization of material movement in factories and mines should result in growing employment.

How to Enter. Apply to local contractors for information on work opportunities. However, for qualifications, training, and the location of apprentice programs write to:

Union of Operating Engineers
1125 17th Street, N.W.
Washington, D.C. 20006

Lathers

Nature of Work. A lather installs supporting backing on ceilings and walls on which plaster or other materials are applied. These supports are usually in the form of metal lath, or perforated gypsum board.

Qualifications. In order to enter this trade the applicant should be between 16 to 26 years old and should be in good physical condition. An eighth grade diploma is required; however, a high school diploma is preferred. The lather's apprenticeship lasts for either two or three years.

Returns. The pay is among the highest in the building trades. However, even with better facilities for working around the calendar, considerable time is lost.

Working Conditions. This is a seasonal occupation; work is both out-doors and indoors. A good deal of climbing and working in cramped positions is required.

Opportunities. Due to the increased use of dry wall construction, job opportunities are decreasing. However, this may be offset somewhat by the increased use of lightweight plaster for fireproofing structural steel and the use of acoustical ceilings for sound proofing.

How to Enter. Further information about apprenticeships or job opportunities in this trade may be obtained from local contractors; the Bureau of Apprenticeship and Training (U.S. Dept. of Labor); the local office of the state employment service; or:

Contracting Plasterers' and Lathers' International Association
304 Landmark Bldg.
1343 H Street, N.W.
Washington, D.C. 20005

National Bureau for Lathing and Plastering
755 Nada Bldg.
2000 K Street, N.W.
Washington, D.C. 20005
The Wood, Wire and Metal Lathers International Union
6530 New Hampshire Avenue
Takoma Park, Maryland 20012

Plasterers

Nature of Work. A plasterer applies plaster to interior walls and ceilings. They also apply stucco to exterior walls, and form and cast ornamental designs in plaster.

Qualifications. Anyone desiring an apprenticeship should be 18 to 25 years old, in good physical condition, and possess manual dexterity. The best way to learn plastering is by a three or four year apprenticeship, although many workers enter by serving many years as helpers or laborers.

Returns. A plasterer's pay ranks among the highest of the skilled building trades. A considerable amount of time is lost because of the seasonal nature of the work.

Working Conditions. Plastering requires considerable standing, stooping, and lifting. Stuccoing is done outdoors; plastering walls and ceilings, and forming and casting ornamental designs are done indoors.

Opportunities. Due to the continued trend toward wider use of dry wall construction, the demand for plasterers is decreasing. There is a continued use of machines to spray plaster on walls.

How to Enter. Further information may be obtained on apprenticeships or job opportunities by contacting the local plastering contractors; the Bureau of Apprenticeship and Training (U.S. Dept. of Labor); the local state employment service; or:

Bricklayers, Masons and Plasterers' International Union of America
815 15th Street, N.W.
Washington, D.C. 20005
Contracting Plasterers' and Lathers' International Association
304 Landmark Bldg.
1343 H Street, N.W.
Washington, D.C. 20005
National Bureau for Lathing and Plastering
755 Nada Bldg.
2000 K Street, N.W.
Washington, D.C. 20005

Marble, Tile, and Terrazzo Workers

Nature of Work. Marble setters, tile setters, and terrazzo workers cover interior and exterior walls and floors with marble, tile, and terrazzo. (The job title indicates the material used.)

Marble setters install marble, shop made terrazzo panels, artificial marble, and structural glass when it is used on the inside of buildings.

A tile setter attaches tile to floors and walls, either by the piece or, as in the case of small tiles, in paper backed strips or sheets.

Terrazzo is an ornamental concrete containing marble chips as the chief ingredient. It is used primarily for floors. After hardening it is ground off and polished, revealing the exposed chips.

Qualifications. Anyone desiring to enter any of these trades should be between 17 to 27 years old and have a high school education or its equivalent. Good physical condition and high manual dexterity are very important assets. The apprenticeship length, is three years.

Returns. The pay compares favorably with other building trades.

Working Conditions. Marble setters and terrazzo workers work both out-doors and in-doors; tile setters work mostly in-doors. Many job opportunities are available because of increased use of tile.

Opportunities. How to Enter. Anyone desiring information on work opportunities or apprenticeships in any of these occupations should contact local contractors; the Apprenticeship and Training Union (U.S. Dept. of Labor); the local state employment office; or:

National Terrazzo and Mosaic Association, Inc.
2000 K Street, N.W.
Washington, D.C. 20005
International Association of Marble, Slate, and Stone Polishers, Rubbers and Sawyers, Tile and Marble Setters' Helpers and Marble Mosaic and Terrazzo Workers' Helpers
821 15th Street, N.W.
Washington, D.C. 20005

Painters and Paper Hangers

Nature of Work. Painting and paper hanging are separate skilled building trades, although many craftsmen do both types of work.

Painters prepare surfaces of buildings and other structures, and then apply paint, varnish, enamel, lacquer, or similar materials.

Paper hangers cover room interiors with paper, vinyls, fabric, or other materials.

Qualifications. A three year apprenticeship is the usual time served before becoming a journeyman. However, qualification may be picked up informally as a helper. The applicant should be from 16 to 26 years old and should be in good physical condition. A high school education is preferred.

Returns. The hourly rate is lower than that of most building trades. Earnings are lowered somewhat by weather and the brief duration of most jobs.

Working Conditions. Although many painters and paper hangers work inside, working conditions are affected by seasonal construction. Prolonged periods of standing are required; paint odors may be very unpleasant.

Opportunities. Apprentice training hasn't kept up with the dropouts, thus creating a shortage of good journeymen.

New types of paints with greater covering power and easier application, spray painting, and roller painting have reduced the requirement for painters.

How to Enter. Information on work opportunities or apprenticeships may be obtained from local contractors; the Bureau of Apprenticeship and Training (U.S. Dept. of Labor); the state employment service; or:

Painters, Decorators and Paperhangers of America
217-219 North 6th Street
Lafayette, Indiana 47901

Glaziers

Nature of Work. Glaziers cut, fit, and install ordinary window glass, plate glass, mirrors, and special items, such as leaded glass panels.

Qualifications. Anyone who desires an apprenticeship as a glazier should be at least 18 years old and should have a high school education or its equivalent. The length of apprenticeship is three years.

Returns. Wages are slightly lower than the average building trade wage.

Working Conditions. Much time is lost between jobs and because of weather conditions.

Opportunities. Replacement, modernization, the increased use of glass in construction is providing additional job opportunities. As a general rule, the chances of entering this occupation are relatively small.

Many windows come to the job already glazed—thus eliminating the need for a glazier.

How to Enter. Information on work opportunities and apprenticeships may be obtained from local glazing contractors, the Bureau of Apprenticeship and Training (U.S. Dept. of Labor); the local state employment office; or:

Painters, Decorators and Paperhangers of America
217-219 North 6th Street
Lafayette, Indiana 47901

Roofers

Nature of Work. A roofer applies composition roofing and other materials, such as slates and tile, to roofs of buildings. He also applies waterproofing and damp proof to masonry walls and other building surfaces.

Qualifications. Apprenticeship applicants must be 18 years old, should be in good physical condition, and should have a good sense of balance. A high school education or its equivalent is required. An apprentice serves a three year program before becoming a journeyman.

Returns. Wage rates are below the average for journeymen in the building trades. Many hours are lost each season because of the brief time on each job, and because of weather conditions.

Working Conditions. The work is sometimes strenuous — prolonged standing, climbing, bending, and squatting is required. Often, particularly when repairing roofs, work is done in all kinds of weather. A worker risks injury from slipping or falling.

Opportunities. Some new job opportunities for roofers are opening. Application of roofs on new construction, and repair jobs on old structures will provide most of the work. Dampproofing and waterproofing are expected to take an increasing amount of the roofer's work time.

How to Enter. Information concerning roofer apprenticeships may be obtained from local roofing contractors, or the local office of Bureau of Apprenticeship and Training (U.S. Dept. of Labor); the state employment service; or:

National Roofing Contractors Association
189 West Madison Street
Chicago, Illinois 60602

United Slate, Tile and Composition Roofers, Damp and Waterproof Workers Association
6 East Lake Street
Chicago, Illinois 60601

Plumbers

Nature of Work. Plumbers are craftsmen who install pipe systems to carry water, steam, air, or other liquids and gases needed for sanitation, industrial production, etc. They also alter and repair existing systems, and install plumbing fixtures, appliances, heating, and refrigerating units.

Plumbers install gas and waste disposal systems, especially those connected to public utility systems. Such installations are made in residential and commercial buildings, schools, churches, industrial plants, and other structures.

Qualifications. An apprentice plumber should be 17 to 25 years old, should have a high school diploma or its equivalent, and should have a high degree of mechanical aptitude and be in good physical condition. A plumber's apprenticeship lasts five years.

Returns. Pay is among the highest of the skilled building trades.

Working Conditions. Employment is less affected by seasonal factors because the work is mostly inside.

A plumber has more accidents than a production worker. Accidents result from ladder falls, sharp tool cuts, and hot pipe or steam burns.

Opportunities. An increase in employment is expected because of the trend toward more bathrooms per dwelling unit, and the installation of washing machines, waste disposals, and automatic heating systems.

The increase in industrial activities and atomic energy use, and the greater use of refrigeration and air conditioning equipment will result in the need for more plumbers.

How to Enter. Anyone interested in plumbing should contact the Bureau of Apprenticeship and Training (U.S. Dept. of Labor); the local state employment office; or:

National Association of Plumbing Contractors
1016 20th Street, N.W.
Washington, D.C. 20006

United Association of Journeymen and Apprentices of the Plumbing and Pipe Fitting Industry of the United States and Canada
901 Massachusetts Avenue, N.W.
Washington, D.C. 20001

Electricians

Nature of Work. Construction electricians perform various jobs related to electrical work. They lay out, install, assemble, and test fixtures, apparatus, and wiring used in electrical systems. An electrician also connects electrical machinery, equipment, and controls.

Qualifications. Anyone desiring to become an electrician should be between 18 to 24 years old and should have a high school education or its equivalent, including math and physics. Most cities require electricians to be licensed. The apprenticeship length varies between three and four years.

Returns. Hourly rates are the highest in the skilled building trades. Electricians work mostly indoors and are less affected by seasonal employment than other trades.

Working Conditions. An electrician has to stand for prolonged periods and sometimes works in cramped quarters. He risks danger of cuts, falls, and burns from live wires.

Opportunities. The number of electricians are expected to rise rapidly due to increased use of appliances requiring rewiring and the installation of electronic equipment in industry and commerce.

How to Enter. Anyone desiring further information on electrician apprenticeship should contact local electrical contractors; the Bureau of Apprenticeship and Training (U.S. Dept. of Labor); the state employment service; or:

National Electrical Contractors Association
610 Ring Building
Washington, D.C. 20006

International Brotherhood of Electrical Workers
1200 15th Street, N.W.
Washington, D.C. 20005

Sheet Metal Workers

Nature of Work. A sheet metal worker installs or fabricates metal ducts for ventilating, air conditioning, and heating systems. He also fabricates and installs other products made from thin metal sheets, such as roofing, gutters, down spouts, flashing, siding, partitions, shelving, and stainless steel kitchen equipment.

Qualifications. Anyone desiring to be a sheet metal apprentice should be 17 to 21 years old, should be in good physical condition, possess good mechanical aptitude, and have a high school education or its equivalent. The term of an apprentice is from four to five years.

Returns. The wages are high in comparison to the average wage rates of other workers in the building trades. Work hours are lost by seasonal and short-duration jobs.

Working Conditions. Sheet metal workers work indoors installing heating, ventilating, or air conditioning systems. Outdoor work may find him working high above the ground installing roofs, flashing, gutters, down spouts, skylights, and cornices. Physically, the job may require working in cramped and almost inaccessible locations.

Opportunities. An increase in employment is expected due to an increased demand for air conditioning systems in residential, commercial, and industrial buildings.

How to Enter. Further information on apprenticeship or job opportunities may be obtained from local sheet metal contractors; the U.S. Bureau of Apprenticeship and Training (U.S. Dept. of Labor); the local state employment office; or:

Sheet Metal and Air Conditioning Contractors' National Association, Inc.
107 Center Street
Elgin, Illinois 60120

Sheet Metal Workers' International Association
1000 Connecticut Avenue, N.W.
Washington, D.C. 20006

Specifications C

The specification shown below is referred to as a "fill-in-form."[1] This is a basic form which may be used for all residences. The architect adds the exact specifications for the particular residence. Specifications are arranged, as far as possible, in the order which the various trades will work on the structure.

The specifications should spell out the responsibilities of both parties. For example, in the specification form given below the contractor is required to provide liability and workmen's compensation insurance. The owner is to provide fire and windstorm insurance during construction. What the contractor will do is commonly introduced by "shall." What the owner will do is commonly introduced by "will."

The working drawings and the specifications function together as a whole. What is mentioned in either is considered to be in both. All items which are necessary for the completion of the structure, even though not mentioned, are considered to be included. If the specifications and the working drawings are in conflict, normally the specifications take precedence. It is the responsibility of the architect, of course, to prevent such conflict. Exactness is especially necessary since the specifications and drawings are used for making the estimate.

The specifications are binding on all parties, including the sub-contractors. Normally, modifications can only be made by mutual agreement.

---

1. This specification was designed by the Miller Planning Service, Kalamazoo, Michigan.

SPECIFICATIONS

The contractor shall provide all necessary labor and materials and perform all work of every nature whatsoever to be done in the erection of a residence for _______________ as owner in accordance with these specifications and drawings.

The location of the residence will be as follows: ______________.

GENERAL

All blank spaces in these specifications that apply to this building are to be filled in. All blank spaces that do not apply to be crossed out. The general conditions herein set forth shall apply to any contract given under these specifications and shall be binding upon every sub-contractor as well as general contractor.

The plans, elevations, sections, and detail drawings, together with these specifications, are to form the basis of the contract and are to be of equal force. Should anything be mentioned in these specifications and not shown in the drawings, or vice versa, the same shall be followed as if set forth in both, as it is the intent of these specifications and accompanying drawings to correspond and to embody every item and part necessary for the completion of the structure. In the event that items which are normally part of a complete house are omitted from both the plans and specifications, it is expected that they will still be supplied as part of the general contract. Example: area walls, bathroom towel bars, soap dishes, etc.; and similar items. The contractor shall comply with all health and building ordinances that are applicable.

EXCAVATION AND GRADING

The contractor shall do all necessary excavating and rough grading. The excavation shall be large enough to permit inspection of footings after the foundation has been completed. All excess dirt shall be hauled away by the contractor. Black surface loam to be piled where directed by the owner for use in grading and will be bulldozed into place by the general contractor. All subsoil and top soil required for fill and/or rough grading shall be paid for by the owner and bulldozed into place by the general contractor. The finish grading shall be done by the owner. Grade level shall be established by the owner, who will also furnish a survey of the lot showing the location of the building. The finish grading, seeding, sodding, and landscaping shall be done by the owner unless specified as follows: _______________.

CONCRETE FOOTINGS

Footings shall be of concrete mixed in the proportion of one part Portland cement, three parts clean, coarse, sharp sand and five parts of gravel or crushed rock. Concrete shall be machine mixed with clean water to the proper consistency, and shall be placed immediately after mixing. Footings shall be thoroughly protected with hay or straw in freezing weather. All footings shall be set below the frost line and rest on firm soil and shall be flat and level on the underside. Footings shall be of sizes shown on plan.

BASEMENT WALLS

Basement walls shall be of poured concrete ______ inches thick. Poured walls shall be straight, level, and plumb,

OR

basement walls will be constructed of ______ inch concrete blocks per plan, of approved quality. Blocks shall be laid in a full bed of mortar, composed of one part of cement to three parts of sand. Mortar joints shall be filled thoroughly with cement mortar, neatly pointed on both sides.

All walls shall have uniform bearing for framing, being straight, plumb, and level. Beam fill to be placed as shown on the plans. Waterproof basement walls with two coats of waterproofing applied according to manufacturer's specifications. Mortar drippings shall be cleaned from footings, and a cement cove trowelled into place.

BASEMENT FLOOR

Basement floor shall be of ______ inch concrete, poured monolithically, with a trowelled finish. Thoroughly tamp the base concrete into place and carefully pitch to floor drains; .004" Polyethylene shall be placed under basement floors under recreation rooms, bedroom, and bathrooms, etc.

CRAWL SPACES

Crawl spaces shall have a skim coat of concrete over .004" Polyethylene. Minimum clearance between joists and slab shall be two feet.

CEMENT WALKS AND STEPS

All cement walks shall be four inches thick, of widths and in locations shown on plans and shall be poured monolithically with a trowelled finish. The steps at the front and rear entrances shall be of wood, cement, or brick construction as indicated on the plan. If rain leaders are not connected to sewer, provide concrete splash blocks for each rain leader.

CHIMNEYS

Chimneys shall be constructed of common brick with face brick top. Provide tile flue lining of size and extent shown on plans for all flues. Thimbles and cleanouts shall be built in as required. If fireplace is required, furnish and install ash dump, damper and cleanouts, fire brick for lining and hearth, facing and outer hearth of material selected by owner. Hearth to be supported on concrete slab of size shown on plan.

All flues shall be cleaned of mortar drippings, and the chimney shall be capped with a concrete cap as shown on plans -- minimum thickness at thinnest point two inches.

Concrete hearth support to be fireproof; hearth floor to be _______.

Chimneys shall be flashed and counter-flashed where they pass through the roof.

Face of fireplace opening, if masonry, shall be ________.

Mantel shelf, if masonry, shall be ________.

Incinerator, if any, shall be _______.

Damper to be _______.

BRICK WORK

All brick work, if any, shall be laid in cement and lime mortar, with all bricks well bedded and shoved into place, with both vertical and horizontal joints on straight lines. Joints to be of color selected by owner.

The price allowed for face brick is $________ per 1,000. Any cost above that amount will be borne by the owner. Lintels to be properly placed above all openings where masonry is shown above.

TILE WORK

The contractor shall furnish and set all tile in a neat and workmanlike manner. Recessed towel bars, paper holder, and soap dish shall be furnished by tile contractor.

The following areas shall be covered with ceramic tile: (Mark "yes" or "no".)

Bathroom floors ______

Bathroom walls to a height 4 ft. above floor ______

Bathroom tub areas to a height 5 ft. above tub ______

Showers to a height 6'-6" above floor ______

Front entrance hall floor ______

Vanity cabinet tops ______

Other ______

CARPENTER WORK

The contractor shall and will provide all necessary labor and perform all carpenter work of every nature whatsoever to be done. He shall lay out all work and be responsible for all measurements and keep a competent foreman in charge. All work shall be done in a workmanlike manner, level, straight, plumb, and true and strictly in accordance with the plans and specifications.

GIRDERS AND COLUMNS

Girders or supporting beams and columns shall be as required by the size of the building and shall be of the size and location shown in the plans.

JOISTS

First floor joists	2" x ___	O. C. Grade #1 Btr. Fir - 15 to 25% #2 permitted.			
Second floor joists	2" x ___	"	"	"	"
Ceiling joists	2" x ___	"	"	"	"
Rafters	2" x ___	"	"	"	"
Collar ties	2" x ___	"	"	"	"
Valley rafters	2" x ___	"	"	"	"

Double joists under partitions and around all openings.

All dimension material covered in the above specification is Douglas Fir, as graded by the West Coast Lumber Inspection Bureau.

STUDDINGS AND PARTITIONS

Studdings shall be sized 2 x 4's, spaced 16" on centers, single plate on bottom and double plate on top of each wall or partition. 2 x 4's shall be doubled around all openings and shall be ________.

BRIDGING

First and second floor joists shall have one row of 1 x 3 wood or approved metal bridging for all spans of 8 to 14 feet. All spans over 14 feet shall have two rows, all fastened securely to joists at each end.

ROUGH FLOORING

Sub-flooring shall be ________ C-D plywood securely nailed. All joints shall be made on joists.

SHEATHING

Outside walls shall be covered with securely nailed ________.

Roof sheathing shall be ________.

SIDING

Siding, if any, to be ________.

ROOFING

Shingles for roof to be __________ laid ________ inches to weather, using galvanized nails.

BUILT-UP ROOFS

Built-up roofs shall be installed to a 15 year specification and covered with gravel, slag, or white aggregate.

INSULATION AND PAPER

Sidewall insulation to be ________.

Top floor ceiling to be insulated with ________.

Building paper under shingles to be ________.

Building paper over sheathing to be ________.

All exterior walls shall be covered on the inside edge of the studs from floor to plate with .004" Polyethylene. Application shall be continuous, with cutouts for windows, elec. openings, etc., being made after lath is applied.

If hot water heat is used, ceilings shall be covered as above -- application to be made to the bottom edge of the ceiling joists.

OUTSIDE FINISH

All lumber required for outside finish shall be ________.

All exterior siding, cornice, and miscellaneous trim shall be woodlife dipped and nailed with non-rusting nails.

WINDOW AND DOOR FRAMES

All window and outside door frames as shown on plans shall be of sound, clear pine, free from objectionable defects. Door sills shall be oak.

Assembled window units, if any, shall be per plan.

Assembled door units, if any, shall be ____________.

WINDOWS, STORM SASH, AND SCREENS

All windows and sash shall be as shown on plans. Storm sash and screens shall be as required for patented units. Double-hung windows and _______ units shall have _______.

FINISHED FLOORS

Finished floors in living room and dining room to be _______.

Finished floors in family room to be _______.

Finished floors in bedrooms to be _______.

Finished floors in front entry to be _______.

Finished floors in kitchen to be _______.

Finished floors in bathrooms to be _______.

Finished floors in toilet to be _______.

Finished floors in _______ to be _______.

Finished floors in rear entry to be _______.

Finished floors in attic to be _______.

All hardwood floors shall be properly nailed and machine sanded to a smooth, even surface. Place 30 lb. red rosin paper between sub-floor and finish floor. Floors under linoleum shall be securely nailed with screw type or annular threaded nails.

SLATE FLOORS

Allow _____ per sq. ft. for slate floors in areas shown on plan.

NON-RIGID FLOOR COVERINGS
(not including carpeting)

Allow $4.50 per sq. yd. for linoleum-type floor covering where required.
Allow $2.00 per sq. ft. for homogenous vinyl floor covering where required.
Allow $0.40 per sq. ft. for vinyl asbestos floor covering where required.

Other _______.

INSIDE FINISH

Trim in the living room, dining room, and front entry shall be _______.

Trim in the kitchen and rear entry shall be _______.

Trim in ________ shall be ________.

Trim in the bedrooms, bathrooms, and hall shall be _______.

DOORS

All of the inside doors shall be 1 3/8" thick as follows: _______.

The front door shall be 1 3/4" thick of _______.

The remaining outside doors shall be 1 3/4" thick of _______.

Provide combination storm and screen doors for all outside doors.

Provide scuttle door to attic and plumbing access doors.

JAMBS AND CASINGS

All inside jambs shall be 3/4" thick and of kinds specified above. Casings shall be 3/4" thick of stock design.

STAIRS

Stairs leading from first to second floor shall be as shown in plans with _______ risers and _________ treads. Basement stairs shall have _______ risers and _______ treads. Three stair horses shall be provided for each stair and shall be _______ x _______. Wall stringers shall or shall not be housed. All stairs to be equipped with hand rails.

CABINET WORK

Built-in medicine cabinet in bathroom -- allow $ _____.

Size of mirrors _______.

Kitchen cabinets shall be _______ and be placed as shown on plan. Mantel and mantel shelf, if any, shall be _______. Kitchen counter tops to be _______. Splash back to be _______. Edging material to be _______. Linen cabinet to be _______. Other cabinet work, if any, shall be as follows: _______.

CLOSETS

All closets shall have one shelf and one clothes rod.

HARDWARE

The contractor shall furnish all rough hardware, such as nails. The amount to be allowed for finish hardware is $_______. Any cost in excess of that amount will be paid by the owner.

ELECTRICAL WORK

Contractor shall provide all necessary labor and material and perform all electrical work of every nature whatsoever to be done. All work to comply with local ordinances. Provide _______ openings, plus special equipment outlets as listed below, plus door bells on _______.

Provide 100 amp. service entrance facilities. All lights and switches to be placed as indicated on plans or as directed by owner. Provide special equipment outlets for

stove _______, water heater ________, washer ________, dryer ________, water pump

________, bathroom exhaust fan ________, kitchen exhaust fan ________. Heating plant

by heating contractor. Other ________.

ELECTRIC FIXTURES

Electric light fixtures to the value of $________ shall be furnished by contractor. Any cost in excess of this amount will be paid by the owner, and any cost lower than this amount listed is to be credited to the owner.

Allow $________ for built-in range and oven.

LATHING, PLASTERING, AND GROUNDS

Lath all walls, ceilings, etc., with gypsum or rocklath applied strictly in accordance with manufacturer's directions. Lath all interior corners throughout with 6 inch strips of angle-shaped metal lath. Provide galvanized corner beads on all exterior corners. All plaster to be two-coat work of a standard brand of hard wall plaster mixed in accordance with manufacturer's directions and shall be straight and true. Finish for each of the several rooms shall be as called for in room finish schedule. Plastering contractor shall repair all defects and do all patching necessary to leave the work in good condition.

Finish to consist of the following: ________.

	Ceilings	Walls
Living room	________	________
Kitchen	________	________
Bedrooms	________	________
Halls	________	________
Bathrooms	________	________
Dining rooms	________	________
Front entry	________	________
Rear entry	________	________
Basement	________	________
Garage	________	________

STUCCO

If stucco is required, it shall be three-coat work applied over self-furring, galvanized, expanded metal lath weighing 3.2 lbs. per sq. yard. Final coat to be of a color selected by owner. Provide a waterproof paper on sheathing under metal lath.

PLUMBING

Contractor shall provide all labor and material and perform all plumbing work of every nature whatsoever to be done. The fixtures shall be as follows:

______ Bath tub ________

______ Toilet combination ________

______ Size ________ Lavatory ________

______ Kitchen sink ________ Size and specification ________

______ Gallon hot water heater (gas, electric, or oil)

Two-compartment laundry tray, swing faucet ______

Dishwasher ________ Garbage disposer ________

Floor drain ________ Sill cocks ________

Towel bars ________ Soap dish ________

Paper holder ________ Shower bath ________

All of the above shall be properly installed and all connections thoroughly tested, and shall be installed according to local ordinance. Hot and cold water connections shall be made with bath tub, shower, lavatory, kitchen sink, and laundry tray. Water connections shall be made with water main in the street, sewer connection shall be made with sewer in the street, gas connections shall be made with gas main in the street, all to be paid for by the contractor. All meters will be paid for by the owner. Private sewage disposal systems, if required, shall be provided and installed in accordance with local codes.

Private water supply systems, if required, shall be provided and installed according to the owner's instructions. Allow $ ________.

HEATING

Contractor shall and will provide all necessary labor and material and perform all heating work of every nature whatsoever to be done, including the installation of __________ heating system of sufficient size to properly heat all parts of the house in coldest weather. If hot air system is to be used, it is to be installed according to the code of the National Society of Heating and Ventilation Engineers.

If hot water, steam, or any other heating system is to be used, such installation shall consist of the following: __________.

SHEET METAL WORK AND FLASHING

Contractor shall and will provide all necessary labor and materials and perform all sheet metal work of every nature whatsoever to be done, including gutters under all eaves with suitable conductors. All joints to be well soldered and securely fastened, and all work to be done in a neat and workmanlike manner. Gutters to be 26 gauge galvanized iron ________ type.

Down spouts to be ________. Proper _________ flashing shall be provided wherever necessary. Clothes chute, if shown on plan, shall be lined with ________.

INTERIOR PAINTING

All woodwork to be carefully cleaned of finger marks, stains, and other defects before any oil, filling, paint, or varnish is applied, and all rough spots to be sandpapered smooth before being filled with colored putty to match color desired. Finish to consist of the following: _________.

	Walls and ceilings	Trim
Living room	_________	_________
Dining room	_________	_________
Dinette	_________	_________
Kitchen	_________	_________
Rear entry	_________	_________
Bedroom	_________	_________
Bedroom	_________	_________
Hall	_________	_________
Front entry	_________	_________
Family room	_________	_________

All hardwood floors shall be sanded, filled, and varnished two coats, excepting ______.

EXTERIOR PAINTING

All exterior woodwork shall have ______ coats of prepared paint of colors to be selected by owner. All sash and trim to be neatly traced. All knots and other defective work to be shellacked and all nail holes to be puttied before applying last coat. All exposed sheet metal shall have one coat of red lead and two coats of finished coat paint. All paint products used on the house, both exterior and interior, shall be manufactured by a reputable firm, suitable for the surface to which they are to be applied, and shall be applied according to the manufacturer's specifications.

EXTRAS OR CREDITS

Any deviation from these specifications or plans involving an extra charge or a credit must be agreed upon in writing between the contracting parties before the change is made. The contractor shall not take advantage of any discrepancies in the drawings and specifications. If any discrepancies are found, they shall be referred to the owner or the architect and be corrected before any contract is entered into.

INSURANCE

The contractor shall provide liability insurance and workmen's compensation insurance in full until completion of the building. Fire and windstorm insurance during construction will be provided by the owner.

CLEANING UP

The contractor shall not remove all debris from the premises when the job is completed. The contractor shall not clean all window glass when job is completed.

Driveway ___________.

Sidewalks ___________.

References D

The following list of books will provide additional information on varying topics that the student may wish to pursue at greater length. The authors have found these books to be extremely useful in their classes. It will be noted that following each entry is a general classification of each book, i.e., perspective, construction, etc.

It would be an impossible task to list all of the catalogs and pamphlets from manufacturers of building supplies and materials, as well as associations and numerous pieces of advertising. It is hoped that this list will aid the student and teacher alike.

Anderson, L. O., and Heyer, O.C. *Wood Frame House Construction*. Washington, D.C.: U.S. Department of Agriculture, 1955. (Building construction—resident)

Baer, Barbara. *How to Improve Your Home by Landscaping*. New York: H. S. Stuttman Co., 1958. (Landscaping)

Book of Successful Fireplaces . . . How to Build Them. Cleveland: The Donley Brothers Company, 1960. (Fireplaces)

Burke, Arthur E. *Architectural Lettering*. Chicago: American Technical Society, 1953. (Lettering)

Burke, Arthur E., Dalzell, J. Ralph, and Townsend, Gilbert. *Architectural and Building Trades Dictionary*. Chicago: American Technical Society, 1955. (Dictionary)

Carpentry and Building Construction. Washington: Department of the Army, 1960. (Building construction-residential)

Dalzell, J. Ralph, Battenberg, Rex, and Paul, W. Rahy. *Building Trades Blueprint Reading: Part 1 Fundamentals*. Chicago: American Technical Society, 1956. (Blueprint reading)

Dalzell, J. Ralph, and Townsend, Gilbert. *Masonry Simplified Vol. 2; Practical Construction*. Chicago: American Technical Society, 1957. (Masonry construction)

Doty, Walter L., and Johnson, Paul C. *Landscaping for Modern Living*. Menlo Park, California: Lane Book Company, 1958. (Landscaping)

Durbahn, Walter E., and Sundberg, Elmer W. *Fundamentals of Carpentry. Vol. 2: Practical Construction*. Chicago: American Technical Society, 1963. (Building construction-residential)

Giachino, J. W., and Beukema, Henry J. *Drafting and Graphics*. Chicago: American Technical Society, 1961. (Engineering drawing)

Godfrey, Robert Sturgis (Ed.) *Building Construction Cost Data 1965*. Duxbury, Mass.: Robert Snow Mean Co., 1965. (Estimating — commercial and residential)

Goodban, William T., and Hayslett, Jack J. *Architectural Drawing and Planning*. New York: McGraw-Hill Book Company, 1965. (Architectural drawing)

Guptill, Arthur L. *Pencil Drawing Step by Step*. New York: Reinhold Publishing Corporation, 1959. (Pencil rendering techniques)

Harris, Charles O. *Elementary Structural Design*. Chicago: American Technical Society, 1951. (Strength of materials and design)

Hepler, Donald E., and Wallach, Paul I. *Architecture Drafting and Design*. New York: McGraw-Hill Book Company, 1965. (Architectural drawing)

How to Build Patio Roofs. Menlo Park, Calif.: Lane Book Company, 1956. (Patio roofs—contemporary)

Huntington, Whitney Clark. *Building Construction*. New York: John Wiley & Sons, Inc., 1963. (Technical aspects of building construction—commercial)

Jones, Richard A. *Household Storage Study*. Urbana, Illinois: University of Illinois—Small Homes Council, 1963. (Storage spaces—residential)

Kaufmann, Edgar, and Raeburn, Ben. *Frank Lloyd Wright: Writings and Buildings*. New York: Meridian Books, Inc., 1960. (Foundations of contemporary architecture)

Light Frame House Construction. Washington, D.C.: U.S. Department of Health, Education, and Welfare. (Building construction—residential)

Load Calculation for Residential Winter and Summer Air Conditioning. Cleveland, Ohio: National Warm Air Heating & Air Conditioning Association, 1964. (Air conditioning)

Lubschez, Ben J. *Perspective: An Elementary Text Book*. New York: D. Van Nostrand Company, 1926. (Perspective)

Marshall, Robert A. *Before You Buy a House*. Washington, D.C.: Kiplinger Washington Editors, Inc., 1964. (Financing the home)

Martin, C. Leslie. *Architectural Graphics*. New York: The Macmillan Co., 1952. (Perspective)

Minimum Property Standards for One and Two Family Living Units. Washington, D.C.: Federal Housing Administration, 1964. (U.S. Government property requirements for FHA and GI loans)

Mix, Floyd M., and Cirou, Ernest H. (Eds.). *Practical Carpentry*. Homewood, Ill.: Goodheart-Wilcox Co., Inc., 1963. (Building construction—residential)

Morgan, Sherley W. *Architectural Drawing: Perspective, Light, and Shadow Rendering*. New York: McGraw-Hill Book Co., 1950. (Perspective and rendering)

Ramsey, Charles George and Sleeper, Harold Reeve. *Architectural Graphic Standards*. New York: John Wiley & Sons, Inc., 1956. (Reference)

Ray, J. Edgar. *The Art of Bricklaying*. Peoria, Ill.: Chas. A. Bennett Co., 1961. (Bricklaying)

Sleeper, Catharine, and Sleeper, Harold R. *The House for You*. New York: John Wiley & Sons, Inc., 1948. (Home planning)

Small Homes Council. *Handbook of Kitchen Design*. Urbana, Ill.: University of Illinois — Small Homes Council, 1950. (Kitchen planning)

Small Homes Council. Urbana, Ill.: University of Illinois.

A 1.3 *Financing the Home.*
A 2.0 *Business Dealings with the Architect and the Contractor.*
B 1.1 *Selecting Livable Neighborhoods.*
B 2.1 *A Guide to Selecting the Home Site.*
B 3.0 *Fundamentals of Land Design.*
C 1.1 *Hazard-Free Houses for All.*
C 2.1 *Designing the House.*
C 2.5 *Split Level Houses.*
C 3.2 *Solar Orientation.*
C 5.1 *Household Storage Units.*
C 5.3 *Planning the Kitchen.*
C 5.31 *Cabinet Space for the Kitchen.*
C 5.32 *Kitchen Planning Standards.*
C 5.33 *Separate Ovens.*
C 5.4 *Laundry Areas.*
C 5.9 *Garages and Carports.*
D 7.0 *Selecting Lumber.*
D 7.2 *Plywood.*
D 9.0 *Plastics as Building Materials.*
E 2.1 *Construction Methods.*
F 2.0 *Basements.*
F 2.5 *Termite Control.*
F 3.0 *Wood Framing.*
F 4.3 *Concrete Floors.*

F 4.4 *Crawl-Space Houses.*
F 4.6 *Flooring Materials.*
F 6.0 *Insulation in the Home.*
F 6.2 *Moisture Condensation.*
F 7.0 *Chimney and Fireplaces.*
F 9.1 *Counter Surfaces.*
F 11.0 *Window Planning Principles.*
F 11.1 *Selecting Windows.*
F 11.2 *Insulating Windows and Screens.*
F 12.3 *Roofing Materials.*
F 15.0 *Hardware.*
F 17.2 *Brick and Concrete Masonry.*
G 3.1 *Heating the Home.*
G 3.2 *Controls for Central Heating Systems.*
G 3.5 *Fuels and Burners.*
G 4.0 *Plans for Electricity.*
G 4.2 *Electrical Wiring.*
G 5.0 *Plumbing.*
G 5.5 *Septic-Tank Systems.*
G 6.0 *Summer Comfort.*
H 1.0 *Interior Design.*

Smith, Ronald C. *Principles and Practices of Light Construction.* Englewood Cliffs, N.J.: Prentice-Hall, Inc., 1963. (Building construction—residential)

Sundberg, Elmer, Battenberg, Rex, and Paul, W. Rahy. *Building Trades Blueprint Reading: Part 2.* Chicago: American Technical Society, 1959. (Print reading)

Sweet's Catalog Service. *Light Construction Catalog File.* New York: F. W. Dodge Corporation, (most current year). (Reference)

Time-Saver Standards. New York: F. W. Dodge Corp. (Reference)

Townsend, Gilbert, Dalzell, J. Ralph, and Battenberg, Rex. *How to Plan a House.* Chicago: American Technical Society, 1958. (Home planning)

Steinberg, Joseph, Stempel, Martin. *Estimating for the Building Trades.* Chicago: American Technical Society, 1965. (Estimating)

Watkins, A. M. *Building or Buying the High-Quality House at Lowest Cost.* Garden City, N.Y.: Dolphin Books, 1952. (Home planning and analysis)

Watson, Ernest, and Watson, Aldren. *The Watson Drawing Book.* New York: Reinhold Publishing Corporation, 1962. (Rendering techniques—different media)

Williams, Henry Lionel, and Williams, Ottalie K. *A Guide to Old American Houses, 1700-1900.* New York: A. S. Barnes and Company, Inc., 1962. (American architecture)

Wright, Frank Lloyd. *The Natural House.* New York: Horizon Press, Inc., 1954. (A portion of Wright's philosophy)

Index and Glossary

Bold face designates illustrations and tables

5-11-67.